AN INTRODUCTION TO MANAGEMENT SCIENCE

Deterministic Models

AN INTRODUCTION TO

MANAGEMENT SCIENCE

Deterministic Models

DANIEL TEICHROEW

Professor of Management

Graduate School of Business

Stanford University

John Wiley & Sons, Inc., New York · London · Sydney

AN INTRODUCTION TO
MANAGEMENT SCIENCE
Deterministic Models

DANIEL TEICHROEW

Professor of Management
Graduate School of Business
Stanford University

John Wiley & Sons, Inc., New York · London · Sydney

"It is a profoundly erroneous truism, repeated by all copy books
and by eminent people when they are making speeches,
that we should cultivate the habit of thinking of what we are doing.
The precise opposite is the case.
Civilization advances by extending the number of important operations
which we can perform without thinking about them."

Alfred North Whitehead

Page	Line	Change	To
589	(a)	$\cdots = h_1 \leq 0$	$\cdots = h_i \leq 0$
589	(c)	$\lambda_i g_i = 0$	$\lambda_i g_i = 0;\ g_i \leq 0$
589	(d)	$\lambda_i \geq 0$	$\lambda_i \geq 0;\ z_i \geq 0$
609	9	$b_{ij} = \dfrac{\partial g_j}{\partial x_i}$	$b_{ji} = \dfrac{\partial g_j}{\partial x_i}$
622	6	Since z_1 and y_1 are ...	Since z_0 and y_1 are ...
629	14	State ensuing from the ...	state existing before the ...

Page	Line	Change	To
261	5 from bottom	$\cdots + \left[\dfrac{\partial f}{\partial y}\dfrac{\partial y}{\partial v} + \cdots\right.$	$\cdots + \left[\dfrac{\partial f}{\partial x}\dfrac{\partial x}{\partial v} + \cdots\right.$
278	2	... of the price in the second period ...	... of the price in the first period and the demand in the second period is a decreasing linear function of the price in the second period ...
295	Eq. (1)	$\cdots c_3$	$\cdots c_8$
308	13	$-\dfrac{5}{2}x + \dfrac{\lambda}{2} = -4 - w$	$-\dfrac{5}{2}x + \dfrac{\lambda}{2} = -4 - w$ and $$2x - \lambda = 2w - 5$$
311	20	... or $v < \frac{23}{4}$	... or $v \leq \frac{23}{4}$
318	15	... $\lambda_3 = \frac{3}{16}$	... $\lambda_3 = \frac{3}{13}$
319	Ex. 5	Add:	The machine is available for 4,800 minutes.
329	2nd last	There are two ...	There are three ...
359	11	$[a_{11}\ a_{12}][c_{21}]$	$[a_{11}\ a_{12}][c_{12}]$
444	7	... $i = 1, 3$	... $i = 1, 2, 3$
447	3 from bottom	$x_i > 0$	$x_i \geq 0$
489	Eq. (15)	$+ (c_0 - c_\tau)S_j$	$+ (c_0 - c_\tau)S_i$
517	15	... of $n + m$ equations in nm ...	... of $k + m$ equations in km ...
517	19	... exactly $n + m - 1$ unknowns	... exactly $k + m - 1$ unknowns
530	4 from bottom	$u_1 \geq 0;\ u_2 \geq 0;\ u_3 \geq 0$	$u_1 \geq 0;\ u_2 \geq 0$
548	2	$\Delta_1 = \dfrac{\partial^2 f}{\partial x_1}$,	$\Delta_1 = \dfrac{\partial^2 f}{\partial x_1{}^2}$,
552	21	Thus sufficient ...	The sufficient ...
553	2	... to one inequality ...	... to one equality ...
572	4	$\cdots + B' \cdots$	$\cdots + B \cdots$
572	16	$= a_{kk'}\quad k \neq k'$	$= a_{kk'} + a_{k'k}\quad k \neq k'$
584	8	... other fluctuate ...	... others fluctuate ...
587	26	The return for ...	The returns for ...
588	15	b_{12}	$b_{1i}b_{i2}$
588	16	$\cdots\ 1\ \ 2\ \ 3$	$\cdots\ 1\ \ 2\ \ 3\ \ 2$

ERRATA

Page	Line	Change	To
14	5	... total cost divided by ...	... total cost to ...
23	1	$\cdots - \sum_i y_{i,j-m} - \cdots$	$\cdots - \sum_i y_{i,j-1} - \cdots$
41	Ex. 4(b)	$s = 0.4$	$s = 0.2$
78	4	... year, than costs ...	... year, then costs ...
81	10	... period i be ...	... period j be ...
85	11	... if this purchase ...	... if his purchase ...
99	Ex. 9	San Franciso	San Francisco
111	4	... over the four years, ...	... over the three years, ...
114	Ex. 4(c)	... parameter.	... parameters.
122	2	$f^{(n)}(1) = (n-1)!\,(-1)^n$	$f^{(n)}(1) = (n-1)!\,(-1)^{n+1}$
122	last	... for $e^{-\lambda}$	... for e^{λ}
137	Ex. 4	$g(x) = \dfrac{3x^2}{1 + 2x + x^2}$	$g(x) = \dfrac{3x^2}{1 - 2x + x^2}$
		$-\infty < \infty x < \infty$	$-\infty < x < \infty$
138	Ex. 10	... is not acquired.	... is not required.
179	Ex. 3(iii)	If $a_2 < A < a_3, \ldots$	If $a_2 < A \leq a_3, \ldots$
194	2nd last	$W = 10{,}000\sqrt{1 + 4}\cdots$	$A_1 = 10{,}000\sqrt{1 + 4}\cdots$
194	last	$L = 10{,}000\sqrt{1 + 9}\cdots$	$A_2 = 10{,}000\sqrt{1 + 9}\cdots$
205	Ex. 2	... the same price as A	... the same price as X
218	Ex. 2	$\cdots = \dfrac{e^{-\delta t}}{\delta^2}(\delta t - 1)$	$\cdots = \dfrac{e^{-\delta t}}{\delta^2}(-\delta t - 1)$
226	2	$\cdots \int \beta t e^{-\delta t} + C$	$\cdots \int \beta t e^{-\delta t}\, dt + C$
226	3	$= \beta\left(\dfrac{t}{\delta}e^{-\delta t} - \right.$	$= \beta\left(-\dfrac{t}{\delta}e^{-\delta t} - \right.$
226	4	$S(t) = \dfrac{\beta t}{\delta} -$	$S(t) = -\dfrac{\beta t}{\delta} -$
226	6	$\cdots + \dfrac{\beta t}{\delta}$	$\cdots - \dfrac{\beta t}{\delta}$
255	8	$a_0 = 24;\ \ldots;\ a_4 = 1$	$a_0 = 1;\ a_1 = -10;$ $a_3 = -50;\ a_4 = 24$

Preface

The purpose of this book is to provide a general introduction to the application of mathematical techniques to business problems *for persons already familiar with differential and integral calculus.* Experience at the Stanford Graduate School of Business has indicated that students find it difficult to apply to business problems the knowledge of mathematics gained from courses in Mathematics or Engineering Departments. Many business schools now require one or two mathematics courses; frequently these are taught in a mathematics department or by mathematicians in a business school. Although such courses may use some business examples, in all likelihood students need an additional "applied mathematics" course before they can use quantitative techniques effectively to study and solve business problems. This book is intended as a text for such a course. It should also be useful to students (and others) who learned their calculus many years ago, have not used it in the meantime, and now find a need to apply it.

The contents and structure of the book have been dictated by this objective. Approximately half of the contents is formal mathematics and half is application. The mathematical subject matter has been selected on the basis of importance in the applications. It includes topics usually covered in an elementary or intermediate calculus course as well as others which are rarely treated. No attempt has been made to make the treatment of the mathematics completely rigorous in the modern sense. This is not only unnecessary but would also cause a needless diversion. The danger in such a lack of rigor, of course, is that students may attempt to apply a rule without realizing the "exceptions." To alleviate this danger to some extent, references are given, where necessary, to rigorous mathematical proofs. In addition, the similarities between the unusual case in the real-life problem and the corresponding exceptions to the rule in the mathematics formulation and solution are emphasized in the business or economic interpretations.

The treatment of each subject begins at a relatively elementary level. The reason for this is the varying mathematical background levels of the students for whom the book is intended. For example, one student who does not know what a matrix is may have had considerable course work in the calculus, whereas another student's experience may be exactly the reverse. The material is therefore described in sufficient detail so that a student can follow areas in which his background is deficient; consequently, it is in more detail than necessary to accommodate a student who is familiar with the material. Summaries are given at the end of some chapters; from these the advanced student should be able to determine which sections he needs to review.

The applied side of the text consists of a large number of examples and exercises, ranging from very short illustrations to extensive examples covering several pages. The examples, in addition to providing motivation for the student and practice in the application of theory, usually make it easier to learn the mathematics, since the business interpretations frequently illuminate abstruse mathematical points. A number of the examples are analyzed by more than one technique. This emphasizes the relationships among the different mathematical tools and frequently helps to clarify the assumptions in the example.

The examples and exercises have been selected to illustrate the application of mathematics to different functional fields of business: organization theory, accounting, finance, production, and marketing. The relatively large number of examples from the different fields makes it possible for an instructor to select those most appropriate for his course if he does not find time to cover them all. The practical application of the models presented is greatly accelerated through the use of electronic computers. Typical computer output is used whenever appropriate.

The topics covered are grouped into five parts. These are arranged, as far as practicable, in order of increasing mathematical difficulty. Within each part each chapter is logically distinct and each section in each chapter has its own exercises. Within each of the five parts, the mathematics is presented first and is then followed by examples, extensions, or proofs. The relationship of the chapters is shown in Table 1.

The basic purpose of Part I is to provide practice in the formulation of business problems; the actual mathematics required is relatively elementary. The major applications are to accounting, organization theory, and mathematics of finance. Part II introduces the concept of optimization models of one variable. After a review of differential calculus of one variable, examples involving polynomials, rationals, transcendental functions, differential equations, and integration are given. The applications are to several different forms of the earnings function, investment problems, and marketing problems. The theory of optimization is extended in Part III to two-decision variable models with no constraints, equality constraints, and inequality constraints. The examples include

Table I Chapter Organization

Part	Mathematics	Chapters					
I	Algebra	1. How to formalize problems	2. Progressions and series	3. Mathematics of interest			
II	Functions of one variable	4. Management science models	5. Optimization of functions of one variable	6. Polynomials and rationals	7. Algebraic exponential logarithm	8. Integration differential equations	
III	Functions of two variables	9. Optimization of functions of two variables	10. Examples	11. Equality and inequality constraints			
IV	Linear systems	12. Matrices	13. Matrix inversion	14. Examples	15. Linear programming	16. Examples	17. Special cases of LP
V	Functions of many variables	18. Optimization of functions of many variables	19. Examples	20. Quadratic forms	21. Dynamic programming		

earnings functions of two variables, curve fitting by least squares, and a production problem. Part IV is concerned with linear systems of many variables and includes an introduction to matrices, solutions to systems of linear equations, applications of the input-output model, linear programming, and a number of examples of applications of linear programming. Part V discusses optimization of models of many variables as a generalization from Part III, using matrix notation from Part IV. The examples are extensions of some of the problems in Parts II, III, and IV. One chapter is devoted to dynamic programming.

The text is designed to provide material for a two-semester undergraduate or graduate sequence. However, the arrangement facilitates selection for a shorter course. A one-quarter (eleven-week) course (such as the one in the first year of the MBA program at Stanford) might contain Part I; Chapters 4, 5, and either 6 or 7, from Part II; Part III; and Chapters 12, 13, and 15 from Part IV.

Considerable flexibility in the order in which the material is used is possible. A course may start with Chapters 1, 4, 12, 13, and 15 since Chapters 12 and 13 on matrices and Chapters 15 and 17 on linear programming are presented from an elementary point of view. (The treatment of the transportation model and the assignment model makes it possible to cover them after Chapter 4 if desired.) This arrangement is particularly advantageous in cases where students are familiar with calculus but not with linear algebra. Covering these subjects early in the course makes it possible to give students a second exposure in the applications in the latter part of the course.

For advanced students, a course could begin with Chapter 4 and go directly to Part IV, if the instructor wishes to emphasize linear programming. On the other hand, if an instructor wishes to emphasize that linear programming is a special case of optimizing a function subject to inequality constraints, Chapter 11 in Part III would be covered first.

In general, the mathematics is presented first and then applied to examples. The order could be reversed so that examples are discussed first; this sometimes helps to provide motivation. The separation of the examples from the mathematical developments makes it convenient to use the examples by themselves in courses where the mathematics is taken from other sources.

Almost all the examples and exercises are based on, adapted from, or were suggested by papers appearing in the literature or by unpublished manuscripts. Acknowledgments appear as footnotes in cases where direct quotations are used; otherwise, the source is stated in the "Notes and References" section at the end of chapters.

In some cases it has not been possible to determine the original source: any failure to acknowledge sources is unintentional. The material in the text has been used in several different courses at the Graduate School of Business during the past six years. Former students have contributed to the form of the material and many of them will undoubtedly recognize the material, especially some of the exercises.

The book could not have been completed without the encouragement and help of the Dean, the Faculty, and staff of the Graduate School of Business. It is a pleasure to acknowledge, in particular, the help of John Haldi and Richard Young, whose comments on the final draft resulted in substantial improvements; and of Jo Ann Weidmann (now Mrs. Edwin Zschau) and Mrs. Eleanor Hendry.

Stanford, California   DANIEL TEICHROEW
April 1964

Contents

Part I   Formulating Business Problems, 1

1. Formalizing Business Problems   **3**
  A. Procedure for formalizing problems, 4
    Determine what is required, 4
    Identify variables or elements and assign symbols, 5
    Express relationships among the elements mathematically, 7
    Simplify and solve, 10
    Verify the correctness of the mathematical formulation and
      the results, 11
    Interpret the results and implement, 12
  B. Breakeven analysis, 14
    Breakeven point, 14
    Allocated costs, 18

2. Problems Involving Progressions and Series   **24**
  A. Mathematics of progressions, 24
    Arithmetic progression, 24
    Geometric progression, 26
    Infinite series, 28
  B. An analysis of depreciation methods, 32
    Change from DDB to SLD, 39
  C. Administrative costs and size of the firm, 42
  D. Organizational efficiency, 48

3. Mathematics of Interest   **53**
  A. Formulas for present and future values, 53
    The value, F, at the end of n periods of a benefit b_0, 54
    Present value, P, of a benefit b_n, 55
    The value, F, at the end of n periods of a benefit of b
      per second, 55
    The present value, P, of a benefit of b per period, 56
    The present value, P, of a non-uniform series, 57
    Nomial and effective interest rates, 57
  B. Investements, 62
    Accept or reject an investment, 62
    More than one possible investment, 64

C. Rent or buy decision, 67
Rent or buy decision, 67
Effect of other depreciation methods and discounting, 70
D. The internal rate of return, 75
Definition, 75
Multiple rates of return, 78
The algorithm for computing the IRRI, 81

Part II   One-Decision Variable Optimization Models, 87

4. Management Science Models   89
A. Formulation of models, 90
Specify the decision variable and list the alternatives, 90
Specify the objective, 91
Identify the uncontrollable variables and parameters, 91
Develop the model, 92
B. Solution of models, 94
Enumeration of alternatives, 94
Graphic solution, 95
Analytic solution, 96
C. Ordered alternatives, 100
Single machine case, 100
Sequence of machines, 103
D. Combinatorial alternatives—least-cost testing sequence, 104

5. Optimization of Function of One Variable   116
A. Review of differentiation, 116
Basic rules, 116
Derivatives of elementary functions, 116
⊗ The Taylor expansion, 121
B. Solving an equation, 123
The interpolation method, 123
Newton's method, 124
C. Optimization of functions of one variable, 128
Local extrema, 129
Global extrema, 134
D. Characteristics of functions of one variable, 139
Concavity and convexity, 139
Other characteristics, 142
E. General earnings function and marginal analysis, 146
General earnings function, 146
Marginal analysis, 148
Average function, 150

6. Models Involving Polynomials and Rational Functions   156
A. Polynomials and rationals, 157
Polynomials of one variable, 157

The rational functions, 160
B. Polynomial objective function: Price wars, 161
C. An investment decision in a life insurance company, 165
   Statement of the problem, 165
   Assumptions, 167
   Qualitative analysis of the problem, 167
   Development of the model, 169
   Verifying the model, 171
   Optimization, 173

7. Models Involving Algebraic and Transcendental Functions   180
A. Algebraic and transcendental functions, 180
   Algebraic functions, 180
   Exponential and logarithmic functions, 181
B. Continuous interest, 185
C. Optimization decisions in the single-project problem with variable
   project life, 190
D. Monotonic transformations, 195
E. Grocery store sales model, 199

8. Models Involving Integration and Differential Equations   208
A. Review of integration, 208
   Elementary integration, 208
   Integration of rational functions, 211
   The definite integral, 213
B. Differential equations, 220
   Definition, 220
   Separable variables, 221
   Homogeneous equations, 222
   Linear equations, 223
C. Differential equation model, 228
   Assumption 1, 228
   Assumption 2, 229
D. Diffusion model, 232
   Basic diffusion model, 232
   Diffusion model incorporating growth and advertising, 234
   An optimization model, 237

Part III   Two-Decision Variable Optimization Models, 243

9. Optimization of Functions of Two-Decision Variables   245
A. Functions of two variables, 245
   Earnings function for a consulting firm, 246
   Polynomials of degree two, 250
   Other functions, 253
B. Calculus of functions of two variables, 255
   Partial derivatives, 255

Higher-order derivatives, 257
The total differential, 258
Differentiation of functions of functions, 261
Implict functions, 262
Taylor expansion, 264
C. Optimization, 266
Conditions for extreme points, 266
Concave and convex functions, 273
D. Nonlinear earnings function of two variables, 275

10. Examples of Optimization with Two-Decision Variables   280
A. The Holt, Modigliani, Muth model, 280
B. Curve fitting by least squares, 284
C. Earnings function: higher-order polynomials in two variables, 287

11. Optimization Subject to Constraints   295
A. Equality constraints, 295
Substitution, 295
Lagrange multipliers, 296
Remarks and discussion, 300
B. Inequality constraints, 302
One inequality constraint, 303
Kuhn-Tucker conditions, 306
Kuhn-Tucker conditions for more than one inequality
constraint, 309
C. Linear objective, linear, and non-negative constraints, 313
Linear objective function, 313
Non-negativity constraint, 315

Part IV   Linear Systems, 323

12. Introduction to Matrices and Linear Systems   325
A. Matrices, 325
Example of matrices, 325
Definitions, 327
Matrix operations, 331
Properties of matrix operation, 341
B. Systems of linear equations in two unknowns, 343
Solution by algebraic elimination, 344
Solution by determinants, 345
Linear independence, 348
Solution by systematic elimination, 350

13. Matrix Inversion and Linear Systems   357
A. Matrix inversion, 357
Definition of the inverse, 357
Computation of the inverse by solving linear equations, 358
Computation of the inverse by determinants, 360

B. Three equations in three unknowns, 362
  Solution by determinants, 363
  Inverse of a 3 × 3 matrix by determinants, 364
  Systematic elimination, 366
C. *n* equations in *n* unknowns, 368
  Solution by determinants, 368
  Properties of determinants, 370
D. Partitioning of matrices, 373
E. *m* equations in *n* unknowns 378
  More equations than unknowns ($m > n$), 379
  More unknowns than equations ($n > m$), 380
  General procedure, 383

14. Examples of the Use of Matrices in Business Problems   **387**
A. Matrices in a production problem, 387
  Graphical solution, 388
  Solution by matrix multiplication, 390
  Production requirements and costs, 394
  Solution by matrix inversion, 395
  Generalization, 396
B. Requirements and cost allocation in joint production, 398
  The problem, 398
  Fictitious processes, 399
  Production requirements, 402
  Cost allocation, 402
C. The input-output model, 411

15. Linear Programming   **415**
A. Introduction, 415
  Formulation of linear programming problems, 415
  The product-mix problem—two products and two machines, 417
B. Solution of simple linear programming problems by graphical
  methods and enumeration of alternatives, 420
  Two products and two machines, 420
  Two products and three machines, 424
  Three products and two machines, 426
C. Management planning information from linear programming
  models, 434
  Slack variables, 434
  Linear programming as an aid to management decision-
    making, 437
  The general LP models with equality constraints, 440
  Verification of optimal solutions, 442
  LP as a special case of nonlinear programming, 447
D. The simplex method for solving linear programming problems, 449
  Algebraic solution, 449
  The simplex tableau, 445

E. Examples of linear programming models, 463
    Example 1, 463
    Example 2, 465

16. **Examples of Linear Programming**   **469**
  A. An Investment Problem, 470
  B. Machine loading, 475
  C. The warehouse problem, 477
  D. Production and employment scheduling, 485
    Introduction, 485
    The cost functions, 485
  E. Alcatraz National Bank, 492
  F. The Personal Toiletries Company, 498

17. **Special Cases of Linear Programming**   **503**
  A. The transportation model, 504
    Statement of the problem, 504
    First feasible schedule, 505
    Evaluation and continuation, 509
    Shortcuts, 511
    Alternate best programs, 512
    Derived optimum programs, 513
    Degenerate solutions, 514
    Summary of procedure, 516
    Linear programming formulation, 519
  B. The assignment problem, 520
    Statement of the problem, 521
    Constructing a first assignment, 521
    Determining if the assignment is feasible, 522
    Revising the assignment, 523
    Summary of procedure, 524
    Linear programming formulation, 524
  C. The dual, 527
    A valuation problem, 527
    The relationship between the primal and the dual models, 532

Part V   Multivariate Optimization Models, 541

18. **Optimization Models with Many Variables**   **543**
  A. Optimization of functions of many variables, 544
    Calculus of functions of many variables, 544
    Extreme values, 547
  B. Optimization subject to equality constraints, 551
    Substitution method, 551
    Lagrange multipliers, 552
    More than one equality constraint, 559

C. Optimization subject to inequality constraints, 561
   The general optimization problem, 561
   General statement of the Kuhn-Tucker conditions, 563

19. Examples of Optimization Models with Many Variables   **569**
A. Polynomials of degree two, 569
   Representation in matrix form, 569
   Differentiation, 571
   Optimization, 572
B. Holt, Modigliani, Muth model, 574
   Matrix formulation, 574
   Optimization, 577
   Optimization using Lagrange multipliers, 579
C. Curve fitting by least squares, 580
D. Portfolio selection, 584

20. Quadratic Forms   **592**
A. Transformations of polynomials of degree two, 592
   Linear transformations, 592
   Reduction to sums of squares, 598
B. Conditions for positive definiteness, 601
   Unconstrained variables, 601
   Positive definiteness under one linear constraint, 602
   Positive definiteness under more than one linear constraint, 604
C. Sufficient conditions for local extrema, 605
   Interior points, 605
   Sufficient conditions for extrema under one constraint, 607
   Sufficient conditions for extrema under more than one
     constraint, 608

21. Dynamic Programming   **610**
A. The backward algorithm, 610
   Analytic solution, 610
   The tabular method, 615
B. The forward algorithm, 621
   Analytic solution, 621
   The tabular method, 623
C. General statement, 627

Appendices   **637**
A. Miscellaneous formulas, 638
B. Interest tables, 640
C. Summary of procedure for reducing polynomial functions of
   second degree in two independent variables to standard form, 690

Answers to Selected Exercises   **695**

Author Index   **709**

Subject Index   **711**

Part One

FORMULATING

BUSINESS PROBLEMS

CHAPTER ONE

Formalizing Business Problems

This book is concerned with the use of mathematics in the formulation and solution of problems arising in business and other organizations concerned with the management of resources. Figure 1.1 shows diagrammatically four main phases in the use of mathematical formulations, or models, as they are usually called.

The sequence begins with identification of a problem area as a situation which requires some action. Ordinarily the initial description will be verbal. The second stage is the translation into a precise mathematical statement of the problem. Analysis is then carried out in the third stage and the result of the analysis is implemented in the real world. A new problem may be created thereby or attention directed to a different problem and the procedure is repeated as necessary.

The major emphasis in the first three chapters is on mathematical formulation of problems; the actions to be taken as a result of the analysis are discussed only briefly. The remaining chapters deal primarily with the selection of the course of action. This first chapter is concerned with outlining and illustrating a procedure to be followed in the formalization of business problems in quantitative terms. Formalization of problems is frequently considered to be an art and something that cannot be taught.

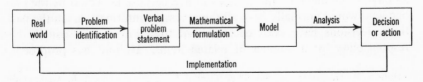

Figure 1.1

3

However, it forms such an essential first step in the application of mathematics to business that an attempt has been made here to develop a procedure. The reader who has difficulty in formulating problems may find it advisable to follow the procedure explicitly until he is familiar with the basic steps. However, no procedure will be applicable to all problems and this one is presented only as a guide.

A. PROCEDURE FOR FORMALIZING PROBLEMS

The following sequence of steps is recommended for attacking business problems which are initially stated in qualitative or semiqualitative terms. Each step is followed by an illustration in a particular example and another example is given in Section B.

Determine What Is Required. Generally, the first requirement is a mathematical statement of the relationship among the various factors in the problem. This statement may be needed for determining the consequences of a set of assumptions, for computing certain numerical values, or for determining particular values of one or more factors which satisfy stated conditions.

Example. This example illustrates the process of converting a verbal problem into a mathematical problem. The mathematics is relatively simple and involves only elementary algebra. Each of the steps in the procedure is illustrated explicitly by this example.

Retail stores have traditionally used "markup" as a measure of the profitability of an item. Used without caution, this would lead to the conclusion that an item with 40% markup is a more desirable item to stock than one that has only 20% markup. A little thought suggests that other factors should be examined. Turnover, for example, is clearly important; an item that "turns over" often is more desirable than one which turns over infrequently. Another important factor to consider is that the direct costs involved in handling the item vary from one item to another. If all these factors were to be taken into account simultaneously, decisions on which items to stock and the price to charge (markup) would all have to be made by the chief executive because he would be the only one who would normally have all the necessary information. In the past, these decisions have been decentralized to a buyer, who usually has responsibility for a number of related items. Holton[1] has proposed a

[1] Holton, R. H. (1961), "A Simplified Capital Budgeting Approach to Merchandise Management," *California Management Review*, III, pp. 82–104.

measure which he calls "contribution return on inventory investment," which incorporates the various factors and still leaves the decision with the buyer. The definition is:

"On any single item being considered for purchase by a department buyer, the contribution-return on inventory investment equals the contribution (in dollars) divided by the average investment (computed as one-half of the purchase price plus one-half of the cost of getting the merchandise into selling position), the whole expression being multiplied by the expected turnover rate and then by 100 to give a percentage figure. . . . The cost of getting the merchandise into selling position is assumed to consist of a direct cost in dollars per unit handled plus a variable cost which depends directly on the selling price. . . . The contribution is the selling price less purchase price and the cost of getting the merchandise into selling position."

Before a buyer can use the contribution return on inventory to select or price merchandise, a formula must be developed. Therefore, this formula and the method for its use are required in this example.

Identify Variables or Elements and Assign Symbols. The "elements" of business problems can be divided into two major groups. The first group consists of sets or classes of objects or entities about which certain statements can be made, e.g., all business corporations with corporate offices in Rhode Island. The second group contains variables whose values can be expressed as numbers, e.g., the annual sales in dollars for a firm with corporate offices in Rhode Island. This distinction is made because different mathematical techniques are employed on quantifiable entities than are employed on sets of discrete and distinct objects.

Usually it is not obvious what elements are important in a particular problem, and considerable experience is necessary to identify them. Frequently it is necessary to take factors which appear to be qualitative and express them in quantitative terms. For instance, a problem in quality control involving color consistency may make it necessary to express color gradations in terms of a numerical scale.

After all the elements are identified, a unique symbol should be assigned to each element. The symbols most frequently used are the individual small and capital Roman letters. Additional symbols are obtained by using letters from other alphabets, subscripts, superscripts, and combinations of letters. There are, therefore, many symbols that can be used, and the assignment should be designed to simplify the statement of the problem and aid in the development of the solution. One way the use of symbols achieves this is by reducing the amount of writing (or printing) required. It is, of course, necessary that the symbols be completely specific and unambiguous; e.g., it must be clear whether TC is the product of the variables represented by the symbols T and C, or whether it represents a single variable. The choice of symbols should take into consideration the complexity of the problem and the means by which it is to be solved. For example, assignment of symbols may be different if an electronic computer rather than a desk calculator is to be used in solving the problem.

Mathematicians have developed a number of conventions for assigning symbols which are followed in this book and which should be adhered to unless there are good reasons to the contrary. These consist of assigning classes of symbols to classes of variables such as constants, parameters, independent variables, and dependent variables. The small and capital letters at the beginning of the alphabet, *a*, *b*, *c*, etc., and small and capital Greek letters (Appendix Table 1) are usually used to represent variables which are treated as constants or parameters in a particular problem. The variables which will vary in a problem are usually designated by the letters near the end of the alphabet, *x*, *y*, *z*. The letters in the middle of the alphabet, *i*, *j*, *k*, *l*, *m*, and *n*, are used for subscripts. For example, the letter *c* may be the symbol for cost. If more than one type of cost is to be considered, the different types of cost must be distinguished. This can be done by using subscripts; e.g., c_1 could denote the first cost, c_2 the second, and c_i the *i*th cost.

One of the characteristics of business problems is that they tend to involve a large number of variables—so large that it becomes difficult to remember what each symbol stands for even if they are divided into classes. One technique that can be used is that of mnemonic symbols which help in recalling the definition of the symbol. We might, for example, use the symbol "*TVC*" to denote "total variable cost." Subscripts can also be mnemonic; c_o might represent ordering cost and c_c might represent carrying cost.

Example. The variables may be identified by italicizing elements in the definition: The *contribution return on inventory investment* equals the *contribution* (in dollars) divided by the *average investment* (computed as one-half of the *purchase price* plus one-half of the *cost of getting the merchandise into selling position*), the whole expression being multiplied by the *expected turnover rate* and then by *100* to give a percentage figure. The *cost of getting the merchandise into selling position* is assumed to consist of a *direct cost in dollars per unit handled* plus a *variable cost which depends directly on the selling price*. The contribution is the *selling price* less *the purchase price* and *the cost of getting merchandise into selling position*.

The symbols assigned to these variables in this example are the capital letters as given in the accompanying table.

Variables	Symbol
Contribution return on inventory investment	C
Contribution	C'
Average inventory investment	I
Purchase price	W
Cost of getting the merchandise into selling position	D
Expected turnover rate	T
Direct cost	D_1
Variable cost rate	D_2
Selling price	S

Express Relationships Among the Elements Mathematically.
The concept of a function is the most important mathematical tool for expressing relationships among variables; once the functional form is established, powerful techniques of mathematical analysis can be used. A function is a mathematical statement of a relationship between variables. It is defined explicitly if the form of the function is given; if $f(x) = a + bx$, the form of the function is a $a + bx$. This function defines the process whereby any number x which is fed into the operation is transformed into $f(x)$ which will be b times as large as x with a added to the product. If the exact form is not given, it may be expressed merely as $f(x)$. Among the more common symbols employed to express functional relationships are $f(x)$, $F(x)$, $g(x)$ and $\phi(x)$. A shorthand form of functional notation used frequently is the letter f by itself; this notation can be used when the variable is self-evident, as $f = a + bx$. Another way of expressing a functional relationship is to let $f(x)$ be represented by another variable; if $f(x) = 5 + 2x$ and if y is defined as equal to $f(x)$, then $y = f(x) = 5 + 2x$, or $y = 5 + 2x$.

It is desirable to distinguish among variables, parameters, independent and dependent variables, and equations. Variables are quantities in a relationship which vary in any given situation. They may assume any value or only values from a restricted group, but they do change. As noted above, variables are commonly represented by letters at the end of the alphabet; e.g., x, y, z. This, in a problem concerning gross pay as a function of hours worked, the number of hours worked and the gross pay are variables. If $y =$ gross pay, $x =$ hours worked, and $b =$ hourly rate, then $y = bx$.

Parameters are quantities which are regarded as fixed constants for a given problem. In the case of the expression of gross pay, b is the hourly rate of pay and is assumed to have a constant value for any given problem.

Consequently, it is considered to be a parameter. This relationship shows the variation in gross pay as the number of hours worked varies, *all other things being constant;* that is, factors which might change, other than hours worked, are held at a predetermined constant value. Consider the situation in which it is assumed that employees will work a given number of hours per week, say, 40, and it is desired to know what the effect on weekly gross pay will be if hourly rates of pay are changed. In this case, the factor held constant is the number of hours worked and the variable is the rate of pay. The roles of variable and parameter are interchanged because the problem itself has been changed.

The importance of understanding the nature of variables and parameters in developing mathematical statements of business problems is hard to overemphasize. In a verbal problem it is not always clear what factors can or should vary. The decision as to what factors are to be considered as parameters and what factors as variables is influenced by the nature of the problem and the requirements of the solution. Skill in making these decisions determines, to a great extent, the success with which mathematical models can be fitted to business problems.

The term "independent variable" refers in a mathematical sense to the variable from which the value of a function can be calculated. When a relationship is expressed as a function of a particular variable, that variable is the independent one. The dependent variable is the result of the operation of the function on the independent variable. In the function $f(x) = bx$ used above to express the relationship between gross pay, hours worked, and hourly rate, x is the independent and $f(x)$ is the dependent variable. This follows logically from the description of what the function represents. The employee works a certain number of hours, x, and from this his gross pay, $f(x)$, is computed. He is not given an arbitrary amount of gross pay and then told to work for it at a particular hourly rate.

The use of the variable notation $y = 5 + 2x$, rather than the functional notation $f(x) = 5 + 2x$, is a convenience in the situation where there is some doubt as to which variable is independent. The expression $y = 5 + 2x$ still implies that values of y are the result of operations on values of x. However, $y = 5 + 2x$ can be expressed as $y - 5 - 2x = 0$, or $5 + 2x - y = 0$. In these two expressions there is no indication as to which variable is independent or dependent. The expression can also be written as $x = y - 5/2$; the indication here is that y is the independent variable and x is the dependent variable.

An equation is a specific statement from which values of the variables in the function can be determined. For example, the expression $f(x) = 5 + 2x$ is recognized as the definition of a particular function of x. However, $5 + 2x = 9$ is an equation because it places constraints on the value of x which can satisfy the equality. Such values are termed the solution to the equation; e.g., the equation $5 + 2x = 9$ has a single solution $x = 2$.

A wide variety of different functions are used in business applications, but the most frequent are the elementary functions:

(*i*) The polynomial of degree n:
$f(x) = a_0 + a_1x + a_2x^2 + \cdots + a_nx^n$, n a positive integer, $a_n \neq 0$

(*ii*) Rational functions: $f(x) = P_m(x)/P_n(x)$ where P_i is a polynomial of degree i

(*iii*) The algebraic function: $f(x) = $ the solution of $P(x, f) = 0$ where $P(x, f)$ is a polynomial in two variables x and f.

(*iv*) The exponential function: $f(x) = e^x$

(*v*) The logarithmic function: $f(x) = \ln x$

Chapters 5, 6, and 7 contain short descriptions of these functions, summarizing the properties which are important in business applications.

The functions listed above are functions of a variable that can take any value in an interval. Frequently in business problems the variable can assume only integer values; for example, the number of units of an item in inventory. Sometimes a variable is continuous, but only measured in discrete units, e.g., time may be measured to the nearest tenth of an hour. Variables which can assume only a limited number of values are said to be *discrete* variables. It is common practice to ignore the fact that variables are discrete and to treat them as though they were continuous; usually no serious difficulty arises from this practice. The fact that a variable is discrete is sometimes emphasized by using a subscript, e.g., writing f_i instead of $f(i)$, or by using the letters i, j, k, l, m, or n to represent the variable.

The relationships among variables are frequently expressed as inequalities rather than as equalities. The notation used is as follows:

$$x > y \qquad x \text{ is greater than } y$$
$$x \geq y \qquad x \text{ is greater than, or equal to, } y$$
$$x < y \qquad x \text{ is less than } y$$
$$x \leq y \qquad x \text{ is less than, or equal to, } y$$

Example. One useful method for expressing relationships among the elements mathematically is to divide the verbal description into small parts, each of which can be translated into a simple mathematical expression. The verbal and mathematical expressions may be placed side by side:

The contribution return on inventory investment equals the contribution divided by the average inventory investment, the whole expression being multiplied by the expected turnover rate and by 100.

$$C = \left(\frac{C'}{I}\right)(T)\,(100) \tag{1}$$

Average investment equals one-half of the purchase price plus one-half the cost of getting the merchandise into selling position.

$$I = \tfrac{1}{2}W + \tfrac{1}{2}D \quad \text{or}$$
$$2I = W + D \tag{2}$$

Cost of getting merchandise into selling position equals direct cost in dollars plus a variable cost which depends directly on the selling price.

$$D = D_1 + D_2 S \tag{3}$$

The contribution is the selling price less the purchase price and the cost of getting the merchandise into selling position.

$$C' = S - W - D = S - 2I \tag{4}$$

A good example of the difficulty of translating from verbal to mathematical statement occurs in deriving (3). The verbal statement merely says variable cost depends directly on the selling price; i.e., is some (unspecified) function of the selling price. This has been interpreted as meaning that variable cost is directly proportional to selling price.

Simplify and Solve. After all the relationships have been expressed mathematically, the set of statements should be reduced to the simplest form. Intermediate variables should be eliminated.

Obtaining the solution will involve the use of appropriate mathematical techniques which can range from simple algebraic manipulations such as the basic operations on numbers and functions: addition, subtraction, multiplication, and division; elementary algebra and geometry; operations on equalities and inequalities, to elementary differentiation and integration and more complex mathematical operations.

Skill in solving problems depends first and foremost on familiarity with the mathematical techniques involved. However, there are "tricks" which are frequently involved. One of the most useful is to take a simple numerical example and work from its solution to the solution of the general problem.

Example. The problem asks for a formula for C as a function of variables T, S, D_1, D_2, and W. Expression (1) gives C as a function of

C', T, and I. I is given as a function of W and D in (2) and hence can be eliminated by substitution. Similarly, D is given as a function of D_1, D_2, and S in (3). C' is given as a function of S, D, and W by (4). Substituting gives:

$$C = \frac{100(S - 2I)T}{I} = 100T\left(\frac{S}{I} - 2\right)$$

$$= 100T\left(\frac{2S}{W + D_1 + D_2S} - 2\right)$$

$$= 100(2T)\left(\frac{S}{W + D_1 + D_2S} - 1\right) \tag{5}$$

The formula gives C as a function of the parameters. The formula for selling price, S, if required, can be obtained by solving (5) for S.

$$1 + \frac{C}{2 \cdot 100 \cdot T} = \frac{S}{W + D_1 + D_2S}$$

$$\left(1 + \frac{C}{2 \cdot 100 \cdot T}\right)(W + D_1) = S - D_2S\left(1 + \frac{C}{2 \cdot 100 \cdot T}\right)$$

$$S = \left[1 - D_2\left(1 + \frac{C}{2 \cdot 100 \cdot T}\right)\right]^{-1}\left(1 + \frac{C}{2 \cdot 100 \cdot T}\right)(W + D_1) \tag{6}$$

Verify the Correctness of the Mathematical Formulation and the Results. This step should frequently be started earlier in the process, but it certainly must be completed before the solution can be accepted. One of the most important requirements is that all statements must be consistent in the units used. Suppose the function is $f(x) = bx$, where x represents hours worked and $f(x)$ represents dollars of gross pay. The variables and parameters in this function obviously are not just pure numbers but have dimensions, and the function must be consistent in these dimensions. In this case, the function can be written

$$f(x) \text{ [dollars]} = (b)(x) \text{ [hours]}$$

$$\frac{f(x) \text{ [dollars]}}{(x) \text{ [hours]}} = b$$

Thus the dimension of b is dollars/hour, or dollars per hour. The dimension of the functional relationship is:

$$f(x) = b(x)$$

gross pay = hourly rate × number of hours worked

$$\text{dollars} = \left[\frac{\text{dollars}}{\text{hours}}\right] \text{[hours]}$$

If it were not obvious beforehand what the parameter b represented, analysis such as the above would soon provide the answer. It should be apparent that this kind of analysis is an excellent means of verifying the form of the mathematical representations.

The correctness of statements can often be verified by computing numerical values for selected values of the variables such as "end points." For example, a problem may involve the tax rate as a parameter. The tax rate may take any value from zero to 100%. The correctness of the solution to the problem can frequently be determined relatively easily at the "end points;" zero and 100% in this example. The correctness may also be examined by investigating the qualitative behavior of the solution. If the tax paid decreases as the tax rate increases, for example, we would suspect an error somewhere. Sketching the functions involved in a problem is also frequently useful. None of these methods guarantees that the solution is correct, but they do help in detecting errors.

It is important to note that there are two levels of verification involved. One must verify first that the statement of the problem is correct, and second that this statement has been formulated correctly in mathematical terms.

Example.   The dimension of S, W, and D_1 is (dollars) and D_2 is a pure number. Furthermore, T is expressed in (number per year). From (1) the dimensions of C are

$$(\text{percent})\left(\frac{\text{number}}{\text{year}}\right)(\text{number})$$

or percent per year.

The qualitative behavior of C as given by (5) may be verified since it increases as T and/or S increases, and it decreases as W, D_1, and D_2 increase.

Interpret the Results and Implement.   Since many mathematical operations may have occurred between the original statement of the problem and the "mathematical" solution, the final result is usually not expressed in the original variables. It is, therefore, necessary to express the results in terms of the physical quantities familiar to the potential user of the results. If the results require computation for use in specific cases, it may be advantageous to prepare aids such as tables or nomograms.

Example.   Suppose a buyer wishes to determine the contribution, for a given set of parameters, for a number of different selling prices. Let

$D_1 = \$4.00$, $D_2 = 0.10$, $W = \$10.00$, and $T = 6$. From (5) C can be computed for any selling price. If $S = \$20.00$,

$$C = (200)(6)\left[\frac{20}{10 + 4 + (0.1)20} - 1\right]$$

$$= (1200)\left[\frac{20}{16} - 1\right] = 300$$

This result can be verified by noting that on each unit there is a profit of $4.00, the total annual profit is $24.00, the average inventory investment is $8.00, and, therefore, the contribution return on inventory investment is 300% per year.

Suppose the buyer requires a certain C, say, 100% per year. Using the same data as above, the necessary selling price can be computed from (6):

$$S = \left[1 - 0.10\left(1 + \frac{100}{200(6)}\right)\right]^{-1}\left[\left(1 + \frac{100}{200(6)}\right)(10.00 + 4.00)\right] = 17.01$$

A table showing C as a function of S and T would facilitate the use of the formula by a buyer. An example of one such table appears below. The buyer would enter the table with the expected turnover rate and find the C corresponding to a given S, or interpolate to find S for a given C. The buyers would therefore be in a better position to evaluate alternative selling prices.

Contribution Return on Inventory for Selected Turnover Rates, T, and Selling Prices, S, for $D_1 = 4.00$, $D_2 = 0.10$, and $W = 10.00$

S \\ T	16.00	17.00	18.00	19.00	20.00
6	30.72	99.36	167.04	234.00	300.00
8	40.96	132.48	222.72	312.00	400.00
10	51.20	165.60	278.40	390.00	500.00
12	61.44	198.72	334.08	468.00	600.00

EXERCISES

1. A retailer is selling a quantity, q_1 per period, at a price, p_1, of an item for which he pays an amount c. His only other cost that varies with selling price is the commission, r, expressed as a fraction of selling price.

   (a) The firm is considering a change to a new price, p_2. Show that the ratio of the quantity that can be sold at the new price, say, q_2, to the quantity that was sold previously, q_1, which will leave the total earnings per period unchanged is

$$\frac{q_2}{q_1} = \frac{m}{m + (1 - r)n_p}$$

where n_p is the change in price divided by p_1 and the contribution, m, is the ratio of the difference between selling price and total cost divided by to the selling price.

(b) An item having a commission rate of 15% has been costing $6.00 and selling for $10.00. A new selling price of $11.00 is being considered. How much would sales have to increase to maintain the same earnings?

(c) Show that if the cost changes and the total earnings and price are to be unchanged, the quantity q_2 that can (or must be) sold is given by

$$\frac{m_1}{m_2} = \frac{q_2}{q_1}$$

(d) The cost of the item in (b) has been increased to $6.50. How much will sales have to increase to maintain the same earnings if selling price remains at $10.00?

B. BREAK-EVEN ANALYSIS

This example illustrates the formulation of a business problem in terms of linear functions of one independent variable. The steps outlined in Section A are followed but are not identified explicitly.

Break-even Point

A firm produces a single product and sells all that it produces at a fixed price. It has a "fixed" cost independent of the number of units produced, plus a variable cost directly proportional to the number of units produced. The Earnings of the firm are equal to the Revenues less Costs. The production level, the number of units produced, is the independent variable and, therefore, it will be denoted by x, i.e.,

$$x = \text{number of units produced}$$

The dependent variables are the total revenue and total cost. Let

$$R = \text{total revenue (dollars)}$$
$$C = \text{total cost (dollars)}$$

and

$$a = \text{fixed cost (dollars)}$$
$$b = \text{variable cost per unit (dollars/unit)}$$
$$e = \text{selling price (dollars/unit)}$$

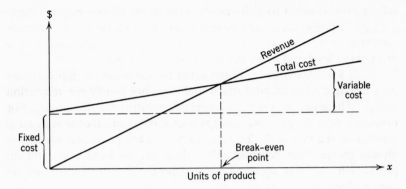

Figure 1.2   Break-even chart.

Then

$$\text{Revenue: } R(x) = ex \qquad x \geq 0; \quad e \geq 0 \qquad (1)$$

$$\text{Cost: } C(x) = a + bx \qquad x \geq 0; \quad a \geq 0; \quad b \geq 0 \qquad (2)$$

Under the assumptions made here, both R and C are linear functions of x. The "break-even point" is defined as the value of x for which total revenue equals total cost; i.e., the value of x which satisfies the equation

$$R(x) = C(x)$$

A geometrical solution can be obtained by drawing the graphs $R(x)$ and $C(x)$ on a "Break-even Chart" (Fig. 1.2). The break-even point is the point of intersection of these two lines. If production (and sales) exceeds the break-even value, revenues exceed costs and earnings are positive. If not, costs exceed revenues and the operations for the period result in a loss.

The algebraic solution is obtained by replacing R and C by their values in terms of x, and by solving for x:

$$R(x) = C(x)$$

or

$$ex = a + bx$$

and the solution is

$$x = \frac{a}{e - b} \qquad (3)$$

This solution will be defined only if $e \neq b$ (because it is not legitimate to divide by zero) and will be positive only if $e > b$. These mathematical observations can be interpreted as follows:

1. If $e = b$, the two linear functions are parallel, and R cannot equal C unless $a = 0$. Where $a = 0$, R is always equal to C. Thus, if unit

selling price is equal to unit variable cost, there cannot be any break-even point unless there are no fixed costs. In the case where there are no fixed costs, revenue exactly balances total cost, regardless of the production level and every point is a break-even point.

2. If $e < b$, a mathematical solution exists for the equation, but it occurs at a negative level of production and does not satisfy the restriction $x \geq 0$. Therefore, it is not an acceptable solution for the model. For positive values of x, the two straight lines diverge and R cannot equal C unless $a = 0$ and $x = 0$. There is no break-even point because cost is always greater than revenue unless there are no fixed costs and no production; if there are fixed costs or production, total costs will be greater than total revenue.

3. If $e > b$, there is a single positive solution for any set of value of a, e, and b. Under the assumptions of this example there is always one single level of production at which the firm breaks even when the unit selling price is greater than the unit variable cost.

The firm may also be interested in determining the production required to produce earnings of $\$k$. Revenues will have to exceed costs by that amount or

$$R(x) - C(x) = k$$
$$ex - (a + bx) = k$$

or

$$x = \frac{k + a}{e - b} \tag{4}$$

Example. Suppose a firm with the following accounting data:

Unit selling price	$	50
Selling and other expenses:		
Fixed	$ 6,000	
Variable	$	2 per unit sold
Manufacturing costs:		
Material	$	18 per unit produced
Direct labor (2 hours at $3)	$	6 per unit produced
Overhead costs:		
Fixed	$60,000	
Variable	$	2 per unit produced

wishes to determine (*i*) the break-even point, and (*ii*) production level yielding net earnings of $22,000. Then

$$a = 6{,}000 + 60{,}000 = \$66{,}000 \quad \text{(fixed costs)}$$
$$b = 18 + 6 + 2 + 2 = \$28 \quad \text{(variable costs per unit)}$$
$$e = \$50$$

(*i*) The break-even point, x, occurs for a production level equal to:

$$x = \frac{a}{e - b} = \frac{66{,}000}{50 - 28} = 3{,}000 \text{ units}$$

At this level revenue is $R = 50(3{,}000) = 150{,}000$
and costs are

$$C = 66{,}000 + 28(3{,}000) = 150{,}000$$

(*ii*) To obtain a net profit of \$22,000, let $k = 22{,}000$ in (4). Then

$$x = \frac{66{,}000 + 22{,}000}{50 - 28} = 4{,}000 \text{ units}$$

These solutions could also be obtained graphically from the break-even chart shown in Fig. 1.3.

Formulas (3) and (4) provide a method for calculating the break-even point and the earnings at any production level. A firm is usually not interested in just breaking even; the owner or the stockholders want to have earnings as large as possible. Under the assumptions of this section the earnings continually increase as the production level increases; hence the "largest" earnings would come from producing an infinite amount. In practical situations, the assumptions that have been made here do not hold for very large production. Frequently the production facility has a limited capacity; it is physically impossible to produce more than a

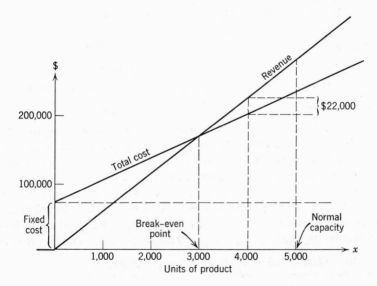

Figure I.3

certain number of units per period. In cases where production can be increased, the "variable cost rate" increases; for example, if production is increased by use of overtime labor. Or, the revenue may not be proportional to production either because not all units can be sold or because the selling price per unit decreases as production increases. The effect of these factors will be analyzed in later sections.

Allocated Costs. Break-even analysis is sometimes used in setting selling price based on a cost per unit. This cost must include fixed costs as well as variable costs. One method for incorporating fixed costs consists of defining a "normal volume" and allocating fixed manufacturing costs at this normal volume.

The data in the example would appear in the following form, if the normal volume were 5,000 units or 10,000 direct labor hours:

Normal volume = 10,000 direct labor hours or 5,000 units of product.

Overhead Burden	Total	Rate/direct labor hour
Fixed costs	60,000	$6
Variable costs	10,000	1
	70,000	$7

Standard Manufacturing Costs (per unit of product)

Material	$18
Direct labor (2 hours at $3)	6
Burden (2 hours at $7)	14
	$38

Selling and other expenses:

Fixed	$6,000
Variable	2 per unit sold

Unit Selling Price	$50

The fixed manufacturing costs have been allocated on a direct labor hour basis, and the rate of allocation is computed assuming production at normal capacity. When production level is less than this normal volume, fixed expenses are understated and a correction, called the "cost of idleness," "activity variation loss," or "the volume variance," has to be made. When the production level is above the normal volume, fixed expenses are overstated. For example, for an actual production level of 3,000 units, the total costs, computed above to be 150,000, is given by

$$\underset{\text{manufacturing costs}}{(38)(3,000)} + \underset{\text{selling costs}}{6,000 + (2)(3,000)} + \underset{\text{volume variance}}{(2,000)(2)(6)}$$

$$= 114,000 + 12,000 + 24,000 = 150,000$$

The last term is the product of the unused capacity (units of product), the number of hours of direct labor per unit, and the burden rate for fixed (overhead) costs (dollars per hour). Note that the burden rate used in computing the volume variance includes only the fixed costs because the variable costs have not actually been incurrred.

The expression of the total cost may be written as

$$C(x) = \alpha + \beta x + \lambda(d - x) \tag{5}$$

where α = fixed costs not included in burden (dollars)

β = standard manufacturing and variable selling cost (dollars per unit)

λ = overhead burden rate for fixed costs per unit of product at normal capacity (dollars per unit)

d = normal capacity (units of products)

As before,

$$R(x) = ex \tag{6}$$

and the break-even point is obtained for $R(x) = C(x)$, or

$$ex = \alpha + \beta x + \lambda(d - x)$$

or

$$x = \frac{\alpha + \lambda d}{e + \lambda - \beta}$$

In the example, $\alpha = 6,000$, $\beta = 40$, $\lambda = 12$, $d = 5,000$ and $e = 50$

$$x = \frac{6,000 + (12)(5,000)}{50 + 12 - 40} = 3,000 \text{ units}$$

The result must, of course, be the same as before, since this accounting procedure does not influence the final earnings. The income computation for a production of 3,000 units might appear as follows:

Sales (3,000 at $50)		$150,000
Less cost of goods sold (3,000 at $38)		114,000
Gross profit:		$ 36,000
Less selling and other expenses:		
Fixed	$6,000	
Variable	6,000	12,000
Operating income:		$ 24,000
Less: Volume variance		
(2,000 units at $12)		24,000
Net income (loss)		$ 0

The mathematical description or model in (1) and (2) contains 3 parameters, a, b, and e, while the model (5) and (6) contains 5 parameters, α, β, λ, d, and e. The latter can be reduced to the former by using appropriate combinations of parameters. The two expressions for the total cost must be equivalent.

$$C(x) = a + bx \qquad \text{from (2)}$$
$$C(x) = \alpha + \beta x + \lambda(d - x) \qquad \text{from (5)}$$
$$= \alpha + \lambda d + x(\beta - \lambda)$$

Therefore

$$a = \alpha + \lambda d$$

and

$$b = \beta - \lambda$$

In general, models should contain as few parameters as possible. Why, then, are these extra parameters introduced? The reason is primarily historical. Firms have frequently found it necessary to incorporate fixed costs as burden to ensure that fixed costs would not be neglected when prices are determined. The use of mathematical models ensures that all factors will be considered and can therefore be simplified as much as possible.

EXERCISES

1. Determine the production level, for the example, for earnings of $55,000.
2. The owner of a travel agency receives 15% commission on all tickets that his agency sells. He employs a supervisor at a salary of $5,000 per year. In addition, he hires temporary help at $2.00 per hour, whenever needed. One hour of temporary help is needed for each $10 received in commission. Other expenses include rent, $10 per day on a long-term contract, and interest expenses equal to 2% of the value of the tickets sold. Assume the office is open 250 days per year.
   (a) Determine the breakeven point, and earnings if ticket sales are $1,200 per day.
   (b) Determine the breakeven point, and earnings if ticket sales are $1,200 per day, if the contract with the supervisor calls for a salary of $5,000 per year, plus 10% of earnings.
3.[1] The Western Paper Company operates a cardboard plant in Seattle. The plant has been operating at 75% capacity, producing 2,700 tons per month at a total cost of $77⅓ per ton. Included in the total cost per ton is the cost of wastepaper, the major raw material. For each 100 tons of product, 80 tons of wastepaper are required. Up to 1,440 tons per month of wastepaper can be purchased locally for $18.75 per ton. Additional wastepaper may be purchased through brokers at $27.50 per ton delivered at the plant. Of the present total

[1] Adapted from: Grant, E. L., and W. G. Ireson (1960), *Principles of Engineering Economy*, Fourth Edition. The Ronald Press Company, New York.

monthly costs at the plant, $59,400 is estimated to be fixed regardless of production level.   The remainder, with the exception of the cost of wastepaper, varies in proportion to output.

(a) Show that if cardboard can be sold F.O.B. the plant at $86, the breakeven point is 1,800 tons per month.

(b) Western Paper has another plant in Oregon which has been operating at 60% capacity, producing 3,600 tons per month at a total cost per ton of $85. Local wastepaper costs $20 per ton and is limited to 4,000 tons per month. Additional wastepaper can be obtained through brokers at $27.50 per ton delivered at the plant. Of the present operating costs, $108,000 per month is regarded as fixed cost. Determine the breakeven point if the same price applies.

Notes and References

Section A

An excellent source on formulating mathematical problems is:

Polya, G. (1945), *How to Solve It*, Princeton University Press, or (Doubleday Anchor Books, Inc., Garden City, N.Y., 1957, 2nd ed.). Parts are reproduced in Newman, J. R., Ed. (1956), *The World of Mathematics*, Simon and Schuster, New York.

Section B

Break-even analysis is widely discussed in the literature on Accounting and Economics. The example used is taken from:

Patrick, A. W. (1958), "Some Observations on the Break-even Chart," *Accounting Review*, **33**, pp. 573–80.

For a mathematical treatment of the problem of cost allocation, see:

Vazsonyi, A. (1956), "Operations Research and the Accountant," Conference Handbook for AMA Special Finance Conference October 3–5, New York.

Cost-Volume-Profit relationships are discussed in:

Willson, J. D. (1960), "Practical Applications of Cost-Volume-Profit Analysis," *N.A.A. Bulletin XLI*, No. 7, pp. 5–18.

Frommer, A. M. (1963), "Determining Compensating Sales Quantities for Price and Cost Changes," *N.A.A. Bulletin XLIV*, No. 9, pp. 35–42.

Tse, J. W. D. (1960), *Profit Planning Through Volume-Cost Analysis*, Macmillan Co., New York.

Chapter Exercises

Exercise 3 is based on:

McGee, C. G. (1956), "Operations Research in the American Thread Company", *Operations Research*, **4**, pp. 587–598.

EXERCISES

1. Define and give an example of:

model	breakeven point
dimensional analysis	normal volume
revenue function	capacity
cost function	subscripts
earnings function	

2. The following bids were received from a construction firm for the construction of an outdoor patio cover:

Width	Length	Bid ($)
8'	30'	872
10'	30'	1,090
12'	30'	1,285
12'	24'	1,055
12'	18'	790

Determine the pricing policy of the firm, assuming that the same quality of material is used regardless of the size of the cover. The pricing policy does not have to give the bids exactly. Look for a simple policy which will approximate the bids received. Interpret the policy in terms of fixed and variable costs.

3. The Acme Playing Card Table Manufacturing Company produces a number of different card tables which vary in finish and design, though the amount of labor and production effort involved is approximately the same for each model. The firm has had very little labor turnover, due primarily to management's policy of maintaining relatively stable production. However, the demand for the different types of tables varies greatly and the policy of maintaining stable production has led to fluctuating inventory. In the past the inventory of the individual models has also fluctuated and management has now established a policy that inventories for the different tables should be approximately the same relative to normal usage. If total inventory is low, inventory of each of the different types should also be low; if total inventory is high, inventory of all types of tables should also be high.

Production is scheduled for four-week periods. The management policy is intrepreted as stating that the difference between available inventory at the end of a period and the allowance for safety, divided by the normal sales during a period, should be equal to a constant and this constant should be the same for each type of table. The available inventory at the end of a period is equal to the available inventory at the present (beginning of the period) plus the production during the period less estimated orders for this period. The allowance for safety is defined as the difference between the maximum sales in any one of the last eight periods and the production during this period. Orders for this period are estimated to be equal to the actual sales during the past period. Normal sales are defined as the average sales during the last eight periods. The total production during a period is the sum of the production of each type of table.

(a) Show that if management sets the total production for the next four-week period (period j) to be equal to C units and

$$y_{ij} = \text{sales of type } i \text{ in period } j$$
$$x_{ij} = \text{production of type } i \text{ in period } j$$
$$z_{ij} = \text{inventory of type } i \text{ at beginning of period } j$$

all expressed in units, then

$$x_{i,j} = \frac{1}{2}\left[\frac{K}{8} \sum_m y_{i,j-m} - z_{ij} + y_{i,j-1} + \max_m \{y_{i,j-m}\}\right]$$

$$m = 1, 2, \ldots 8 \qquad (1)$$

where
$$K = \left[\frac{8}{\sum_i \sum_m y_{i,j-m}} \right]\left[2C + \sum_i z_{ij} - \sum_i y_{i,j-1} - \sum_i \max_m \{y_{i,j-m}\} \right]$$

(b) Show that if management sets the total inventory at the end of the period to be equal to I, then x_{ij} is given by (1) where

$$K = \left[\frac{8}{\sum_i \sum_m y_{i,j-m}} \right]\left[2I - \sum_i z_{ij} + \sum_i y_{i,j-1} - \sum_i \max_m \{y_{i,j-m}\} \right]$$

CHAPTER TWO

Problems Involving Progressions and Series

Many business problems involve a sequence of numbers in which each number is related in some way to others near it in the sequence. A *progression* is a particular kind of sequence of numbers, usually called terms, with the property that each number in the sequence may be determined from the *preceding* number by some rule. Let t_n denote the nth term, then t_{n-1} will denote the term preceding the nth term or the $(n-1)$st term, and t_i will denote the ith term. The "rule" or "property" of the progression can be expressed by

$$t_i = f(t_{i-1})$$

that is, the ith term is some function, f, of the $(i-1)$st term. The first term, t_1, is given.

Some problems associated with progressions are to determine f, the rule by which a term can be computed from the preceding one, to develop a formula for the nth term when t_1 and the rule as given, and to determine the sum of the first n terms.

Two types of progressions, the arithmetic progression and the geometric progression, are of particular interest; both are discussed in detail in Section A. Applications using progressions are given in Sections B, C, and D.

A. MATHEMATICS OF PROGRESSIONS

Arithmetic Progression

An arithmetic progression is a sequence of numbers such that any term after the first may be obtained by adding a constant, known as the common difference, d, to the previous term, i.e.,

$$t_i = f(t_{i-1}) = t_{i-1} + d \qquad (1)$$

If the first term is a, then the second term will be $a + d$, the third term $a + 2d$, and the nth term will be $a + (n - 1)d$. Examples of arithmetic progressions are:

$$2, \quad 4, \quad 6, \quad 8, \quad \cdots$$
$$3, \quad 2, \quad 1, \quad 0, \quad \cdots$$
$$7, \quad 9\tfrac{1}{2}, \quad 12, \quad 14\tfrac{1}{2}, \quad \cdots$$

The difference in these series is 2, -1, and $2\tfrac{1}{2}$, respectively. Note that the common difference, d, may be positive or negative.

A formula for the sum of the first n terms of the arithmetic progression may be obtained by noting that if the nth term is denoted by L, then

$$L = a + (n - 1)d \qquad (2)$$

and the next to last term, the $(n - 1)$st term, is $a + (n - 2)d$ or $L - d$. The sum, s, of the first n terms can then be written as:

$$s = (a) + (a + d) + (a + 2d) + \cdots + (L - 2d) + (L - d) + (L)$$

Rewriting in the reverse order gives:

$$s = (L) + (L - d) + (L - 2d) + \cdots + (a + 2d) + (a + d) + (a)$$

Adding the two expressions for s, term by term, gives:

$$\begin{aligned}
2s &= (a + L) + (a + L + d - d) + (a + L + 2d - 2d) + \cdots \\
&\quad + (a + L + 2d - 2d) + (a + L + d - d) + (a + L) \\
&= (a + L) + (a + L) + (a + L) + \cdots \\
&\quad + (a + L) + (a + L) + (a + L) \\
&= n(a + L)
\end{aligned}$$

and

$$s = \frac{n(a + L)}{2} \qquad (3)$$

$$= \frac{n}{2}[2a + (n - 1)d] \qquad \text{since } L = a + (n - 1)d \qquad (4)$$

Example 1. The progression 2, 4, 6, 8 ... has $a = 2$, $d = 2$, and therefore the nth term, from (2), is $2 + (n - 1)2 = 2n$ and the sum of the first n terms, from (4), is

$$s = \frac{n}{2}[4 + (n - 1)2] = n^2 + n$$

Example 2. The sum of five terms in an arithmetic progression is 50 and the common difference is 4. Find a and L. Substituting $s = 50$, $n = 5$, $d = 4$ in (3) gives

$$50 = \frac{5(a + L)}{2} \quad \text{or} \quad a + L = 20$$

Substituting $n = 5$, $d = 4$ in (2) gives

$$L = a + 4(4)$$

Solving these two equations gives $a = 2$ and $L = 18$.

Example 3. A creditor agrees to allow a debt of $416.00 to be repaid by taking $11.00 the first month and a payment increased by $2.00 each month thereafter until the debt is fully repaid. What is the amount of the last payment, and how many months are required to complete payment if no interest is charged? Here $a = \$11.00$, $d = \$2.00$, $s = \$416.00$. Substituting in (4) gives

$$416.00 = \frac{n}{2}[2(11) + (n - 1)2]$$

This may be rewritten as the quadratic equation

$$n^2 + 10n - 416.00 = 0$$

Recalling that the solution of

$$ax^2 + bx + c = 0$$

is given by

$$x = \frac{-b \pm \sqrt{b^2 - 4ac}}{2a}$$

gives the solutions in this case as

$$n = \frac{-10 \pm \sqrt{10^2 + (4)(416.00)}}{2} \quad ; \quad n = \frac{-10 + 42}{2}, \text{ or } n = \frac{-10 - 42}{2}$$

$n = 16$ months or -26. Since n cannot be negative, the solution is $n = 16$ months. The last payment is

$$L = a + (n - 1)d = 11.00 + (16 - 1)2 = \$41.00$$

Geometric Progression

A geometric progression is a sequence of numbers such that any term after the first may be obtained from the preceding term by multiplying it by a constant called the common ratio, r; i.e.,

$$t_i = f(t_{i-1}) = rt_{i-1}$$

If the first term is a, the second term will be ar, the third term ar^2, and the nth term will be
$$ar^{n-1} \tag{5}$$

Examples of geometric progressions are

$$3, \qquad 9, \qquad 27, \qquad 81, \qquad \cdots$$
$$-4, \qquad -2, \qquad -1, \qquad -\tfrac{1}{2}, \qquad -\tfrac{1}{4}, \qquad \cdots$$
$$64, \qquad -32, \qquad 16, \qquad -8, \qquad 4, \qquad -2, \qquad 1, \qquad \cdots$$

The common ratios in these progressions are 3, $\tfrac{1}{2}$, and $-\tfrac{1}{2}$, respectively. The sum, s, of the first n terms is given by:

$$s = a + ar + ar^2 + \cdots + ar^{n-2} + ar^{n-1}$$

Multiplying both sides of the equation by r gives

$$rs = ar + ar^2 + ar^3 + \cdots + ar^{n-1} + ar^n$$

Subtracting the second equation from the first, term by term, gives:

$$s - rs = a - ar^n$$

or

$$s = \frac{a(1 - r^n)}{1 - r} = \frac{a(r^n - 1)}{r - 1} \qquad \text{provided } r \neq 1 \tag{6}$$

If $r = 1$, the sum is na.

Example 4.   A forest has 343,600 acres of timber; 10% of the acreage at the beginning of each year is cut during that year. How many acres of original timber will have been cut at the end of 10 years?

The number of acres left at the end of the first year is $(343,600)0.90$. The number of acres left at the end of the second year is $[(343,600)0.90]0.90$. Therefore, the acreage remaining at the end of $1, 2, 3, \ldots,$ years forms a geometric progression with

$$a = (343,600)(0.90) \qquad \text{and} \qquad r = 0.90$$

The nth term is given by (5) with n equal to 10.

Substituting the values in this equation gives

$$L = (343,600)(0.90)(0.90)^9 = (343,600)(0.90)^{10}$$

Using logarithms gives

$$\log_{10} L = \log_{10} 343,600 + 10 \log_{10} 0.90$$
$$\log_{10} L = 5.536 - 0.458 = 5.078$$

Therefore,

$$L = 119,800$$

and hence the total number of acres that have been cut are

$$343,600 - 119,800 = 223,800$$

Infinite Series

If the sequence of terms t_i is unending, the sequence of the sums of the first n terms:

$$S_n = t_1 + t_2 + t_3 + \cdots + t_n$$

is called an infinite series. The sum of the sequence is the limiting value of S_n as n goes to infinity:

$$S = \lim_{n \to \infty} S_n$$

For the geometric progression

$$S_n = a + ar + ar^2 + ar^3 + \cdots + ar^n$$

$$\lim_{n \to \infty} S_n = \lim_{n \to \infty} \frac{a(1 - r^n)}{1 - r} = \lim_{n \to \infty} \frac{a}{1 - r} - \frac{a}{1 - r} \lim_{n \to \infty} r^n$$

$$= \frac{a}{1 - r} - \frac{a}{1 - r} \lim_{n \to \infty} r^n \tag{7}$$

The sum will be finite if the $\lim_{n \to \infty} r^n$ exists.

If $-1 < r < 1$, $\lim_{n \to \infty} r^n = 0$ and $S = \frac{a}{1 - r}$.

If $|r| > 1$, $\lim_{n \to \infty} r^n = \pm \infty$ and $\lim_{n \to \infty} S_n$ does not exist. S_n increases or decreases without limit as n increases.

If $r = +1$, $S = \lim_{n \to \infty} S_n = a + a + a + \cdots$ and S increases without limit as n increases.

If $r = -1$, $S = \lim_{n \to \infty} S_n = a - a + a - a + a - a \cdots$

$$= 0 \text{ or } a$$

and again the limit does not exist.

Example 5. The United States banking laws require most banks to maintain a reserve equivalent to a certain proportion of their outstanding deposits. This enables such banks, when they wish and when they can find borrowers, to loan out a certain proportion of the funds that have been deposited in them. Assume that this latter proportion, call it r, is 0.8.

Now, suppose a miner mines a quantity of gold, sells it to the government, and receives a check for $1,000. If the miner deposits his $1,000 in a bank which, subsequently, is able to loan the maximum legally possible amount, and this loan is redeposited elsewhere, etc., what is the total amount of money placed in circulation by this gold?

The miner deposits his check and the bank credits $1,000 to his account. The bank then loans $800 to, say, A. A, in turn, deposits the $800 loan in his bank which credits $800 to his account and loans ($800) (0.8) or $640 to B. B deposits the $640 in his bank which credits $640 to his account and loans out ($640) (0.8) or $512 to C, and so on. The total additional amount of money in circulation is

$1,000 + (1,000)(0.8) + (1,000)(0.8)(0.8) + (1,000)(0.8)(0.8)(0.8) + \cdots$

$1,000 + (1,000)(0.8) + (1,000)(0.8)^2 + (1,000)(0.8)^3 + \cdots$

The terms form a geometric progression and the sum for any given number of terms can be obtained from (7) by using $a = \$1,000$, $r = 0.8$.

$$S = \frac{a}{1 - r} = \frac{1,000}{0.2} = \$5,000$$

and the total amount in circulation approaches $5,000.

Example 6. *Learning Curves.* Industrial firms have found that the manufacturing cost of the second unit of a product is less than that of the first, the cost of the third is less than that of the second, etc. This phenomenon occurs because as employees learn, they perform the operations faster, waste less material, eliminate unnecessary motions, and so on. A method for predicting the total cost of producing n units is essential for determining the selling price, delivery date, etc. Let

n = number of units to be produced

$U(i)$ = cost (dollars) to produce the ith unit

$T(n)$ = total cost (dollars) to produce n units

If there were no learning effect, the cost of the ith unit would be the same as that of the first; i.e., $U(i) = U(1)$, and the total cost would be directly proportional to the number of units to be produced:

$$T(n) = nU(1)$$

Whenever the cost of the ith unit is less than the $(i - 1)$th because of the influence of learning, $U(i)$ will decrease as i increases. Assume, first, that the decrease in cost from the ith to the $(i + 1)$th unit is the same as the decrease in cost from the $(i - 1)$th and the ith,

Let: b = reduction in cost achieved as the result of building one unit.
Then:

$$U(2) = U(1) - b$$

$$U(3) = U(2) - b = U(1) - 2b$$

$$U(i) = U(1) - (i - 1)b$$

$$T(n) = \sum_{i=1}^{n} U(i) = U(1) + U(2) + \cdots + U(i) + \cdots + U(n)$$

$$= U(1) + [U(1) - b] + \cdots + [U(1) - (i - 1)b] + \cdots \quad (8)$$

$$+ [U(1) - (n - 1)b]$$

$$= nU(1) - [b + 2b + \cdots + (n - 1)b]$$

$$T(n) = \sum_{i=1}^{n} U(i) = nU(1) - \sum_{i=1}^{i=n}(i - 1)b = nU(1) - \frac{n(n - 1)}{2} b$$

There are usually limits to the effect of learning. In many cases it will become more and more difficult to reduce the production cost as more units are produced. The decrease in cost per unit will then not be constant, as assumed above, but will itself be decreasing. One reasonable assumption is that $U(i)$ is some fraction of $U(i - 1)$ or

$$\frac{U(i)}{U(i - 1)} = b$$

where $b(<1)$ is the learning parameter.

The formula for $U(i)$ then becomes

$$\frac{U(2)}{U(1)} = b \quad \text{or} \quad U(2) = bU(1)$$

similarly,

$$U(3) = bU(2) = b^2U(1)$$

and in general

$$U(i) = b^iU(1) \quad (9)$$

Empirical studies have indicated that $U(i)$ does not decrease as rapidly as this assumption would imply. The model which is widely used in practice, because it does approximate experience, is

$$U(i) = U(1)i^b; \quad b < 0 \quad (10)$$

where again b is the learning parameter. The rate of decrease depends on the value of b.

Suppose the production cost per unit is decreased to 80% each time production is doubled; i.e.,

$$U(2) = 0.8U(1)$$
$$U(4) = 0.8[U(2)] = 0.64U(1)$$
$$U(8) = 0.8[U(4)] = 0.512U(1)$$

and so forth.

Solving from $U(2) = U(1)2^b = 0.8U(1)$, or $2^b = 0.8$, for b gives $b = -0.322$. Other values of b are:

Production Cost Decreased to, If Production Is Doubled	b
0.75	−0.415
0.80	−0.322
0.90	−0.152
0.95	−0.074

The parameter b is negative, and the more negative it is, the greater is the decrease in production cost. The total cost of producing n units is:

$$T(n) = \sum_{i=1}^{n} U(i) = U(1)[1^b + 2^b + 3^b + \cdots + n^b]$$

It can be shown that

$$\sum_{i=1}^{n} i^b = \frac{n^{b+1}}{b+1} + \frac{1}{2}n^b + \frac{1}{6} \cdot \frac{b}{2!} n^{b-1} - \frac{1}{30} \frac{b(b-1)(b-2)}{4!} n^{b-3} + \cdots$$

Therefore,

$$T(n) = \sum_{i=1}^{n} U(1)i^b \approx \frac{U(1)n^{b+1}}{b+1} \qquad (11)$$

where the $\approx$ sign denotes is approximately equal to. Since b is negative, the remaining terms in the sum are small compared to the first term when n is large.

EXERCISES

1. Verify that the sum of the first n odd integers, 1, 3, 5, . . . , is n^2.
2. Find the general expression for the sum of the first n integers, 1, 2, 3, . . . n.
3. For the situation discussed in Example 5, show graphically how the total amount of money in circulation, as a result of the sale of $1,000 worth of gold to the government, would vary as a function of the proportion r.

4. Verify the result of Example 4 by developing and summing a geometric series for the number of acres cut each year.

5. Verify that it will take almost 9 years to reach sales of $37,000,000, if sales increase by 18% per year and the sales this year are $10,000,000.

6. Three quantities, a, b, and c, are said to be in harmonic progression when

$$\frac{a}{c} = \frac{a - b}{b - c}$$

and a series, u_1, u_2, ..., u_m, ..., is said to be a harmonic series if any three successive quantities are in harmonic progression. Show that the reciprocals of quantities in harmonic progression are in arithmetical progression.

7. Verify that

$$T = 1 + 2r + 3r^2 + \cdots + nr^{n-1} = \left[\frac{1 - r^n}{(1 - r)^2} - \frac{nr^n}{1 - r} \right]$$

[*Hint*: Find $(1 - r)T$.]

8. The Apex Toy Manufacturing Co. is introducing a new toy. From past experience the firm has found that manufacturing costs are subject to "learning curves."

(*a*) Determine the average manufacturing cost per unit under each of the three learning curves (8), (9), and (10).

(*b*) The policy of Apex is to set retail selling price at 300% of average manufacturing cost. If the manufacturing cost of the first unit is $1,000 and the 80% learning curve (10) applies, what will be the selling price at expected sales of 1,000, 10,000, and 100,000 units. [*Hint*: $10^{0.322} \approx 2.1$]

B. AN ANALYSIS OF DEPRECIATION METHODS

The federal government taxes the gross earnings of each taxpayer. Expenses and "deductions" are subtracted from total income to give gross earnings. If a taxpayer purchases property, such as a machine, which will be used in the production of income for several years, the total cost cannot be deducted in the year the property is purchased. Instead, the taxpayer receives a depreciation allowance each year which is included in the "deductions" for that year. The sum of the depreciation allowances, over the life of the property, in general is equal to the original cost of the equipment.

The 1954 Internal Revenue Code, Section 167, provides for the computation of depreciation allowances or deductions as follows:

(*a*) *General Rule.* There shall be allowed as a depreciation deduction a reasonable allowance for the exhaustion, wear and tear (including a reasonable allowance for obsolescence)

(1) of property used in the trade or business, or

(2) of property held for the production of income.

(b) *Use of Certain Methods and Rates.* For taxable years ending after December 31, 1953, the term "reasonable allowance" as used in subsection (a) shall include (but shall not be limited to) an allowance computed in accordance with regulations prescribed by the Secretary or his delegate, under any of the following methods:

(1) the straight line method;
(2) the declining balance method, using a rate not exceeding twice the rate which would have been used had the annual allowance been computed under the method described in paragraph (1),
(3) the sum of the years-digits method, and
(4) any other consistent method productive of an annual allowance which, when added to all allowances for the period commencing with the taxpayer's use of the property and including the taxable year, does not, during the first two-thirds of the useful life of the property, exceed the total of such allowances which would have been used had such allowances been computed under the method described in paragraph (2).

Nothing in this subsection shall be construed to limit or reduce an allowance otherwise allowable under subsection (a).

(c) *Limitations on Use of Certain Methods and Rates.* Paragraphs (2), (3) and (4) of subsection (b) shall apply only in the case of property (other than intangible property) described in subsection (a) with a useful life of 3 years or more [to the owner].

(d) *Agreement as to Useful Life on Which Depreciation Rate Is Based.* Where, under regulations prescribed by the Secretary or his delegate, the taxpayer and the Secretary or his delegate have, after the date of enactment of this title, entered into an agreement in writing specifically dealing with the useful life and rate of depreciation of any property, the rate so agreed upon shall be binding on both the taxpayer and the Secretary in the absence of facts or circumstances not taken into consideration in the adoption of such agreement . . . .

(e) *Change in Method.* In the absence of an agreement under subsection (d) containing a provision to the contrary, a taxpayer may at any time elect in accordance with regulations prescribed by the Secretary or his delegate to change from the method of depreciation described in subsection (b)(2) to the method described in subsection (b)(1).

(f) *Basis for Depreciation.* The basis on which exhaustion, wear and tear, and obsolescence are to be allowed in respect of any property shall be the adjusted basis provided in section 1011 for the purpose of determining the gain on the sale or other disposition of such property.

In most cases, business firms find it advantageous to accelerate depreciation allowances as much as the law will allow. Without depreciation, for any one year,

Earnings = Revenue − Costs

After-tax Earnings = Earnings − t(Earnings)   where t is the tax rate

With a depreciation allowance,

After-tax Earnings = Earnings − t(Earnings − Depreciation)

$$= (1 - t) \text{ Earnings} + t(\text{Depreciation})$$

since depreciation is allowed as a deduction in computing the amount taxable.

Over the total life of the asset, the amount of depreciation is in general equal to the initial book value and hence is independent of the method of calculating allowances for each year. However, the acceleration of an allowance is in effect an interest-free loan of amount t times the accelerated allowance during the period for which it is accelerated.

The three methods of computing depreciation specifically defined in the Revenue Code are:

The Straight-Line Method.   Under this method the adjusted basis for depreciation (frequently, but not always, the book value or cost of the property), less the estimated salvage value, is recovered *evenly* over the useful life of the property. There are no limitations on the use of this method except that the allowance must be "reasonable."

Declining-Balance Method.   A uniform rate of depreciation may be applied, not exceeding twice the straight-line rate without adjustment for salvage factor, to the undepreciated balance of the property. Frequently, the maximum rate is allowed on equipment purchased new and 1.5 times the straight line rate if used equipment is purchased. To be eligible for this method, property must have a useful life of 3 or more years.

Sum-of-the-Years-Digits Method.   Under this method the depreciation rate for any year is a fraction, the numerator of which is the remaining life of the property at the beginning of each year, and the denominator of which is the sum of the digits representing the years of estimated life. For example, if the useful life is 5 years, the depreciation rate would be

$$\frac{5}{1 + 2 + 3 + 4 + 5} = \frac{5}{15} = 0.333 \text{ for the first year,}$$

$$\tfrac{4}{15} = 0.267 \text{ for the second year,}$$

$$\tfrac{3}{15} = 0.200 \text{ for the third year,}$$

$$\tfrac{2}{15} = 0.133 \text{ for the fourth year,}$$

$$\tfrac{1}{15} = 0.067 \text{ for the fifth year.}$$

Table 2-1

Year	Straight Line (SLD)		Double Declining Balance (DDB)		Sum of Years Digits (SYD)	
	Dep.	Book Value	Dep.	Book Value	Dep.	Book Value
1	200	800	400	600	333.33	666.67
2	200	600	240	360	266.67	400
3	200	400	144	216	200	200
4	200	200	86.40	129.50	133.33	66.67
5	200	0	51.80	77.70	66.67	0

Under this method, cost must be reduced by estimated salvage value before computing depreciation. Like the declining-balance method, eligible property must have a life of 3 or more years.

Table 2-1 shows the depreciation allowance and book value, which is original cost less accumulated depreciation, at the end of each year for each of the three methods for an asset which was purchased for $1,000, has a book life of 5 years, and no salvage value. The maximum rate is used for the declining balance method.

A property owner may select any of the methods to calculate depreciation. Once the choice is made it can be changed only to the extent permitted by the Code. To aid in this choice, formulas for the amount of depreciation for any year, total depreciation for any period, and the book value at the end of any year for each method of depreciation must be developed.

The first step is to identify the variables and assign symbols. The variables dealing with the asset are:

A = book value at initial point in time

N = remaining life in years

s = salvage value at the end of N years as a fraction of initial book value.

For each method of computing depreciation, let

$r_i(t)$ = depreciation rate

$D_i(t)$ = depreciation allowed for the tth year

$C_i(t)$ = depreciation allowed for all years up to and including the tth

$A_i(t)$ = book value of the asset at the end of the tth year

where t = time in years measured from the initial point in time

and i = the method of computing depreciation

= 1 denotes straight-line method (SLD)

= 2 denotes double declining-balance method (DDB)

= 3 denotes sum-of-the-years-digit method (SYD)

The formulas desired are for $D_i(t)$, $C_i(t)$ and $A_i(t)$ for each i where $0 \leq t \leq N$. They will be developed here for the case where salvage value is assumed to be zero.

In general, the cumulative depreciation, $C(t)$, is the sum of all depreciation taken in this and previous years. Thus

$$C(t^*) = \sum_{t=1}^{t^*} D(t)$$

The book value at the end of year t, $A(t)$, is last year's book value, $A(t-1)$, minus this year's depreciation.

$$A(t) = A(t-1) - D(t)$$

$A(t)$ is also initial book value minus all accumulated depreciation.

$$A(t) = A - C(t)$$

Under the *straight-line method* ($i = 1$) the depreciation is received evenly and, therefore, $r_1 = 1/N$; $1/N$th of the cost is allowed each year. Then

$$D_1(t) = Ar_1 = \frac{A}{N}$$

$$C_1(t) = \frac{A}{N} t$$

and
$$A_1(t) = A - \frac{At}{N} = A\left(1 - \frac{t}{N}\right)$$

Under the *double declining-balance method* ($i = 2$), the rate of depreciation is a fixed number independent of time; Section 167-b(2) states that the rate must not exceed twice that under SLD. Therefore:

$$\frac{1}{N} < r_2 \leq \frac{2}{N}$$

The rate is applied to the remaining book value, and consequently the amount of depreciation changes each year. The depreciation and book value for years 1, 2, 3, and t are:

$$D_2(1) = r_2 A \qquad\qquad A_2(1) = A - r_2 A = A(1 - r_2)$$

$$D_2(2) = r_2 A_2(1) = r_2 A(1 - r_2) \qquad A_2(2) = A_2(1) - r_2 A_2(1)$$
$$= A_2(1)(1 - r_2) = A(1 - r_2)^2$$

$$D_2(3) = r_2 A_2(2) = r_2 A(1 - r_2)^2 \qquad A_2(3) = A_2(2) - r_2 A_2(2)$$
$$= A_2(2)(1 - r_2) = A(1 - r_2)^3$$

$$\cdot\ \cdot\ \cdot\ \cdot\ \cdot\ \cdot\ \cdot\ \cdot\ \cdot\ \cdot \qquad \cdot\ \cdot\ \cdot\ \cdot\ \cdot\ \cdot\ \cdot\ \cdot\ \cdot\ \cdot\ \cdot\ \cdot$$

$$D_2(t) = r_2 A(1 - r_2)^{t-1} \qquad\qquad A_2(t) = A(1 - r_2)^t$$

and
$$C_2(t) = A - A_2(t) = A - A(1 - r_2)^t = A[1 - (1 - r_2)^t]$$

Under the *sum-of-years-digits method* ($i = 3$), the rate is applied to the initial book value, but the rate changes each year:

$$r_3(1) = \frac{N}{1 + 2 + 3 + \cdots + N}$$

$$r_3(2) = \frac{(N - 1)}{1 + 2 + 3 + \cdots + N}$$

$$\cdots \cdots \cdots \cdots \cdots \cdots \cdots \cdots$$

$$r_3(t) = \frac{(N - t + 1)}{1 + 2 + 3 + \cdots + N}$$

The denominator is an arithmetic series whose sum can be obtained by applying the formula (4), Section A, or by the method used in obtaining the formula. Let

$$D = 1 + 2 + 3 + \cdots + N$$

Then

$$D = N + (N - 1) + (N - 2) + \cdots + 1$$

Adding gives

$$2D = (N + 1) + (N + 1) + \cdots + (N + 1) = N(N + 1)$$

and

$$D = \frac{N(N + 1)}{2}$$

Then

$$r_3(t) = \frac{2(N - t + 1)}{N(N + 1)}$$

The depreciation is obtained by multiplying A by this rate:

$$D_3(t) = Ar_3(t) = \frac{2A(N - t + 1)}{N(N + 1)}$$

The book value is

$$A_3(1) = A - D_3(1) = A - \frac{2NA}{N(N + 1)} = A\left(1 - \frac{2}{N + 1}\right)$$

$$A_3(2) = A - D_3(1) - D_3(2) = A - \frac{2NA}{N(N + 1)} - \frac{2(N - 1)A}{N(N + 1)}$$

$$= A\left\{1 - \frac{2[N + (N - 1)]]}{N(N + 1)}\right\}$$

$$A_3(t) = A\left\{1 - \frac{2[N + (N - 1) + \cdots + (N - t + 1)]]}{N(N + 1)}\right\}$$

Let

$$M_1 = N + (N - 1) + (N - 2) + \cdots + (N - t + 1)$$

then

$$M_1 = (N - t + 1) + (N - t + 2) + \cdots + N$$

or

$$2M_1 = (2N - t + 1) + (2N - t + 1) + \cdots + (2N - t + 1)$$

$$= t(2N - t + 1)$$

$$M_1 = \frac{t}{2}(2N - t + 1)$$

Then

$$A_3(t) = A\left[1 - \frac{t(2N - t + 1)}{N(N + 1)}\right]$$

$$= A\left[\frac{(N - t)(N - t + 1)}{N(N + 1)}\right]$$

and

$$C_3(t) = A - A_3(t) = A - A\left[\frac{(N - t)(N - t + 1)}{N(N + 1)}\right]$$

$$= At\left[\frac{2N - t + 1}{N(N + 1)}\right]$$

The three functions, $A_1(t)$, $A_2(t)$, and $A_3(t)$, are shown in Fig. 2.1 for

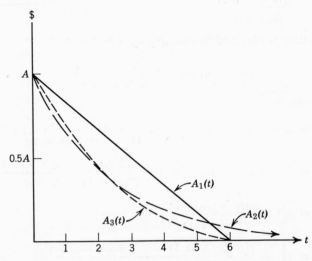

Figure 2.1 Book value as a function of time for three methods of depreciation.

$N = 6$ and $A = \$1,000$. This figure suggests a number of conjectures for the case where salvage value is zero:

(a) Under SLD and SYD the asset is fully depreciated over its life but under DDB a residual remains.

(b) DDB method ($r_2 = 2/N$) provides more total depreciation in the first two years than SYD, but less thereafter.

(c) To accelerate depreciation as much as possible, the change from DDB to SLD permitted by the Code should be made approximately at the middle of the asset's life.

The last conjecture is examined below. The others, and the effect of a positive salvage value, are left as exercises.

Change from DDB to SLD

The double declining-balance method of depreciation is often used because it provides larger allowances in early years. However, the book value, original cost less any depreciation taken, will not be zero at the end of the asset's book life. In order to fully depreciate the asset, at some point during the book life of the asset the method of depreciation may be changed in accordance with the Revenue Code from DDB to the straight-line method of depreciation which will be based on the book value *at that time* and the remaining years of the book life. The question then is: at what point in the book life of the asset should the change from the double declining-balance to straight-line method be made to obtain the most rapid depreciation allowed by law, if the asset has no salvage value at the end of its book life?

It is clear that in the first year the depreciation allowance under DDB is greater than under SLD;

$$D_2(1) > D_1(1)$$

since

$$Ar_2 > \frac{A}{N} \quad \text{if} \quad r_2 > \frac{1}{N}$$

It follows that initially the DDB results in a larger depreciation. However, after a certain number of years the depreciation under DDB will be less than that allowable under a change to SLD.

After $t - 1$ years under the DDB method, book value is

$$A_2(t - 1) = A(1 - r_2)^{t-1}$$

If changeover is made to SLD for year t, the depreciation for year t and all succeeding years will be:

$$\frac{\text{Remaining book value}}{\text{Remaining life (years)}} = \frac{A(1 - r_2)^{t-1}}{N - t + 1}$$

If DDB is continued, depreciation for year t will be

$$D_2(t) = r_2[A(1 - r_2)^{t-1}]$$

Therefore, the change should be made for the smallest value of t for which

$$\frac{A(1 - r_2)^{t-1}}{N - t + 1} \geq Ar_2(1 - r_2)^{t-1}$$

or

$$\frac{1}{N - t + 1} \geq r_2$$

Table 2-2

t	Depreciation (DDB)	Book Value	Depreciation for year t and for each succeeding year if change to SLD is made for year t
1	333.33	666.67	166.67
2	222.22	444.45	133.33
3	148.15	296.30	111.11
4	98.77	197.53	98.77
5	65.84	131.69	98.77
6	43.30	87.79	131.69

In the particular case where $r_2 = 2/N$, the value of t is the smallest value of t for which

$$N \geq 2N - 2t + 2 \qquad 2t \geq N + 2 \qquad t \geq \frac{N + 2}{2}$$

Since t must be an integer, the correct time to change is $t = (N + 2)/2$ if N is even, and $t = (N + 3)/2$ if N is odd. However, if N is even, the depreciation is the same under both methods for year $t = (N + 2)/2$ and, therefore, the change can be delayed to year $t = (N + 4)/2$ without any loss. The example considered in Table 2.1 (page 35), can be used to illustrate the result. For $t = 3$, the depreciation under DDB is 144, and if the change were made for year 3, the depreciation under SLD would be only 120. However, for $t = 4$ the depreciation is 86.40 under DDB, and 108 if the change to SLD is made. If the book life had been 6 years, the depreciation and book value under double declining-balance method would be as given in Table 2.2. The change can be made for either year $(N + 2)/2 = 4$ or $(N + 4)/2 = 5$.

EXERCISES

1. (a) Verify that $A_1(N) = A_3(N) = 0$ and $A_2(N) > 0$, when salvage value is zero.

   (b) Determine the value of $A_2(N)$ when salvage value is zero, $A = 1,000$, $r_2 = 2/N$ when $N = 6$ and when N is very large.

2. In the analysis, t has been treated as a continuous variable. However, depreciation allowances are calculated for each year, and technically t should be discrete: $t = 1, 2, 3, \ldots$. Does this affect the accuracy of the results and conclusions?

3. Determine values of t at which $A_2(t)$ and $A_3(t)$ cross when salvage value is zero and $r_2 = 2/N$. Of what significance is the fact that they cross?

4. (a) Verify that the formulas for SLD, SYD, and DDB in the accompanying table are correct for the case where a positive salvage value exists at the end of the book life. State a policy for determining which method should be used to accelerate depreciation as much as possible. Here

$$s = \frac{\text{Salvage value}}{\text{Initial book value}}$$

Method	Depreciation	Book Value	Accumulated Depreciation
i	$D_i(t)$	$A_i(t)$	$C_i(t)$
1: SLD	$\dfrac{A(1 - s)}{N}$	$A\left[1 - \dfrac{t}{N}(1 - s)\right]$	$A(1 - s)\dfrac{t}{N}$
2: DDB	$r_2 A(1 - r_2)^{t-1}$	$A[1 - r_2]^t$	$A[1 - (1 - r_2)^t]$
3: SYD	$\dfrac{A(1 - s)2(N - t + 1)}{N(N + 1)}$	$A\left[1 - \dfrac{(1 - s)t(2N - t + 1)}{N(N + 1)}\right]$	$A(1 - s)t\left[\dfrac{2N - t + 1}{N(N + 1)}\right]$

However $A_i(t) \geq sA$ for $t > 0$; $i = 1, 2, 3$ 0·2

   (b) Graph $A_i(t)$ for $i = 1, 2, 3$ when $A = 1,000$, $N = 6$, $s = 0·4$.

5. One tax authority makes the following recommendation: "Use double declining-balance for tax purposes whenever salvage value exceeds 13.53 per cent of cost." How can this rule be justified?

6. "Law: Section 167(b) of the Internal Revenue Code states that the term 'reasonable allowance'. . . shall include . . . an allowance computed in accordance with regulations prescribed . . . under any of the following methods:

   (1) the straight-line method
   (2) the declining-balance method . . . not exceeding twice the rate . . . in paragraph (1),
   (3) the sum of the years-digits methods, and
   (4) any other consistent method . . . [which is not faster than (2) during the first 2/3 of life]."

One method that falls under (4) is the units-of-production method in which

$$D(u) = \frac{A - sA}{P}$$

where A = initial book value
 sA = salvage value
 P = total units of production over life
 $D(u)$ = depreciation allowance per unit of production
  A timber company has spent \$50,000 to build a sawmill in a remote area, primarily to handle the production from a certain tract of timber in which the mill is located. After the timber in adjoining areas has been logged off, the mill will remain on a standby basis to handle occasional small lots. Useful life of the buildings is 10 years, after which salvage value will be zero. Estimated total production from the area is 15 million board feet of lumber, with production likely to occur mostly during the first couple of years:

1st year:	7,500,000 board feet
2nd year:	5,000,000 board feet
3rd year:	2,000,000 board feet
4th year:	100,000 board feet
5th year:	100,000 board feet
6th year:	100,000 board feet
7th to 10th years:	50,000 board feet per year

What method of depreciation should be used to accelerate depreciation as much as possible?

C. ADMINISTRATIVE COSTS AND SIZE OF THE FIRM

  The hierarchical organizational structure of a simple manufacturing firm is illustrated in Fig. 2.2. In this example there are three levels of administrators and one level of production workers. The number of subordinates reporting to one administrator is termed his "span of

Administrative Level

3

2

1

Production Workers

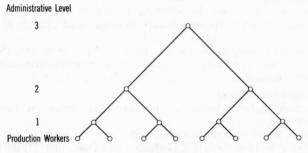

Figure 2.2

control" in organization theory. If the span of control is constant throughout the organization, every administrator has the same number of subordinates reporting to him as does any other administrator. In Fig. 2.2 the span of control is 2; every administrator has two subordinates. More generally, let

n = number of administrative levels and

a = span of control

There will be one administrator, usually the president, at level n (the highest level), a administrators at level $n - 1$, a^2 administrators at level $n - 2$, and a^{n-1} administrators at level 1. The total number of administrators is

$$1 + a + a^2 + \cdots + a^{n-1} = \frac{a^n - 1}{a - 1}$$

The number of workers in such an organization is a^n. Thus the firm shown in Fig. 2.2 has

$$1 + 2 + 4 = \frac{2^3 - 1}{2 - 1} = 7 \text{ Administrators}$$

and $2^3 = 8$ production workers.

One of the interesting problems in the "Theory of the Firm" is how size of the firm affects earnings. Economists speak of "diseconomies of scale," meaning that as the size of the firm increases, its cost per unit of its output increases. For example:[1]

"The main factor causing diseconomies of scale has to do with certain managerial problems which typically arise as a firm becomes a large-scale producer. In a small plant a single key executive may render all the basic decisions relative to his plant's operation. Because of the firm's smallness he is close to the production line. He can therefore comprehend the various aspects of the firm's operations and digest the information fed to him by his subordinates to the end that efficient decision making is possible.

"This neat picture changes, however, as a firm grows. The management echelons between the executive suite and the assembly line become many; top management is far removed from the actual production operations of the plant. It becomes impossible for one man to assemble, understand, and digest all the information essential to rational decision making in a large-scale enterprise. Authority must be delegated to innumerable vice-presidents, second vice-presidents, and so forth. This expansion in the depth and width of management entails problems of coordination and bureaucratic red tape which can eventually impair the efficiency of a firm and lead to higher costs."

[1] From: McConnell, Campbell R. (1962), *Economics: Principles, Problems, and Policies*, McGraw-Hill Book Company, Inc., New York. Used by permission.

In this example, the effect of increasing size will be studied quantitatively under some simple assumptions. The earnings of the firm may be written as:

Earnings
    = Net Revenue − Worker Cost − Administrator Cost − Fixed Cost

where the Net Revenue is the difference between the revenue obtained from the sales of the product and the cost of the material used. Worker cost and Administrator cost are the cost of all the workers and administrators, respectively, and the Fixed cost is all costs which do not vary with production level.

Suppose the final output of the firm is directly proportional to the number of production workers; then dividing by Worker Cost and rearranging gives

$$\frac{\text{Earnings} + \text{Fixed Cost}}{\text{Worker Cost}} = \frac{\text{Net Revenue} - \text{Worker Cost}}{\text{Worker Cost}}$$
$$- \frac{\text{Administrator Cost}}{\text{Worker Cost}}$$

By the assumption the Net Revenue and the Worker Cost are directly proportional to Worker Cost. The Earnings, over and above Fixed Costs, per unit of Worker Cost will then increase, remain constant, or decrease as the size of the firm increases, if the last term decreases, remains constant, or increases respectively.

Consider first the case of an organization which has the same span of control regardless of the number of administrative levels. An organization with a span of control $a = 4$ and four levels will have $\dfrac{4^4 - 1}{4 - 1} = 85$ administrators and $4^4 = 256$ workers. As this firm grows, it will arrive at the point where it has five levels of administrators still with a span of control of 4, which would mean that the number of administrators is $\dfrac{4^5 - 1}{4 - 1} = 341$ and that there are $4^5 = 1024$ production workers. The ratio of administrators to workers has increased slightly from

$$\frac{85}{256} = 0.3320 \quad \text{to} \quad \frac{341}{1024} = 0.3330$$

In general the ratio of the number of administrators to workers is

$$\frac{\text{Number of administrators}}{\text{Number of workers}} = \frac{\left(\dfrac{a^n - 1}{a - 1}\right)}{a^n} = \frac{a^n - 1}{a^n(a - 1)} = \frac{1 - \dfrac{1}{a^n}}{a - 1}$$
$$= \frac{1}{a - 1} - \frac{1}{a^n(a - 1)}$$

As the number of levels increases, the second term becomes smaller and smaller, and hence the ratio tends to the limit $1/(a - 1)$. The ratio of the number of administrators to workers never exceeds $1/(a - 1)$ regardless of how large the firm becomes.

However, the administrators at the different levels do not all receive the same salary. The case where the span of control is constant but the salary increases with the level of the administrator is considered next. In particular, suppose that each administrator receives a salary of b times the salary of his immediate subordinates and that the salary of a worker is given by W.

Level	Number	Salary
n	1	$b^n W$
$n - 1$	a	$b^{n-1} W$
.	.	.
.	.	.
.	.	.
1	a^{n-1}	bW
Production worker	a^n	W

The Administrator Cost at any given level is the product of the salary at that level and the number of administrators at that level. The total Administrator Cost is the sum of the Administrator Cost at all levels, or

$$\text{Total Administrator Cost} = a^{n-1}bW + a^{n-2}b^2W + \cdots + ab^{n-1}W + b^nW$$

$$= a^{n-1}bW[1 + b/a + \cdots + (b/a)^{n-1}]$$

$$= a^{n-1}bW\left[\frac{1 - (b/a)^n}{1 - b/a}\right]$$

The total Worker Cost is given by the product of the number of workers and the salary per worker, $= a^nW$; hence the ratio of Administrator Cost to Worker Cost is

$$\frac{\text{Administrator Cost}}{\text{Worker Cost}} = \frac{a^{n-1}bW}{a^nW}\left[\frac{1 - (b/a)^n}{1 - b/a}\right]$$

$$= \frac{b/a}{1 - b/a} - \frac{(b/a)^{n+1}}{1 - b/a} \tag{1}$$

Thus the ratio of Administrator Cost to Worker Cost depends on the ratio b/a which is the "salary increase factor" divided by the span of control. The first term in (1) is a constant and does not depend on the size of the organization. The second term in (1) will become smaller as the size of the organization increases, provided the ratio b/a is less than 1, which will usually be the case. Typically a will be between 3 and 7, while b very seldom exceeds 3.

The conclusions reached above can be shown to hold even if the assumptions are relaxed still further. Suppose the span of control a and the salary increase factor b are not constant throughout the firm; in particular suppose that there is a lower bound on the span of control (every administrator has at least a administrators reporting to him) and the salary increase factor has an upper bound (each administrator receives no more than b times the salary of any one of his subordinates). The number of administrators and their salaries are:

Level	Number	Salary
n	$N_n = 1$	$W_n \leq bW_{n-1}$
$n-1$	$N_{n-1} \geq aN_n$	$W_{n-1} \leq bW_{n-2}$
...	...	...
2	$N_2 \geq aN_3$	$W_2 \leq bW_1$
1	$N_1 \geq aN_2$	$W_1 \leq bW$
Production workers	$N_0 \geq aN_1$	W

The number of administrators at the ith level, N_i, is at least aN_{i+1} and each receives a salary W_i which is no greater than $b^i W_{i-1}$. As before, the total Administrator Cost is obtained by summing the costs at each level:

$$\text{Administrator Cost} = N_1W_1 + N_2W_2 + \cdots + N_nW_n$$

and the ratio of administrator cost to worker cost is

$$\frac{\text{Administrator Cost}}{\text{Worker Cost}} = \frac{N_1W_1 + N_2W_2 + \cdots + N_nW_n}{N_0W}$$

$$= \frac{N_1}{N_0}\frac{W_1}{W} + \frac{N_2}{N_0}\frac{W_2}{W} + \cdots + \frac{N_n}{N_0}\frac{W_n}{W} \qquad (2)$$

The equality can be replaced by an inequality if each term is replaced by a term which is larger. Since

$$N_{n-1} \geq aN_n$$
$$N_{n-2} \geq aN_{n-1} \geq a^2N_n$$
$$\cdot$$
$$\cdot$$
$$\cdot$$
$$N_0 \geq aN_1 \geq a^nN_n$$

or

$$\frac{N_n}{N_0} \leq \frac{1}{a^n} \quad \text{and} \quad \frac{N_i}{N_0} \leq \frac{1}{a^i} \quad i = 1, \ldots, n$$

Similarly,

$$\frac{W_1}{W} \leq b; \quad W_2 \leq bW_1 \leq b^2 W \quad \text{or} \quad \frac{W_2}{W} \leq b^2, \ldots, \frac{W_i}{W} \leq b^i$$

Therefore,

$$\frac{N_i}{N_0} \frac{W_i}{W} \leq \left(\frac{1}{a^i}\right)(b^i) \tag{3}$$

Replacing each one of the terms in (2) with the appropriate one from (3) gives

$$\frac{\text{Administrator Cost}}{\text{Worker Cost}} \leq \left[\frac{b}{a} + \left(\frac{b}{a}\right)^2 + \cdots + \left(\frac{b}{a}\right)^n\right]$$

$$\leq \left(\frac{b}{a}\right)\left[\frac{1 - (b/a)^n}{1 - b/a}\right]$$

$$\leq \frac{b/a}{1 - b/a} - \frac{(b/a)^{n+1}}{1 - b/a} \tag{4}$$

The ratio of Administrator Cost to Worker Cost still will not increase above the same limit no matter how large n gets.

In the analysis made up to this point it has been assumed that output per worker is constant regardless of the size of the firm. This assumption might be questioned because the larger an organization gets, the more administrative levels it has to have if the span of control does not change. Hence more time may be required to make decisions. This case will be studied under the following assumptions: (a) all situations requiring decisions arise at the worker level; (b) the time required to transmit a question up, or a decision down, the hierarchy is a constant per level and (c) all administrators make the same number of decisions.

For example, a three-level firm with a span of control a equal to 2, shown in Fig. 2.2, has seven administrators. Under the assumption, one-seventh of the decisions must go to the administrator at level 3 and will require three time periods to reach the top and three time periods for the decision to come back down. Similarly, two-sevenths of the decisions will reach level 2 and will require a total of four time periods. Four-sevenths of the decisions will be made at level 1 and will require a total of two time periods. The average number of time periods required for the decisions will then be

$$\frac{\sum_{i=1}^{3} 2 \text{ (Time required to reach level } i) \text{ (Number of administrators at level } i)}{\text{Number of administrators}}$$

$$= \tfrac{1}{7} [2(3)(1) + 2(2)(2) + 2(4)(1)] = \tfrac{22}{7}$$

In general, if there are n levels and a is the span of control, the average time required to make a decision is

$$\frac{\dfrac{2}{a^n - 1} \{2n + 2(n - 1)a + 2(n - 2)a^2 + \cdots 2[n - (n - 1)]a^{n-1}\}}{a - 1}$$

Using the formula developed in Exercise 6, Section B, this is equal to

$$\frac{2a}{a - 1} - \frac{2n}{a^n - 1} \qquad (5)$$

As n increases, the second term becomes small, and hence the average number of time periods required to make a decision is always less than a fixed quantity which is independent of the size of the organization.

Under the assumptions made here, the ratio of administrator cost to worker cost and the average time required to make decisions, do not grow indefinitely but approach a limit as the firm increases in size. Thus, under these assumptions, there should be no serious diseconomies in the cost of administration when the size of the firm increases. Since this conclusion is at variance with the statements frequently encountered in other textbooks, further empirical investigations are required to determine whether the assumptions are valid.

D. ORGANIZATIONAL EFFICIENCY[2]

One of the problems not considered in the previous example was whether one span of control is "better" in some sense than another. In this example, efficiency of an organization as a function of the span of control will be studied with reference to an organization which has three levels and an arbitrary span of control equal to a. The criterion of "better" which will be used is the average efficiency of the organization defined as the total efficiency of all individuals divided by the total number of individuals, or

$$\text{Average efficiency of organization} = \frac{\text{Sum of efficiency of all individuals}}{\text{Total number of individuals}}$$

$$(1)$$

[2] The example is adapted from: Fordham, S. (1958), "Organization Efficiency," *J. Industrial Economics*, VI, 3, pp. 209–215.

The efficiency of an individual will be defined as the time he has available for his primary work multiplied by his effectiveness:

Efficiency of an individual

$$= \text{(Time available for primary task)(Effectiveness)} \quad (2)$$

An individual spends his time either on accomplishing his primary task or on contacts with his superior, his equals, and his subordinates. Let c denote the amount of time, in fractions of basic time unit, which an administrator spends with each of the individuals with whom he is in contact. For example, an administrator at level 2 has a subordinates, $a - 1$ equals, and 1 superior. The total amount of time that he spends with them, then, is

$$ac + (a - 1)c + c = 2ac \quad (3)$$

This time will be regarded as not directly useful and hence the time available for an individual at level 2 to devote to his primary task is 1 minus the time wasted on these contacts, or

Time available for an administrator at level $2 = 1 - 2ac$ \quad (4)

This time that an administrator spends with others is, of course, not completely wasted. In fact, this is what makes it possible for him to specialize. Assume that the effectiveness of an individual working by himself is 1 and that the parameter s denotes the increase in effectiveness due to specialization. In particular, if an administrator has $a - 1$ equals, his effectiveness becomes

Effectiveness of an administrator at level $2 = 1 + (a - 1)s$ \quad (5)

The same definitions and assumption can be applied to the other two levels, assuming that the coefficients c and s are the same for all levels. A summary of the time available and the effectiveness is given in the table on page 50.

The average efficiency of the organization is, by (1), the sum of the efficiencies of all individuals divided by the total number of individuals in the organization, or

$$\text{Average efficiency} = \frac{\begin{array}{ccc} \text{Total} & \text{Total} & \text{Total} \\ \text{efficiency} + & \text{efficiency} + & \text{efficiency} \\ \text{(level 3)} & \text{(level 2)} & \text{(level 1)} \end{array}}{\text{Total number of administrators}}$$

$$= \frac{(1 - ac) + a(1 - 2ac)[1 + (a - 1)s] + a^2(1 - ac)[1 + (a - 1)s]}{1 + a + a^2} \quad (6)$$

Level of Administrator	3	2	1
Number of direct contacts with subordinates	a	a	0
Direct contacts with equals	0	$a-1$	$a-1$
Number of direct contacts with superiors	0	1	1
Total number of direct contacts	a	$2a$	a
Time per contact	c	c	c
Total time spent in contacts	ac	$2ac$	ac
Time available	$(1-ac)$	$(1-2ac)$	$(1-ac)$
Effectiveness of the individual	1	$[1+(a-1)s]$	$[1+(a-1)s]$
Efficiency of the individual	$(1-ac)$	$(1-2ac)[1+(a-1)s]$	$(1-ac)[1+(a-1)s]$
Number of administrators	1	a	a^2

The average efficiency for a firm with three levels of administrators can be determined for any given values of c and s for the different levels of span of control. Figure 2.3 shows the relationship between average efficiency and span of control for some particular values of a.

The values of c, 0.05, 0.10 and 0.20, represent spending 5, 10, and 20% respectively, of total available time on each contact; $c = 0.10$ means that 10% or 48 minutes out of an eight hour working day is spent on each contact. The values of s of 0.05 and 0.10 represent 5 and 10% improvement in effectiveness due to specialization. Figure 2.3 shows that if $c = 0.05$ and $s = 0.1$, the average efficiency is highest at approximately 6; for lower values of s and/or higher values of c, the average efficiency decreases from $a = 1$.

One way to increase the efficiency might be to add specialists. In particular, suppose a specialist is added at level 2 and he is given one assistant who is regarded as being at level 1. Suppose that the specialist and his assistant spend the same amount of time per contact as do the other members of the organization, and suppose that c and s are the same as they were before. The formula for average efficiency then

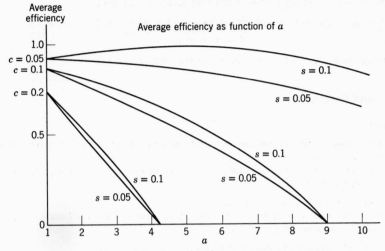

Figure 2.3   Average efficiency as function of a.

becomes

Average efficiency

$$= \frac{1 - (a + 1)c + a[1 - (2a + 1)c][1 + as] + a^2[1 - (a + 1)c][1 + as]}{3 + a + a^2}$$

(7)

Another possible way to increase the average efficiency might be to hire a consultant. Suppose the consultant has no direct responsibility and is approached only at the choice of the individual members of the organization. The consultant is not considered as an immediate contact for the other members of the organization and a fraction of his working time is spreadout to other members of the organization. The formula for average efficiency then becomes, if

$$T = (1 - ac) + a\left[1 - 2ac - \frac{1}{2(a + a^2)}\right](1 + as),$$

Average efficiency $= \dfrac{T + a^2\left[1 - ac - \dfrac{1}{2(a + a^2)}\right][1 + as]}{2 + a + a^2}$

(8)

EXERCISES

1. Does the addition of a specialist and his assistant increase average efficiency if $a = 5$, $c = 0.05$, and $s = 0.1$?

2. Does the addition of a consultant increase average efficiency if $a = 5$, $c = 0.05$, and $s = 0.1$?

3. Show that if the organization has four levels, (6) becomes

$$\frac{1 - ac + a(a + 1)(1 - 2ac)[1 + (a - 1)s] + a^3[1 - ac][1 - (a - 1)c]}{1 + a + a^2 + a^3}$$

4. Generalize the result in Exercise 3 to the case of n levels.

Notes and References

Section A

For a discussion of the convergence of the infinite series in general and the geometric series in particular, see:
Courant, R. (1934), *Differential and Integral Calculus*, Blackie and Sons, Ltd., London, Vol. 1, Chapter VIII.

For a discussion of learning curves, see:
Conway, R. W., and A. Schultz (1959), "The Manufacturing Progress Function," *J. Industrial Engineering*, **10**, pp. 39–53.

For a useful collection of sums of series, see:
Jolley, L. B. W. (1961), *Summation of Series*, 2nd ed., Dover Publications, New York.

Section B

Depreciation formulas for the 1954 Internal Revenue Code are developed in:
Myers, J. H. (1958), "Useful Formulae for DDB and SYD Depreciation," *Accounting Review*, **33**, pp. 93–95.
Myers, J. H. (1960), "Influence of Salvage Value upon Choice of Tax Depreciation Methods," *Accounting Review*, **35**, No. 4, pp. 598–602.
Van Ness, P. H. (1961), "Mathematics of Accelerated Depreciation," *N.A.A. Bulletin XLII*, No. 8, pp. 5–14.

Section C

The example is based on
Beckmann, M. J. (1960), "Some Aspects of Return to Scale in Business Administration." *Quart. J. Economics*, **74**, pp. 464–471.

CHAPTER THREE

Mathematics of Interest

Many management problems involve commitments for expenditures now and at various times in the future in the expectation of receiving benefits now and/or at various times in the future. The "value" of costs or benefits payable or received at different times cannot be compared directly. Before decisions can be made, therefore, a method for putting the costs and benefits on a common basis must be developed. The concept commonly used is that of "interest" which states the value of the cost or benefit in terms of its "equivalent" value at some fixed point in time.

A. FORMULAS FOR PRESENT AND FUTURE VALUES

The costs and benefits may involve (a) a single cost or benefit, (b) a sequence in which the costs and/or benefits in different periods are equal from one period to another, or (c) a sequence in which the costs and benefits in the different periods are not equal. In this section, the formulas for reducing a sequence of costs and benefits to a single point in time are developed for the case where the point is either now, or n-periods from now. In some problems it may be convenient to use other reference points and the formulas can be modified as necessary.

The following notation is used in this chapter:

1. A dollar deposited in a savings account today will be worth $1 + i$ dollars at the end of a period if i is the interest for the period. $i =$ interest rate per period (expressed as a number; e.g., 0.03, 0.01, etc. or as a percentage; e.g., 3%, 1%)

2. We may borrow an amount v and repay the bank at the end of the period by one dollar; that is, $v(1 + i) = 1$. The interest rate may be expressed in terms of v as

$$i = \frac{1 - v}{v}$$

3. Small (lower-case) letters are used to denote costs or benefits:
   c_j = a cost incurred at the end of the jth period
   b_j = a benefit received at the end of the jth period
   $a_j = b_j - c_j$ = net benefit received at the end of the jth period
In particular, c_0 and b_0 denote the cost and benefit, respectively, at the end of the 0th period; or just before the beginning of the first period.
4. Capital (upper-case) letters denote the value of a series of amounts (which may consist of one term); in particular:

   P = the present value of a series; i.e., the value now
   F = the value of a series n-periods from now.

Sometimes it will be desirable to indicate the interest rate used for computing P and F for a particular series; for example, the value of a series, A, which has costs $c_0, c_1, c_2, \ldots$, and benefits $b_0, b_1, b_2, \ldots$, at interest i, will be denoted by $P(i; A)$ and $F(i; A)$ for the value now and n-periods from now, respectively.

The formulas for computing present and future values of single cost or benefit and a sequence of costs and benefits are developed below and are summarized in Table 3.2, page 61.

The value, F, at the end of n periods of a benefit, b_0, received now:
   A benefit of b_0 now is worth b_0 now,
   $$b_0(1 + i) \text{ one period hence,}$$
   $$b_0(1 + i)^2 \text{ two periods hence, and}$$
   · · · · · · · · · · · ·
   $$b_0(1 + i)^n \text{ } n \text{ periods hence}$$
Therefore,
$$F = b_0(1 + i)^n \tag{1}$$

For any given values of b_0, i and n, F can be evaluated by multiplication. When n is large, it is usually more convenient to use logarithms. An even more convenient method is to use available tables such as Appendix Table 1 which gives $(1 + i)^n$ for selected values of i and n from 0.01 to 0.50 (1 % to 50%) and n from 1 to 50. The value of F for any specified b_0 is then readily obtained by multiplying the value of $(1 + i)^n$ by b_0.

Example.   If $i = 0.05$, then:

$(1 + i)^1 = 1.0500$

$(1 + i)^2 = (1.05)(1.05) = 1.1025$

$(1 + i)^3 = (1.05)(1.1025) = 1.157625$ (rounded to 1.15763 in Table 1)

If $b_0 = \$1,000$, F at the end of three periods is $\$1,157.625$, or $\$1,157.63$, if Appendix Table 1 is used.

The present value, P, of a benefit b_n to be received n periods from now:
A benefit of b_n at the end of n periods is worth
    b_n at the end of the nth period,
    $b_n v$ at the end of the $(n - 1)$st period,
    $b_n v^2$ at the end of the $(n - 2)$nd period, and
    $b_n v^n$ at the end of the 0th period; i.e., now.
Therefore,

$$P = b_n v^n = \frac{b_n}{(1 + i)^n} \tag{2}$$

Appendix Table 2 gives v^n for selected values of i and n ranging from $i = 0.01$ to 0.50 $(1\% \text{ to } 50\%)$ and n from 1 to 50. For example, if $i = 0.05$:

Table 2 Values

$v^1 = \dfrac{1}{1 + i} = 0.9523\ 8095$	0.952381
$v^2 = \dfrac{1}{(1 + i)^2} = 0.9070\ 2948$	0.907029
$v^3 = \dfrac{1}{(1 + i)^3} = 0.8638\ 3760$	0.863838

Values of v^n can also be obtained from Appendix Table 1 since $(1 + i)^n v^n = 1$, or

$$v^n = \frac{1}{(1 + i)^n}$$

for example, for $n = 3$; $i = 0.05$; $(1 + i)^n = 1.15763$; and $\dfrac{1}{1.15763} = $
0.863838. Thus a benefit of $\$1,000$ to be received at the end of three periods (assuming 5% interest rate per period) is worth $\$863.84$ now.

The value, F, at the end of n periods, of a benefit of b received at the end of each of the n periods. The first payment will draw interest for $n - 1$ periods, the second for $n - 2$ periods, and the last payment will not draw any interest. The total value, F, is:

$$F = b(1 + i)^{n-1} + b(1 + i)^{n-2} + b(1 + i)^{n-3} + \cdots + b(1 + i)^1 + b$$
$$= b + b(1 + i) + \cdots + b(1 + i)^{n-2} + b(1 + i)^{n-1}$$

The right-hand side is a geometric progression with the first term $= b$ and a ratio of $(1 + i)$, and therefore the sum is

$$F = b\left[\frac{1 - (1 + i)^n}{1 - (1 + i)}\right] = b\left[\frac{(1 + i)^n - 1}{i}\right] \tag{3}$$

Values of $\dfrac{(1 + i)^n - 1}{i}$ are given in Appendix Table 3 for selected values of i and n ranging from $i = 0.01$ to 0.50 (1% to 50%) and n from 1 to 50. These values can also be obtained by summing values from Appendix Table 1. For example, a value of 1 at the end of each of three periods at interest 0.05 will be worth, at the end of the three periods,

$$(1.05)^2 + (1.05) + 1 = 3.1525$$

The present value, P, of a benefit of b received at the end of each of n periods. The present value of the series of payments at interest i is:

$$P = bv + bv^2 + bv^3 + \cdots + bv^n$$

The first payment is discounted for one period, the second for two periods, and the last for n periods. The right-hand side is a geometric series with a ratio of v and first term equal to bv; therefore,

$$P = \frac{bv(1 - v^n)}{1 - v} = \frac{b}{i}(1 - v^n) = b\left[\frac{1 - (1 + i)^{-n}}{i}\right] \tag{4}$$

Values of $\dfrac{(1 - v^n)}{i}$ are given in Appendix Table 4 for selected values of i and n ranging from $i = 0.01$ to 0.50 (1% to 50%) and n from 1 to 50.

Example. If $i = 0.05$, $n = 3$, and $b = 1$, there will be three payments:

the value now of the 1st payment is $v = 0.952381$
the value now of the 2nd payment is $v^2 = 0.907029$
the value now of the 3rd payment is $v^3 = 0.863838$
and the sum is

$$0.952381 + 0.907029 + 0.863838 = 2.72325$$

This is the value given in Appendix Table 4 for $i = 0.05$ and $n = 3$. It may be noted that the relationship between P, given by (4), and F, given by (3), is

$$F = P(1 + i)^n$$

or

$$b\left[\frac{(1 + i)^n - 1}{i}\right] = b\left[\frac{1 - (1 + i)^{-n}}{i}\right](1 + i)^n$$

$$= \frac{b}{i}[(1 + i)^n - 1]$$

The present value, P, of a non-uniform series of costs and benefits for n periods. If there are costs of c_i at the end of each period (c_0 is the initial cost), and benefits of b_i at the end of each period (b_0 is the initial benefit), then

Present value = Present value of benefits − Present value of costs

$$P = \left(b_0 + \frac{b_1}{1 + i} + \cdots + \frac{b_n}{(1 + i)^n}\right) - \left(c_0 + \frac{c_1}{1 + i} + \cdots + \frac{c_n}{(1 + i)^n}\right)$$

$$= (b_0 - c_0) + (b_1 - c_1)v + (b_2 - c_2)v^2 + \cdots + (b_n - c_n)v^n$$

$$= \sum_{j=0}^{n}(b_j - c_j)v^j = \sum_{j=0}^{n}a_j v^j \qquad (5)$$

Since b_i and c_i can assume any values, it is not feasible to prepare tables for P. However, Appendix Table 2 can be used to obtain the necessary values of v^j. These are then multiplied by $(b_j - c_j)$ and the products summed to obtain P.

Nominal and Effective Interest Rates.   Interest rates are usually quoted as annual rates, but interest may actually be added to the principal at more frequent intervals—often on a quarterly or semi-annual basis. The amount accumulated at the end of a year will clearly depend on the frequency with which interest is compounded during the year, as well as on the quoted annual or "nominal" rate. For example, if the nominal rate is 6% and interest is compounded annually, the amount accumulated per dollar at the end of one year is 1.06 and hence the "effective" rate is 6%. If the interest is compounded semi-annually, the amount accumulated per dollar at the end of the first half-year is

$$\left(1 + \frac{0.06}{2}\right)$$

and at the end of the second half-year the amount is

$$\left(1 + \frac{0.06}{2}\right)\left(1 + \frac{0.06}{2}\right) = (1.03)^2 = 1.0609$$

and the effective annual rate is 6.09%. In general *if i is the effective rate and j is the nominal rate, and interest is compounded m times per year* ($m \geq 1$), then

$$(1 + i) = \left(1 + \frac{j}{m}\right)^m \quad \text{or} \quad i = \left(1 + \frac{j}{m}\right)^m - 1 \quad (6)$$

The identity (6) can be solved for j in terms of i and m to determine the nominal rate which must produce a required effective rate with m compoundings per year. In practical problems, it is usually not necessary to

Table 3-1

Nominal Annual Rate of Interest	Effective Rate when Compounded			
	Annually	Semi-Annually	Quarterly	Monthly
0.02	0.0200	0.0201	0.0201	0.0202
0.05	0.0500	0.0506	0.0509	0.0511
0.10	0.1000	0.1025	0.1038	0.1047
0.20	0.2000	0.2100	0.2155	0.2194
0.40	0.4000	0.4400	0.4641	0.4821
0.50	0.5000	0.5625	0.6018	0.6321

compute effective rates if the tables have the necessary entries. For example: What is the value in five years of $1 deposited now if interest is 8% per year compounded quarterly? The amount in five years will be the same as the amount in 20 periods compounded at 2% per period. From Appendix Table 1 $(1 + 0.02)^{20} = 1.48595$; and consequently the value is $1.49.

The effect of compounding at different periods with different nominal interest rates is shown in Table 3-1. The effective rate is greater than the nominal rate except if $m = 1$ and then they are equal.

Example I. The Apex Manufacturing Co. has purchased a machine for $50,000. The use of this machine is expected to yield a net benefit of $18,000 per year for four years. What is the present value of the investment if the interest rate is 0.20? From (4):

$$P = -50,000 + \frac{18,000}{1+i} + \frac{18,000}{(1+i)^2} + \frac{18,000}{(1+i)^3} + \frac{18,000}{(1+i)^4}$$

$$= -50,000 + \frac{b[1-(1+i)^{-n}]}{i} \quad \text{with } b = 18,000, \ i = 0.20, \text{ and } n = 4$$

From Appendix Table 4:

$$\frac{1-(1+0.20)^{-4}}{0.2} = 2.58873$$

Therefore, rounding to four decimal places,

$$P = -50,000 + 18,000\,(2.5887)$$

$$= -50,000 + 46,596.60 = -3,403.40$$

If the benefits were obtained semi-annually and interest compounded semi-annually,

$$\frac{1}{0.1}\left[1 - \left(1 + \frac{0.20}{2}\right)^{-8}\right] = 5.33493$$

and

$$P = -50,000 + 9,000(5.3349)$$

$$= -50,000 + 48,014.10 = -1,985.90$$

or if quarterly,

$$\frac{1}{0.05}\left[1 - \left(1 + \frac{0.20}{4}\right)^{-16}\right] = 10.8378$$

and

$$P = -50,000 + 4,500(10.8378)$$

$$= -50,000 + 48,770.10 = -1,229.90$$

Example 2. The Mulholland Company owns and operates a small lead and zinc mine. Its annual net earnings are $20,000 before payment of $10,000 on a note. The outstanding balance of the note ($160,000) must be paid at the end of five years. The Alpaca Hill Company is considering acquiring the Mulholland Company by purchase from its owners. Acquisition of Mulholland will require no initial outlay other than the purchase price and will produce immediate income. The net income at the end of each of the first five years will be $10,000, (20,000 − 10,000), and at the end of the fifth year $160,000 will have to be spent to pay the note in full. Subsequently, income of $20,000 per year will be received each year until the ore is exhausted at the end of the twentieth year. At the end of 20 years, there will be no salvage value for any of the facilities. What is the maximum amount that Alpaca Hill can afford to give for the Mulholland Company, if it does not wish to exceed the present value of the future benefits less future costs? Assume its interest rate is 20%.

Since the costs and benefits are not uniform, (5) must be used. Here:

$$c_j = 10,000 \qquad j = 1, \ldots, 4$$

$$c_s = 170,000$$

$$c_j = 0 \qquad j = 6, \ldots, 20$$

$$b_j = 20,000 \qquad j = 1, \ldots, 20$$

$$P = \sum_{j=1}^{20}(b_j - c_j)v^j = \sum_{j=1}^{5}(10,000)v^j - 160,000v^5 + \sum_{j=6}^{20}(20,000)v^j$$

$$= \sum_{j=1}^{5}(10,000)v^j - (160,000)v^5 + \sum_{j=1}^{20}(20,000)v^j - \sum_{j=1}^{5}(20,000)v^j \quad (7)$$

These terms may be evaluated using Tables II and IV.

$$P = 10,000(2.9906) - 160,000(0.4019) + 20,000(4.8696) - 20,000(2.9906)$$

$$= 29,906 - 64,304 + 97,392 - 59,812 = 3,182$$

Alpaca Hill could afford to pay $3,182 in cash for the assets and liabilities of the Mulholland Co.

Example 3. A fund which will accumulate a given amount, S, at the end of a given number of periods is frequently called a *sinking fund*. The payments, b, are called sinking fund payments.

If $n = 3$, there will be three payments. At the end of the third period the value of the first payment will be $b(1 + i)^2$, the value of the second payment will be $b(1 + i)$ and the value of the last payment will be b. Therefore, if $i = 0.05$,

$$S = b(1.1025) + 1.05 + 1 = 3.1525b$$

The sinking fund payment will be $b = \dfrac{S}{3.1525}$

In general the sinking fund payment required for an amount S at the end of n periods at interest rate i per period is

$$b = \frac{S}{\dfrac{(1 + i)^n - 1}{i}} \quad (8)$$

The annual sinking fund payments required if the fund must be $350,000 at the end of five years and the interest rate is 0.06 is

$$b = \left[\frac{(1 + i)^n - 1}{i}\right]^{-1} S$$

or

$$b = \$62,088.77$$

Table 3-2 Summary of Interest Formulas

Payment		Value		
When	Amount	When	\multicolumn{2}{c}{Amount}	

Payment When	Payment Amount	Value When	Formula	Appendix Table
			Compounding Each Period	
Now	b_0	n periods hence	$F = b_0(1 + i)^n$	1
n periods hence	b_n	Now	$P = b_n(1 + i)^{-n} = b_n v^n$	2
At the end of each period	b	n periods hence	$F = b[(1 + i)^{n-1} + \cdots (1 + i) + 1]$ $= b\left[\dfrac{(1 + i)^n - 1}{i}\right]$	3
At the end of each period	b	Now	$P = b[v + v^2 + \cdots + v^n]$ $= \dfrac{bv(1 - v^n)}{1 - v} = \dfrac{b}{i}[1 - v^n]$	4
At the end of each period $j = 0, \ldots, n$	$b_j - c_j$	Now	$P = \sum\limits_{j=0}^{n} (b_j - c_j)v^j$	

EXERCISES

1. (*a*) Show that the present value of net benefits of \$5,000 per year received at the end of each year for five years at an interest rate of 10% is \$18,954.

(*b*) Show that if the benefits are received semiannually and interest compounded twice a year, the present value is \$19,304.

2. (*a*) What is the present value of \$3,000 net income per year received at the end of each year for ten years? Assume $i = 0.30$

(*b*) What is the present value if income is received semiannually and compounded twice a year?

3. The Baxter Co. is considering the purchase of a machine which requires an initial cost of \$20,000 and will yield a net benefit of \$10,000 the first year, \$8,000 the second year, \$6,000 the third year, \$4,000 the fourth year, and \$2,000 the fifth year. Show that the present value of the investment at an interest rate of 6% is \$6,255.

4. What is the present value of a project which will cost \$20,000 initially, and will yield net income of \$2,500 the first year, \$5,000 in the second year, \$7,500 in the third year, and \$10,000 in the fourth year? Assume $i = 0.10$.

5. A company is enjoying a favorable growth rate. To attract more capital, it has indicated that annual dividend payments will be increased by an amount $y each year after payment of next year's dividend of $x, due exactly one year from now. What is the present value of dividends to be paid during the next n years, if interest rate is i? Use this result to check the answers to (3) and (4).

6. The Bayshore Industrial Park Company leases buildings to tenants on long-term contracts. The annual rental charge is increased each year by a constant ratio, r. A new lease being negotiated calls for the first year's rent payable one year hence to be a, the second year's rent payable two years hence to be ar, the third ar^2, etc. What is the present value of the rental payments if the leases are to run for n years and the interest rate is i?

7. The Alpaca Hill Co. (Example 2) has a preferred stock which pays a semi-annual dividend of $3 per share. How many shares should the owners of the Mulholland Co. accept, assuming they are interested only in (perpetual) income and their other investments earn 6% per year? Comment on the answer.

B. INVESTMENTS

Accept or Reject an Investment

A simple form of the investment problem occurs when a firm has an opportunity to commit itself to some project, say, denoted by A, with known costs and benefits:

$c_0, c_1, c_2, \ldots, c_n$ where c_j is the cost (money paid out) at the end of period j

and

$b_0, b_1, b_2, \ldots, b_n$ where b_j is the benefit (money received) at the end of period j

A widely used rule for deciding whether or not to undertake the project is:

Undertake the project if $P(i;\ A) \geq 0$

Do not undertake it if $P(i;\ A) < 0$

where $P(i;\ A)$ is present value, at interest i, of project A with the given costs and benefits, that is,

$$P(i;\ A) = \sum_{j=0}^{n} \frac{(b_j - c_j)}{(1 + i)^j} \tag{1}$$

The interest rate, i, that a firm expects from the use of its money is regarded as fixed and known. The rationale underlying this rule is that undertaking a project with positive present value will increase the firm's future amount of money. The firm will have more money at the end of n periods if it undertakes a project with positive value than if it does not undertake it (provided, of course, that it can borrow, or invest, money at the rate i).

Example 1. The Centaur Missile and Space Co. is considering the purchase of a machine, A, for $50,000 which will yield a net benefit of $18,000

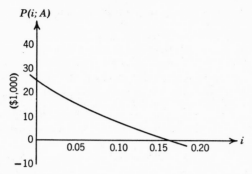

Figure 3.1 Present value of purchase of machine, A, as a function of the interest rate i.

for four years and will have no salvage value at the end of that period. Should the machine be purchased?

If the interest rate is 20%, the present value of the investment is $\$-3,403.40$ (Example 1, page 58), and the machine would not be purchased. However, the decision depends on the value of the interest rate i; in general,

$$P(i; A) = -50,000 + \frac{18,000}{1+i} + \frac{18,000}{(1+i)^2} + \frac{18,000}{(1+i)^3} + \frac{18,000}{(1+i)^4}$$

$$= -50,000 + 18,000 \left[\frac{(1-(1+i)^{-4}}{i} \right]$$

Using Appendix Table 4 gives for two other interest rates:

i	$P(i;\ A)$
0	22,000.00
0.10	7.058.20
0.20	−3,403.40

The present value is shown as a function of i in Fig. 3-1. The machine will be purchased if the firm's required interest rate is (approximately) 0.163 or less, and will not be purchased if it is greater.

Example 2. The machine purchase problem may be stated more generally. Let

c = initial cost of the machine ($\$$)
b = net benefit received at the end of each period ($\$$ per period)
i = interest rate per period
n = life of the machine (periods)
b_n = salvage value at the end of n periods ($\$$)

The present value of the investment in the machine is

$$P(i) = -c + b\left[\frac{1 - (1 + i)^{-n}}{i}\right] + b_n(1 + i)^{-n} \tag{2}$$

If c, b, b_n, n, and i are known, the present value can be computed and the rule applied. The formula can also be rearranged to give the minimum value of b which will make $P(i)$ positive. Since $P(i)$ increases as b increases, the minimum value of b is the one which satisfies the equation

$$P(i) = 0 \quad \text{or} \quad -c + b\left[\frac{1 - (1 + i)^{-n}}{i}\right] + b_n(1 + i)^{-n} = 0$$

Multiplying by i, adding and subtracting $b_n i$, and rearranging gives

$$b[1 - (1 + i)^{-n}] = ci - b_n i(1 + i)^{-n} + b_n i - b_n i$$
$$= (c - b_n)i + b_n[i - i(1 + i)^{-n}]$$
$$b = (c - b_n)\left[\frac{i}{1 - (1 + i)^{-n}}\right] + b_n i \tag{3}$$

More Than One Possible Investment

The problem just discussed has been concerned with whether or not the firm should commit itself to an investment. Many practical problems are concerned with choosing among several alternative investments.

The present value investment rule can be extended to situations where there is more than one possible investment:

Compute $P(i)$ for each investment
Rank the investments with positive present value in order
of present value

$$P(i; A_1) \geq P(i; A_2) \geq \cdots \geq P(i; A_m) \geq 0 \tag{4}$$

A_1 is the investment with the largest present value; A_2 has the next largest present value, etc., and m is the number of investments with positive present value. The order given by (4) is the order in which the investments should be undertaken.

The rationale for this rule is the same as that given for accepting or rejecting a single project on the basis of present value. The firm will have more money at the end of the investment period if it follows the rule than if it does not.

Example 3. The Centaur Missile and Space Co. (Example 1) has examined other machines and has located one machine, B, which costs

$37,000 and would result in net benefits of $14,000 per year for four years, and would also have no salvage value at the end. Either machine would be satisfactory but both would not be needed. Which one should be purchased?

$$P(i; B) = -37,000 + 14,000\left[\frac{1 - (1 + i)^{-4}}{i}\right]$$

or

i	P(i; B)
0	19,000.00
0.10	7,378.60
0.15	2,970.00
0.20	−758.20

If machine B were considered by itself, it would be purchased if the interest rate were approximately 18.9% or less and not purchased if it were greater.

Table 3-3 Present Value of Investments in Machines A and B as Functions of the Interest Rate i

i	$\dfrac{1 - (1 + i)^{-4}}{i}$	$P(i; A)$	$P(i; B)$
0	4.0000	22,000.00	19,000.00
0.06	3.4651	12,371.80	11,511.40
0.08	3.3121	9,617.80	9,369.40
0.10	3.1699	7,058.20	7,378.60
0.12	3.0373	4,671.40	5,522.20
0.15	2.8550	1,390.00	2,970.00
0.16	2.7982	367.60	2,174.80
0.17	2.7432	−622.40	1,404.80
0.18	2.6901	−1,578.20	661.40
0.20	2.5887	−3,403.40	−758.20
0.22	2.4936	−5,115.20	−2,089.60
0.24	2.4043	−6,722.60	−3,339.80

If both machines are being considered, machine A would be recommended if $i = 0$ since

$$P(0; A) > P(0; B)$$

machine B would be recommended at $i = 0.10$ since

$$P(0.10; B) > P(0.10; A)$$

and neither would be recommended at $i = 0.20$ because the present values are both negative. Machine A is preferred at low interest rates and

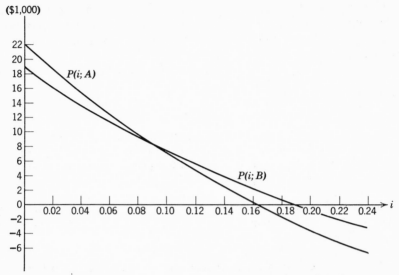

Figure 3.2 Present value of investments A and B as a function of the interest rate i.

B at higher rates. To determine the crossover point more precisely values of $P(i;\ A)$ and $P(i;\ B)$ for more values of i are required. These are given in Table 3-3. $P(i;\ A)$ and $P(i;\ B)$ are shown in Fig. 3.2.

If the rule were followed, machine A would be purchased if $i \leq 0.088$, and B would be purchased if $i > 0.088$.

EXERCISES

1. A firm is considering a project which will involve an immediate cost of $10,000 and will yield a net income of $3,000 per year at the end of each year for four years. Show that this project would be undertaken if $i \leq 0.078$, and not undertaken if $i > 0.078$.

2. An inventor, X, has licensed the Diane Manufacturing Co. to produce a product based on a patent which he owns. Diane will pay a royalty of $5,000 a year at the end of each of the next five years. However, X has other income and for tax reasons would prefer to receive a single payment at the end of seven years. He approaches an investor Y and offers to sell the license agreement to him for $32,000 to be paid seven years from now. Should Y accept the offer?

3. Show that the project in Exercise 3, p. 61, would be undertaken if $i \leq 20\%$.

4. Determine the range of value of i for which the project in Exercise 4, p. 61, would be undertaken.

5. An investment costs $10,000 at present. The returns on the investment will be $10,000 a year for ten years, with the first return one year from the present. A rate of interest of 100% will prevail for the next six years, then there will be two years in which the interest rate will be 50% and two more years in which the interest rate is zero. Compute the present value and indicate whether the investment is advisable.

6. Show how the payment (positive or negative) which the Alpaca Hill Company (Example 2, p. 59) would make to the Mulholland Co. depends on the value of *i*.

C. RENT OR BUY DECISION; EFFECT OF DEPRECIATION ALLOWANCES AND DISCOUNTING

Buisiness firms must consider the effect of taxes in investment decisions. Probably the single most important effect is through the depreciation allowances. The quotation under heading 1 deals with the problem of whether an electronic data processing system should be purchased or rented. Straight-line depreciation is assumed. The development will be extended under heading 2 to include other methods of depreciation and to take into account the time value of money.

I. Rent or Buy Decision[1]

"In determining whether to rent or purchase an electronic system the basic problems are: (1) actual costs incurred by renting versus those incurred by buying, (2) the probability of obsolescence before the investment on the system is at least recaptured, and (3) tax advantages. We discuss how to analyze a particular situation as to costs and taxes, and then discuss obsolescence.

"Disregarding obsolescence in the decision to rent or buy, it is reasonable to say that the choice will be that which has the lowest yearly costs. (We assume a computer has already been justified in general by direct clerical savings and/or other benefits.) The costs may be analyzed as follows:

"Some equations are derived for determining when to rent, when to buy: Let

C_e = those costs of changing to a computer which are part of the investment, but are called expenses under the usual accounting system; these would be programming, training, cost of change-over of methods, etc.

C_s = capital expenditures which are 'sunken' or non-recoverable costs, such as physical changes to accommodate the computer, also equipment which cannot be rented, such as especially constructed units.

[1] "Some Notes on Renting Versus Buying an Electronic Data Processing System," *Data Processing Digest*, March 1957, pp. 15–17.

"Note that $C_e + C_s$ are costs incurred whether the system is rented or purchased, and so will not appear in an equation comparing the two.

C_p = cost of purchasing the equipment

C_m = cost of maintenance, if system is purchased

R = yearly rental of system including maintenance

J = yearly operating costs including personnel for continuing programming, operation and supervision; power, space overhead, tape, and paper. (This also is the same whether renting or buying.)

d = fraction of investment depreciated each year (we assume a straight line depreciation; more sophisticated methods could be used, if desired). The entire actual investment will be depreciated at this rate.

t = tax rate (as a fraction) which the company pays on net profit.

r = the rate of return which the company can obtain by using its capital in the best way it knows at the time, other than for a computer (i.e., highest rate-of-return possible).

"The basis for the derivation that follows is that management will always invest its money so as to get the maximum return. (Note that a company does not always have the easy choice of using its own or someone else's capital. If the best investment is to expand a sales force, the company has to use its own capital or perhaps use some long-range financing technique; it cannot "rent" a sales force.)

"A company will have to make some investment in a computer, i.e., $C_e + C_s$; the remainder may be rented or purchased.

"The basic yearly cost of renting is:

$$d(C_e + C_s) + R + J - rC_p = a \qquad (1)$$

"The first term accounts for the depreciation of the 'investment' in programming and installation. The last is the income from the 'freed' capital being used elsewhere.

"The yearly cost of purchasing is:

$$d(C_e + C_s + C_p) + J + C_m = b \qquad (2)$$

"Combining terms and subtracting a from b to get the benefit of renting, we have:

$$(r + d)C_p - R + C_m = c \qquad (3)$$

"To include the effect of taxes consider as follows: Assume a study has shown that a computer will result in a saving of S dollars per year (direct clerical saving plus estimates of saving through improved control, etc.).

"The 'profit' in renting a computer is:

$$(S + rC_p) - [d(C_e + C_s) + R + J]$$
$$- t\{(S + rC_p) - [d(C_e + C_s) + R + J]\}$$

where the first term is 'income,' the second expenses and the third taxes on the profit. Rearranging, this is merely

$$(S - a) - t(S - a)$$

or

$$(1 - t)S - (1 - t)a \tag{4}$$

Likewise, when buying, the profit is

$$(1 - t)S - (1 - t)b \tag{5}$$

"Here the difference in favor of renting, (4) — (5), is:

$$-(1 - t)a + (1 - t)b$$

or

$$(b - a) - t(b - a)$$

or

$$(1 - t)c \tag{6}$$

"So the tax effect has not changed the validity of equation (3) but has reduced its effect by $(1 - t)$.

"Thus, to determine whether to rent or buy we calculate:

$$D = (1 - t)[(r + d)C_p - R + C_m] \qquad \text{if } D > 0 \text{ rent,} \tag{7}$$

since, if $D > 0$, the purchase costs (2) are greater than the rental costs (1): the net difference reduced by the effect of taxes.

"For example, if $C_p = \$1,500,000$
$\qquad C_m = \$150,000$ per year
$\qquad R = \$600,000$ (2-shift rental)
$\qquad d = 0.2$ (5-year depreciation)
$\qquad r = 0.25$ (25% return)
$\qquad t = 0.5$ (50% tax rate)

Then $D = +\$112,500$, hence one would rent so as to realize this much per year over buying.

"Note that if the best investment (other than in a computer) brings 5% so that $r = 0.05$ then D is $- \$37,500$. In this case purchase is a somewhat more economical course; that is, management would be wisest to "invest" in the purchase of a computer, rather than some other investment with a 5% return. The effect of other variations is shown in Fig. 3.3. Note that a high tax rate (e.g., $t = 0.7$) reduces the importance of the decision (lower D), but cannot reverse the decision. Increasing R makes buying more

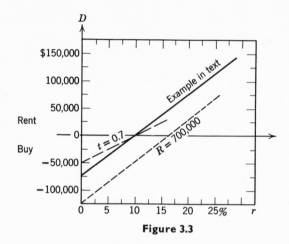

Figure 3.3

attractive even at high 'next-best' rates of return. Decreasing maintenance costs or depreciation would have a similar effect."

2. Effect of Other Depreciation Methods and Discounting

If the costs and benefits of renting (and buying) are identical for each year, the interest rate does not affect the relative desirability of renting or buying, because if one alternative is more desirable in one year, it is also more desirable for each year and hence for all years. In the example given above, the costs and benefits are identical for each year because straight-line depreciation results in the same allowance for each year and all other costs and benefits are the same for each year.

If one of the other methods of depreciation is used, the costs and benefits will be as follows:

	Rent			Buy		
Year	Cost	Benefits	Depreciation	Cost	Benefits	Depreciation
0	$C_e + C_s$			$C_p + C_e + C_s$		
1	$R + J$	S	$d_1 C_s$	$C_m + J$	S	$d_1(C_p + C_s)$
2	$R + J$	S	$d_2 C_s$	$C_m + J$	S	$d_2(C_p + C_s)$
3	$R + J$	S	$d_3 C_s$	$C_m + J$	S	$d_3(C_p + C_s)$
...	...	...	...	...	...	...
n	$R + J$	S	$d_n C_s$	$C_m + J$	S	$d_n(C_p + C_s)$

where d_j is the rate of depreciation, applied to original cost, in year j. It is assumed that C_s, C_e, and C_p are paid at the end of year zero and other costs and benefits occur at the end of the year.

The after-tax present value of renting if the interest rate is i, $PV(i;$ Rent), is the sum of the discounted after-tax (benefits minus cost):

$$PV(i; \text{Rent}) = [-(C_e + C_s) + v(S - R - J) + \cdots + v^n(S - R - J)]$$
$$- t[v(S - R - J) + \cdots + v^n(S - R - J)$$
$$- (vd_1 + v^2 d_2 + \cdots + v^n d_n)C_s]$$
$$= \left[-(C_e + C_s) + (1 - t)\sum_{j=1}^{n} v^j(S - R - J) + t\sum_{j=1}^{n} v^j d_j C_s \right]$$

Note that the depreciation allowance is a credit against the net benefits that are taxed. Similarly, the after-tax present value of buying is:

$$PV(i; \text{Buy}) = -(C_p + C_e + C_s)$$
$$+ (1 - t)\sum_{j=1}^{n} v^j(S - C_m - J) + t\sum_{j=1}^{n} v^j d_j(C_s + C_p)$$

It is assumed that there is no salvage value; that the tax rate is constant, and that if the taxable amount is negative (as it frequently is in the first few years) the firm has other taxable income against which this loss can be applied. It is also assumed that d_j is the same for C_p and C_s.

A firm will rent if

$$PV(i; \text{Rent}) > PV(i; \text{Buy})$$

or

$$PV(i; \text{Rent}) - PV(i; \text{Buy}) > 0$$

that is, if

$$B = C_p + (1 - t)\sum_{j=1}^{n} v^j(C_m - R) - t\sum_{j=1}^{n} v^j d_j C_p > 0$$

$$B = C_p + (1 - t)(C_m - R)\left(\frac{1 - v^n}{i}\right) - C_p t\sum_{j=1}^{n} v^j d_j > 0 \tag{8}$$

$$B = C_p\left(1 - t\sum_{j=1}^{n} v^j d_j\right) + (1 - t)(C_m - R)\left(\frac{1 - v^n}{i}\right) > 0$$

The variables C_s, C_e, S, and J do not appear in (8). They are the same under both alternatives and could have been omitted from the analysis right from the beginning.

Further analysis requires the explicit formulas for the d_j which were developed in Chapter 2.

Straight-Line Depreciation:

$$d_j = \frac{1}{n}$$

$$\sum v^j d_j = \frac{v}{n}\left(\frac{1 - v^n}{1 - v}\right) = \frac{1 - v^n}{ni} \tag{9}$$

Substituting in (8) gives

$$B = C_p + \left[-\frac{t}{n} C_p + (1 - t)(C_m - R) \right] \left[\frac{1 - v^n}{i} \right] > 0$$

as the condition under which the machine should be rented.

Sum-of-the-Years Digits Depreciation:

$$d_1 = \frac{n}{1 + 2 + \cdots + n} = \frac{2n}{(n + 1)n}$$

$$d_2 = \frac{2(n - 1)}{n(n + 1)}$$

$$\cdots \quad \cdots$$

$$d_n = \frac{2}{n(n + 1)}$$

$$\sum_{j=1}^{n} d_j v^j = \frac{2v}{n(n + 1)} [n + (n - 1)v + (n - 2)v^2 + \cdots + v^{n-1}]$$

$$v \left(\sum_{j=1}^{n} d_j v^j \right) = \frac{2v}{n(n + 1)} [nv + (n - 1)v^2 + \cdots + 2v^{n-1} + v^n]$$

$$(v - 1) \left(\sum_{j=1}^{n} d_j v^j \right) = \frac{2v}{n(n + 1)} [-n + v + v^2 + \cdots + v^{n-1} + v^n]$$

$$\sum_{j=1}^{n} d_j v^j = \frac{2v}{n(n + 1)(v - 1)} \left[-n + \frac{v(1 - v^n)}{1 - v} \right]$$

$$= \frac{2}{(n + 1)i} - \frac{2(1 - v^n)}{n(n + 1)i^2} \tag{10}$$

Double-Declining Balance Depreciation:

$$d_1 = \frac{2}{n}$$

$$d_2 = \left(1 - \frac{2}{n} \right) \frac{2}{n}$$

$$\cdots \quad \cdots$$

$$d_n = \left(1 - \frac{2}{n} \right)^{n-1} \frac{2}{n}$$

Then

$$\sum_{j=1}^{n} v^j d_j = \sum_{j=1}^{n} v^j \left(1 - \frac{2}{n}\right)^{j-1} \frac{2}{n}$$

$$= \frac{2/n}{1 - (2/n)} \sum_{j=1}^{n} \left[v\left(1 - \frac{2}{n}\right)\right]^j$$

$$= \frac{2v}{n} \left\{\frac{1 - [v(1 - (2/n))]^n}{1 - v(1 - (2/n))}\right\} \tag{11}$$

Double-Declining Balance with Change to Straight-Line Depreciation after k Years:

$$\sum_{j=1}^{n} v^j d_j = \sum_{j=1}^{k} v^j \frac{2}{n} \left(1 - \frac{2}{n}\right)^{j-1} + \sum_{j=k+1}^{n} v^j \frac{1 - (2/n)^k}{n - k}$$

$$= \frac{2}{n} v \frac{1 - v^k(1 - (2/n))^k}{1 - v(1 - (2/n))} + \frac{v^k(1 - (2/n))^k}{n - k} \frac{1 - v^{n-k}}{i} \tag{12}$$

The optimum value of k is $n/2 + 1$ or $n/2 + 2$ if n is even, and $\frac{n + 3}{2}$ if n is odd.

Example. Using the same data as above, namely,

$$C_p = 1{,}500{,}000$$

$$C_m = \$150{,}000$$

$$R = \$600{,}000$$

$$n = 5 \text{ years}$$

$$t = 0.5$$

and substituting in (8) gives B, in units of $\$1{,}000{,}000$, as

$$B = 1.5 - 0.75 \, \Sigma \, v^j d_j + 0.5(-0.45)\left(\frac{1 - v^n}{i}\right)$$

B as defined here is five times the value of D used in heading 1, page 69, because B here represents the total present value, not just the value for one year. Values of B for various values of i for each method of depreciation are given in Table 3-4 and shown in Fig. 3.4. The double declining balance method assumes a change to straight-line depreciation for years 4 and 5.

The straight line is obtained by multiplying the figures for the line in the example in heading 1 by 5, the life of the machine. B under straight-line depreciation is zero for i approximately 7.8%, rather than the 10%

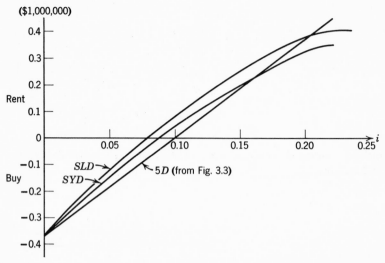

($1,000,000)

Figure 3.4 Present value of rent versus purchase for two methods of depreciation.

obtained when the time value of money was not taken into account. If the firm can earn 7.8% or more on its money, it should rent rather than buy if straight-line depreciation is used. If either of the other methods is

Table 3-4 Depreciation Allowance and B for Rent versus Purchase for Various Values of i

i	$\dfrac{1-v^5}{i}$	$\Sigma v^j d_j$			B		
		SLD	SYD	DDB	SLD	SYD	DDB
0.00	5.0000	1.0000	1.0000	1.0000	−0.375	−0.375	−0.375
0.05	4.3295	0.8659	0.8940	0.8965	−0.124	−0.145	−0.146
0.10	3.7908	0.7582	0.8061	0.8110	0.079	0.043	0.039
0.15	3.3522	0.6704	0.7324	0.7394	0.243	0.196	0.191
0.20	2.9906	0.5981	0.6698	0.6788	0.379	0.325	0.318
0.30	2.4356	0.4871	0.5699	0.5821	0.587	0.525	0.515
0.50	1.7366	0.3473	0.4351	0.4516	0.849	0.786	0.771

used, the firm should rent rather than buy if it can earn 8.8% or more elsewhere. The difference between sum-of-the-years digit and double-declining balance method in this case is very small.

The tax rate will have a major effect on the rent or buy decision. If the tax rate is zero (8) reduces to

$$B = C_p + (C_m - R)\left[\frac{1 - v^n}{i}\right]$$

Depreciation allowances are now irrelevant. In the example, the machine should be rented if $i \geq 0.14$

If the tax rate is 1, (8) reduces to

$$B = C_p - C_p \Sigma v^j d_j$$

which is always positive, and hence the machine will always be rented. As the tax rate increases, the minimum interest rate at which the machine will be rented rather than purchased decreases from 0.14 to zero.

EXERCISES

1. Modify (8) to include the effect of state income taxes. Assume that state depreciation methods are the same as federal methods and that state taxes are allowed as costs in the computation of federal taxes, but that federal taxes are not allowed as costs in the computation of state taxes.

2. Modify (9), (10), (11), and (12) to incorporate a salvage value of sA ($0 \leq s \leq 1$) at the end of its life.

3. Modify (8) to include the effect of the salvage value of the system. Assume that the difference between book value and salvage value is treated as a capital gain or loss and taxed at a rate t_3 for the federal tax and t_4 for the state tax if a gain, and allowed as a cost, if a loss, for both.

4. Modify (8), assuming the firm can borrow the amount C_p necessary to purchase the system at interest rate r and repays the loan with n equal installments at the end of each year.

5. Is (8) with (9) substituted consistent with (7)? Explain.

6. In the example there was very little difference between the sum-of-the-years digit method and the double-declining balance method. However, one tax authority has made the following recommendation:

> "For interest rates between 0.02 and 0.10, the double declining balance with change to straight line method should be used if $n = 3, 4$ or 5; and the sum of the years digits method is better if $n \geq 6$."

Use one of the available depreciation tables (some are listed in Notes and References) and determine whether this advice is correct.

D. THE INTERNAL RATE OF RETURN

Definition

The use of the Present Value as a criterion for investment decisions has frequently been questioned because it depends on an externally determined interest rate. One of the alternative criteria that have been developed is the internal rate of return. In Figs. 3.1 and 3.2 the present values of the investments are positive for i near zero; they decrease as i increases and eventually become negative when i becomes large. This form of P is typical of many projects. If P is positive for some value of i and negative for some other value of i, there must exist a value of i for which P is equal to zero. The value of i for which $P = 0$ is called the internal rate of return (IRR) and will be denoted by $i*$. Formally $i*$ is the solution of the equation

$$P(i) = 0$$

The internal rate of return is that value of i for which the present value of the benefits equals the present value of the costs. In other words, it is the rate at which the project is earning benefits which just balance the costs. It is called an "internal rate" because it depends solely on the costs and benefits associated with the project and not on any rate determined outside the investment.

The higher the internal rate of return, the more desirable is the investment. The investment rules based on this criterion may be stated as follows:

(a) Given i_{min}, the minimum acceptable rate of return, undertake an investment if and only if $i* \geq i_{min}$.

(b) If several investments are being considered, the one with the largest internal rate of return is preferred, if its rate is greater than i_{min}.

Again, the rationale for these rules is that if the rules are followed, they result in the firm having a larger amount of money at the end of the investment than if they are not. The minimum rate, i_{min}, is set at the rate which the firm must pay for borrowing or otherwise acquiring money (that is, the firms' cost of capital). Any project which has a rate of return greater than this will result in a positive increase in the firm's amount of money. If one project has a greater rate of return than another, it will result in a greater positive increase.

The internal rate of return usually cannot be computed directly but must be obtained by interpolation. In Example 1, page 62,

$$P(0.10; \ A) = 7,058.20$$
$$P(0.20; \ A) = -3,403.40$$

Graphical interpolation, Fig. 3.1, gives a value of $i*$ of approximately 0.163. To check this $P(0.163; A)$ should be computed. Unfortunately the rate $i = 0.163$ does not usually appear in the interest tables. There are numerical interpolation techniques which could be used and some of these will be discussed in Chapter 5. However, the computational difficulty is a disadvantage of the internal rate of return. The relative disadvantage over other methods is minor when computers are used.

Example I. Investment in machine A has an internal rate of return i^* of approximately 0.163%. Therefore, the machine will be purchased if $i_{min} \leq 0.163$ and not undertaken if $i_{min} > 0.163$. Investment in machine B has an internal rate of return equal to approximately 0.19, and would be preferred over machine A if the internal rate of return is used.

Example 2. What is the internal rate of return to the Alpaca Company, if it could acquire the Mulholland Company by merely accepting responsibility for its debt?

The present value of the investment for various values of i can be computed, starting with $i = 0$ and continuing until the present value becomes negative:

i	$P(i)(\$1,000)$
0	190.00
0.10	33.04
0.15	12.11
0.20	3.19
0.25	−0.25

At this point it is known that $P(i)$ is zero for i between 20 and 25% and further computation would show that $P(i)$ is zero for i near 0.24.

Is this the internal rate of return? The answer, unfortunately, is "no" because the computation of $P(i)$ for larger values of i shows that $P(i)$ becomes positive.

i	$P(i)$
0.30	−1.13
0.40	−0.14
0.45	+0.70
0.50	1.52

$P(i)$ is also zero for i between 40 and 45%. $P(i)$ is shown as a function of i in Fig. 3.5. There are, therefore, projects which have more than one

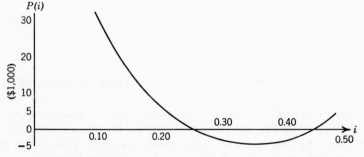

Figure 3.5 Present value of acquisition of Mulholland Co.

internal rate of return. The reason for this and a solution are discussed in the next section.

Multiple Rates of Return

A project costs \$1 now, pays \$5 at the end of the first year, then costs \$6 at the end of the second year. The present value of the project at interest rate i is

$$P(i) = -1 + \frac{5}{1+i} - \frac{6}{(1+i)^2}$$

The internal rate of return (IRR) is defined as the rate (or rates) for which $P(i)$ is zero:

$$-6\left(\frac{1}{1+i}\right)^2 + 5\left(\frac{1}{1+i}\right) - 1 = 0 \qquad (1)$$

It will be recalled that the solutions to the equation

$$ax^2 + bx + c = 0$$

are given by

$$x = \frac{-b \pm \sqrt{b^2 - 4ac}}{2a}$$

Here

$$\frac{1}{1+i} = \frac{-5 \pm \sqrt{25 - 24}}{-12} = \frac{-5 \pm 1}{-12} = \frac{1}{3} \quad \text{or} \quad \frac{1}{2}$$

Hence, $P(i) = 0$ if the interest rate is 100% or 200%.

The internal rate of return can also be computed from the value, F, of the project at the end of its life. Here

$$F = -1(1 + i)^2 + 5(1 + i) - 6 \qquad (2)$$

and $F = 0$ if

$$-(1 + i)^2 + 5(1 + i) - 6 = 0$$

or if

$$(1 + i) = \frac{-5 \pm \sqrt{25 - 24}}{-2} = \frac{-5 \pm 1}{-2} = 2 \quad \text{or} \quad 3$$

The internal rate of return must be identical because (2) can be obtained by multiplying (1) by $(1 + i)^2$.

The basic reason for the occurrence of two internal rates of return in this example is that the project is not only an investment; it is also a lender, since the firm borrows money from the firm. During the first year, the firm has money (\$1) invested in the project which is returned at the end of the year with interest at rate i. The remainder (provided $i < 4.0$) of the \$5 received at the end of the first year, $\$5 - (1 + i)$, is in effect being loaned *by* the project *to* the firm and the \$6 represents a repayment at interest rate i or

$$6 = [5 - (1 + i)](1 + i)$$
$$6 = 5(1 + i) - (1 + i)^2$$
$$0 = -(1 + i)^2 + 5(1 + i) - 6$$

The crucial assumption in this formulation is that the firm assigns the same interest rate when it borrows from the project as it requires when it invests in the project. In this example the Present Value of the project will be zero if

1. The firm expects 100% when it invests and pays 100% when it borrows.
2. The firm expects 200% when it invests and pays 200% when it borrows.

In practical situations, firms will have available sources from which to borrow money, say, at some interest rate k. The firm is seeking projects in which money can be invested; any project which has a return of less than k would not be considered. Ranking projects on the basis of IRR as defined above or on the present value of the project computed at a fixed interest rate leads to nonsensical results when money is both invested in, and borrowed from, a project.

A more realistic approach is to define different interest rates. A project will "receive" interest at the rate k whenever the firm "borrows" money from it. The return on the investment is then computed at the interest rate r which makes the value of the project equal to zero at the end of its life and will be termed the *internal rate of return for investment* (IRRI). It serves as an investment criterion in the same way that IRR does when it is unique; if several projects are available, the one with the highest internal rate of return for investment will be preferred (all other factors being equal).

In the example, the IRRI for investment is the solution of the equation

$$6 = [5 - 1(1 + r)](1 + k) \tag{3}$$

since the one dollar invested for one year must be returned with interest at the rate r and the difference is loaned to the firm which pays interest on it at the rate k. Solving (3) gives

$$1 + r = 5 - \frac{6}{1 + k}$$

or

$$r^* = 4 - \frac{6}{1 + k}$$

if

$$k = 0 \qquad 1 + r^* = 5 - 6 \qquad IRRI = -2$$

$$k = 20\% \qquad 1 + r^* = 5 - 5 = 0 \qquad IRRI = -1$$

$$k = 50\% \qquad 1 + r^* = 5 - 4 = 1 \qquad IRRI = 0$$

$$k = 100\% \qquad 1 + r^* = 5 - 3 = 2 \qquad IRRI = 1$$

As we would expect, the IRRI increases as k increases; the higher the rate paid by the firm to the project for borrowing money, the higher the rate the project can afford to pay to the firm on its investments. If the firm pays a low rate for borrowing, the equation (3) can be solved only by negative values of r. Figure 3.6 shows IRRI as a function of k, and the line IRRI $= k$ which intersects the curve at $k = 1$ and $k = 2$. It should be

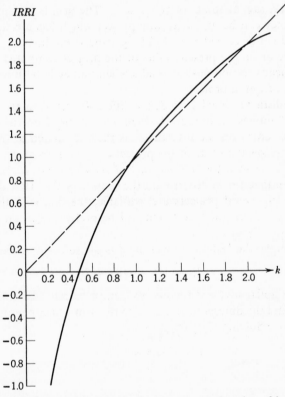

Figure 3.6 Internal rate of return for investment as a function of borrowing rate k for data in example.

noted that (3) is correct only for $r \leq 4.0$. For $r \geq 4.0$, the equation is

$$6 = [5 - 1(1 + r)](1 + r)$$

because the project is an investment for both years. However, there is no value of $r > 4.0$ which will satisfy this equation.

The Algorithm for Computing the IRRI

The first step in the computation of IRRI is the specification of k. Once this is given, the algorithm below is used to compute $F_n(r, k)$, the value of the project at the end of its life, for different values of r. The value of r for which $F_n(r, k)$ is zero is the IRRI.

Let the net benefits at the end of period j be given by:

$$a_0, a_1, \ldots, a_n \quad \text{where} \quad a_j = b_j - c_j$$

The actual value of the project at the present is a_0. During the first period the project earns interest at the rate r if it is an investment during the period or at the rate k if it is a loan to the firm. Let F_j be the value at the end of the jth period. Then

$$F_0 = a_0$$

$$F_1 = a_0(1 + r) + a_1 \quad \text{if} \quad F_0 < 0$$

$$= a_0(1 + k) + a_1 \quad \text{if} \quad F_0 > 0$$

$$= a_1 \quad \text{if} \quad F_0 = 0$$

Similarly, during the second period the project earns interest during the period at the rate r if it is an investment and k if it is a loan, or

$$F_2 = F_1(1 + r) + a_2 \quad \text{if} \quad F_1 < 0$$

$$= F_1(1 + k) + a_2 \quad \text{if} \quad F_1 > 0$$

$$= a_2 \quad \text{if} \quad F_1 = 0$$

And, in general,

$$F_j = F_{j-1}(1 + r) + a_j \quad \text{if} \quad F_{j-1} < 0$$

$$= F_{j-1}(1 + k) + a_j \quad \text{if} \quad F_{j-1} > 0$$

$$= a_j \quad \text{if} \quad F_{j-1} = 0$$

IRRI is the value of r for which

$$F_n(r, k) = 0$$

For the example,

$$F_0 = -1 \qquad\qquad F_0 \le 0$$
$$F_1 = -1(1 + r) + 5 \qquad F_1 > 0 \quad \text{if} \quad 1 + r < 5$$
$$F_2 = [-1(1 + r) + 5](1 + k) - 6$$
$$F_2 = 0 \qquad \text{if} \qquad [-(1 + r) + 5](1 + k) = 6$$
$$\text{or if} \quad 5 - (1 + r) = \frac{6}{1 + k}$$

The internal rate of return will be studied in more detail later; the following results can be proven:

(a) If the sign of a_0 is different from the sign of the other a_j's, there will be at most one positive internal rate of return. In Example 1, page 62, the a_j are

$$-50{,}000, \; +18{,}000, \; +18{,}000, \; +1800$$

There is only one change of sign and therefore only one root. An example of a project with no positive rate of return is

$$1, \, -1, \, 2$$

(b) If the sign of the sequence of net benefits changes more than once, there may or may not be multiple roots. In the example, page 78 the a_j are

$$-1, \, 5, \, -6$$

the sign of the coefficients changes twice: positive to negative, and then back to positive. There are, therefore, two possible internal rates of return. However, the project with a_j

$$-1, \, 0.6, \, -0.45, \, 1.1$$

which has three changes in sign has only one rate of return (10%).

(c) the internal rate of return for investment defined above will always be unique for a given value of k and it increases (or at least never decreases) as k increases.

EXERCISES

Determine whether the following projects in Exercises 1, 2, 3, and 4 have unique internal rates of return; if so, compute them. If not, compute the internal rate of return for investment as a function of the rate k.

1. A project costs $4 now and pays $7 two years from now and $3 three years from now.

2. A project pays $100 now, costs $150 a year from now, pays $200 two years from now, costs $250 three years from now.

3. A project costs $1 now, $5 two years hence, and returns $3 at the beginning of the next year and $3 two years in the future.

4. A project costs $1 now, $7 one year hence, and $15 two years hence. It returns $13 one year hence, $4 two years hence, and $6 three years hence.

5. In Example 2, p. 63, a formula is developed for the case where an investment costs c now, returns a net benefit of b for n periods, and has a salvage value of b_n at the end of n periods. Under these assumptions, the internal rate of return is the solution of

$$-c + \frac{b}{i}(1 - v^n) + b_n v^n = 0$$

However, considerable numerical computation may be required. A number of the investment criteria that have been proposed for this special case can be considered as first approximations to the internal rate of return.

(a) A criterion sometimes used to make investment decisions is the payback or payout period, which is defined as the number of years required to recover the invested capital. Here the payout period is c/b. Show that if an investment has a single initial cost, and has the same return every year for n years, and $i_1 = b/c$, then i_1 approaches i^* (where i^* is the internal rate of return) as n tends to ∞; i.e.,

$$\lim_{n \to \infty} i_1 = i^*$$

(b) Another criterion sometimes used to evaluate investment decisions is the Return on the Investment, defined as the annual income after depreciation divided by the initial cost. If the depreciation is calculated by the straight-line method, the annual income is

$$b - \frac{c - b_n}{n}$$

and the "return on the investment," i_2, is

$$i_2 = \frac{b - \dfrac{c - b_n}{n}}{c} = \frac{b}{c} - \frac{1}{n} + \frac{b_n}{nc}$$

For what values of n and i^* will i_2 be a good approximation for i^*? (Hint: use the binomial theorem to approximate $(1 + i)^n$ by $(1 + ni)$.)

(c) Another criterion sometimes used is to calculate the rate of return on an investment as the annual income divided by the average investment (or one-half the original investment plus the salvage value); i.e.,

$$i_3 = \frac{b - \dfrac{c - b_n}{n}}{\frac{1}{2}(c + b_n)}$$

Show that this is the rate obtained by approximating (3), p. 64, by

$$b = (c - b_n)\left[\frac{1}{n} + \frac{i}{2}\right] + b_n i$$

(d) Compute the i_1, i_2, i_3, and i^* if $c = \$10,000, b = \$3,000, n = 5$, and $b_n = 0$

(e) Repeat (d), using $b_n = \$4,000$.

Notes and References

Section A

Extensive interest tables are available; for example, see:

Bierman, H. and Smidt, S. (1960), *The Capital Budgeting Decision*, Macmillan Co., New York.

Brachen, J. and Christenson, C (1961), *Tables for the Analysis of Capital Expenditures*, Harvard Business School (ICH 7Cl3 EA-C 561).

Sections B and D

The current literature on investment decisions is large and increasing rapidly. A few selected, relatively current, sources are:

Dougall, H. E. (1961), "Payback as an Aid in Capital Budgeting," *Controller*, pp. 3–7.

Grant, E. L., and Ireson, W. G. (1960), *Principles of Engineering Economy*, 4th ed., The Ronald Press, New York.

McKean, R. N. (1958), *Efficiency in Government through Systems Analysis*, John Wiley and Sons, New York.

National Association of Accountants, (1959), "Return on Capital as a Guide to Managerial Decisions," *N.A.A. Research Report No. 35*.

Solomon, E., Ed. (1959), *Management of Corporate Capital*, University of Chicago, Chicago, Ill.

Young, B. (1963), "Overcoming Obstacles to Use of Discounted Cash Flow for Investment Choices," *N.A.A. Bulletin XLIV*, No. 7, pp. 15–26.

Section C

Depreciation methods are discussed in:

Bernhard, R. (1963), "On the importance of reinvestment rates in appraising accelerated depreciation plans," *J. Industrial Engineering XIV*, pp. 135–137.

U.S. Treasury Department (1962), "Depreciation, Guidelines and Rules," Publication 456 (9–62).

―――― (1962), "Tables for Applying Revenue Procedure 62–21," Publication 457 (8–62).

Section D

Exercise 5 is based on:

Swalm, R. O. (1958), "On calculating the rate of return on an Investment," *J. Industrial Engineering*, IX, pp. 99–103.

Pinger, R. W. (1958), "Reader Comment," *J. Industrial Engineering*, IX, pp. 275–276.

Chapter Exercises

Exercise 2 is based on:

Churchman, C., and Ackoff, R. L. (1955), "Operational Accounting and Operations Research," *J. Accountancy*, **99**, 36.

Levary, G. (1956), "A Pocket-Sized Case Study in Operations Research Concerning Inventory Markdown," *Operations Research*, p. 739.

CHAPTER EXERCISES

1. Define: interest   sinking fund

                present value   internal rate of return

                future value

2. A number of items sold in retail stores are characterized by a very heavy initial demand when first introduced, and then a much lower but steady demand over a number of years. Examples of such items are books, certain fashion goods, sports items, and toys. A retail sports store has purchased an item that has recently been introduced and, after the initial heavy demand, finds itself with n units remaining in inventory.

The retailer now has two alternatives. He can maintain the selling price and sell the units, say, at an expected rate of v units per year, or he can reduce the price in the hope of selling the units immediately so that the money can be invested in items which sell at his "normal" rate.

The retailer normally uses a mark-up of k; i.e., if his purchase price is u, the selling price is $s = u(k + 1)$. For example, if u is $7.50 and k is $\frac{1}{3}$, the selling price, $s = 7.50(4/3) = \$10$. The average time items are in inventory for normal items is m years. (turnover is $1/m$ times per year.)

One criterion that has been suggested for determining the sales price under the second alternative is that the money received at the new price and reinvested in items that turn over at the normal rate will after $n/2v$ years be equal to the initial selling price (n/v is divided by two because the items will, on the average, be in stock for half that time). For example, if $s = 10.00$, $k = \frac{1}{3}$, $n = 20$, $v = 2$, $m = \frac{1}{6}$, and s_p is the "sales" price, then s_p invested in normal items will be turned over six times per year ($1/m$) for five years ($n/2v$) at a mark-up of $\frac{1}{3}(k)$ and will be equal to $10 if

$$(s_p)(6)(5)(\tfrac{1}{3}) + s_p = \$10.00 \quad \text{or} \quad s_p = \$0.91$$

(a) Show that the price that will satisfy the criterion is given by

$$s_p = \frac{s}{1 + kn/2mv}$$

(b) Develop the formula for s_p, incorporating any time value for money and assuming that the interest rate is i. Comment on the answer.

Part Two

ONE-DECISION VARIABLE

OPTIMIZATION MODELS

CHAPTER FOUR

Management Science Models

A number of examples in the previous three chapters have illustrated the application of mathematics to the formulation of business problems. These concepts will now be extended to the class of problems requiring an action or a decision. In this chapter the procedure, outlined in Chapter 1 for formulating general business problems in quantitative terms, will be modified to aid in management decision making. The chapter is titled "Management Science Models" because the word *model* is generally accepted as meaning the mathematical statement of a problem and *Management Science* refers to a mathematical (or more accurately, a quantitative) study of management problems.

A decision maker is confronted with a problem in which he must choose one from among a set of alternative courses of action. For each alternative, the decision maker foresees a certain specified outcome. To each possible outcome he associates a value which "measures" how much the outcome is to his liking or how much the outcome accomplishes his objectives. The decision maker will choose that alternative whose outcome has the "best" value.

The decision-making process based on Management Science Models is a special case of the process of formulating problems described in Chapter 1. The relation between the steps in Chapter 1 and the steps to be followed here is:

General Steps in Chapter 1	*Management Science Models*
1. Determine what is required.	Specify the controllable or decision variable and list alternatives. Specify the objective.

2. Identify variables or elements and   Identify the uncontrollable variables.
   assign symbols.

3. Express relationships   Develop the model.
   mathematically.

4. Simplify and solve.   Solve the model.

5. Verify the correctness.   Verify the correctness.

6. Interpret the results and implement.   Interpret the results and implement.

These steps are described and illustrated in Sections A and B. More extensive examples are given in Sections C and D.

A. FORMULATION OF MODELS

Specify the Decision Variable and List the Alternatives

In any situation there are variables or factors which influence the outcome or result of whatever decision is made. These variables can be classified as those which the decision maker controls, called decision variables, and those which he does not control, called uncontrollable variables. The first step in making a decision is to identify the variables over which the decision maker has control, and then to generate all the values of these variables that could be taken as the decision. These will be called the feasible alternatives.

A wholesale auto parts supply house sells only one item, a battery. There is a definite and known uniform demand for 7,800 batteries in the coming year. These batteries are ordered from a manufacturer and delivery is immediate. The decision maker has no control over demand; it is a fixed number: 7,800 units per year. The number of orders placed per year, however, is under the control of the decision maker and is, therefore, the decision variable in this problem. The feasible alternatives are limited because at least one order per year is required and not less than one battery can be ordered. The alternatives, therefore, range from one order per year to 7,800 orders per year. This problem may be summarized as follows:

Example I. Let x denote the decision variable, then

$$x = \text{number of orders placed per year}; \ 1 \leq x \leq 7{,}800$$

As a different type of example, consider the problem of travelling from A (say, a residence) to B (a city). If this is the only specification of the problem that is available, there are a number of possible decision variables: the mode of transportation, the route to be used, etc. For each of these decision variables, a number of alternatives could be listed. For illustration purposes, assume that there is a single decision variable, the mode of transportation, and that the feasible alternatives are the different modes that are available: personal automobile, train, bus. Other alternatives, such as walking, hitchhiking, use of a helicopter, have been rejected. This example may be summarized as follows.

Example 2. Decision variable: What mode of transportation shall be used to travel from A to B? The alternatives are:

$$1 = \text{personal automobile}$$
$$2 = \text{train}$$
$$3 = \text{bus}$$

The difference in the method of listing alternatives in these two examples should be noted. In Example 1, all alternatives are generated by the statement that the alternatives are all the integers, x, which satisfy $1 \leq x \leq 7,800$. In Example 2, the list of alternatives cannot be generated so simply. Since the alternatives are not directly related, each alternative must be listed and assigned a number.

Specify the Objective

In Example 2, if it made no difference which method of transportation were used, a decision would not be necessary because any one of the alternatives would be equally acceptable. An essential part of decision theory is the specification of criteria by which the outcome of one alternative is preferred over that of another. For example, if it were necessary to get to B as fast as possible, one of the feasible alternatives would be preferred over the others since the different alternatives would presumably result in different travel times. Assume that in Example 2 the objective is to minimize the time required, and, therefore, the alternative selected will be the one which requires the minimum travel time.

In Example 1, it will be assumed that the objective is to minimize the total operating cost expressed in dollars.

Identify the Uncontrollable Variables and Parameters

The uncontrollable variables were defined previously as those factors which affect the objective but over which the decision maker exercises no control. In any particular case, the number of such factors will be very large, and for practical purposes it is necessary to limit the list to those which "significantly" affect the outcomes and desirability of these outcomes as measured by the objective function.

In Example 1, the uncontrollable variables could include the following:

(*a*) Demand   7,800 units per year
(*b*) Operating costs
  (1) Fixed cost per order
     (delivery charges, etc.) $75.00
  (2) Inventory carrying costs
     (i) Annual interest charge
          per battery $0.96
     (ii) Storage, insurance, etc.   0.24
          Total annual cost per unit $1.20

The decision maker incurs a cost of $75.00 each time he orders and an annual carrying cost of $1.20 for each battery.

In Example 2, the list of uncontrollable variables might include:

(*a*) The time and cost required by the decision maker to get from his present location to the point at which he can start using the transportation.
(*b*) The transportation time itself.
(*c*) The time and cost required to get from the point at which the transportation stops to the destination.

Develop the Model

The next step in determining the optimum alternative is the development of a model. *A model is the function which gives the value of the objective function for each alternative, for particular values of the uncontrollable variable.* Mathematically, the model can be represented by

$$E = f(x; z)$$

where E = the objective
$\quad x$ = the decision variable
$\quad z$ = the uncontrollable variables
$\quad f$ = the model; i.e., the functional relationship between the objectives and the alternatives and uncontrollable variables

When a numerical value for z is given, the relationship f gives a numerical value for E for each particular value of x which is inserted in the function.

Note that the model, as defined here, actually consists of the combination of two functions:

(*a*) Let $y = h(x; z)$ denote the outcome resulting from a selection of x as the alternative.

(b) Let $E = g(y)$ denote the objective as a function of the outcome.

$$\therefore\ E = g(y) = g[h(x; z)] = f(x; z)$$

The function h may be called the predicting function since it predicts the outcome of a particular course of action; the function g measures desirability of a particular outcome. In some problems, it may be necessary to determine functions h and g explicitly; in others, it is simpler to determine the function f directly.

The model for Example 2 is

$$C(i) = z_1(i) + z_2(i) + z_3(i) = \sum_{j=1}^{3} z_j(i) \qquad i = 1, 2, 3 \tag{1}$$

where $C(i)$ = total cost in minutes for alternative i

$z_1(i)$ = the time in minutes required to get from the present location to the point of starting to use the ith transportation alternative

$z_2(i)$ = the time in minutes on the ith transportation alternative

$z_3(i)$ = the time in minutes required to get from the point at which the ith transportation alternative stops to the destination

The model for Example 1 is somewhat more difficult to develop. As before, let x = number of orders per year. The costs will be represented by c with a subscript to indicate their nature:

c_o = cost of placing an order

c_c = carrying cost per unit per year

C = total cost

Let r = the total demand (requirement) for the year.

The total cost is the sum of the cost of placing orders, plus the cost of carrying inventory. Each of these component costs must be expressed in terms of the decision variable. This can be done as follows:

Total ordering cost = $c_o x$

Total inventory carrying cost is developed as follows:

Quantity ordered in one order = $\dfrac{r}{x}$

Therefore, the average inventory on hand = $\left(\dfrac{1}{2}\right)\left(\dfrac{r}{x}\right)$

and the yearly inventory carrying cost = $\left(\dfrac{1}{2}\right)\left(\dfrac{r}{x}\right) c_c$

The model then is:

$$\text{Total cost} = C = c_0 x + \frac{rc_c}{2x} \tag{2}$$

B. SOLUTION OF MODELS

After the model has been developed and numerical values are available for the uncontrollable variables, the alternative which results in the optimum value of the objective function can be selected. Several different methods may be used. In Example 2, the solution would be obtained by computing $C(1)$, $C(2)$, and $C(3)$; i.e.,

$$C(1) = z_1(1) + z_2(1) + z_3(1)$$
$$C(2) = z_1(2) + z_2(2) + z_3(2)$$
$$C(3) = z_1(3) + z_2(3) + z_3(3)$$

and selecting that alternative, 1, 2, or 3, for which C has the lowest value.

Enumeration of Alternatives. The first step in solving the model in Example 1 is to consider the range of possible alternative courses of action. The alternatives or values of the decision variable in this case can range from 1 order (of 7,800 batteries) to 7,800 orders (of 1 battery per order).

Table 4-1   Ordering Cost, Inventory Carrying Cost and Total Cost as a Function of Number of Orders Per Year (Data from Example 1)

(1) Number of Orders Per Year	(2) Order Quantity	(3) Ordering Cost	(4) Average Inventory	(5) Carrying Cost	(6) Total Cost of Alternative
3	2,600	$225.00	1,300	$1,560.00	$1,785.00
4	1,950	300.00	975	1,170.00	1,470.00
6	1,300	450.00	650	780.00	1,230.00
7	1,114	525.00	557	668.40	1,193.40
8	975	600.00	488	585.60	1,185.60
9	867	675.00	434	520.80	1,195.80
10	780	750.00	390	468.00	1,218.00
16	488	1,200.00	244	292.90	1,492.80
30	260	2,250.00	130	156.00	2,406.00

Column 1 contains various possible numbers of orders per year. The range to be tested could either cover the entire possible range of alternatives or a segment within which a minimum cost point is expected to be found. Column 2 is determined by dividing, 7800 (the total known demand) by the number of orders per year. Column 3 is orders per year (column 1) times $75 (order cost per order). Column 4 is the average inventory which is equal to the order quantity divided by 2. Column 5 is annual carrying cost; $1.20 per unit times average inventory. Column 6 is the sum of columns 3 and 5.

The case of one order of 7,800 batteries would certainly minimize ordering cost, but would lead to high inventory-carrying costs. Likewise, 7,800 orders of 1 battery per order would minimize inventory-carrying costs, but would maximize order costs. Somewhere between these extremes there should be an alternative with a minimum cost. Table 4-1 gives the ordering cost, inventory carrying cost, and total cost for a number of values of the decision variable. The value of the decision variable which minimizes the cost can be determined from this list by inspection.

From the last column it can be seen that the number of orders which minimizes total cost is 8 orders per year.

Enumeration of alternatives has the advantage of proceeding directly and logically from a real-life problem situation to numerical computations. It requires no great degree of mathematical sophistication on the part of either the analyst or the person interpreting the results. One disadvantage of enumeration is that, as the number of alternatives which must be examined becomes very large, the computations become time-consuming and the tables become cumbersome.

Graphic Solution.   Graphic solution consists of plotting the various costs as functions of the decision variable; e.g., Figure 4.1 is a plot of ordering

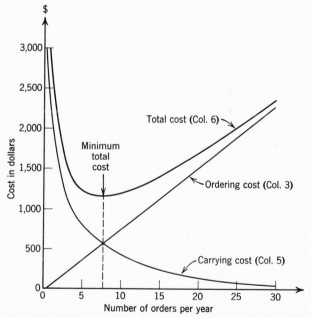

Figure 4.1   Cost as a function of numbers of orders per year.

cost, carrying cost, and the total cost (all taken from Table 4-1) versus the number of orders per year. The desired value is the point of minimum elevation in the total cost curve (6).

The main advantage of graphic presentation over tabular analysis is that over-all relationships can be seen at a glance because more information can be presented on a graph than in a table. An additional factor to be noted from Figure 4.1 is that there is little difference in cost as between 6 and 10 orders per year, but that total cost increases sharply when less than 6 orders per year are placed. The major limitation of this method is that graphs are two-dimensional, and when more than two variables are involved, graphs become difficult to prepare and interpret.

Analytic Solution. An analytic solution can be obtained by treating $C(x)$ as though it were a continuous function of x. A basic theorem in differential calculus (which will be described in detail in Chapter 5) states that a function $f(x)$ has a minimum at a point x^* if $f'(x^*) = 0$ and $f''(x^*)$ is positive.

The model for Example 1 as developed in (2):

$$C(x) = c_o x + \left(\frac{1}{2}\right)\left(\frac{r}{x}\right)(c_c)$$

The problem is to determine the value of x for which C is a minimum.

$$\frac{dC}{dx} = c_o - \left(\frac{1}{2}\right)\left(\frac{r}{x^2}\right)(c_c) = 0 \qquad (1)$$

and solving for x gives

$$x^* = +\left(\frac{c_c r}{2c_o}\right)^{\frac{1}{2}}$$

Equation (1) actually has two solutions; however, the one with the negative sign does not satisfy the condition that x be non-negative. The solution is a minimum point because

$$\frac{d^2C}{dx^2} = \frac{rc_c}{x^3}$$

which is definitely positive.

The solution to numerical Example 1 can be obtained by substituting the numerical values for the parameters,

$$r = 7,800 \qquad c_c = 1.20 \qquad c_o = 75$$
$$x^* = \sqrt{62.4} = 7.9$$

The quantity to be ordered in this case is $7,800/7.9 = 987$

The reason for a non-integral value for x is that the model as stated here did not require x to be an integer. Under the definition of the problem, $x = 7.9$ is not an acceptable solution. The correct solution can be obtained by computing C for $x = 7$ and $x = 8$, and since $x = 8$ yields a lower value for C, the optimum number of orders per year is 8.

Table 4-2   Summary of Decision-Making Procedure for Two Examples

Step	Example 1	Example 2
Decision variable Alternatives	x = number of orders per year $1 \leq x \leq 7{,}800$ x must be an integer	Mode of transportation 1 = personal automobile 2 = train 3 = bus
Objective Uncontrollable variables	C, total cost to be minimized c_o = ordering cost c_c = carrying cost r = demand	C, travel time to be minimized z_1 = time to get to transportation z_2 = travel time z_3 = time to get to destination
Model	$C = c_o x + \dfrac{r c_c}{2x}$	$C(i) = \sum_{j=1}^{3} z_j(i) \quad i = 1, 2, 3$
Solution	$x = +\left(\dfrac{r c_c}{2 c_o}\right)^{1/2}$ If x is not an integer, compute C for the integer on either side of x and choose the one with lowest C.	i^* is the i for which $C(i)$ is a minimum

There are many advantages to an analytical solution. Once relationships between variables have been established, a solution can be computed for any value of the uncontrollable variable. Problem formulation and model construction are separated from the mechanics of problem solution and, once the solution has been determined, clerks (or a computer) can go through the mechanics of calculating the solution for any particular values of the uncontrollable variables. A formula which gives the optimum value of the decision variable as a function of the uncontrollable variables is called a decision rule.

The formulation and solution of Examples 1 and 2 is summarized in Table 4-2.

EXERCISES

(Exercises 1, 2, 3, and 4 refer to Example 1 discussed in the text.)

1. Develop and solve an analytical model for the case where the decision variable is the number of units per order.

2. How much money would be saved per year by ordering 987 instead of 975 units per order? Assume the same demand conditions hold for an indefinite number of years so that the number of orders per year need not be an integer. What conclusion can be drawn from the magnitude of the difference?

3. (a) Describe in qualitative terms how the decision rule varies with changes in the uncontrollable variables.

   (b) How much would the decision and the total cost change if one of the parameters, c_c, c_o, or r, were in error by $\pm 10\%$?

4. Show that the model and formula for x are expressed correctly in terms of dimensions.

5. Develop a model for the situation in Example 1 where the objective is to maximize the total profit. Let u = unit purchase cost and p = unit selling price of a battery. Make the same assumptions regarding demand and uncontrollable variables that are made in Example 1 and include all the costs included there. Solve the model. How does the solution to this model differ from that obtained in Example 1 in the text?

6. A certain machine produces parts at a uniform rate of 800 per day. The parts have a market price of $1.00 each and can be sold immediately after manufacture. Production cannot be varied above or below this rate.

Adjustment of the machine is critical and the number of defective parts is dependent on the number of adjustments made during the day. Company records indicate that the number of deflective parts out of the 800, produced in a day is equal to 100 divided by the number of adjustments made. Each part regardless of its salability costs $0.70 and defective parts are worthless. The machine is adjusted once each morning before operations are begun, but the foreman is free to make as many additional adjustments as he desires. Each adjustment, including the initial adjustment, costs $4.00 and no production is lost because of this operation.

   (a) Identify the decision variable.
   (b) Identify the alternatives.
   (c) Identify the objective.
   (d) Identify the uncontrollable variable.
   (e) Construct a model of this situation and formulate the decision rule.
   (f) Compute the optimal decision.

7. Define the following terms:
   (a) Decision variable
   (b) Alternatives
   (c) Objectives
   (d) Uncontrollable variables
   (e) Model
   (f) Decision rule

8. Identify each of the above terms for the following situations (not all terms may apply in every case):

   (a) The general manager of a chain of supermarkets was interested in what instructions he should give his store managers as to how many checkout counters should be open at any time. A research team made a study and found that the labor cost would be minimized if one checkout counter was open for every 30 customers that entered the store during any hour.

   (b) The Carson Company has been engaged in wholesale operations in the Los Angeles area for over 50 years. During this time its business has grown steadily and further increases are predicted for the future. The company maintains a number of warehouses and also rents space in commercial warehouses. The profit margin is considered too low and one of the factors frequently cited is the high cost of maintaining many distribution points. The president instructed the Finance Department to compile a list of available warehouses which would have sufficient capacity and suitable transportation facilities to serve as central warehouses. He then engaged a consulting firm to aid him in determining whether the distribution system should be changed to utilize one or more of these centralized warehouses. There was general agreement that the selection should be based on minimizing the operating cost provided, however, that the level of service now furnished would not be decreased. The consultants computed the operating cost for each combination of warehouses as the sum of the transportation costs, the handling cost, the cost of the warehouse, and the inventory holding cost. A centralization to three warehouses turned out to have the lowest operating cost and resulted in improved service because the number of "out-of-stocks" was reduced.

(c) A manufacturer produces four products, using three machines. Each machine is used for each product, but the order in which the machines are used is not important. Each month the manufacturer is faced with the problem of deciding how many units of each product to produce. In the past, this decision was made on the basis of reducing idle time on machines. After some consideration, it occurred to the manufacturer that this procedure might not lead to the largest profit. Now he computes the profit on each unit of each product and, knowing the amount of time one unit of each product requires on each machine, he determines the most profitable combination which does not exceed the machine time available. He assumes that he will be able to sell everything he produces.

9. A large office equipment firm in San Francisco acts as both retailer and wholesaler for one line of office furniture. The manager is concerned about whether he is pursuing an optimal policy in stocking a standard secretarial desk. This desk has a fairly constant demand (about 200 per month) and requires considerable floor space for storage.

The present policy for determining when to reorder a new supply, and how many to order, is quite simple. The firm has a standing order with its supplier to ship 200 on the first of each month. Upon questioning, the firm's accountant states that the cost of shipping, handling, and processing these monthly orders is $1,418, which represents fixed costs of $18 per order plus a variable cost of $7 per desk for packing, shipping, and handling. The net cost of each desk is $200, and the firm finances inventory with an 8% bank loan. The desks are 3' wide by 5' long and one desk thus requires about 16 square feet of floor space. However, they are stacked 2 high in the warehouse so that on the average each desk requires only 8 square feet of storage space. The ten-year lease on the warehouse amounts to $1.00 per square foot per year. The firm could use additional warehouse space to good advantage.

(a) From the above data, determine the firm's optimal size order and the number of orders it should place each year.

(b) What would be the optimal policy if each desk cost $380, the interest rate was 10%, and warehouse space cost $2.00 per square foot per year?

(c) Prepare a lucid statement for the manager showing why, *for this particular problem*, the "fixed costs" are in fact variable and the "variable costs" are, in fact, fixed.

C. ORDERED ALTERNATIVES

The examples given in the previous section have illustrated cases where alternatives were completely unordered (Example 2) on the one hand, and where they consist of all values of a continuous variable (Example 1) on the other. Actually the alternatives in Example 1 are limited to integer values, but continuous values can be assumed in the analysis. The optimum solution is rounded to the nearest integer, if necessary. Another example in which the feasible alternatives are limited to integer values of the decision variable is the machine replacement problem.

A firm uses a machine which "wears out" after a certain amount of time and is then replaced by a new machine of the same type. For each year of operation the machine produces a certain revenue, each year there is a maintenance cost, and at the end of any year the machine may be sold for salvage for a certain amount. In general, with the age of the machine the net revenue decreases, the maintenance cost increases, and the salvage value decreases. The simplest case occurs where it can be assumed that the machine is of a standard type, that the market for the product is stable so revenue, maintenance, salvage value, and cost can be assumed to be known for the indefinite future, that there will be no technological improvement in the machine, and that there will be no change in the price level. The "Replacement Problem" is concerned with how frequently the machine should be replaced.

Single Machine Case

Consider, first, the case where a single machine is to be purchased and the problem is to determine when the machine should be sold for salvage.

Decision variable: k = number of periods the machine is used

Alternatives: $k = 1, 2, 3, \ldots$

Objective: maximize present value of all net earnings plus salvage value

Uncontrolled variables: e_j = net revenue (value of goods produced by the machine less cost of raw material, labor, and operating cost) during period j, received at the end of period j

m_j = maintenance cost during period j paid at the end of period j

s_j = salvage value obtainable at the end of period j

C = purchase price

i = interest rate; $v = (1 + i)^{-1}$

Model. The present value of the machine, if kept for k periods, is

$$P(k) = -C + \sum_{j=1}^{k} e_j v^j - \sum_{j=1}^{k} m_j v^j + s_k v^k$$

$$= -C + \sum_{j=1}^{k} (e_j - m_j)v^j + s_k v^k \qquad (1)$$

Data. A study of records indicates that revenue, maintenance cost, and salvage value can be closely approximated by linear functions; e.g.,

$$e_j = a + bj$$
$$m_j = c + dj \qquad (2)$$
$$s_j = C - uj$$

Solution. If the machine is kept for k periods, the present value is given by (1); if it is kept for $k + 1$ periods, the present value is

$$P(k + 1) = -C + \sum_{j=1}^{k+1} (e_j - m_j)v^j + s_{k+1}v^{k+1}$$

$$= P(k) - s_k v^k + (e_{k+1} - m_{k+1})v^{k+1} + s_{k+1}v^{k+1}$$

The change in present value due to holding the machine for the $(k + 1)$st period is

$$P(k + 1) - P(k) = (e_{k+1} - m_{k+1})v^{k+1} + s_{k+1}v^{k+1} - s_k v^k \qquad (3)$$

Assuming that the change will be positive if k is 1, 2, . . . , the machine should be kept for the period $k + 1$ if this change, (3), is positive and should not be kept if the change is negative. The optimum value of k is the first value of k for which (3) is negative. Substituting (2) and dividing by v^k gives the condition as

$$[a + b(k + 1) - c - d(k + 1)]v + [C - u(k + 1)]v - [C - uk] < 0 \qquad (4)$$

The machine should be sold at the end of year k, for that k for which the inequality first holds. In other words the condition states that at the end of period k, the decision should be to hold the machine for another period, if the discounted net earnings for the year exceed the discounted decrease in the salvage value.

If the salvage value is zero for all j, (4) would reduce to

$$[a + b(k + 1) - c - d(k + 1] < 0$$

or

$$a - c + (b - d) + k(b - d) < 0$$

$$\frac{a - c}{b - d} + 1 + k < 0 \qquad \text{if} \qquad b - d > 0 \qquad (5)$$

The inequality is reversed if $(b - d) < 0$.

Note that the initial cost of the machine, C, does not explicitly appear in (4) or (5), except insofar as the salvage value depends on C. The value of C does appear in $P(k)$ and, if $P(1)$ were negative, the optimum decision would be not to buy the machine at all.

Example.   Let $e_j = 160 - 10j$
$$m_j = 10 + 10j$$
$$s_j = 225 - 25j$$

Table 4-3 shows the net revenue, maintenance, net earnings and salvage value.

Table 4-3

Period	Net Revenue	Maintenance	Net Earnings	Salvage
1	150	20	130	200
2	140	30	110	175
3	130	40	90	150
4	120	50	70	125
5	110	60	50	100
6	100	70	30	75
7	90	80	10	50
8	80	90	−10	25
9	70	100	−30	0
10	60	110	−50	

If the salvage value were always zero, the machine would be replaced at the end of period 7. When the salvage value is as given, the optimum value of k depends on the interest rate. The machine would be replaced at the end of period 5, if

$$\frac{125}{150} < v < \frac{100}{105}$$

that is, the interest rate is between 5 and 20%, because substituting in (4) gives

$$30v + 75v - 100 < 0$$

If

$$\frac{100}{105} < v < 1$$

that is, if the interest rate is less than 5%, the machine would be replaced after six periods.

Sequence of Machines

Suppose now that the machine is to be replaced by another of the same type and that that machine will be replaced by another, and so on. If all the assumptions stated above actually hold, the optimum number of periods that the machine is used will be the same for all machines. The model may then be formulated as follows:

Decision variable: k = number of periods each machine is used before being replaced by a new one.

Alternatives: $k = 1, 2, 3, \ldots$

Objective: maximize present value of net earnings and salvage value for all future machines

Uncontrolled variables: (Same as above)

Model.   The present value of the first machine is given by (1). The present value of the second machine will be the same as that of the first, except that it must be multiplied by v^k; the present value of the third machine must be multiplied by v^{2k}, etc. The present value of the entire sequence is

$$E(k) = P(k) + v^k[P(k)] + v^{2k}[P(k)] + v^{3k}[P(k)] + \cdots$$

$$= P(k)[1 + v^k + v^{2k} + v^{3k} + \cdots]$$

$$= \frac{P(k)}{1 - v^k} \quad \text{since } |v| < 1 \tag{6}$$

Data.   (Same as above)

Solution.   The optimum value of k is the first value of k for which

$$E(k + 1) - E(k) = \frac{P(k + 1)}{1 - v^{k+1}} - \frac{P(k)}{1 - v^k} < 0 \tag{7}$$

The condition cannot be simplified in general; it can be applied directly in a specific example.

Example.   The computation for the data given above and using $C = 250$ and $i = 25\%$ are shown in Table 4-4 on page 104. The optimum value of k is 2.

Table 4-4

j	$e_j - m_j$	$v^j(e_j - m_j)$	$\Sigma \, v^j(e_j - m_j)$	$s_j v^j$	$P(j)$	$E(j)$
1	130	104.00	104.00	160.00	14.00	70.00
2	110	70.40	174.40	112.00	36.40	101.11
3	90	46.08	220.48	76.80	47.28	96.88
4	70	28.67	249.15	51.20	50.35	85.28
5	50	16.38	265.53	32.77	48.30	71.84
6	30	7.86	273.39	19.66	43.05	58.34
7	10	2.10	275.49	10.49	35.98	45.33

EXERCISES

1. Show that

$$P(k) = \frac{v(1 - v^k)}{1 - v}\left[a - c + \frac{b - d}{1 - v}\right] - \left[(b - d)\frac{v}{1 - v} + u\right]kv^k - C(1 - v^k)$$

if net revenue, maintenance, and salvage are given by (2).

2. Modify this example to include depreciation and federal taxes on income.

3. Determine the optimum replacement period for Exercise 2, if the income tax rate is 50%.

4. An investment firm has purchased property for $100,000 with $10,000 cash and a mortgage calling for eight semiannual payments of $11,559.06, beginning six months from now. The property consists of a lot worth $20,000 and a building which has just been constructed for $80,000. The property has been leased for the next four years for a semiannual rent of $11,559.06. In addition, the leasee agrees to pay all insurance, taxes, and other costs associated with the upkeep of the property. The building can be depreciated with a four-year life. The owner can sell the property together with the mortgage and rental agreement at the end of any year for $10,000. How long should he hold the property and what is his internal rate of return, if his tax rate is 50% and he has other income to balance depreciation allowances?

D. COMBINATIONAL ALTERNATIVES—LEAST-COST TESTING SEQUENCE

In many problems enumeration of all possible alternatives is not practical because their number is too great. This occurs particularly when the alternatives are actually obtained by combining sub-alternatives. An example is the "least-cost testing sequence" problem. There are n non-destructive tests which are to be performed on an item. The sub-alternatives are: given that m tests have been performed, which test should be carried out next? A complete statement of the alternative then is the sequence in which all the n tests are performed. Since any one of the tests can be performed first (n possibilities), any of the remaining can be performed next $(n - 1$ possibilities), etc., the total number of possible alternatives is

$$n(n - 1)(n - 2) \cdots (1) = n!$$

The following quotation[1] illustrates how the optimum alternative can be determined for this particular problem.

"[Price] discussed the arrangement of a series of n non-destructive tests in such a sequence that the cost per item tested would be a minimum. The tests were such that at each stage only those items found to be acceptable were subjected to the next test. It was suggested that the least-cost sequence be found by first calculating the cost per item tested of all $n!$ possible sequence of tests, and then selecting the sequence which gave the least cost. There is, however, a very simple rule for finding the least-cost sequence. The items should be arranged in order of increasing cost per item rejected,

$$\frac{C_1}{R_1} < \frac{C_2}{R_2} < \cdots < \frac{C_n}{R_n},$$

where R is the average rejection rate of a test, and C is the average cost per item tested.

"This is similar to the rule given by Gluss for finding the optimum policy for detecting a single fault in a complex system, but we are here concerned with the testing of items which may have a number of faults or none at all.

Proof of the Rule: Suppose we have a series of tests $T_1, T_2, \ldots, T_n$ costing $C_1, C_2, \ldots, C_n$ per item tested, with average acceptance rates $A_1, A_2, \ldots, A_n$ and average rejection rates $R_1, R_2, \ldots, R_n$ (equal to $1 - A_1, 1 - A_2, \ldots, 1 - A_n$). We assume that the C's, A's, and R's are unaffected by the order in which we do the tests, and are mutually independent.

"If we arrange the tests in a particular sequence $(T_1, T_2, \ldots, T_n)$, the sequence will cost $C(T_1, T_2, \ldots, T_n)$ per item tested, and this cost will alter if we alter the sequence.

"In order to show that the least-cost sequence is given by the rule, we prove first a lemma and then the main theorem.

Lemma:

"If

$$\frac{C_j}{R_j} < \frac{C_{j+1}}{R_{j+1}} \qquad C(\ldots, T_j, T_{j+1}, \ldots) < C(\ldots, T_{j+1}, T_j, \ldots)$$

---

[1] Boothroyd, H., "Least-cost Testing Sequence," *Operational Research Quarterly*, II, 3, September 1960, pp. 137–38.

Proof of the Lemma:
"Because the A's and C's are independent,

$$C(T_1, T_2, \ldots, T_n) = C_1 + A_1C_2 + A_1A_2C_3 + \cdots$$
$$+ (A_1A_2 \cdots A_{n-1})C_n$$

If we reverse the order of the jth and $j + 1$th tests, we only change the jth and $j + 1$th terms on the right-hand side of the equation. Hence,

$$C(\ldots, T_j, T_{j+1}, \ldots) - C(\ldots, T_{j+1}, T_j, \ldots)$$
$$= (A_1A_2 \cdots A_{j-1})(C_j + A_jC_{j+1} - C_{j+1} - A_{j+1}C_j)$$
$$= (A_1A_2 \cdots A_{j-1})(C_jR_{j+1} - C_{j+1}R_j)$$
$$< 0,$$

and the lemma is proved.
Theorem:
    If

$$\frac{C_1}{R_1} < \frac{C_2}{R_2} < \cdots < \frac{C_n}{R_n} \quad \{T_1, T_2, \ldots, T_n\}$$

is a least-cost sequence of tests.
Proof:
"Consider the transformation of any other sequence of the same tests $\{T_{n_1}, T_{n_2}, \ldots, T_{n_n}\}$ to $\{T_1, T_2, \ldots, T_n\}$ by successively bringing $T_1, T_2, \ldots, T_{n-1}$ to first, second, $\ldots$, $(n-1)$th position by repeated interchange of the test being moved with the test preceding it at that stage. By the lemma, the total cost per item tested is reduced at each stage of the transformation. Hence,

$$C(T_{n_1}, T_{n_2}, \ldots, T_{n_n}) > C(T_1, T_2, \ldots, T_n),$$

and $\{T_1, T_2, \ldots, T_n\}$ is a least-cost sequence of tests."

EXERCISES

1. Identify the following for the problem discussed above.
(a) Decision variable (state the alternatives)
(b) Objective
(c) Uncontrollable variables
(d) Model
(e) Data
(f) Method of solution
(g) Solution

2. Use the decision rule to determine the least-cost testing sequence for the following case:

Test	Accept rate	Reject rate	Test cost per item in man-hours
Visual	0.998	0.002	0.08
Shock	0.95	0.05	0.584
Distortion	0.965	0.035	0.124
Electrical	0.95	0.05	0.232
Vibration	0.35	0.65	0.64

3. Do you agree with the author in his contention that the decision rule minimizes the cost if the assumptions hold?

SUMMARY

The development and use of Management Science models requires a number of distinct steps. The order in which the steps are followed may vary from problem to problem. Frequently several steps may be carried out simultaneously or the sequence may be repeated several times in one problem.

The most logical place to begin is with the identification of the variable over which the decision maker can exercise control. The next step is to list the feasible values of the decision variable (the feasible alternative decisions). The set of feasible values may consist of all real numbers in any interval or it may consist of a discrete set of numbers. The feasible alternatives may or may not have a natural order. The alternatives in the decision as to the mode of transportation (Example 2), or the sequence in which tests should be used (Section C), are examples of situations where the numbering of the alternatives is purely arbitrary. The alternatives in the inventory example (Example 1) are all the integers in a certain range. In some problems the decision variable can (theoretically, at least) be any real non-negative number.

The next logical step is the specification of the objective. Problems may be stated either as maximizing or as minimizing the objective; the term optimizing is used to include either case. Conceptually there is no difference between maximizing and minimizing; many problems can be stated in either form.

By this time the other variables, uncontrollable or controlled variables, and parameters have been defined. They appear either in the statement of the objective function or in the conditions which define the feasible alternatives. The distinction between controllable variables on one hand and uncontrollable variables and parameters on the other hand is usually very clear. However, the distinction between uncontrollable variables and parameters is frequently arbitrary. Both are represented by symbols and both are regarded as constants in a particular problem. One possible distinction is that if the problem were to be examined again, under slightly different conditions, the uncontrollable variables might have different values whereas the parameters are likely to have the same value. In the inventory example (Example 1) the demand r might change from one period to another while the ordering and carrying costs would not. If this were the case, demand would be treated as an uncontrollable variable and ordering and carrying costs would be treated as parameters.

The model is the statement which gives the value of the objective function for each feasible alternative. The next major step is the solution of the model; the determination of which of the feasible alternatives optimizes the objective. The method of solution depends on the feasible alternatives. If the feasible alternatives are discrete and have no natural order, the only general possibility is to enumerate all the alternatives, compute the objective function for each one, and select the optimum. It may be possible, as in the least-cost testing sequence (Section D) to develop an ordering of the alternatives according to the value of the objective function. In the inventory example (Example 1), the decision variable is the number of orders placed per year and the alternatives are discrete but have a natural order. The method of enumeration may be used in this case. However, if the number of alternatives is large, it may be possible to limit examination to a smaller number of alternatives. In general, the alternatives can be placed into a one-to-one correspondence with the the integers and labeled as

$$n_1, n_2, \ldots$$

The objective function $f(n_i)$ has a "local" maximum value at n_i if $f(n_i)$ is greater than the objective for alternatives on either side of n_i; i.e.,

$$f(n_{i-1}) < f(n_i) > f(n_{i+1})$$

In general, there may be more than one n_i with this property and all such local "maximum" values must be examined to determine the global or over-all maximum value.

Another possibility in this case is to assume that the variable is continuous and use appropriate techniques from the differential calculus. If the optimum obtained is not one of the feasible discrete alternatives, the "closest" discrete values must be checked to determine the feasible optimum.

If the decision variable can, theoretically (or is treated as though it can),

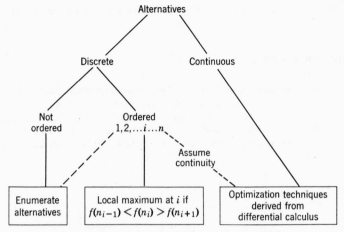

Figure 4.2   Solving management science models.

assume any real value, the possible optimum alternatives can be determined by setting the derivative equal to zero and solving the resulting equation. The second (or higher) derivative or direct examination may be used to determine whether the function has "local" maxima or "local" minima, at this point.

The different possibilities are illustrated in Fig. 4.2. The techniques based on differential calculus will be discussed in detail in Chapter 5.

Notes and References

Traditional management problems are discussed in many texts; see in particular:
Jones, M. H. (1962), *Executive Decision Making*, rev. ed., Richard D. Irwin, Homewood, Ill.
Albers. H. H. (1961), *Organized Executive Action*, John Wiley and Sons, New York.

An annotated bibliography is:
Wasserman, P., and Silander, F. S. (1958), *Decision-Making: An Annotated Bibliography*, Graduate School of Business and Public Administration, Cornell University, Ithaca, N.Y.

The Management Science approach is discussed in detail in:
Churchman, C. W., et al. (1957), *Introduction to Operations Research*, John Wiley and Sons, New York.

Section C

A general discussion of the equipment replacement problem with an extensive bibliography is given by:
Reisman, A., and Buffa, E. S. (1962), "A general model for investment policy," *Management Science*, VIII, pp. 304–310.

Section D

The least-cost testing sequence problem is also discussed in:
Mitten, L. G. (1960), "An Analytic Solution to the Least Cost Testing Sequence Problem," *J. Industrial Engineering*, XI, p. 17.

Price, H. W. (1959), "Least-Cost Testing Sequence," *J. Industrial Engineering*, X, pp. 278–279.

CHAPTER EXERCISES

1. Fabrication Department 15 of a large manufacturing plant is laid out as shown in Fig. 4.3. The intersecting lines represent aisles along which all work must be moved from machine to machine. Machines A, B, and C are located at the intersections of aisles 1 and 101, 3 and 105, and 6 and 103, respectively. Because of possible congestion, only one machine can be located at an intersection.

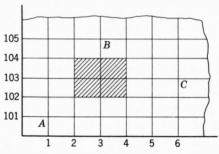

Figure 4.3

Two machines now in Department 14, D and E, are being transferred to Department 15 and are to be located within the shaded area bounded by aisles 2, 4, 102, and 104. The average number of pallet loads of partially fabricated work that will be moved between the existing machines and the new machines each day is given in the following table.

	D	E
A	10	1
B	6	8
C	1	4

Compute the total work in terms of pallet-load distance moved for each possible location of the machines D and E. Determine the assignment which will result in minimum total work.

2. A firm operates a rubber plantation of four square miles in a country which has just passed a law expropriating, without compensation, all foreign-owned land at the end of three years from the present. In the meantime, the government will purchase any amount of land offered in units of full square miles at the following price:

Square Miles Offered at One Time	Purchase Price ($10,000)
1	4
2	7
3	9
4	10

at the beginning of a year. Land used for rubber production produces a net revenue of $10,000 per square mile per year.

(*a*) Determine the optimum sales and production decisions for the firm, if it wishes to maximize total net income over the four years, by enumerating and evaluating all alternatives. (One alternative is to sell one square mile now; produce rubber on the remaining three square miles for two years and then sell all three at the beginning of the third year. The total net income would be

$$40,000 + 30,000 + 30,000 + 90,000 = 190,000)$$

(*b*) Develop the formula for determining the total number of alternatives if the firm had *m* square miles and the law expropriated land in *n* years.

3. For each of the following, identify the decision variable, the alternatives, the objective, and list the uncontrollable variables. Develop and solve the model where possible.

(*a*) A manufacturer produces steel bars in 20-foot lengths. He has a customer who orders nine 1-foot sections every week. When the manufacturer cuts the bar into 1-foot sections he must, of course, cut the complete bar, and therefore each time he cuts a bar, he obtains twenty 1-foot sections. What is the average number of 1-foot bars which the manufacturer must hold in inventory because the quantity ordered by the customer does not equal the quantity that must be obtained in one production lot? Develop a general formula for the average inventory for the case of any size production line and any size order. Assume that the orders are made periodically and equal amounts are ordered. What could the manufacturer do to decrease the average inventory?

(*b*) A trucking concern operating in the Los Angeles area sends out 90 pickup trucks a day to pick up shipments in the Los Angeles area going to the ten destinations which this firm serves. (These include San Francisco, Western, and Eastern cities.) The pick-up trucks are sent out during the working day and arrive at the transfer point at 5 P.M. At the transfer point the shipments are sorted by the ten destinations and loaded onto long-haul trucks. A problem arises because competitors offer overnight service to San Francisco. For this trucking firm to meet this competition, it is necessary that its long-haul trucks leave for San Francisco not later than 8 P.M. The normal procedure would be for the sorting operations to take place between 5 P.M. and 1 A.M. The trucking firm would like, in order to save workers' salaries, to use the full time from 5 P.M. to 1 A.M. to unload the pick-up trucks, sort, and load the long-haul trucks. However, because of the competition, it is faced with the choice of either providing inferior service or increasing the manpower so that the complete operation can be carried out in 3 hours, which means that the workers would be paid for the regular 8-hour shift for doing 3 hours work. Show how it might be possible to provide competitive service without increasing labor costs proportionately.

(*c*) The actual operation at the transfer point consists of using a rectangular warehouse with room for 80 trucks on each of the long sides. The pick-up trucks arrive at one side and the long-haul trucks are loaded and leave from the other side. The shipments are unloaded, put on a small cart, and attached to a moving track. When the cart arrives at the long-haul truck marked for that destination, the cart is taken off and the shipment transferred to the truck. The problem which arose was that a considerable amount of congestion developed. A number of remedies, such as increasing the number of carts or increasing the number of workers, were suggested. Because of physical limitations the speed of the track could not be increased. Are there any other remedies which are better than the suggested ones?

(d) A bus company operates a large number of buses. On the average, 250 engines are pulled out of buses each year and rebuilt. When an engine is rebuilt, it is brought into the shop, completely disassembled, the parts are tested, and any wornout parts are discarded. The reusable parts are stored in inventory and, as required, new engines are assembled out of the parts in inventory. The charges for this operation are as follows: $500 for disassembly and testing; $250 for the reassembly plus $1,500 for parts which are not in inventory and must therefore be purchased new. Since it costs $3,500 to buy a new engine there is a saving of $1,250 by rebuilding instead of buying; on the average one-third of the parts, by value, going into a reassembled engine are new. Show that it is possible to reduce the cost of repair operations.

4. The Federal government in recent years has followed a policy of leasing post offices from private owners. The pertinent data on one such opportunity is as follows:

Lot Size: Approximately 22,352 sq ft (irregular).

Improvements: 7,325 sq ft one-storey concrete, stucco, and brick, air-conditioned commercial building. Balance of property landscaped, paved for parking and drive-ways.

Lease Terms: Firm 20 years from U.S. Government at $14,787.60 per year with options as follows:

RENTALS		GOVERNMENT REPURCHASE OPTIONS	
Base 20 years	$14,787.60	end of base 20 years	$135,000.00
1st 5-year option	14,787.60	end of 1st option	120,000.00
2nd 5-year option	14,000.00	end of 2nd option	115,000.00
3rd 5-year option	13,600.00	end of 3rd option	110,000.00
4th 5-year option	13,300.00	end of 4th option	107,500.00
5th 5-year option	13,000.00	end of 5th option	105,000.00
6th 5-year option	13,000.00	end of 6th option	102,500.00

Gross Annual Income: (First 20 years) · · · · · · · · · · · · · · · $14,787.60

Expenses:

Taxes (Government pays increase)	$3,500.00
Insurance & Maintenance (est.)	700.00
	$4,200.00

Estimated Net Annual Income: · · · · · · · · · · · · · · · · · · · $10,587.60

Price: $162,000

Anticipated Loan: 20 years; $140,000; $5\frac{1}{4}\%$; payable $10,500 per year.

The following table has been compiled by the investment counselor:
Projected flow of depreciation and interest charges for Post Office, assuming 200% declining-balance method of depreciation. Total project cost $162,000; Land value of $35,000; net rental income of $10,500 per year after property operational expenses; mortgage of $140,000; $5\frac{1}{4}\%$; payable $10,500 per year, principal and interest. These figures are calculated on annual basis.

Year	Loan Payment	Annual Int. Paid	Unpaid Loan Bal.	Annual Depreciation	Book Value of Building	Net Tax Deduction*
1	$10,500	$7,274	$136,774	$6,350	$127,000	$13,624
2	10,500	7,101	133,375	6,032	120,650	13,133
3	10,500	6,916	129,791	5,730	114,617	12,646
4	10,500	6,728	126,019	5,444	108,886	12,172
5	10,500	6,526	122,045	5,172	103,442	11,698
6	10,500	6,307	117,852	4,913	98,270	11,220
7	10,500	6,081	113,443	4,668	93,357	10,749
8	10,500	5,844	108,777	4,434	88,689	10,278
9	10,500	5,594	103,871	4,213	84,255	9,807
10	10,500	5,331	98,702	4,002	80,042	9,333
11	10,500	5,052	93,254	3,802	76,040	8,854
12	10,500	4,760	87,514	3,612	72,238	8,372
13	10,500	4,449	81,463	3,431	68,626	7,880
14	10,500	4,124	75,087	3,259	65,195	7,383
15	10,500	3,783	68,370	3,096	61,936	6,879
16	10,500	3,420	61,290	2,942	58.840	6,362
17	10,500	3,041	53,831	2,794	55,898	5,835
18	10,500	2,638	45,969	2,655	53,104	5,293
19	10,500	2,216	37,685	2,522	50,449	4,738
20	10,500	1,771	28,956	2,396	47,927	4,167
21	10,500	1,299	19,755	2,276	45,531	3,575
22	10,500	806	10,061	2,162	43,255	2,968
23	10,500	764	7,210	2,054	41,093	2,818

* To apply against rental income (total of interest and depreciation charges).

Note: This office recommends that the rate of depreciation used by a prospective property owner be discussed with their own tax counsel.

A tax advisory service has given the following opinion:
You have requested our advice regarding the depreciation allowances that will be applicable to the post office building under consideration as an investment.

According to the information provided to us, this property will cost $162,000, about $34,000 being allocable to land and $128,000 allocable to the improvements. The improvements consist of a one-story, concrete, stucco, and brick, air-conditioned building to be used as a post office. It will be leased to the Government for a base period of 20 years with six 5-year renewal option periods thereafter. In addition, at the end of each renewal option period, there is a repurchase option available to the lessee.

The allowance for depreciation is a function of the useful life of the building and the method of depreciation claimed. The method of depreciation is elective by the taxpayer without Government permission. We have, therefore, assumed that depreciation will be claimed, using an accelerated method of depreciation, namely, declining-balance method at 200% of straight-line rates. The sum-of-the-years-digits method is another accelerated method and produces results substantially the same as the declining-balance method.

The determination of the useful life of the building is also elective, but is subject to review by the Commissioner. This is an area in which there has been constant controversy between taxpayers and the Treasury Department. An attempt to alleviate this controversy was made by the issuance of certain guidelines for depreciation. These guidelines were intended to "up-date" determination of useful life. Buildings generally are assigned useful lives of from 40 to 60 years under the guidelines, but this excludes special purpose structures. The post office building should qualify as special purpose, at least to some extent, for although it could be used at some future date as a warehouse or office building, substantial remodeling expenditures would have to be incurred to convert it to this feature.

The minimum life that could be assigned to this building is 20 years. The theory for assigning a 20-year life would have to be that the owner could not be assured of the specialized tenant for any period after 20 years, and since remodeling expenditures would be so substantial, the owner must recover his cost over this 20-year period. The Treasury Department would undoubtedly disagree with such a useful life and the reviewing authorities would probably agree with the Treasury Department. On the other hand, the maximum useful life that should be assigned to this building is 40 years, simply because the economic factors indicate that this building would be obsolete after 40 years, even if the tenant should renew the lease. In all probability, a life would ultimately be determined of somewhere between 25 years and $33\frac{1}{3}$ years. Probably the Treasury Department would agree to a $33\frac{1}{3}$ year life. We would be more inclined toward a 25-year life as a sort of compromise between the 20-year and $33\frac{1}{3}$-year position.

In conclusion, we would advise one of our clients to claim depreciation based on a 20-year life. We would further advise him that this life would be challenged, but that it would be our hope to settle on a 25-year basis.

For your convenience, we are enclosing a schedule setting forth the estimated annual depreciation allowances which could be claimed for each of the first 10 years, assuming useful lives of 20, 25, $33\frac{1}{3}$, and 40 years. We hope this will be helpful to you in making your cash forecast projections.

(a) Develop the formulas for the rate of return on the investment for each of the three methods of depreciation, assuming that the investors tax rate is a constant t and using n year life.

(b) Compute the rate of return for the $t = 0.25$ and $n = 20$.

(c) Develop the formula for a general case, using the following parameter.

$$a = \text{initial cost of building}$$
$$b = \text{initial cost of land}$$
$$i = \text{interest rate}$$
$$u = \text{amount of mortgage}$$

(d) Develop the formula for determining, for each year, the minimum value the investor should accept for his equity in the investment.

Estimated Annual Depreciation Allowance First Ten Years

	Assumed Useful Life			
	40 Years (5%)*	33⅓ Years (6%)*	25 Years (8%)*	20 Years (10%)*
Total cost	$162,000			
Less land (rounded)	34,000			
Depreciable basis	$128,000	$128,000	$128,000	$128,000
First year	$ 6,400	$ 7,680	$ 10,240	$ 12,800
Second year	6,080	7,219	9,421	11,520
Third year	5,776	6,786	8,667	10,368
Fourth year	5,487	6,379	7,974	9,331
Fifth year	5,213	5,996	7,336	8,398
Sixth year	4,952	5,636	6,749	7,558
Seventh year	4,705	5,298	6,209	6,803
Eighth year	4,469	4,980	5,712	6,122
Ninth year	4,246	4,682	5,255	5,510
Tenth year	4,034	4,401	4,835	4,959
Depreciation, 1st 10 years	$ 51,362	$ 59,057	$ 72,398	$ 83,369
Remaining basis, building	$ 76,638	$ 68,943	$ 55,602	$ 44,631

* Depreciation computed on declining balance method at twice straight-line rates. Sum-of-the-years-digits method would produce slightly higher allowances in early years, but not significantly higher. Straight-line depreciation would produce annual allowances as follows:

40 years	$3,200
33⅓ years	3,840
25 years	5,120
20 years	6,400

CHAPTER FIVE

Optimization of Functions of One Variable

One of the most important aspects of Management Science is the set of optimization techniques available for solving models. Examples in the last chapter have illustrated that the techniques based on the differential calculus do not apply in all models. Nevertheless, a thorough understanding of the basic elements of differential calculus is necessary in the study of Management Science.

This chapter is intended primarily as a review of the basic differentiation formulas; the differentiation of the elementary function; techniques for determining local and global maxima and minima; and the definition of concavity, convexity, and other general characteristics of functions. In addition, a brief description of marginal analysis is presented.

A. REVIEW OF DIFFERENTIATION

Basic Rules

The basic rules of differentiation are:

(a) The derivative of a sum (difference) of two functions is equal to the sum (difference) of their derivatives; if u and v are functions of x, then

$$\frac{d}{dx}(u \pm v) = \frac{du}{dx} \pm \frac{dv}{dx}$$

For example, if $u = 2x + 1$ and $v = 4x - 6$, $du/dx = 2$, $dv/dx = 4$, $u + v = 6x - 5$, and

$$\frac{d}{dx}(u+v) = \frac{du}{dx} + \frac{dv}{dx}$$

$$\frac{d}{dx}(6x - 5) = \frac{d}{dx}(2x - 1) + \frac{d}{dx}(4x - 6)$$

$$6 = 2 + 4$$

(b) The derivative of a product of two functions is given by

$$\frac{d}{dx}(uv) = v\frac{du}{dx} + u\frac{dv}{dx}$$

For example, if $u = x$ and $v = x^2$, then

$$\frac{du}{dx} = 1; \qquad \frac{dv}{dx} = 2x; \qquad \frac{d}{dx}(x \cdot x^2) = x^2\frac{dx}{dx} + x\frac{d(x^2)}{dx}$$

$$3x^2 = x^2 \cdot 1 + x \cdot 2x$$

(c) The derivative of a quotient of two functions is given by

$$\frac{d}{dx}\left(\frac{u}{v}\right) = \frac{v(du/dx) - u(dv/dx)}{v^2}$$

For example, if $u = x^3$ and $v = x - 1$,

$$\frac{d}{dx}\left(\frac{u}{v}\right) = \frac{(x - 1)3x^2 - x^3(1)}{(x - 1)^2}$$

$$= \frac{2x^3 - 3x^2}{(x - 1)^2}$$

This result may be verified by writing u/v, in this case, as $x^3(x - 1)^{-1}$ and using rule (b):

$$\frac{d}{dx}[x^3(x - 1)^{-1}] = (x - 1)^{-1}3x^2 + x^3(-1)(x - 1)^{-2}$$

$$= (x - 1)^{-2}[(x - 1)3x^2 - x^3] = (x - 1)^{-2}(2x^3 - 3x^2)$$

(d) The derivative of a function $f(g)$ where g is a function of x is given by

$$\frac{df}{dx} = \left(\frac{df}{dg}\right)\left(\frac{dg}{dx}\right) = [f_g(g)][g_x(x)]$$

For example, if $g(x) = x^2 + 2x$, and $f(g) = g^2 - 1$,

$$\frac{df}{dx} = \left(\frac{df}{dg}\right)\left(\frac{dg}{dx}\right) = (2g)(2x + 2)$$

$$= 2(x^2 + 2x)(2x + 2)$$

$$= 4x^3 + 12x^2 + 8x$$

This result may be verified directly, since $f(x) = (x^2 + 2x)^2 - 1 = x^4 + 4x^3 + 4x^2 - 1$, and differentiating this function gives

$$\frac{df}{dx} = 4x^3 + 12x^2 + 8x$$

(e) If $y = g(x)$, and a unique inverse function $x = g^{-1}(y)$ exists, then

$$\frac{dy}{dx} = \frac{1}{dx/dy}$$

For example, for $x = y + \frac{1}{3}y^3 + \frac{1}{5}y^5$

$$\frac{dx}{dy} = 1 + y^2 + y^4 \quad \text{and} \quad \frac{dy}{dx} = \frac{1}{dx/dy} = \frac{1}{1 + y^2 + y^4}$$

(f) If y and x are implicitly defined by $F(x, y) = 0$, then dy/dx (or dx/dy) may be obtained by differentiating the terms of the equation on the assumption that y is a function of x (or x is a function of y). The derivative thus derived is defined only for pairs (x, y) which satisfy the original equation. For example, if y and x are related by the equation $2.35x + 0.18y + 0.007xy = 0$, then

$$\frac{dy}{dx} = -\frac{2.35 + 0.007y}{0.18 + 0.007x} = -\frac{0.423}{(0.18 + 0.007x)^2}$$

Derivatives of Elementary Functions

Formulas for the derivatives of some of the elementary functions are:

(a) The derivative of a constant function is 0; e.g., if $f(x) = 12$; $f'(x) = 0$.

(b) The derivative of x^n is

$$\frac{d(x^n)}{dx} = nx^{n-1}$$

For example,

$$\frac{d}{dx}(x^5) = 5x^4$$

(c) The derivative of e^x is

$$\frac{de^x}{dx} = e^x \quad \text{and} \quad \frac{de^{f(x)}}{dx} = f'(x)e^{f(x)}$$

For example,

$$\frac{d}{dx}(e^{-ax}) = -ae^{-ax}$$

(d) The derivative of the logarithmic function is

$$\frac{d(\ln x)}{dx} = \frac{1}{x} \quad \text{and} \quad \frac{d(\ln v(x))}{dx} = \left(\frac{1}{v}\right)\left(\frac{dv}{dx}\right)$$

For example,

$$u = x^2; \quad \frac{d}{dx}(\ln u) = \left(\frac{1}{u}\right)\left(\frac{du}{dx}\right) = \left(\frac{1}{x^2}\right)(2x) = \frac{2}{x}$$

(e) The derivative of a^x is

$$\frac{d}{dx}(a^x) = \frac{d}{dx}(e^{x\ln a}) = (\ln a)e^{x\ln a}$$

$$= (\ln a)(a^x)$$

since $a = e^{\ln a}$ and $a^x = (e^{\ln a})^x = e^{x\ln a}$

Example I.   Find the first and second derivatives of $g(x)$ where $g(x) = (x^2 - 5x + 2)^3$. Let $u(x) = x^2 - 5x + 2$; and then

$$g(u) = u^3$$

The derivative is

$$g'(x) = \frac{d}{dx}g(x) = \left[\frac{d}{du}g(u)\right]\left(\frac{du}{dx}\right) = (3u^2)(2x - 5)$$

$$= 3(x^2 - 5x + 2)^2(2x - 5)$$

and

$$g''(x) = 3[2(2x - 5)^2(x^2 - 5x + 2) + 2(x^2 - 5x + 2)^2]$$

$$= 30x^4 - 300x^3 + 972x^2 - 1110x + 324$$

Example 2.   Determine the first and second derivatives of $g(x)$ where

$$g(x) = \frac{ax^2}{1 + bx + cx^2}$$

where a, b, and c are constants.

$$g'(x) = \frac{(1 + bx + cx^2)(2ax) - (ax^2)(b + 2cx)}{(1 + bx + cx^2)^2}$$

$$= \frac{ax(2 + bx)}{(1 + bx + cx^2)^2}$$

$$g''(x) = (2a + 2abx)(1 + bx + cx^2)^{-2}$$

$$- (2ax + abx^2)(2)(b + 2cx)(1 + bx + cx^2)^{-3}$$

$$= \frac{2a(1 - 3cx^2 - bcx^3)}{(1 + bx + cx^2)^3}$$

Example 3.   Determine the first and second derivatives of $f(x)$ where

$$f(x) = cxe^{ax^2 + bx}$$

where $a < 0$; $b > 0$; $c > 0$ are constants.   Then

$$f'(x) = ce^{ax^2 + bx} + cx(2ax + b)e^{ax^2 + bx}$$

$$= ce^{ax^2 + bx}(2ax^2 + bx + 1)$$

and

$$f''(x) = ce^{ax^2 + bx}(4ax + b) + c(2ax + b)e^{ax^2 + bx}(2ax^2 + bx + 1)$$

$$= ce^{ax^2 + bx}[4a^2x^3 + 4abx^2 + (6a + b^2)x + 2b]$$

Example 4.   Find dy/dx where $y(x)$ is defined by

$x^5 + 3x^2y^3 - y^6x = 0$.   To find dy/dx, differentiate term by term:

$$\frac{d}{dx}(x^5) + \frac{d}{dx}(3x^2y^3) - \frac{d}{dx}(y^6x) = 0$$

$$\frac{dy}{dx}[9x^2y^2 - 6y^5x] = y^6 - 6xy^3 - 5x^4$$

$$\frac{dy}{dx} = \frac{y^6 - 6xy^3 - 5x^4}{9x^2y^2 - 6y^5x}$$

Note that the derivative contains both x and y.

Example 5.   Find dy/dx where $x = \sqrt{y} + \sqrt[3]{y}$.   Then

$$\frac{dy}{dx} = \frac{1}{dx/dy} = \frac{6y^{2/3}}{3y^{1/6} + 2}$$

The Taylor Expansion

If a function $f(x)$ has continuous derivatives of all orders in an interval containing a point $x = a$, the value of the function at a nearby point in the interval $x = a + h$ may be obtained from the equality

$$f(a + h) = f(a) + h[f'(a)] + \frac{h^2}{2!}[f''(a)] + \frac{h^3}{3!}[f'''(a)] + \cdots$$

$$+ \frac{h^n}{n!}[f^{(n)}(a)] + R_n$$

where $[f^{(i)}(a)]$ denotes the value of the ith derivative evaluated at the point $x = a$, and R_n denotes the "remainder" or the difference between the left-hand side and the sum of the other $n + 1$ terms on the right. Under very general conditions R_n tends to zero as n increases.

The series of terms on the right is known as the Taylor series or the Taylor expansion of the function f. This expansion is one of the most important tools in analysis of functions and frequently the most convenient method for computing numerical values of a function.

Example I.   Determine the Taylor expansion for:

$$f(x) = e^x \qquad \text{Let} \qquad a = 0$$

Then

$$f' = e^x, f'(0) = 1; \qquad f'' = e^x, f''(0) = 1, \ldots f^{(n)}(x) = e^x,$$

and

$$f^{(n)}(0) = 1$$

Hence,

$$e^h = 1 + h + \frac{h^2}{2!} + \frac{h^3}{3!} + \cdots$$

Example 2.   Determine the Taylor expansion for:

$$f(x) = \ln x \qquad \text{let} \qquad a = 1$$

Then

$$f(1) = \ln 1 = 0$$

$$f'(x) = \frac{1}{x} \qquad f'(1) = 1$$

$$f''(x) = -\frac{1}{x^2} \qquad f''(1) = -1$$

$$f'''(x) = +\frac{2}{x^3} \qquad f'''(1) = 2$$

and in general

$$f^{(n)}(1) = (n - 1)!(-1)^n$$

Hence,

$$\ln (1 + h) = h - \frac{h^2}{2} + \frac{h^3}{3} - \frac{h^4}{4} + \cdots \qquad -1 < h \leq 1$$

Example 3. Evaluate $e^{0.5}$ to four significant decimal places.

$$e^{0.5} = 1 + 0.5 + \frac{0.25}{2} + \frac{0.125}{6} + \frac{0.0625}{24} + \frac{0.03125}{120} + \frac{0.015625}{720} + \cdots$$

$e^{0.5} =$	1.0	1.0	one term
	+0.5	1.5	two terms
	+0.125	1.625	three terms
	+0.020833	1.645833	four terms
	+0.002604	1.648437	five terms
	+0.000260	1.648697	six terms

The true value to five places is 1.64872. Note the rapid improvement in accuracy resulting from the first few terms. This is characteristic; the first several terms often give sufficient accuracy for practical purposes. Any desired degree of accuracy could be obtained by including enough terms. In the series for the logarithm (Example 2) this statement is true only for $-1 < h \leq 1$.

EXERCISES

Find the first and second derivatives of the following functions:
1. $g(x) = a_0 + a_1 x + a_2 x^2 + a_3 x^3 + a_4 x^4$ a_i are parameters
2. $g(x) = a \ln x + b$ a and b are parameters
3. $g(x) = c - de^{-hx-m}$ c, d, h, and m are parameters
4. $g(x) = \dfrac{ax^2 + bx^3}{1 + cx + dx^2}$ a, b, c, and d are parameters
5. $g(x) = cx^2 a^{bx^3 + dx}$ a, b, c, and d are parameters
6. $g(x) = a_0 + a_1 x + \dfrac{a_3}{a_4 - a_{5/x}}$ a_i are parameters
7. $g(n) = kn^v v^n$ k and v are parameters
8. $g(x) = x \ln c + \left(\dfrac{c}{x} - x\right) \ln x$ c is a parameter
9. $g(v) = \left(\dfrac{c}{v}\right)^v v^{c/v}$ c is a parameter
10. Determine the formula for the sum

$$\sum_{=0}^{\infty} \frac{e^{-\lambda} \lambda^x}{x!} \qquad \text{where } \lambda \text{ is a constant and } x = 0, 1, 2, \ldots$$

(*Hint:* Use the Taylor expansion for e^{λ}.)

B. SOLVING AN EQUATION

The extreme points of $E(x)$ are given by the "zeros" or "roots" of the derivative; i.e., by those values of x which satisfy the equation $E'(x) = 0$. In general, $E'(x)$ contains parameters $a, b, c, \ldots$ as well as the variable x, and may be written as $E'(x, a, b, \ldots)$. Solving the equation

$$E'(x, a, b, \ldots) = 0$$

is equivalent to finding the implicitly defined function

$$x = g(a, b, \ldots)$$

In some cases this is relatively simple; e.g., if the derivative is of the form

$$E'(x) = x - a \qquad \text{or} \qquad E'(x) = ae^{x/c} - d$$

the equation $E'(x) = 0$ can be easily solved for x, and the solution can be expressed as

$$x_0 = a \qquad \text{and} \qquad x_0 = c \ln \frac{d}{a}$$

respectively. Any solution of $f(x) = 0$ is said to be a root of the equation.

However, in cases where an explicit, and computable, inverse function cannot be derived analytically, the solutions to the equation $f(x) = 0$ must be found by numerical methods. In this section two such methods are described. Starting with an initial approximate solution, both provide a formula for computing a sequence of values of x which, in general, converges toward the exact value of the root. The effectiveness of the methods is measured by rate of convergence, or number of iterations, required for a desired accuracy.

The Interpolation Method

Suppose that it is known that $f(x_0) > 0$ and $f(x_1) < 0$; then if $f(x)$ is known to be continuous, there will be a value α, $x_1 < \alpha < x_0$, for which $f(\alpha) = 0$. Such a case is shown in Fig. 5.1. One can approximate the value of α by the value x_2; the abcissa of the point where the chord AB intersects the x-axis. The value of x_2 can be found numerically by observing that triangle Ax_1x_2 is similar to triangle Bx_0x_2 and hence that

$$\frac{x_2 - x_0}{x_2 - x_1} = \frac{f(x_0)}{f(x_1)} \qquad \text{or} \qquad x_2 = \frac{x_0 f(x_1) - x_1 f(x_0)}{f(x_1) - f(x_0)}$$

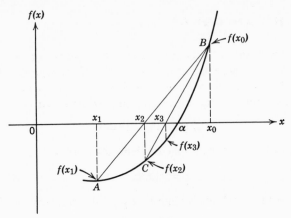

Figure 5.1

The value $f(x_2)$ will be either positive or negative. (If it is zero, the root has been found.) The case where $f(x_2)$ is negative is illustrated in Fig. 5.1. The same method can be applied to the chord BC to provide a value for x_3. The procedure can be continued until $f(x_n)$ is sufficiently close to zero. The general formula for x_{i+1} is:

$$x_{i+1} = \frac{(x_{i-1})f(x_i) - (x_i)f(x_{i-1})}{f(x_i) - f(x_{i-1})}$$

After x_{i+1} has been computed, x_i is chosen so that $f(x_i)$ and $f(x_{i+1})$ have opposite signs.

Newton's Method

This procedure is based on the replacement of a curve by a straight line, the tangent, in the neighborhood of a root. Assume that, by a graph or by trial computations, it has been found that x_0 is close to a root α of $f(x) = 0$, Fig. 5.2. The curve can be replaced by the tangent AT which intersects the x-axis at the point T. From the definition of the derivative

$$f'(x_0) = \frac{f(x_0)}{x_0 - x_1}$$

and, therefore,

$$x_1 = x_0 - \frac{f(x_0)}{f'(x_0)}$$

The same procedure can be applied at the point B and leads to another

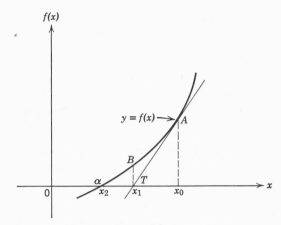

Figure 5.2

(and better approximation), x_2, and so on, until the desired accuracy is reached. In general,

$$x_{i+1} = x_i - \frac{f(x_i)}{f'(x_i)}$$

The major difference between the two methods is that the interpolation method requires only the calculation of the values of the function while Newton's method requires also the values of the derivative. In general, however, the Newton method will converge more rapidly (require fewer iterations) than the interpolation method.

The applicability of Newton's method depends essentially on the nature of the curve $y = f(x)$, and on the choice of the starting value x_0. In Fig. 5.2 the successive estimates converge rapidly to the required root. However, for a poor choice of x_0 the method may not converge. In Fig. 5.3, x_2 is further than x_0 from the true root α.

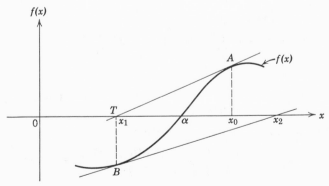

Figure 5.3

Example. The function

$$g(x) = [\ln C - 1] + \frac{C}{x^2} - \left[1 + \frac{C}{x^2}\right] \ln x$$

which appears as the derivative of an objective function in Chapter 7, is known to have a root between 3 and 4 in the case where $C = 120$. Use the interpolation method and Newton's method to compute the root to two decimal places.

Solution by the Interpolation Method. For $C = 120$, $\ln C = 4.7875$, and

$$f(x) = 3.7875 + \frac{120}{x^2} - \left[1 + \frac{120}{x^2}\right] \ln x$$

$$f(4.0) = 3.7875 + \frac{120}{4.0000^2} - \left[1 + \frac{120}{4.0000^2}\right] \ln 4.0000$$

$$= 3.7875 + 7.5000 - [8.5000]1.3863 = -0.4961$$

$$f(3.0) = 3.7875 + 13.3333 - [14.3333]1.0986 = 1.3742$$

Thus $f(4.0)$ and $f(3.0)$ have opposite signs; this verifies that there is a root somewhere between 3.0 and 4.0.
Then

$$x_2 = \frac{x_0 f(x_1) - x_1 f(x_0)}{f(x_1) - f(x_0)}$$

$$= \frac{(4.0000)(1.3742) - (3.0000)(-0.4961)}{1.3742 - (-0.4961)} = 3.7348$$

$$f(x_2) = -0.2634$$

The root must lie between 3.0 and 3.7348. Then

$$x_3 = \frac{x_1 f(x_2) - x_2 f(x_1)}{f(x_2) - f(x_1)}$$

$$= \frac{(3.0000)(-0.2634) - (3.7348)(1.3742)}{(-0.2634) - (1.3742)} = 3.6166$$

and

$$f(x_3) = 3.7875 + \frac{120}{(3.6166)^2} - \left[1 + \frac{120}{(3.6166)^2}\right] \ln 3.6166 = -0.1173$$

The root must lie between 3.0 and 3.6166:

$$x_4 = \frac{(3.0)(-0.1173) - (3.6166)(1.3742)}{(-0.1173) - (1.3742)} = 3.5681$$

$$f(x_4) = -0.0316$$

The root must lie between 3.0 and 3.5681:

$$x_5 = 3.5553$$

Two further iterations gives $x_7 = 3.5396$; $f(x_7) = -0.0053$, and hence the root is approximately $x = 3.54$

Solution by Newton's Method.   Starting with $x_0 = 3.0000$ gives

$$f(x_0) = 1.3742$$

as before. In addition, the value of the derivative

$$f'(x) = \frac{1}{x}\left[\frac{C}{x^2}(2\ln x - 3) - 1\right]$$

must be computed.

$$f'(x_0) = \frac{1}{3}\left\{\frac{120}{3^2}[-3 + 2(1.0986)] - 1\right\} = -3.9013$$

Therefore,

$$x_1 = x_0 - \frac{f(x_0)}{f'(x_0)}$$

$$= 3.0000 - \frac{1.3742}{-3.9013} = 3.3522$$

$$f(x_1) = 0.3396$$

and

$$f'(x_1) = \frac{1}{3.3522}[10.6788(-3 + 2.4192) - 1] = -2.1484$$

The next iteration gives

$$x_2 = x_1 - \frac{f(x_1)}{f'(x_1)} = 3.5103$$

$$f(x_2) = 0.0417$$

and

$$f'(x_2) = -1.6411$$

The third iteration gives

$$x_3 = x_2 - \frac{f(x_2)}{f'(x_2)} = 3.5357$$

and $f(x_3) = -0.0045$.

Newton's method in this example gives the same accuracy in three iterations as the interpolation method did in seven.

EXERCISES

1. There is another root at approximately $x = 35$. Locate this root by using numerical methods.

2. Another root is suspected at $x = 10$. Determine its value by Newton's method.

3. A well-known rule for computing the approximation to a square root of a positive number, G, from an initial approximation x_0 is

$$x_n = \frac{[G/x_{n-1}] + x_{n-1}}{2}$$

For example, let $G = 144$ and $x_0 = 2$. Then

$$x_1 = \frac{1}{2}\left[\frac{144}{2} + 2\right] = 37$$

$$x_2 = \frac{1}{2}\left[\frac{144}{37} + 37\right] = 20.4$$

$$x_3 = 13.73$$

$$x_4 = 12.109$$

and

$$x_5 = 12.0005$$

Use Newton's method to develop this rule.

C. OPTIMIZATION OF FUNCTIONS OF ONE VARIABLE

A function which increases as x increases in an interval is said to be a strictly increasing function of x in that interval, and a function which decreases is said to be strictly decreasing. If the function increases or remains constant (decreases or remains constant) the word "strictly" is omitted and the function is said to be an increasing (decreasing) function, or sometimes, non-decreasing (non-increasing). A (strictly) monotonic function is one which is either (strictly) increasing or (strictly) decreasing.

The function shown in Fig. 5.4a is strictly monotonically increasing; the one in 5.4b is strictly monotonically decreasing; the function in 5.4c is monotonically increasing (non-decreasing) and the one in 5.4d is monotonically decreasing (non-increasing).

By definition, the slope of the curve $y = f(x)$ at the point x_0 is given by

Figure 5.4a   Strictly increasing function.
Figure 5.4b   Strictly decreasing function.

 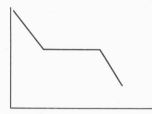

Figure 5.4c   Increasing function.
Figure 5.4d   Decreasing function.

the derivative $f'(x)$, if it exists at a point x_0. If $f'(x)$ exists for all $x_1 < x < x_2$, and if for all x' in $x_1 < x < x_2$,

$f' > 0$, then f is strictly increasing in $\qquad x_1 < x < x_2$

$f' \geq 0$, then f is increasing (non-decreasing) in $x_1 < x < x_2$

$f' \leq 0$, then f is decreasing (non-increasing) in $x_1 < x < x_2$

$f' < 0$, then f is strictly decreasing in $\qquad x_1 < x < x_2$

Local Extrema

A function has a local *maximum* value at a point x_0 if the values of the function on either side of x_0 are less than $f(x_0)$, and a local *minimum* value at the point x_0 if the values of the function on either side are greater than $f(x_0)$. Such maximum values and minimum values of a function are called local *extreme* values or local extrema. The values of x at which a function has extreme values are called extreme points.

Assume that a function $f(x)$ has a continuous first derivative in an interval including the point x_0. Then if f has a minimum value at x_0, the first derivative must change from negative to positive as x increases through x_0, and if f has a maximum at x_0, the derivative must change from positive to negative. Therefore, at x_0 the first derivative must be zero. Any point at which $f' = 0$ is said to be a *stationary* point. A necessary condition for x_0 to be an extreme point (in an interval in which $f(x)$ is differentiable) is that x_0 be a stationary point. For example, the function

$$f(x) = x^3 - 48x$$

has a continuous first derivative for all x. It has two stationary points, $x = -4$; $x = 4$, which may or may not be extreme points.

At a stationary point, a differentiable function may have either a maximum, a minimum, or neither. The following functions all have a single stationary point at $x = 0$, but at this point

$$f(x) = x^4 \quad \text{has a minimum}$$
$$f(x) = -(x^4) \quad \text{has a maximum}$$
$$f(x) = x^3 \quad \text{has neither a maximum nor a minimum}$$

The *sufficient* conditions for a stationary point of a differentiable function to be a local maximum or local minimum can be obtained by examining the Taylor expansion. By definition, the first derivative is zero at a stationary point x_0. Hence the expansion takes the form

$$f(x_0 + h) = f(x_0) + 0 + \frac{h^2}{2!}[f''(x_0)] + R_2$$

For any small value of h, the remainder R_2 will be less in absolute value than the term containing f''. Then, since $h^2/2!$ is always positive for any positive or negative h.

$f(x_0 + h) > f(x_0)$ if $f''(x_0) > 0$, and therefore x_0 is a local *minimum*

$f(x_0 + h) < f(x_0)$ if $f''(x_0) < 0$, and therefore x_0 is a local *maximum*

At x_0 in Fig. 5.5c, f' is changing from positive to negative, hence $f'' < 0$ and f has a maximum at x_0. At x_0 in Fig. 5.5d, f' is changing from negative to positive; hence $f'' > 0$ and f has a minimum at x_0.

If $f''(x_0) = 0$ the term in the Taylor series containing the third derivative must be examined. The value of the third derivative at $x = x_0$ may also be zero, in which case the fourth derivative must be examined, and so on. Suppose the ith derivative is the lowest order derivative which is not zero at $x = x_0$. Then the Taylor expansion is:

$$f(x_0 + h) = f(x_0) + 0 + 0 + \cdots + \frac{h^i}{i!}[f^{(i)}(x_0)] + R_i$$

If i *is even*, then h^i is positive for any h and

$f(x_0 + h) > f(x_0)$ if $f^{(i)}(x_0) > 0$, and therefore x_0 is a local *minimum*

$f(x_0 + h) < f(x_0)$ if $f^{(i)}(x_0) < 0$, and therefore x_0 is a local *maximum*

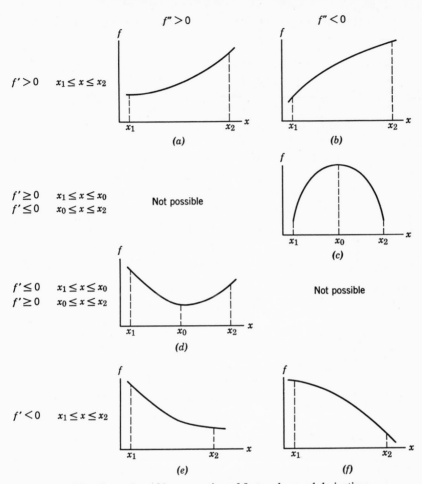

Figure 5.5   Illustration of interpretation of first and second derivatives.

If *i is odd*, then h^i is negative if h is negative, and positive if h is positive.

Then if	when $h > 0$	when $h < 0$
$f^{(i)} > 0$	$f(x_0 + h) > f(x_0)$	$f(x_0 + h) < f(x_0)$
$f^{(i)} < 0$	$f(x_0 + h) < f(x_0)$	$f(x_0 + h) > f(x_0)$

In neither case is x_0 an extreme point; the function has an *inflection* point at x_0 rather than a local extreme value. A point x_0 is an inflection point if $f''(x_0) = 0$, and if f'' changes sign in going through x_0. (Note that an inflection point does not have to be a stationary point; a function can have an inflection point where the first derivative is not zero.)

The procedure for identifying the local extrema of a differentiable function may be summarized as follows:

1. Determine the solutions to the equation $f' = 0$. The function can have local extreme values only at these stationary points.
2. For each of the stationary points, determine the value of the lowest order derivative which is not zero at that point.
   (*a*) If the order is even and the value of the derivative is positive, the function has a local minimum at the stationary point.
   (*b*) If the order is even and the value of the derivative is negative, the function has a local maximum at the stationary point.
   (*c*) If the order is odd the stationary point is an inflection point.

Example I. Determine the local extrema for the function $g(x) = (x^2 - 5x + 2)^3$. In Example 1, p. 119, the first derivative was derived

$$g'(x) = 3(x^2 - 5x + 2)^2(2x - 5)$$

The solutions of $g'(x) = 0$ are obtained by solving each term. For the first term,

$$x = \frac{5 \pm \sqrt{25 - 8}}{2} = \frac{5}{2} \pm \sqrt{4.25} = 2.5 \pm 2.062$$

and for the second term

$$x = \frac{5}{2}$$

Thus the stationary points are $x_1 = 4.562$, $x_2 = 0.438$, $x_3 = 2.500$ The second derivative is

$$g''(x) = 30x^4 - 300x^3 + 972x^2 - 1{,}110x + 324$$

The point $x_1 = 4.562$ is an inflection point because

$$g''(4.562) = 12{,}994.2 - 28{,}483.2 + 20{,}229.3 - 5{,}063.82 + 324 \sim 0$$

and g'' changes sign in going through 4.562.

The point $x_2 = 0.438$ is an inflection point because
$$g''(0.438) = 1.11 - 25.20 + 186.62 - 486.18 + 324 \sim 0 \quad \text{and} \quad g''$$

changes sign in going through 0.438. The point $x_3 = 2.5$ is a minimum because

$$g''(2.5) = 1{,}171.8 - 4{,}689 + 6{,}075 - 2{,}775 + 324 = +106.8$$

Example 2. Determine the local extrema for the function $g(x)$ where

$$g(x) = \frac{-2x^2}{1 + x + 2x^2}$$

Then
$$g'(x) = \frac{2x(2+x)}{(1+x+2x^2)^2}$$

The equation $g'(x) = 0$ has solutions at
$$x = 0 \qquad x = -2$$

The second derivative is
$$g''(x) = \frac{-4(1 - 6x^2 - 2x^3)}{(1+x+2x^2)^3}$$

The point $x = 0$ is a maximum because
$$g''(0) = -4$$

The point $x = -2$ is a minimum because
$$g''(-2) = \frac{(-4+96-64)}{(1-2+8)^3} = 0.082 > 0$$

Note that the denominator is never zero.

Example 3. Determine the local extrema for the function $f(x) = cxe^{ax^2+bx}$. From Example 3, p. 120, $f'(x) = (2ax^2 + bx + 1)ce^{ax^2+bx}$ and the zeros of $f'(x)$ are given by
$$2ax^2 + bx + 1 = 0$$

since $c > 0$ and $e^{ax^2+bx} > 0$.
The solutions to the quadratic are given by
$$x_1 = \frac{-b + \sqrt{b^2 - 8a}}{4a} \qquad \text{and} \qquad x_2 = \frac{-b - \sqrt{b^2 - 8a}}{4a}$$

Substituting the values of x_1 and x_2 in $f''(x)$ will determine the nature of the extreme point for these values of x in terms of the given coefficients a, b, c. If, for example,
$$a = -2 \qquad b = 3 \qquad c = 1$$
then,
$$x_1 = \frac{-3 - \sqrt{9 + 16}}{-8} = 1 \qquad \text{and} \qquad x_2 = \frac{-3 + \sqrt{25}}{-8} = -\frac{1}{4}$$

The values of the second derivative at these points are:
$$f''(1) = e[16 - 24 - 3 + 6] = -5e < 0$$
$$f''(-\tfrac{1}{4}) = e^{-7/8}[-\tfrac{1}{4} - \tfrac{3}{2} - \tfrac{3}{4} + 6] = 5e^{-7/8} > 0$$

and hence the function has a maximum at $x = 1$ and a minimum at $x = -\frac{1}{4}$.

Global Extrema

The extrema discussed above were defined in terms of the behavior of a function in a small interval and are therefore known as local extrema. The function shown in Fig. 5.6 has local extrema at x_2, x_5, and x_6; the one at x_5 is a local minimum and the ones at x_2 and x_6 are local maxima.

The global maximum is the largest value in a closed interval (including the end points) and similarly the global minimum is the smallest value. For example, in the interval $x_1 \leq x \leq x_7$, the function in Fig. 5.6 has a global minimum at x_1 and a global maximum at x_6.

A *critical* point is any point which is a "likely" candidate for a global extrema. For the function represented in Fig. 5.6, for example, solving $f' = 0$ would locate the points x_3 and x_5 as stationary points. However, the global maximum is at x_6, where f is discontinuous. If the interval of interest is $x_1 \leq x \leq x_3$, the global maximum is at x_2. At x_2 the derivative is discontinuous and hence the point x_2 cannot be found by solving $f' = 0$. The critical points which must be examined for global extrema, therefore, are:

(*a*) end points of the intervals
(*b*) points at which f is discontinuous
(*c*) solutions of $f' = 0$

A flow chart of the procedure for locating global extrema is shown in Fig. 5.7.

One reason for the detailed analysis of critical points is that most Management Science models are of the form

$$E = f(x;\ a, b, c, \ldots)$$

where the a, b, c, etc., are parameters. Strictly speaking, the function f,

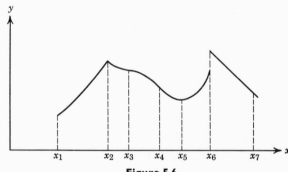

Figure 5.6

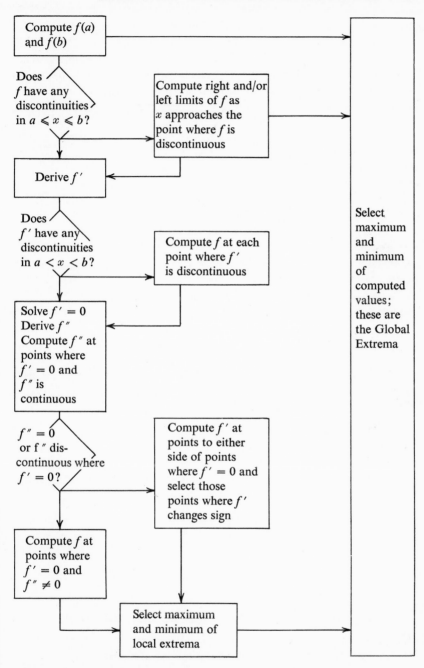

Figure 5.7. Procedure for locating global extrema of $f(x)$ for $a \leq x \leq b$.

and its derivatives, are considered to be functions of x for any specific values of the parameters. However, it is usually necessary to examine the model or find extrema for a range of values of the parameters. Thus it is of interest to differentiate the function with respect to its parameter and when this occurs, discontinuities frequently appear.

Example 4. To find the global extrema for the function defined in $-3 \leq x \leq 2$ by

$$\begin{aligned} f(x) &= x - 1 & 0 \leq x \leq 2 \\ &= (2 + \sqrt{2}) + 2\sqrt{2x} + x^2 & -\sqrt{2} \leq x < 0 \\ &= 3\sqrt{2} + x + \frac{2}{x} & -3 \leq x \leq -\sqrt{2} \end{aligned}$$

f must be analyzed by the procedure shown in Fig. 5.7. The values of f at the end points of the interval are:

$$f(2) = 1 \qquad f(-3) = 0.575$$

Computation of f at the end points of the subintervals shows that f is discontinuous at $x = 0$ and has one value defined there as

$$f(0) = -1$$

as $x \to 0$ from the right, but also approaches the limit $2 + \sqrt{2}$ as x approaches zero from the left, i.e., through negative values. The derivative is:

$$\begin{aligned} f' &= 1 & 0 \leq x \leq 2 \\ &= 2\sqrt{2} + 2x & -\sqrt{2} \leq x < 0 \\ &= 1 - \frac{2}{x^2} & -3 \leq x < -\sqrt{2} \end{aligned}$$

and there is one stationary point at $x = -\sqrt{2}$. However

$$\begin{aligned} f'' &= 2 > 0 & -\sqrt{2} \leq x < 0 \\ &= \frac{4}{x^3} < 0 & -3 \leq x < -\sqrt{2} \end{aligned}$$

or

$$f'' = 2 \quad \text{or} \quad -\sqrt{2} \quad \text{when } x = -\sqrt{2}$$

that is, f'' is discontinuous at $x = -\sqrt{2}$.

Letting δ be any small positive number: for $x > -\sqrt{2}$,

$$f'(-\sqrt{2} + \delta) = 2\sqrt{2} + 2(-\sqrt{2} + \delta) = 2\delta > 0$$

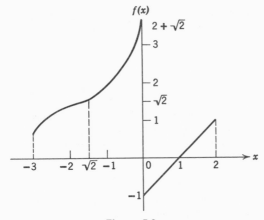

Figure 5.8

and for $x < -\sqrt{2}$,

$$f'(-\sqrt{2} - \delta) = 1 - \frac{2}{(-\sqrt{2} - \delta)^2} = \frac{2\sqrt{2}\delta + \delta^2}{2 + 2\sqrt{2}\delta + \delta^2} > 0$$

Thus f' does not change sign at $x = -\sqrt{2}$, which means that $x = -\sqrt{2}$ is not local extreme point. Note that f' and f'' are also discontinuous at the point $x = 0$. The set of critical points, or possibilities for global extrema, are the end points $(2, -3)$, the points at which f is discontinuous (0) and the stationary points $(-\sqrt{2})$. The values of f at these points are 1.0 at $x = 2$, 0.575 at $x = -3$, -1 at $x = 0$, $2 + \sqrt{2}$ at $x = 0^-$, and $\sqrt{2}$ at $x = -\sqrt{2}$. f has a global maximum as x approaches zero through negative values and a global minimum at $x = 0$. A graph of $f(x)$ is shown in Fig. 5.8.

EXERCISES

Determine the critical points and global extrema of the functions in Exercises 1 to 9 in the interval shown. Indicate the intervals in which the functions are increasing or decreasing.

1. $g(x) = 2 - 8x + x^2 - 10x^3 + 9x^4$ $-\infty < x < \infty$

2. $g(x) = 2 \ln x + 3$ $x > 0$

3. $g(x) = 2 - 3e^{-2x+5}$ $x \geq 0$

4. $g(x) = \dfrac{3x^2}{1 + 2x + x^2}$ $-\infty < \infty x < \infty$

5. $g(x) = 2x^2 e^{x^3 - x}$ $-\infty < x < \infty$

6. $g(x) = 1 + \dfrac{x}{\sqrt{3}} + \dfrac{-3/4}{2 - 4/x}$ $-\infty < x < \infty$

7. $g(n) = 3n^2 2^n$ $-\infty < n < \infty$

8. $g(x) = (x + 1)^2(x - 2)^2$ $-\infty < x < \infty$

9. $g(x) = |x|^{3/2}|x - 18|^{-1/2}$ $-\infty < x < \infty$

10. Graph the missing functions as they would appear in Fig. 5.5, if a continuous first derivative is not acquired.

11. The earnings of a firm are $\$E$ per period when it produces x units of a certain commodity, where

$$E = 2500 + 15x^2 - 2x^3$$

What is the optimum output per period?

12. The total cost of producing x lbs of livestock feed in a flour mill per month is

$$x^2 + 30x + 100$$

How many pounds should be produced each month to obtain maximum earnings if the price per pound at which all the feed may be sold is $(150 - 2x)$?

13. A lumber mill produces y units of quality lumber per period. By-products (x units) in the process are given by

$$x = \frac{10y - 30}{y - 4}$$

Determine the optimum output per period, if the quality lumber sells for twice as much per unit as the by-product.

14. A private fishing resort owner builds cabins to rent to fishermen. The rental obtainable depends on the total number of cabins. Suppose that the rent is x dollars per day per cabin,

$$x = \tfrac{1}{4}(512 - 16y)^{1/2}$$

if y cabins have been built. How many cabins should be built to maximize the rental income?

15. The cost of supplying electricity is the sum of two components: fixed costs (overhead), including such charges as rent, interest, etc., which do not vary with production level: and variable costs, which are proportional to the supply of electricity produced. Assume that variable costs are directly proportional to production volume at all levels of production. Thus the average cost per unit, c, may be expressed as

$$c = c_1 + c_0/n \tag{1}$$

where c_1 represents variable cost, per unit produced; c_0 is the total annual overhead, or fixed cost; and n is the number of units sold per year.

The demand for electricity is such that there is a limiting price p_1 above which no sales will be made, and that as the price is reduced, sales will increase indefinitely. There are many functions which will satisfy these assumptions; one is

$$n = a \left[\frac{p_1 - p}{p} \right] \qquad (2)$$

where p is selling price. Determine the maximum earnings, if the functions have the form given by (1) and (2).

D. CHARACTERISTICS OF FUNCTIONS OF ONE VARIABLE

Concavity and Convexity

A function is said to be strictly concave, if a line segment drawn between any two points on its graph falls entirely below the graph (Fig. 5.9a). A function is strictly convex, if the line segment falls entirely above the graph (Fig. 5.9b). A strictly convex function increases more rapidly than a straight line (Fig. 5.9c), or decreases less rapidly (Fig. 5.9d). A strictly concave function increases less rapidly than a straight line (Fig. 5.9c) or decreases more rapidly (Fig. 5.9d).

If $f(x)$ has a continuous second derivative in an interval, it is *concave* if and only if $f'' \leq 0$ for all x in the interval. The functions shown in Figs. 5.5b, 5.5c and 5.5f are concave in $x_1 \leq x \leq x_2$. Similarly, a function with a continuous second derivative in an interval is *convex* if and only if $f'' \geq 0$ for every x in the interval. The functions shown in Figs. 5.5a, 5.5d and 5.5e are convex in $x_1 \leq x \leq x_2$.

More generally, even if a function is not differentiable, a line segment drawn between any two points x_1 and x_2 in an interval in which the function is convex will never underestimate the value of the function for any $x_1 \leq x_0 \leq x_2$ (Fig. 5.10).
Let

$$t = \frac{x_0 - x_1}{x_2 - x_1}$$

Then $0 < t < 1$ or
$$x_0 = (1 - t)x_1 + tx_2$$

The value on the line segment at x_0, say, $g(x_0)$, is

$$g(x_0) = f(x_1) + t[f(x_2) - f(x_1)]$$
$$= (1 - t)f(x_1) + tf(x_2)$$

By definition if f is strictly convex

$$f(x_0) < g(x_0)$$

or
$$f[(1 - t)x_1 + tx_2] \leq (1 - t)f(x_1) + tf(x_2) \qquad (1)$$

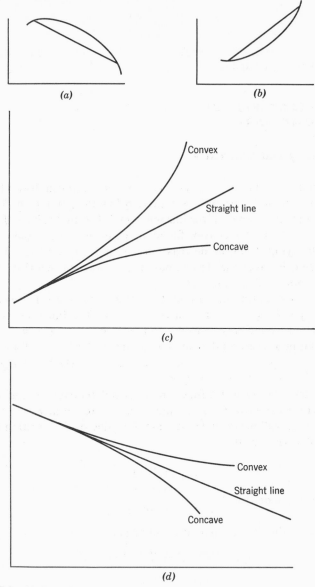

Figure 5.9 (*a*) Function that is concave downward. (*b*) Function that is convex downward.

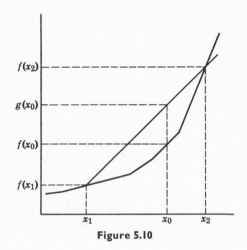

Figure 5.10

This condition may be used to determine whether a function is strictly convex, or strictly concave, if the inequality is reversed. If this condition holds throughout an interval with $<(>)$ replaced by $\leq(\geq)$, the function is convex (concave).

Example. If $f(x) = a + bx$, then substituting in (1)

$$a + b[(1 - t)x_1 + tx_2] \leq (1 - t)[a + bx_1] + t[a + bx_2]$$

$$a + x_1 b(1 - t) + x_2 bt \leq [(1 - t) + t]a + x_1(1 - t)b + x_2 tb$$

In this case the *equality sign* holds for any two points x_1 and x_2 and a linear function is both convex and concave, but not strictly convex or strictly concave.

The concept of concavity and convexity is useful in determining global extrema. From Fig. 5.5 it is clear that if a function is convex throughout an interval, the minimum occurs at an interior stationary point if one exists; if not, the minimum occurs at an end point. The maximum value

	Convex	Concave
Minimum	At a stationary point if it exists in the interval; otherwise, at one of the end points	At one of the end points
Maximum	At one of the end points	At a stationary point if one exists in the interval; otherwise, at one of the end points

of a convex function occurs at one of the end points. For a concave function, the role of minimum and maximum are interchanged.

Other Characteristics

Asymptotes. The behavior of functions for very large positive or negative values of the independent variable is frequently of interest. A function is said to be asymptotic to a given value, if the function approaches but never reaches the given value. In Fig. 5.11 the function $f(x) = 1/(x + 1)$ is asymptotic to zero, since it approaches 0 as x becomes very large in either a positive or negative direction.

The concept is usually applied as the independent variable approaches $+\infty$ or $-\infty$, but is also useful for cases in which the independent variable approaches other points. The function in Fig. 5.11 also approaches an asymptote when the independent variable x approaches -1. The asymptote is the line $x = -1$. It approaches but never reaches the value $-\infty$ as x approaches -1 through values less than -1. As x approaches -1 through values greater than -1, the function is also asymptotic to the line $x = -1$ and approaches the value $+\infty$.

Periodic Functions. An example of a function which has the same extreme values for many values of the independent variable is the periodic function. A function $f(x)$ is periodic with period T if, for any value of x,

$$f(x + nT) = f(x) \qquad \text{for} \quad n = 1, 2, 3, \ldots$$

Fig. 5.12 shows two examples of functions which are periodic with period $T = 2$.

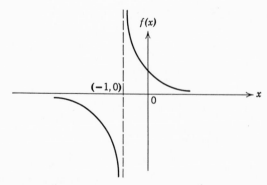

Figure 5.11   Graph of $f(x) = \dfrac{1}{x + 1}$.

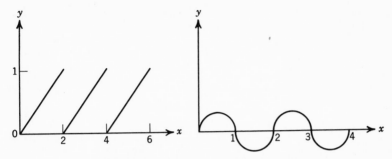

Figure 5.12   Examples of periodic functions.

Symmetrical Functions.   A function $f(x)$ is said to be an *even function* about the y-axis if $f(-x) = f(x)$ (see Fig. 5.13). More generally, $f(x)$ is an even function about the point $x = a$, if $f(a - x) = f(x - a)$. A function $g(x)$ is said to be an *odd function* about the point $x = a$, if $g(a - x) = -g(x - a)$ (see Fig. 5.13).

Inverse Functions.   A function $y = f(x)$ has an inverse function $x = f^{-1}(y)$ which is unique if $f(x)$ is continuous and strictly monotonic. Figure 5.14a shows a function f which is continuous and strictly monotonic for $x_1 < x < x_2$; the inverse function shown in Fig. 5.14b is also continous and strictly monotonic in $y_1 < y < y_2$, where $y_1 = f(x_1)$ and $y_2 = f(x_2)$. If f is not monotonic, the inverse function may not be unique over a whole interval, but may be unique for a smaller interval. The function $y = x^2$ shown in Fig. 5.13a has a unique inverse $x = +\sqrt{y}$ for $x > 0$, and a different unique inverse $x = -\sqrt{y}$ for $x < 0$.

Example I.   From a knowledge of the maximum, minimum, and inflection points, as well as the value of the function at these points, it is possible

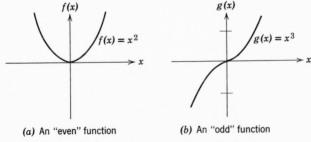

(a) An "even" function   (b) An "odd" function

Figure 5.13   Examples of symmetrical functions.

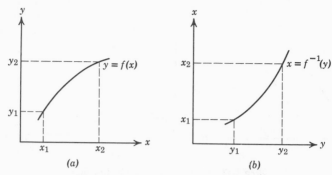

Figure 5.14   A function and its inverse.

to sketch the graph of the polynomial (Example 1, Section A) of degree 6,

$$g(x) = (x^2 - 5x + 2)^3$$

$$g(0.438) = (0.192 - 2.192 + 2)^3 = 0$$

$$g(2.5) = (6.25 - 12.5 + 2)^3 = -76.78$$

$$g(4.56) = (20.82 - 22.82 + 2)^3 = 0$$

also

$$g(0) = 8$$

The function increases monotonically in the intervals not shown in the figure, i.e., for x greater than 4.56 or less than 0. (Fig. 5.15.)

Example 2.   The function considered in Example 2, Section C, was

$$g(x) = \frac{-2x^2}{1 + x + 2x^2}$$

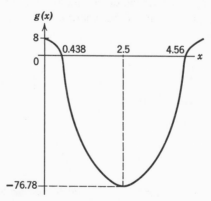

Figure 5.15 $g(x) = (x^2 - 5x + 2)^3$.

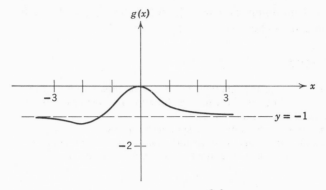

Figure 5.16 $g(x) = \dfrac{-2x^2}{1 + x + x^2}$.

This is a rational function which has a local maximum at $x = 0$ and a local minimum at $x = -2$, with $g(0) = 0$ and $g(-2) = -1.14$. An analysis of g'' shows that there are three inflection points x_0, x_1, and x_2 with $-3 < x_0 < -2$, $-1 < x_1 < 0$, and $0 < x_2 < 1$. Since $\lim\limits_{x \to \pm\infty} g(x) = -1$, $x = 0$ and $x = -2$ are global extrema as well as local extrema. (Fig. 5.16.)

Example 3.   The function

$$f(x) = xe^{-2x^2+3x}$$

considered in Example 3, Section C, is the product of a polynomial and an exponential. f has a local and global maximum at $x = 1$, and a local

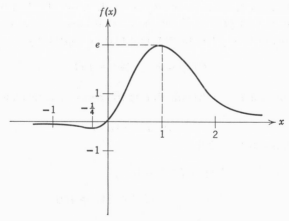

Figure 5.17 $f(x) = xe^{-2x^2+3x}$.

and global minimum at $x = -\frac{1}{4}$. Since $\lim\limits_{x \to \pm\infty} f(x) = 0$, the function has the form shown above (Fig. 5.17).

EXERCISES

1–9. For each of the functions given in Exercises 1 to 9, p. 137,

(*a*) Give the intervals in which the function is concave or convex.

(*b*) State the asymptotes, if any.

(*c*) Describe the periodicity or symmetry, if any.

(*d*) Give the intervals in which the function has a unique inverse.

(*e*) Sketch a graph of the function in the intervals given.

E. GENERAL EARNINGS FUNCTIONS AND MARGINAL ANALYSIS

General Earnings Functions

Linear "Earnings" functions of the general form

$$\text{Earnings } (x) = \text{Revenue } (x) - \text{Cost } (x)$$

$$E(x) = R(x) - C(x)$$

were developed in Chapter 1. The objective of "break-even analysis" discussed there was to find the value of x for which $E(x) = 0$. The revenues and costs were *linear* functions of the variable x. In many business situations, revenue and cost functions can be adequately approximated by linear functions; in others, the functions are clearly nonlinear.

Example I. A firm is producing a single product which sells in the market for a fixed price, \$52 per unit, regardless of quantity produced. The cost of producing x units during a period is given by:

$$C(x) = x^2 + 24x + 160$$

If all units produced can be sold during the period, the revenue per period is:

$$R(x) = 52x$$

The earnings function then is

$$E(x) = R(x) - C(x)$$

$$= 52x - (x^2 + 24x + 160)$$

$$= -x^2 + 28x - 160$$

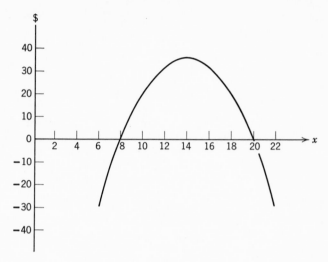

Figure 5.18 $E(x) = -x^2 + 28x - 160$.

The function is shown in Fig. 5.18. Earnings are negative for $x < 8$ and for $x > 20$ and positive for $8 < x < 20$. There are, therefore, two levels of production at which the firm "breaks even." However, the firm would be more interested in the production level which results in maximum earnings.

Since

$$\frac{dE(x)}{dx} = -2x + 28 \qquad \text{or} \qquad x^* = 14$$

and

$$\frac{d^2E(x)}{dx} = -2$$

the stationary point is a maximum and the firm will have maximum earnings at a production level of 14 units per period.

Example 2.   In Example 1, the selling price was considered fixed (at $52) and the quantity to be produced (and sold) was the decision variable. In some problems, the number of units that can be sold is assumed to be a function of the price; the problem then becomes one of determining the optimum price.

In the example, page 16, the cost is the sum of manufacturing cost, selling cost, and overhead cost, and each of these includes fixed costs and variable costs. Frequently, material costs decrease because larger quantities are purchased as the production level increases. Suppose the firm can purchase the material for the xth unit at a cost of $$(18 − 0.001x)$ where, as before, the x is the number of units produced in one period. Then the total cost in the example is:

$$C(x) = 66,000 + (6 + 2 + 2 + 18 - 0.001x)x$$
$$= 66,000 + 28x - 0.001x^2$$

Normally the number of units that the firm can sell decreases as the prices increase. Suppose the number of units x the firm can sell if it charges a price y is given by:

$$y = 55 - 0.0035x$$

A function relating price and quantity such as this one is known as a *demand function*.

Then revenue is:
$$R(x) = (55 - 0.0035x)x$$
and
$$E(x) = 55x - 0.0035x^2 - 66,000 - 28x + 0.001x^2$$
$$= -0.0025x^2 + 27x - 66,000$$

Again the breakeven point is no longer unique; there are two production levels at which earnings are zero. Furthermore, there is one production level, $x = 5,400$, at which earnings are greater than at any other production level.

$$E'(x) = 0.005x + 27$$

$$x^* = \frac{27}{0.005} = 5,400 \text{ units}$$

$$E''(x^*) = -0.005 < 0$$

If this production level were feasible, i.e., if the capacity of the plant is greater than or equal to 5,400 units, the firm would receive maximum earnings by operating at this level.

If the earnings function is truly linear, the maximum earnings are obtained by operating at plant capacity; if the earnings function is non-linear, it is possible that maximum earnings may be obtained by operating at less than capacity.

Marginal Analysis

Let the level of an activity be denoted by the (non-negative) variable x, the revenue function, $R(x)$, give the revenue for each value of x, and the cost function $C(x)$ give the cost for each value of x. The earnings function is:

$$E(x) = R(x) - C(x)$$

The optimum value of x, x^*, is given by

$$\frac{dE(x)}{dx} = 0$$

or

$$R'(x^*) - C'(x^*) = 0$$

or

$$R'(x^*) = C'(x^*)$$

This states that the optimum level of the activity is the one where the rate of change of revenue is equal to the rate of change of cost. In economics and accounting literature, the rate of change of revenue is called *marginal revenue* and the rate of change of cost is called *marginal cost*. The method of marginal analysis is usually stated as:

The level of an activity should be increased until the revenue of the next unit (marginal revenue) is equal to the cost of that unit (marginal cost.)

To ensure that the optimum level actually results in a maximum earning, the second derivative must be negative:

$$R''(x^*) - C''(x^*) < 0 \qquad \text{or} \qquad R''(x^*) < C''(x^*)$$

Implicit in the usual statement of marginal analysis is the assumption that at lower activity levels the revenue per unit has been greater than the cost per unit.

Example 1 (Continued).

$$\frac{dR(x)}{dx} = 52 \qquad \frac{dC(x)}{dx} = 2x \overset{+}{-} 24$$

According to marginal analysis, the optimum value of x is the value which satisfies

$$52 = 2x \overset{+}{-} 24 \qquad \text{or} \qquad x^* = 14 \text{ units}$$

Example 2 (Continued).

$$\frac{dR(x)}{dx} = 55 - 0.0070x \qquad \frac{dC(x)}{dx} = 28 - 0.002x$$

The optimum value is the solution of

$$55 - 0.0070x = 28 - 0.002x \qquad \text{or} \qquad x^* = 5,400 \text{ units}$$

Average Function

The optimization method and the method of marginal analysis both depend on a knowledge of marginal revenue and marginal cost. A firm, however, may not know these values; it is frequently easier to estimate average revenue and average cost from company records. It is, therefore, relevant to investigate how averages may be used in optimization.

Let x be the level of some activity and let $y(x)$ denote the function of interest which may be the revenue, cost or earnings function. From the results on optimization:

y is increasing if $y' > 0$, and decreasing if $y' < 0$

y is convex if $y'' > 0$, and concave if $y'' < 0$

x^* is an extreme point if $y'(x^*) = 0$, and $y''(x) \neq 0$

x^* is a maximum if $y''(x^*) < 0$, and a minimum if $y''(x^*) > 0$

Let $a(x)$ be the average value of y, or

$$a(x) = \frac{y(x)}{x} \quad \text{or} \quad y(x) = xa(x)$$

Then $y' = a(x) + xa'(x)$. The error made in using a instead of y' is $xa'(x)$ which may be positive or negative, depending on whether a is increasing or decreasing.

EXERCISES

1. The demand function for a firm is given by

$$y = \alpha - \beta x$$

where y is the price and x is the quantity produced (and sold). The cost function is

$$C(x) = ax^2 + bx + c$$

Assume that all parameters α, β, a, b, and c are positive. Determine other conditions on these parameters that are necessary for the existence of a unique nonnegative optimum production level.

2. In normal situations the cost function, C, is an increasing function of x. Show that the average cost is an increasing (decreasing) function of x, if it is less (greater) than the marginal cost. Plot the average cost and marginal cost curves on the same diagram, and verify that they intersect at the minimum point of the average cost curve, where

$$C = 5x^3 - 30x^2 + 60x + 160$$

What is the number of units which yields minimum average cost?

3. Answer Exercise 2 for the general case where

$$C(x) = ax^3 - bx^2 + cx + d$$

Assume that the parameters a, b, c, d are positive and $b^2 < 3ac$.

4. The elasticity of a function $f(x)$ is defined as

$$\pm \frac{x}{f(x)} \frac{df}{dx}$$

If $f(x)$ is the demand for a product at a price x, the elasticity of demand is usually denoted by η and the minus sign is used because $f(x)$ normally decreases as x increases:

$$\eta = - \frac{x}{f(x)} \frac{df}{dx}$$

If $R(x)$ is the revenue obtained at a price x, show that

$$\frac{dR}{dx} = f(x)(1 - \eta)$$

Summary

Let x be a real variable which can take any value in a closed interval, $x_1 \leq x \leq x_2$, and let $f(x)$ be a function with a continuous derivative. The optimization problem consists of locating the extreme points: i.e., points at which $f(x)$ has extreme (maxima or minima) values. A point x_0 is a local maximum at any point at which $f(x_0) > f(x)$ for x close to x_0. A point x_0 is a local minimum, if $f(x_0) < f(x)$ for x close to x_0. The point x_0 is the global maximum (minimum), if $f(x_0) > (<) f(x)$ for all x in the interval.

The first step in the procedure for determining global extreme points consists of locating the critical points. The set of critical points consists of the end points of the interval; points at which f is discontinuous and the stationary points (points at which $f' = 0$).

Second, each critical point is classified as a local maximum, local minimum, or neither. An end point is a local maximum (minimum) if the adjacent interior points are smaller (greater). At a point where f is discontinuous, values of f at adjacent points are examined. A stationary point is (1) a local maximum if $f'' < 0$, or if $f'' = 0$ and $f''(x_0 \pm \varepsilon) < 0$, and neither if f'' changes sign as x goes through x_0. The global maximum is then selected as the largest local maximum and the global minimum as the smallest local minimum.

A function is concave (convex) in an interval if a line segment joining any two values of the function always underestimates (overestimates) the function. If the function is convex throughout the interval of definition, it can have only one stationary point at which the function has a global minimum. If it does not have a stationary point, the minimum is at one of the ends of the interval. If the function is concave through the interval, it can have only one stationary point at which it has a global maximum.

If it does not have a stationary point, the maximum is at one of the ends of the interval.

Other relevant properties of the functions are the following:

Increasing (decreasing): A function is increasing (decreasing) in an interval if $f(x_2) \geq (\leq) f(x_1)$ for $x_2 > x_1$.

Asymptotic: A function is asymptotic to another if it approaches but never quite reaches it.

Symmetrical: A function is symmetrical about a point a if
$$f(a + h) = \pm f(a + h).$$

Periodic: a function is periodic if $f(x + n) = f(T)$.

The method of marginal analysis, which appears in economic and accounting literature, may be considered as a special case of the general technique of optimization. The earnings function may be written as

$$\text{Earnings} = \text{Revenue} - \text{Cost}$$
$$E(x) = R(x) - C(x)$$

The optimum value of x by the general optimization technique is given by
$$E'(x) = 0 \quad \text{or} \quad R'(x) = C'(x)$$
if
$$E''(x) < 0 \quad \text{or} \quad R''(x) - C''(x) < 0$$

The method of marginal analysis states that x should be increased until marginal revenue equals marginal cost or until

$$R'(x) = C'(x)$$

Notes and References

Section A, B, C

A standard reference work, as well as a readable textbook, on differential calculus is:
Courant, R. (1934), *Differential and Integral Calculus*, 2 vol., Blackie and Sons, Ltd., London.

Other texts are
Johnson, R. E., and Kiokemeister, F. E. (1957), *Calculus*, Allyn and Bacon, Boston.
Taylor, H. E., and Wade, T. L. (1962), *University Calculus*, John Wiley and Sons, New York.

Section D

Marginal analysis is discussed in textbooks on microeconomics:
Allen, R. G. D. (1956), *Mathematical Analysis for Economists*, Macmillan & Co., New York.
Baunol, W. J. (1961), *Economic Theory and Operations Analysis*, Prentice-Hall, Inc., Englewood Cliffs, N.J.

Henderson, J. M., and Quandt, R. E. (1958), *Microeconomic Theory, A Mathematical Approach*, McGraw-Hill Book Co., New York.

Chapter Exercises

Exercise 2 is based on:
Hadley, G. F. (1959), "Dynamic Programming—A new tool for maximization" *Product Engineering*, **30**, pp. 84–86.

Exercise 4 is based on:
Eilon, S. (1960), "A Note on the Optimal Range," *Management Science*, **7**, pp. 56–61.

CHAPTER EXERCISES

1. In the inventory example, Example 1 in Chapter 4, the cost function was of the form

$$c(x) = c_1(x) + c_2(x)$$

where $c_1(x)$ is a monotonically increasing function of x and $c_2(x)$ is a monotonically decreasing function of x. Let x^* denote the optimum value of x which minimizes $c(x)$. In the example it was noted that the minimum value of $c(x)$ occurs where

$$c_1(x^*) = c_2(x^*)$$

Is this result true for any functions, $c_1(x)$ and $c_2(x)$? If so, prove it. If not, give a counter example.

2. A manufacturer of consumer products is considering marketing his products in several new regions. A given level of sales support will produce different sales in the different regions because of such factors as varying consumer tastes, different competitive products, availability of different advertising media, differing rate structures. Based on previous experiences, the firm's market research department has estimated expected sales per period for different levels of sales support expenditures in each of five new regions.

Sales Support Expenditure (in units of $10,000)	Expected Sales by Region (in units of $10,000)				
	A	B	C	D	E
0	0	0	0	0	0
1	190	316	181	259	272
2	362	447	330	451	495
3	518	548	451	593	677
4	659	632	551	699	826
5	787	707	632	777	948
6	902	775	699	835	1048
7	1006	837	753	878	1130
8	1101	894	798	909	1197
9	1186	949	834	933	1252
10	1264	1000	864	950	1297

(a) Use marginal analysis to determine the optimum allocation, to the five regions, of a sales support budget of $200,000 per period.

(b) Formulate a general rule for problems of this type.

3. A company has ten machines that can be used to make three products, A, B, or C. An assignment of machines to products for the entire year must be made at the beginning of the year. The earnings that result from assigning X_A machines to product A, X_B machines to product B and X_C machines to product C are to be maximized. The annual profit, as a result of assigning X_i machines to a product, is given by:

Number of Machines Assigned to Product:	Annual Earnings (Dollars)		
	A	B	C
0	0	0	0
1	500	800	900
2	1100	1400	1600
3	1800	2300	1900
4	2500	3100	2400
5	3100	3600	2700
6	3900	4600	3100
7	4900	5400	3600
8	6000	6000	4300
9	6300	5900	5200
10	5900	5700	6200

(a) Use marginal analysis to determine the optimum allocation of machines to products.

(b) Comment on the difference, if any, between this problem and the one in Exercise 2.

4. In practical situations it is not always convenient to use exactly that value of a decision variable which optimizes the objective function. It may be easier to implement a model if a permissible range for the decision variable is given. The objective function $E(x)$ can always be written as the sum of a fixed component which is independent of the decision variable, x, and a component $f(x)$ which depends on x:

$$E(x) = c + f(x)$$

Suppose the concept of permissible range is expressed in the form of a parameter $p(p > 1)$:

$$p = \frac{\text{largest permissible value of the variable component of the objective}}{\text{optimum value of the variable component of the objective}}$$

Expanding $E(x)$ in a Taylor series about the optimum point x^* gives

$$f(x^* + h) = f(x^*) + hf'(x^*) + \frac{h^2}{2!}f''(x^*) + \frac{h^3}{3!}f'''(x^*) + \cdots$$

and by definition then

$$p = \frac{f(x^* + h)}{f(x^*)}$$

(a) Show that

$$\frac{h}{x^*} = [2(p-1)v]^{\frac{1}{2}} \qquad \text{where} \qquad v = \frac{1}{x^{*2}}\frac{f(x)^*}{f''(x^*)}$$

if all derivatives higher than the second are discarded as negligible.

(b) Show that for the case of the economic lot size, Example 1, p. 90, where

$$C(x) = + c_0 x + \frac{c_e r}{2x}$$

$$v = 1 \text{ and } \frac{x}{x^*} = 1 \pm \sqrt{2(p-1)}$$

Describe a chart that could be prepared to simplify the use of this formula.

(c) Show that if

$$E(x) = c + ax^n + \frac{b}{x^m} \qquad m, n > 0$$

$$x^* = \left(\frac{mb}{na}\right)^{\frac{1}{m+n}} \qquad \text{and} \qquad v = \frac{1}{mn}$$

Describe the chart that could be used for this case.

CHAPTER SIX

Models Involving Polynomials and Rational Functions

Once the form of the objective function and the values of the parameters are completely specified, mathematical techniques can be used to determine optimum values. However, mathematical manipulations are empty gestures unless the objective function is a realistic representation of the actual relationship between the objective and the variables. Even "rough" or "approximate" graphs of functions are frequently sufficient to detect inconsistencies between verbal assumptions and the mathematical relationships expressed in the model. A little time spent in graphing the objective function during the initial stages of a problem may reduce much wasted effort later on. It is also worthwhile to become familiar with examples of some of the functions which are most widely used in practical problems.

Figure 6.1 A piece-wise linear function.

A useful guide in selecting the form of the objective function is to use the simplest form and the smallest number of parameters which will be a reasonably close approximation to the situation being modelled. For many business problems it is sufficient to restrict considerations to the elementary functions. Examples of linear functions have already been given in Chapter 1. One simple extension of the class of linear functions is the function which is known as a "piecewise" linear function. An example of such a function is shown in Fig. 6.1. Each segment of the function is linear, but the function for the interval $0 \leq x \leq \infty$ is not linear.

An example of a business relationship which could be represented by a piecewise linear function is the total cost as a function of the quantity ordered when price discounts are given in fixed quantity increments.

Polynomials and rational functions are discussed in Section A. An example of the case of a polynomial as an objective function is given in Section B. The objective function in the model in Section C is a rational function. Additional elementary functions of one variable are discussed and illustrated in the next chapter.

A. POLYNOMIALS AND RATIONALS

Polynomials of One Variable

A function $f(x)$ of one variable x is said to be a polynomial of degree m, if $f(x) = a_0 + a_1x + a_2x^2 + \cdots + a_mx^m$ and $a_m \neq 0$, where $m = 0, 1, 2, \ldots$. If $m = 0$, the function is a constant. When $m = 1$, the function is linear. Hence, both constant and linear functions are special cases of the general class of polynomials. A polynomial to be of degree m needs only the one term a_mx^m; if all the coefficients from a_0 to a_{m-1} are zero, the polynomial is still of degree m if $a_m \neq 0$.

A polynomial of one variable of degree 2,

$$f(x) = a_0 + a_1x + a_2x^2$$

is known as a quadratic. The function is convex if $a_2 > 0$ (Fig. 6.2a), and concave if $a_2 < 0$ (Fig. 6.2b)

Since $f' = a_1 + 2a_2x, f'' = 2a_2$, and $f''' = 0$, the function is decreasing up to some value of x and then increasing after that if $a_2 > 0$, or vice versa if $a_2 < 0$. The extreme point is $x = -a_1/2a_2$.

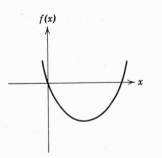

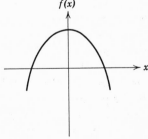

Figure 6.2a Example of quadratic function with $a_2 > 0$.

Figure 6.2b Example of quadratic function with $a_2 < 0$.

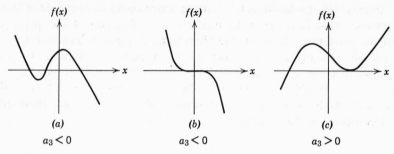

Figure 6.3 Examples of cubic functions.

A polynomial of degree 3,

$$f(x) = a_0 + a_1 x + a_2 x^2 + a_3 x^3$$

is known as a cubic. Here

$$f' = a_1 + 2a_2 x + 3a_3 x^2$$

$$f'' = 2a_2 + 6a_3 x$$

$$f''' = 6a_3$$

and the higher derivatives are all zero. The stationary points are given by the solution of $f' = 0$ and there may be two, one, or zero stationary points

$$x = \frac{-2a_2 \pm \sqrt{4a_2{}^2 - 12a_1 a_3}}{6a_3}$$

depending on whether $4a_2{}^2$ is greater than, equal to, or less than $12a_1 a_3$.

Examples of cubics with two stationary points are shown in Fig. 6.3a and c, and an example of a cubic with one stationary point is shown in Fig. 6.3b. The behavior of a cubic at $\pm\infty$ depends on the sign of a_3, because the x^3 term dominates the other terms when $|x|$ is large. If a_3 is negative, the cubic is $+\infty$ at $x = -\infty$ and $-\infty$ at $x = +\infty$.

Examples of the behavior for $a_3 < 0$ are shown in Fig. 6.3a and b, and for $a_3 > 0$ in Fig. 6.3c.

These results can be generalized to an nth degree polynomial. The behavior of the polynomial as x approaches $\pm\infty$ depends on the sign of a_n and on whether n is even or odd, since the x^n term dominates the others when $x \to \pm\infty$. As shown above, a polynomial of degree one has one real root, and a polynomial of degree two has zero, one, or two real roots. A polynomial of degree three can have one, (Fig. 6.3b), two (Fig. 6.3c), or three (Fig. 6.3a) roots. In general, if n is even, the number of (real) roots may be $0, 1, 2, \ldots$ or n; if n is odd, the number of real roots may be $1, 2, \ldots$ or n.

A polynomial of degree n with roots, $\alpha_1, \alpha_2, \ldots \alpha_m$ may be written as the product of factors

$$(x - \alpha_1)(x - \alpha_2) \cdots (x - \alpha_m)$$

The highest power of x in this product is m. If m is less than n, the additional powers may arise from factors which are raised to a power greater than one, or from factors of the form $ax^2 + bx + c$, in which $b^2 - 4ac < 0$. For example, the polynomial of degree five

$$x^5 + x^4 - 4x^3 - x^2 + 5x - 2$$

may be written as

$$(x - 1)^2(x + 2)(x^2 + x - 1)$$

The factorization of polynomials is especially useful in the integration of rational functions (Chapter 8).

Example I. The internal rate of return for a project which has net benefits of a_j at the end of the jth period has been defined, page 76, as the solution of the equation

$$P(i) = a_0 + \frac{a_1}{1 + i} + \frac{a_2}{(1 + i)^2} + \cdots + \frac{a_n}{(1 + i)^n} = 0$$

$P(i)$ is a polynomial of degree n in $1/(1 + i)$; hence, there may be up to n real roots which may be either positive or negative. Some conditions on the number of positive real roots can be obtained from Descartes' Rule of Signs: the number of positive real roots cannot exceed the number of sign changes in the sequence of coefficients and can differ from this only by an even number. A polynomial which has one change of sign in the coefficients can have at most one positive real root.

This statement guarantees a unique internal rate of return for the simplest type of investment problem: a firm buys a machine for \$3 now which results in net savings of \$1 per year for the next four years. The internal rate of return is the solution of $P(i) = 0$ where

$$P(i) = -3 + v + v^2 + v^3 + v^4 \quad \text{where} \quad v = \frac{1}{1 + i}$$

The polynomial has only one change of sign in the coefficients, and hence has either one or zero positive real roots in v. Since $P = 1$ when $i = 0$ ($v = 1$), it follows that the root must be for some $i > 0$.

For situations in which more than one sign change occurs in the sequence of cash flows, Descartes' Rule of Signs states that multiple positive roots may occur. The necessary and sufficient conditions for a sequence of cash flows to have a unique positive internal rate of return may be developed from the function $F_n(k,r)$ defined on page 81 and discussed further on page 254.

The Rational Functions

The simplest types of functions are obtained by repeated application of the elementary operations: addition, multiplication, and subtraction. Applying these operations to an independent variable x and any real numbers gives the polynomials

$$f(x) = a_0 + a_1x + \cdots + a_nx^n$$

If the operation of division is used, expressions of the form

$$f(x) = \frac{a_0 + a_1x + \cdots + a_nx^n}{b_0 + b_1x + \cdots + b_mx^m},$$

are obtained. These are called rational functions, and are defined and continuous at all points where the denominator differs from zero.

Rational functions are extremely useful in business problems because they can be used to represent relationships in cases where polynomials are not suitable. One such case occurs when $f(x)$ must remain finite as x increases to ∞. Any polynomial of degree n approaches $\pm\infty$ as $x \to \pm\infty$. A rational function on the other hand may approach a finite value as $x \to \pm\infty$ if $n < m$.

The simplest rational functions occur when $n = 0$, $m = 1$; e.g.,

$$f(x) = \frac{a_0}{b_0 + b_1x}$$

The case $a_0 = 1$, $b_0 = 0$, $b_1 = 1$ is shown in Fig. 6.4a. If $a_0 = 1$, $b_0 \neq 0$, $b_1 = 1$, the function has the form shown in Fig. 6.4b.

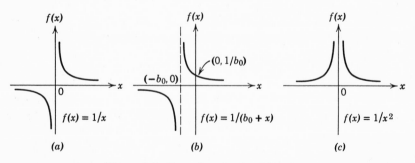

(a)   (b)   (c)

Figure 6.4 Examples of rational functions.

Another class of rational functions frequently encountered is that obtained when $n = 1$, $m = 2$, i.e.,

$$f(x) = \frac{a_0 + a_1 x}{b_0 + b_1 x + b_2 x^2}$$

The simplest example of the class is $a_0 = 1$, $a_1 = b_0 = b_1 = 0$, $b_2 = 1$ shown in Fig. 6.4c.

EXERCISES

1. The internal rate of return in a simple case of the investment problem is the solution i to the following equation

$$C = \sum_{j=1}^{n} \frac{a_j}{(1 + i)^j}$$

where C is the initial capital and a_j is the net cash flow in period j. Use differentiation to show that the appropriate polynomial is monotonic, and hence that sufficient conditions for one and only one positive solution are that all the a_j are ≥ 0 and their sum exceeds the initial capital cost, C, of the project.

2. Develop a procedure for finding roots of a general cubic.

3. In a model in Chapter 2, p. 48, the average efficiency of an organization with three administrative levels was given, as a function of the span of control, a, as

$$E(a) = \frac{(1 - ac) + a(1 - 2ac)[1 + (a - 1)s] + a^2(1 - ac)[1 + (a - 1)s]}{1 + a + a^2}$$

State the conditions for the optimum span of control for any set of values for the parameters c and s. Determine the optium for $c = 0.05$ and $s = 0.1$.

B. POLYNOMIAL OBJECTIVE FUNCTION: PRICE WARS

Retail price wars occur in a number of different types of commodities. Consider the case of a retailer who is selling, say, gasoline. Assume that there are many other retailers selling the same commodity, and that each retailer has only a small fraction of the total market. Each retailer has certain "normal" sales; there exists a "normal" price for the commodity, and the unit cost of the commodity is the same for all the retailers and is not changed when the retailers change their prices. At a certain time one of the retailers, A, lowers his price in an effort to increase his sales at the expense of the other retailers. Develop an equation for the earnings of one of the other retailers, B, under the assumption that B's sales will:

1. Be decreased by an amount proportional to the difference between B's price and A's price.

2. Be decreased by an amount proportional to the difference between the normal price and A's price.
3. Be increased by an amount proportional to the difference between the normal price and B's price.
   Also assume that these three effects are additive.

The problem will be analyzed following the procedure given in Chapter 4.

Solution. (a) *Identify the Decision Variable.* The variable that B controls is his own price:

$$x = \text{the price } B \text{ should charge}$$

(b) *Specify the Objective.* B will attempt to maximize his earnings (revenue less cost).

(c) *List the Uncontrollable Variables.* The variables not under the control of B which must be considered, the symbols assigned to them, and numerical values are:

$y = A$'s new price
$d = B$'s normal demand $\qquad = 2,000$ gallons
$p = $ normal price $\qquad = 30$ cents per gallon
$s = $ unit cost $\qquad = 20$ cents per gallon
$a = $ proportionality constant in 1. $\quad = 100$
$b = $ proportionality constant in 2. $\quad = 20$
$c = $ proportionality constant in 3. $\quad = 5$

(d) *Develop the Model.*

$$\text{Earnings} = \text{Revenue} - \text{Cost}$$

here

$$E(x) = xg(x) - sg(x) = (x - s)g(x)$$

where $g(x)$ is quantity sold.

From (1)–(3),

$$E(x) = (x - s)[d - a(x - y) - b(p - y) + c(p - x)]$$

or

$$E(x) = -x^2(a + c) + x[(a + b)y + s(a + c) + p(c - b) + d]$$

$$-s[d + ay - b(p - y) + cp]$$

(e) *Solve the Model.* For a given y, B will maximize his profit if

$$\frac{dE(x)}{dx} = -2x(a + c) + (a + b)y + s(a + c) + p(c - b) + d = 0$$

The optimum value is:

$$x = \left[\frac{a+b}{2(a+c)}\right]y + \frac{s(a+c) + p(c-d) + d}{2(a+c)}$$

For the assumed values of the parameters and uncontrollable variables,

$$E(x) = (x-20)[1{,}550 - 105x + 120y]$$
$$= -105x^2 + 3{,}650x + 120xy - 2{,}400y - 31{,}000 \tag{1}$$

$$\frac{dE(x)}{dx} = 0 \quad \text{gives } x = \frac{120}{210}y + \frac{3{,}650}{210} = 0.57y + 17.38$$

$$\frac{d^2E(x)}{dx} = -210$$

Therefore, in order to maximize his earnings B should charge a price

$$x = 0.57y + 17.38 \tag{2}$$

when A charges a price y. The negative second derivative shows that this gives the maximizing value of x or B's optimum price. A graph of the derived relation between A's price and B's optimum price is shown in Fig. 6.5.

B is also interested in knowing what his optimum earnings will be for each y in order to determine, for example, if they are sufficient to cover distribution costs. One way to ascertain his optimum earnings is to plot a set of curves $E(x)$ for different values of y, and then link by a smooth curve all the maximum values of $E(x)$ (Fig. 6.6).

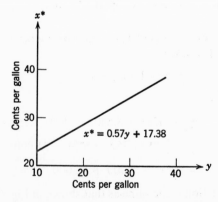

Figure 6.5 Optimum price, x^*, as a function of competitor's price, y.

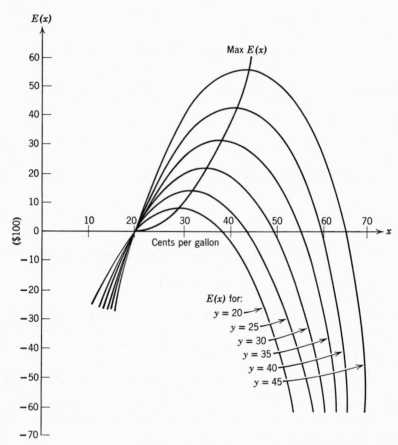

Figure 6.6   Maximum earnings, Max $E(x)$, as a function of price, x. Earnings, $E(x)$, as a function of price, x. For various competitors' prices, y.

Another way to solve the model is to eliminate y between the two equations (1) and (2). From (2)

$$y = 1.75x - \tfrac{365}{12}$$

Substituting this in (1),

$$\text{Max } E(x) = -105x^2 + 3{,}650x + 120x(1.75x - \tfrac{365}{12})$$

$$-2{,}400(1.75x - \tfrac{365}{12}) - 31{,}000$$

$$= 105x^2 - 4{,}200 + 42{,}000 \qquad (3)$$

A graph of this function is the same as that shown in Fig. 6.5 as linking the maximum values of $E(x)$.

B has reduced his price problem to a model represented by two curves Figs. 6.5 and 6.6.

If A changes his price, B can immediately read on Fig. 6.5 what optimum price he should charge, and, from this, go to Fig. 6.6, and see what his corresponding earnings will be. Or, he can solve for x from (2) and find the corresponding value for Max $E(x)$ from (3).

EXERCISES

Using the values of the parameters assumed in the example, A would charge

$$x = 0.57(30) + 17.38 = 34.48 \text{ cents per gallon}$$

when y charges the normal price of 30 cents per gallon. This contradicts the initial assumption that there is a "normal" price for the product. What changes are necessary in the model and/or the parameters to ensure that A should charge the normal price when B does?

C. AN INVESTMENT DECISION IN A LIFE INSURANCE COMPANY[1]

Statement of the Problem

Under the 1959 Life Insurance Company Tax Act, the interest earned by a company on its investments in any one year is taxed in the following manner:

(a) The difference between the total interest earned and the sum of the allowable deductions is taxed at a rate t $(0 \le t \le 1)$ if the total interest earned is greater than the sum of the allowable deductions.

(b) The first deduction is of a fixed amount, I, which does not vary with the amount of interest earned. It represents the deduction for a special reserve which is allowed life insurance companies [Sec. 809(a)].

(c) The second deduction is allowed for interest earned on tax-exempt bonds. The amount of the second deduction is obtained by multiplying the difference, between total interest earned and the fixed deduction, by the ratio of tax-exempt earnings to total earnings [Sec. 809(d)8].

[1] Adapted with permission from Robichek, A. A., and Teichroew, D. (1961), "An Investment Decision in a Life Insurance Company," *Management Technology*, **1**, pp. 24–35.

The computation of the tax is illustrated by the following example. Assume that:

(1) Fixed reserve deduction $600,000
(2) Interest from taxable bonds $600,000
(3) Interest from non-taxable bonds $400,000
(4) Total interest earned $1,000,000

The ratio of tax-exempt earnings to total earnings is

$$\frac{400,000}{1,000,000} = 40\%$$

The second deduction is

$$(\$1,000,000 - 600,000) \times 40\% = \$400,000 \times 0.4 = \$160,000$$

It is assumed in the law that the proportion of tax-exempt earnings in the fixed deduction I is the same as the ratio of tax-exempt earnings to total interest earnings of the company. Thus, out of a total $1,000,000 interest earned, of which $400,000 came from tax-exempt bonds, it is assumed that the reserve deduction I is composed of interest earned from the two sources in the same proportion; i.e., 40% from tax-exempt and 60% from taxable sources. Thus the portion of tax-exempt interest in the $600,000 is 40% or $240,000. However, $400,000 was earned from tax-exempt bonds; therefore, an additional deduction of

$$\$400,000 - \$240,000 = \$160,000$$

should be added to the initial fixed deduction.

In this example the total deduction is 600,000 + (400,000)(0.4) or $760,000. If the tax rate is 50%, the tax on the remaining interest is $120,000 and hence the amount remaining after taxes is $880,000.

Suppose a life insurance company has an amount of money, A, which it can invest either in tax-exempt bonds which yield interest at an annual rate y_1 or in taxable bonds which yield interest at the annual rate y_2. The company has the options of investing the entire amount, A, in either type, or it can invest in both types in any proportion it wishes as long as the total investment is equal to A.

The problem facing the company is to determine how much should be invested in each of the two types of securities. Let $x =$ the proportion of total funds which are to be invested in tax-exempt securities. Then Ax is the amount of money invested in tax-exempt securities and $A(1 - x)$ is the amount of money invested in taxable bonds.

Assumptions

Before a general mathematical solution to this problem can be obtained, certain additional information is necessary in order to establish the complete setting of the problem. For example, we might ask whether or not the entire investment must be made at one time; whether or not interest rates can be assumed to change in the future; whether or not tax considerations of the current period affect future operations; whether or not past conditions affect current tax considerations. Since the statement of the problem did not provide the necessary information, assumptions have to be made. Before the solution obtained under these assumptions is applied to practical problems, we must verify that the assumptions hold.

The assumptions that will be made in this illustrative case are:

1. The amount, A, is the only money available for investment during a given period.

2. The investment decision is to be made at the beginning of the period, at which time the entire amount will be invested.

3. The interest rates, y_1 and y_2, are constant and do not depend on the decision; the tax rate, t, is constant for all levels of earnings.

4. The risk of loss of investment money in both types of bonds is equal and so insignificant that risk of loss can be ignored.

5. There is no tax rebate or credit to be gained if the total interest earned is less than the allowed deductions.

6. The firm has no underwriting gains or losses or other items which affect the taxes that it must pay.

The effects of conditions 1, 2, and 3 above, together with taking the period to coincide with the tax year, are to eliminate any timing considerations in the problem. Varying interest rates, varying amounts of money to be invested, and the option of taking advantage of future changes in conditions are not considered. The problem is reduced to a static situation in which the decision with regard to the investments is evaluated independently of all other decisions in the company.

Qualitative Analysis of the Problem

The problem is now defined as being one of devising optimum rules for making the investment decision under the given assumptions. First, it is necessary to state the criteria for judging the excellence or effectiveness of the rules; i.e., the measure of effectiveness. In this problem it will be

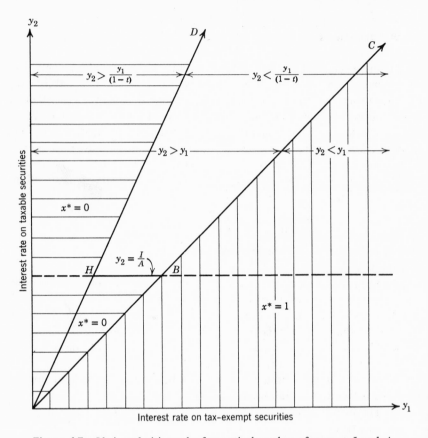

Figure 6.7   Obvious decision rules for particular values of y_1, y_2, t, I, and A.

assumed that the objective is to earn the maximum interest possible after taxes under the given conditions and, therefore, the effectiveness of the rules will be measured by the amount of the after-tax earnings resulting from using the decision rule.   The value of x which maximizes the after-tax earnings will be denoted by an asterisk, e.g., x^*.

Before attempting to solve the problem mathematically, it is desirable to examine it qualitatively to see if there really is a problem.   The answer to the problem in certain situations is obvious:

(*a*) If the interest obtainable from tax-exempt securities is greater than that obtainable from taxable securities, then all funds should be invested in tax-exempt securities regardless of the values of I; i.e., if $y_1 > y_2$, then the optimum solution is $x^* = 1$.

(*b*) If (*a*) does not apply, i.e., if $y_2 > y_1$, and the maximum interest obtainable from taxable securities is less than the fixed deduction, then no tax-exempt securities should be purchased; i.e., $y_1 < y_2$ and $Ay_2 < I$, then the optimum solution is $x^* = 0$.

(c) If the interest obtainable from taxable securities, less the tax that has to be paid, is greater than the interest obtainable from tax-exempt securities, then no exempt securities should be purchased; i.e., if $Ay_2(1 - t) > Ay_1$, then the optimum solution is $x^* = 0$.

These obvious rules are illustrated in Fig. 6.7; for combinations of values of y_1 and y_2 lying in the area $HBCD$, it is reasonable to suppose that it may be possible to maximize after-tax earnings by choosing an x greater than zero and less than one.

Development of the Model

The first step in solving this problem in general is to identify and assign symbols to the variables in the problem; some have already been assigned and are summarized here. The uncontrollable variables are:

A = the total amount of money to be invested
I = the first deduction
y_1 = interest rate on tax-exempt bonds
y_2 = interest rate on taxable bonds
t = tax rate

and the decision variable is:

x = proportion of A invested in tax-exempt bonds

The analysis will be simplified if certain additional variables are defined as follows:

$y_3 = y_2 - y_1$ — i.e., y_3 is the excess interest rate earned by investing in taxable bonds

$y_4 = y_1 - y_2(1 - t)$ — i.e., $-y_4$ is the after-tax excess interest earned by investing in taxable bonds, assuming all of it is taxed at the rate, t.

The next step is to determine how interest earnings after taxes are related to the decision variable. From the statement of the problem and the assumption made, the total pre-tax earnings, $E(x)$, are:

$$E(x) = Axy_1 + A(1 - x)y_2 \qquad (1)$$

The interest earnings after taxes will be equal to the before-tax earnings minus the tax. The tax is equal to the total earnings less allowable deductions, multipled by the tax rate t, i.e.,

Interest earnings after taxes = total earnings − taxes

Interest earnings after taxes = total earnings − (total earnings − allowable deductions)(tax rate)

Interest earnings after taxes = total earnings − tax rate [total earnings − (fixed deduction + deduction for tax-exempts)]

Let $P(x)$ denote the interest earnings after taxes if a proportion x, is invested in tax-exempt bonds; then

$$P(x) = E - t\left\{E - \left[I + \frac{Axy_1}{E}(E - I)\right]\right\} \tag{2}$$

The next step is to simplify this objective function as much as possible. In (2), $P(x)$ is a function of x, $E(x)$, and the uncontrollable variables. However, $E(x)$ is itself a function of x and the uncontrollable variables and hence can be eliminated by substituting (1) into (2). The "interest earnings after taxes" function then becomes

$$P(x) = Axy_1 + A(1 - x)y_2 - t\left(Axy_1 + A(1 - x)y_2\right.$$

$$\left. - \left\{I + \frac{Axy_1}{Axy_1 + A(1 - x)y_2}[Axy_1 + A(1 - x)y_2 - I]\right\}\right)$$

$$P(x) = [Ay_2(1 - t) + It] + Ax[y_1 - y_2(1 - t)] + \frac{Iy_1t}{y_2 - y_1 - y_2/x} \tag{3}$$

$$= [Ay_2(1 - t) + It] + Axy_4 + \frac{Iy_1t}{y_3 - y_2/x} \tag{4}$$

This formula gives the objective function $P(x)$ as a function of the decision variable x and the uncontrollable variables y_1, y_2, t, A, and I. The range of x for which this function is of interest is by definition

$$0 \leq x \leq 1$$

The range of the uncontrollable variables is the region $HBCD$ in Fig. 6.7 which is

$$\frac{y_1}{1 - t} > y_2 > y_1 \quad \text{and} \quad y_2 > \frac{I}{A} \quad \text{or} \quad y_3 > 0; \quad y_4 > 0 \quad \text{and} \quad y_2 > \frac{I}{A}$$

The term

$$[Ay_2(1 - t) + It] + Axy_4$$

is a linear function of x. The last term of equation (4) is a rational function of x. Let the denominator of the term be $g(x) = y_2(1 - 1/x) - y_1$. As $x \to 0$, $g(x) \to -\infty$ and at $x = 1$, $g(x) = -y_1$. Furthermore, as x increases from 0 to 1, $g(x)$ is an increasing function, reaching its maximum in the interval $0 \leq x \leq 1$ at $x = 1$. Before determining the optimum by the use of calculus, it is desirable to verify the correctness of the objective function, (4).

Verifying the Model

(a) Dimensional analysis. $P(x)$ is the after-tax earnings expressed in dollars. The variables y_1, y_2, t, and x are pure numbers, and I and A are expressed in dollars. Each term in $P(x)$ is therefore expressed in dollars.

(b) $P(x)$ for particular values of x

(1) When $x = 0$, $P(x)$ reduces to

$$P(x) = Ay_2(1 - t) + It$$
$$= Ay_2 - t(Ay_2 - I)$$

This states that when all investments are in taxable bonds the profit is equal to earnings before taxes (Ay_2), less the tax which is computed on all earnings in excess of the fixed deduction I. This conclusion agrees with what is intuitively obvious from the information in the case.

(2) When $x = 1$

$$P(1) = Ay_2(1 - t) + It + Ay_1 - Ay_2(1 - t) - It$$
$$= Ay_1$$

This states that when all the money is invested in tax-exempt bonds, the after-tax earnings are equal to the total interest earned.

(3) Numerical example. In the example given in the first section

$$y_1 = 4\%, \quad y_2 = 5\%, \quad t = 50\%,$$
$$y_4 = 0.04 - 0.05(0.5) = 0.015, \quad y_3 = 0.01,$$
$$I = 600,000, \quad A = 22,000,000, \quad x = \tfrac{10}{22}$$

then

$$P(\tfrac{10}{22}) = (22,000,000)(0.05)(0.5) + 600,000(0.5)$$

$$+ \ 22,000,000(\tfrac{10}{22})(0.015) + \frac{600,000(0.04)(0.5)}{0.01 - 0.05(22)/10}$$

$$= 550,000 + 300,000 + 150,000 - 120,000$$

$$= \$880,000$$

(c) Verification of conclusion that $x^* = 1$, if $y_1 > y_2$. When $y_1 > y_2$, the tax-exempt bonds earn at a higher interest rate than the taxable bonds. This is the case where it is obvious that all the money should be invested in tax-exempt bonds, i.e., $x^* = 1$. To show that $x = 1$ does produce the maximum interest after taxes, if $y_1 > y_2$, write the profit function from (2) in the form

$$P(x) = E(1 - t) + tI + tAxy_1\left(1 - \frac{I}{E}\right)$$

When $y_1 > y_2$, $E(x) = Axy_1 + A(1 - x)y_2$ increases as x increases since x and $1 - x$ vary linearly in opposite directions and y_1 is a larger multiplier than y_2. It is obvious, therefore, that to increase $E(x)(1 - t)$ as much as possible, x should be as large as possible. The next term tI is constant relative to x and, therefore, does not enter into consideration. The last term

$$tAxy_1\left[1 - \frac{I}{E}\right]$$

has its maximum value if $E(x)$ is as large as possible, since $E(x) \geq I$, and if the multiplier, $tAxy_1$, is as large as possible. For both cases, the optimum value is $x = 1$. The result of this analysis shows that if $y_1 > y_2$, $P(1) > P(x)$ for $0 \leq x < 1$, $x^* = 1$.

(d) Verification that $x^* = 0$ when $y_1 < y_2(1 - t)$. If the interest rate of the taxable securities is greater than the interest rate of the tax-exempt securities by an amount which more than compensates for the taxes which have to be paid, then all the money, A, should be invested in taxable securities. Algebraically this means, if

$$Ay_2(1 - t) > Ay_1,$$

that is, $y_4 < 0$, then x^* should be 0.

To show that this result holds for $P(x)$ given by (4) it is merely necessary, since the first term is independent of x and is positive by definition, to show that the last two terms have their maximum value at $x = 0$.

The term, Axy_4, is negative if y_4 is negative and, therefore, the maximum value is $x = 0$. The last term was shown above to be negative for all $0 < x < 1$.

This shows that if $y_4 < 0$, $P(x)$ decreases as x increases, and therefore the maximum value occurs at $x = 0$, i.e., $x^* = 0$.

Optimization

The optimum value of x, given $y_3 > 0$, $y_4 > 0$, and $y_2 > I/A$, is obtained by setting the derivative of $P(x)$ with respect to x equal to zero and solving the resulting equation, i.e.,

$$P'(x) = \frac{dP(x)}{dx} = Ay_4 + (Ity_1)(-1)\left(y_3 - \frac{y_2}{x}\right)^{-2}(-y_2)(-1)x^{-2}$$

$$= Ay_4 - \frac{Ity_1y_2}{x^2(y_3 - y_2/x)^2} \tag{5}$$

The second derivative must be examined to determine whether some value of x yields an optimum P.

Differentiating a second time yields:

$$\frac{d^2P(x)}{dx^2} = (-Ity_1y_2)(-2)(xy_2 - xy_1 - y_2)^{-3}y_3 = \frac{2Iy_1y_2y_3}{(xy_2 - xy_1 - y_2)^3} \tag{6}$$

The numerator of equation (6) is always > 0, if $y_3 = y_2 - y_1$. The denominator is always < 0 as long as $y_2 > y_1$ and $0 \leq x \leq 1$. Consequently,

$$\frac{d^2P(x)}{dx^2} < 0 \qquad \text{for all } 0 \leq x \leq 1$$

and hence $P(x)$ is concave over its entire range and the solution of (5) in the interval $0 \leq x \leq 1$ gives a value of x for which $P(x)$ is a maximum. At $x = 0$, the slope of $P(x)$, from (5), is

$$P'(0) = Ay_4 - \frac{Ity_1}{y_2} \tag{7}$$

The slope at $x = 0$ is positive if $Ay_4 > Ity_1/y_2$, and negative if $Ay_4 < Ity_1/y_2$.

The constraints $y_4 > 0$, $y_3 > 0$, and $y_2 > I/A$ permit $P'(0)$ to assume either positive or negative values. Since $P''(x) < 0$ for all $0 \le x \le 1$, the fact that $P'(0)$ can be negative implies that within the region $HBCD$ there is a sub-region where $P(x)$ reaches a maximum at $x = 0$. If $P'(0) > 0$, the maximum of $P(x)$ must exist for some x greater than zero.

To determine the dividing line for the sub-region within $HBCD$ where $x^* = 0$, let

$$y_2 = \frac{y_1}{b} \qquad \text{where } (1 - t) < b < 1$$

This is equivalent to considering a line passing through the origin which intersects the line $y_2 = I/A$ somewhere between H and B.

Substituting for y_4 and y_1 in (7) and setting $P'(0) = 0$ gives

$$A[by_2 - y_2(1 - t)] = \frac{Itby_2}{y_2}$$

Regrouping and solving for b

$$b = \frac{Ay_2(1 - t)}{Ay_2 - It} \tag{8}$$

b is a function of I, A, t, and y_2. As $y_2 \to I/A$, $b \to 1$, i.e., as the rate on taxable investments approaches the rate of allowed deduction, the rate on tax-exempt investment will have to approach the rate on taxable investments to keep the entire amount, A, invested in taxable securities. On the other hand, as $y_2 \to \infty$, $b \to (1 - t)$, i.e., as $(y_2 - I/A)$ increases, the ratio between the tax-exempt and taxable rates can decrease up to the point where b approaches $(1 - t)$ and still maintain the entire investment in taxable securities.

The slope at $x = 1$ is

$$P'(1) = Ay_4 - \frac{Ity_2}{y_1} \tag{9}$$

which is negative if $Ity_2/y_1 > Ay_4$, and positive if $Ity_2/y_1 < Ay_4$.

The restrictions $y_4 > 0$, $y_3 > 0$, and $y_2 > I/A$ permit $P'(1)$ to assume either positive or negative values. Since $P''(x) < 0$ for all $0 \le x \le 1$, the fact that $P'(1) > 0$ implies that within the region $HBCD$ there is a sub-region where $P(x)$ reaches a maximum at $x = 1$. If, on the other hand, $P'(1) < 0$, $P(x)$ must have a maximum for some x less than one.

To determine the dividing line for the sub-region within $HBCD$ where $x^* = 1$, let

$$y_2 = \frac{y_1}{a} \qquad \text{where } (1 - t) < a < 1$$

Substituting for y_4 and y_1 in (9), setting $P'(1) = 0$, and solving for a gives:

$$a = \frac{(1 - t) \pm \sqrt{(1 - t)^2 + 4It/Ay_2}}{2} \tag{10}$$

a is a function of I, A, t, and y_2. As $y_2 \to I/A$, $a \to 1$, i.e., as the rate on taxable investments approaches the fraction I/A the rate on tax-exempt investments will have to approach the rate on taxable investments to keep the entire amount, A, invested in tax exempts. On the other hand, as $y_2 \to \infty$, $a \to (1 - t)$, i.e., as $(y_2 - I/A)$ increases, the spread between the taxable and tax-exempt rates can increase up to the point where a approaches $(1 - t)$ and still maintain the entire investment in tax-exempt securities. Graphs of a and b as functions of y_2, holding I, A, and t constant, are shown in Fig. 6.8.

The optimum value of x, i.e., x^*, must satisfy the equation

$$Ay_4 - \frac{Ity_1y_2}{(xy_2 - xy_1 - y_2)^2} = 0 \qquad \text{or} \qquad (xy_2 - xy_1 - y_2)^2 = k \tag{11}$$

which is obtained by setting $P'(x) = 0$ and setting $Ity_1y_2 = kAy_4$. Multiplying and collecting like terms of x give the equation which may be written as

$$x^2y_3^2 - 2xy_2y_3 + [y_2^2 - k] = 0$$

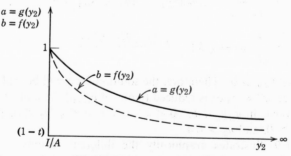

Figure 6.8 Graph of a and b.

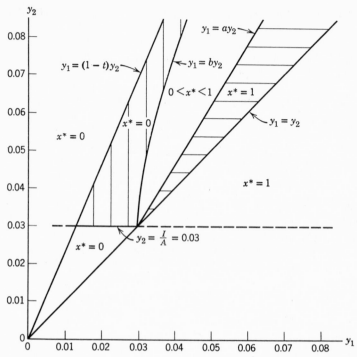

Figure 6.9   Decision rules for various values of y_1 and y_2 for $t = 0.5$, $A = \$100,000,000, I = \$3,000,000$.

This quadratic equation in x has the solution

$$x^* = \frac{2y_2y_3 \pm \sqrt{4y_2^2y_3^2 - 4y_3^2(y_2^2 - k)}}{2y_3^2}$$

This equation can be simplified to

$$x^* = \frac{y_2}{y_3} \pm \frac{1}{2y_3^2} \sqrt{y_3^2[4y_2^2 - 4y_2^2 + 4k]} = \frac{y_2}{y_3} \pm \frac{1}{y_3} \sqrt{k}$$

$$= \frac{1}{y_3} [y_2 \pm \sqrt{k}] = \frac{y_2 \pm \sqrt{Ity_1y_2/Ay_4}}{y_3} \tag{12}$$

k is positive if $y_4 > 0$. Therefore, the solution for x will be real if $y_4 > 0$. Furthermore, $x^* = 1$, or is reduced to one, if $y_1/y_2 > a$, and $x^* = 0$, or is raised to zero, if $y_1/y_2 < b$. $0 < x^* < 1$ if $b < y_1/y_2 < a$, given that $y_3 > 0$, $y_4 > 0$, and $y_2 > I/A$.

Figure 6.9 illustrates graphically the different regions of optimum solutions, given $I = \$3,000,000$, $A = \$100,000,000$, and $t = 0.5$.

Numerical Example. Let

$$A = \$100,000,000$$
$$I = \$3,000,000$$
$$t = 0.5$$
$$y_2 = 0.05$$

Then, from equations (8) and (10) we obtain

$$a = 0.852 \qquad ay_2 = 0.0426$$
$$b = 0.7143 \qquad by_2 = 0.0357$$

In each case, x^* is obtained from equation (12).

CASE I
$$y_1 = 0.044; \text{ i.e., } y_1 > ay_2 = 0.0426$$
$$x^* = 1.38 \qquad \text{or} \qquad \text{since } 0 \leq x^* \leq 1, x^* = 1$$

CASE II
$$y_1 = 0.04; \text{ i.e., } 0.0357 = by_2 < y_1 < ay_2 = 0.0426$$
$$x^* = 0.53$$

CASE III
$$y_1 = 0.037; \text{ i.e., } 0.0357 = by_2 < y_1 < ay_2 = 0.0426$$
$$x^* = 0.146$$

CASE IV
$$y_1 = 0.035; \text{ i.e., } 0.0357 = by_2 > y_1$$
$$x^* = -0.08 \qquad \text{or} \qquad \text{since } 0 \leq x^* \leq 1, x^* = 0$$

The difference in $P(x)$ for Cases II and III above, under the conditions $P(0)$, $P(x^*)$, and $P(1)$, are tabulated below:

CASE II ($y_1 = 0.04$):

$P(x)$	$x = 0$	$x = x^* = 0.53$	$x = 1$
	\$4,000,000	\$4,083,591	\$4,000,000

CASE III ($y_1 = 0.037$):

$P(x)$	$x = 0$	$x = x^* = 0.146$	$x = 1$
	\$4,000,000	\$4,006,708	\$3,700,000

Summary

The optimum procedure to be followed is given in Fig. 6.10.

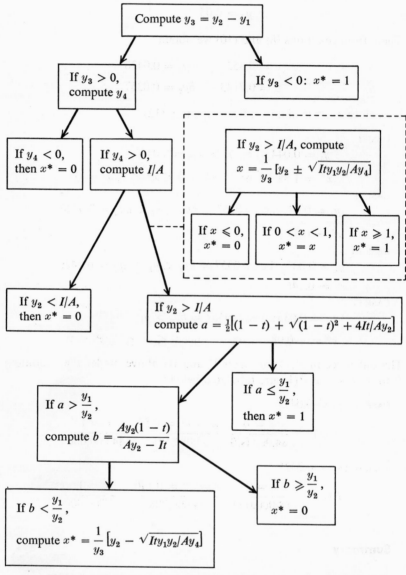

Figure 6.10 Flow chart for the computation of the optimum solution.

EXERCISES

1. Assume that $(1 - t)y_2 \leq y_1 \leq y_2$ and let

$$a_1 = \frac{I}{y_2}, \qquad a_2 = \frac{Ity_1}{y_2y_4} \qquad \text{and} \qquad a_3 = \frac{Ity_2}{y_1y_4}$$

Show that

(a) $a_1 = a_2 = a_3$ if $y_1 = y_2$

(b) $a_1 < a_2 < a_3$ if $y_1 < y_2$

2. Show that if an amount A has been invested in taxable securities, a small increase in investment will earn more, after taxes, if invested in taxable than in tax-exempt securities if $A < a_2$, and that it will earn more, after taxes, if invested in tax-exempt if $A > a_2$.

(*Hint:* At $A = a_2$ the marginal interest earned after taxes is $\left[y_1 - \dfrac{tIy_1}{Ay_2} \right]$ for tax-exempt securities and $[(1 - t)y_2]$ for taxable securities. Hence, the marginal returns for a small increase in investment are equal at $A = a_2$.

3. Show that the optimum decision, for the case specified in Exercise 2, may be stated as:

(*i*) If $A \leq a_1$, invest A in tax-exempt securities.

(*ii*) If $a_1 < A \leq a_2$, invest A in taxable securities.

(*iii*) If $a_2 < A < a_3$, invest a_2 in taxable securities and $A - a_2$ in tax-exempt securities.

(*iv*) If $a_3 < A$, invest A in tax-exempt securities.

(*v*) Explain fully why the equating of marginal returns does not give the correct solution for (*iv*).

4. Show that the rule in Exercise 2 is identical to the one given in Figure 6.10.

5. Comment on the implications of the decision rule, as stated in Exercise 3, for investment decisions as A increases.

CHAPTER SEVEN

Models Involving Algebraic and Transcendental Functions

A brief review of algebraic, logarithmic, and exponential functions is given in Section A. Examples of the application of these types of function are given in Sections B, C, D, and E.

A. ALGEBRAIC AND TRANSCENDENTAL FUNCTIONS

Algebraic Functions

The variable y is said to be an algebraic function of another variable x, if it can be defined implicitly by $P(x, y) = 0$ where P is a polynomial in x and y. The simplest is the function defined by $y - x^n = 0$. The solution of this equation for x as the dependent and y as the independent variable is given by

$$x = \sqrt[n]{y} = y^{1/n}$$

which is the inverse of the function $y = x^n$

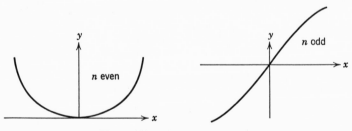

Figure 7.1   The function $y = x^n$.

For $x > 0$, $x = \sqrt[n]{y}$ exists and is unique. The derivative may be obtained directly:

$$\frac{dx}{dy} = \frac{1}{n} y^{\frac{1}{n} - 1}.$$

or by using the rule for the derivative of an inverse:

$$\frac{dy}{dx} = n x^{n-1} \quad \text{and} \quad \frac{dx}{dy} = \frac{1}{dy/dx} = \frac{1}{n} x^{-n+1}$$

$$= \frac{1}{n} (y^{1/n})^{-n+1} = \frac{1}{n} y^{\frac{1}{n} - 1}$$

Exponential and Logarithmic Functions

Two functions which play a fundamental role in the theory and application of mathematics are the exponential and logarithmic functions. They are the most widely used of the transcendental functions [those which cannot be obtained as a solution to $P(x, y) = 0$ where P is a polynomial].

The exponential function is given by

$$y = e^x \qquad -\infty < x < \infty \tag{1}$$

The function (Fig. 7.2a) is strictly monotonically increasing from close to zero when x approaches $-\infty$, to $+\infty$ when x approaches $+\infty$. The parameter e is the number defined as $e = \lim_{t \to \infty} (1 + 1/t)^t$, and has the value of approximately 2.7178. The function

$$y = a^x \qquad -\infty < x < \infty \tag{2}$$

defined for any positive base, a, different from one, is sometimes also called the exponential function. The function has the same form as (1) if $a > 1$, and the form shown in Fig. 7.2b if $a < 1$.

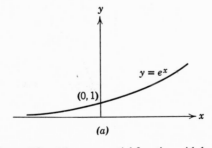

(a)

Figure 7.2a   The exponential function with base e.

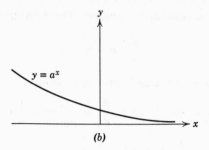

Figure 7.2*b*   The exponential function with base a, $0 < a < 1$.

One of the reasons for the importance of the exponential function (1) in theoretical work is that

$$\frac{dy}{dx} = e^x \tag{3}$$

It is the one function whose derivative at any point is equal to the value of the function at that point.

The logarithmic function

$$y = \log_a x \qquad 0 < x < \infty;\ a > 0;\ a \neq 1 \tag{4}$$

is a monotonically increasing function (Fig. 7.3). It is the inverse function of (2). If

$$z = a^x \qquad \text{then} \qquad x = \log_a z. \tag{5}$$

Since $de^x/dx = e^x$, it follows from (4) that the inverse function

$$x = \log_e y = \ln x$$

has the derivative

$$\frac{dx}{dy} = \frac{1}{dy/dx} = \frac{1}{e^x} = \frac{1}{y}$$

or, interchanging variables, if $y = \ln x$, then

$$\frac{dy}{dx} = \frac{1}{x} \tag{6}$$

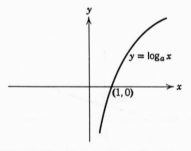

Figure 7.3   The logarithmic function.

The general exponential function (2) has the derivative

$$\frac{dy}{dx} = a^x \ln a \qquad (7)$$

The properties of exponential and logarithmic functions are derived from the properties of exponents. If a and b are any positive numbers different from one, x and y are any positive numbers; and $a^x = u$, $a^y = v$, then $x = \log_a u$ and $y = \log_a v$.

EXPONENTIAL	LOGARITHMIC
$a^1 = a$	$\log_a a = 1$
$a^0 = 1$	$\log_a 1 = 0$
$1^x = 1$	
$a^x \cdot a^y = a^{x+y}$	$\log_a uv = \log_a u + \log_a v$
$(a^x)^y = a^{xy}$	$\log_a u^{\,y} = y \log_a u$
$\dfrac{a^x}{a^y} = a^{x-y} = \dfrac{1}{a^{y-x}}$	$\log_a \dfrac{u}{v} = \log_a u - \log_a v = -\log_a \dfrac{v}{u}$
$(ab)^x = a^x b^x$	
$\left(\dfrac{a}{b}\right)^x = \dfrac{a^x}{b^x}$	

The logarithms of a number y to two different bases, a and b, are related by the formula

$$\log_a y = \frac{\log_b y}{\log_b a}$$

From $x = \log_a y$ we have $y = a^x$. Taking logarithms of both sides to the base b gives

$$\log_b y = \log_b a^x = x \log_b a = (\log_a y) \log_b a$$

or

$$\log_a y = \frac{\log_b y}{\log_b a}$$

EXERCISES

1. Show that if $y = a^{2 \log_a x}$, then $y = x^2$.

2. Show that if $\log_{10} \dfrac{x}{y} = y - 3$, then $1{,}000x = y10^y$.

3. Solve each of the following equations for the variable indicated.

(a) $e^{x/2} = M$ for x

(b) $at^{x+3} = b$ for x

(c) $x = [\tfrac{1}{4}] \ln \left(\dfrac{y}{a}\right)$ for y

4. Learning curves, described in Chapter 2, p. 29, give a formula for the manufacturing cost of the ith unit of a product. In particular, one form was

$$U(i) = U(1)i^b$$

where $U(i)$ = manufacturing cost of the ith unit.

(a) Show that $U(i)$ is a straight line when plotted as a function of i on logarithmic paper.

(b) The Leisure Manufacturing Co. markets a skin diver kit consisting of goggles, swim fins, etc. Suppose the manufacturing cost of each of the components (goggles, fins, etc.) is given by

$$U_j(i) = U_j(1)i^{b_j}$$

where b_j is the learning parameter for the jth component. Under what conditions will the formula also give the total manufacturing cost of the complete kit?

(c) The average manufacturing costs for i units is given by

$$\frac{1}{i} T(i) = \frac{1}{i} \sum_{k=1}^{i} U(k)$$

In some cases it has been found that

$$\frac{T(i)}{i} = U(1)i^{-b}$$

gives a better approximation to manufacturing costs than the formula given above. Develop the formula for $U(i)$ and show that it is asymptotic to a straight line on logarithmic paper.

5. An investment advisory service has developed a formula for the "payout" of a growth stock because it believes that the corporate manager's concept of "payout" applied to capital investment in plant and equipment can also be used by the growth stock investor. The term "payout" is the time required for per share earnings, compounding at a given growth rate, to accumulate to current market price, and is equal to its price divided by the first year's earnings, plus the second year's earnings, plus the third, plus ... n year's earnings:

$$n = \frac{\ln\,[1 + r(P/E + 1)]}{\ln\,(1 + r)} - 1$$

where n = payout, in years
   r = compound growth rate
   P/E = ratio of current price to current annual earnings.
Develop the formula from the definitions.

6. Show that elasticity of a function $f(x)$ defined on p. 151 may be written as

$$-\frac{d \ln f(x)}{d \ln x} .$$

B. CONTINUOUS INTEREST

The effect of compounding interest more frequently than once a year was briefly mentioned in Chapter 3. For many investment decisions, the choice of the compounding period is somewhat arbitrary, because benefits and costs occur continuously over time. It is, therefore, more natural to assume that interest is compounded continuously. The effective rate i when a nominal annual rate j is compounded m times per year is given by (6), page 58.

$$1 + i = \left(1 + \frac{j}{m}\right)^{j}$$

$$1 + i = 1 + m\frac{j}{m} + \frac{m(m-1)}{2!}\left(\frac{j}{m}\right)^{2} + \cdots + \left(\frac{j}{m}\right)^{m}$$

$$= 1 + j + \frac{1}{2!}\left(\frac{m-1}{m}\right)j^{2} + \cdots + \left(\frac{j}{m}\right)^{m}$$

For large m, the series on the right approaches the expansion of the exponential function and

$$1 + i = \lim_{m \to \infty} \left(1 + \frac{j}{m}\right)^{m} = e^{j}$$

The symbol, δ, will be used to denote the effective instantaneous rate of interest:

$$1 + i = e^{\delta} \quad \text{or} \quad \delta = \ln(1 + i)$$

Similarly, discounting m times per year at a nominal annual rate i will produce an effective rate δ; as m becomes infinite,

$$\frac{1}{1+i} = \lim_{m \to \infty} \left(1 - \frac{j}{m}\right)^{m} = e^{-j} \quad \text{or} \quad e^{-\delta}$$

$$\frac{1}{1+i} = e^{-\delta} \quad \text{and} \quad (1+i)^{-1} = e^{-\delta} \quad \text{or} \quad \delta = \ln(1 + i)$$

The instantaneous rates of interest and discount for the same nominal rate of interest are both equal to $\ln(1 + i)$.

An amount b invested now will grow to be $be^{\delta t}$ at time t if interest is compounded continuously at rate δ. The relation between nominal and effective interest rates is illustrated in Fig. 7.4. If interest were compounded once a year at the rate of 20% a year, the amount would be as shown by the staircase function. If interest were compounded continuously at the rate

$$\ln(1 + i) = \ln(1.2) = 0.1823$$

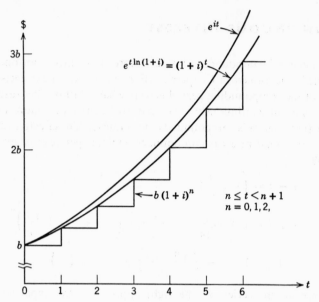

Figure 7.4 Value of an amount b compounded at discrete interest i per period or continuous interest at $\ln(1+i)$ and i per period ($i = 0.20$).

the amount would be given for any value of t by

$$e^{t\ln(1+i)} \qquad \text{or} \qquad (1+i)^t \tag{1}$$

This function has the same values at the end of each year as the function obtained by compounding once a year. Hence numerically or mathematically there is no difference between the continuous or discrete compounding methods as long as only the amount at the end of a year is desired.

There is, however, a difference if the *interest rate $i = 0.20$ is used as the continuous rate $\delta = 0.20$*; as shown by the function e^{it} in Fig. 7.4. Even then, when the period of time under consideration is fairly short and the rate fairly small, the difference between an amount developed by continuous compounding and that developed by annual compounding is small. When large rates or extended periods are involved, the difference becomes significant.

As in the case of compounding at discrete intervals, continuous compounding is facilitated through the use of tables. A set analogous to Appendix Tables 1 through 4 are given as Tables 5 through 8. Their derivation and their relationships to the formulas in Table 3-2 are presented here and summarized in Table 7-1. The value, F, of an amount,

1, n periods hence with continuous compounding at rate δ is

$$F(\delta, n) = e^{\delta n}$$

Appendix Table 5 gives $F(\delta, n)$ for various values of δ and n; this is a table of the exponential function e^x in which $x = \delta n$.

The present value, P, of an amount of 1 to be received at some point in time, with continuous compounding at the rate δ is

$$P(\delta, n) = e^{-\delta n} \tag{2}$$

Appendix Table 6 gives values of $P(\delta, n)$ for various values of δ and n. Again this is a table of the exponential function e^x with $x = -\delta n$.

The value at the end of n periods of a benefit b at the end of each period with continuous compounding at rate δ per period is, by analogy with (3), p. 56,

$$F = be^{\delta(n-1)} + be^{\delta(n-2)} + \cdots + be^{\delta} + b$$

or

$$F = \frac{b(e^{\delta n} - 1)}{e^{\delta} - 1}$$

Similarly, the present value P of a benefit b received at the end of each of n periods is by analogy with (4), p. 56,

$$P = be^{-\delta} + be^{-2\delta} + \cdots + e^{-n\delta}$$

$$= be^{-\delta}\left[\frac{1 - e^{-\delta n}}{1 - e^{-\delta}}\right] \tag{3}$$

The value at the end of n periods of an amount bn received uniformly over the n periods and compounded continuously at an interest rate i per period may be obtained from the formula for benefits received at the end of the period. (3), p. 56.

$$F = b\left[\frac{(1 + i)^n}{i} - 1\right]$$

If each period is divided into m very short intervals, the amount received at the end of each short interval is b/m and the interest rate is i/m for the short interval, or

$$F = \frac{b}{m}\left\{\frac{[1 + (i/m)]^n - 1}{i/m}\right\}$$

$$\lim_{m \to \infty} F = b\left(\lim \frac{1}{i}\right) \lim\left[\left(1 + \frac{i}{m}\right)^n - 1\right]$$

$$F(\delta, n) = \frac{b}{\delta}[e^{\delta n} - 1] \tag{4}$$

Table 7-1 Summary of Interest Formulas

Payment		Value	Compounding Each Period		Compounding Continuously	
When	Amount	When	Formula	Appendix Table	Formula	Appendix Table
Now	b	n periods hence	$F = b_0(1+i)^n$	1	$F = b_0 e^{\delta n}$	5
n periods hence	b	now	$P = b_n(1+i)^{-n} = b_n v^n$	2	$P = b_n e^{-\delta n}$	6
At the end of each period	b	n periods hence	$F = b[(1+i)^{n-1} + \cdots + (1+i) + 1]$ $= b\left[\dfrac{(1+i)^n - 1}{i}\right]$	3	$F = \dfrac{b(e^{\delta n} - 1)}{(e^\delta - 1)}$	
At the end of each period	b	now	$P = b[v + v^2 + \cdots + v^n]$ $= \dfrac{bv(1 - v^n)}{1 - v}$	4	$P = \dfrac{be^{-\delta}(1 - e^{-\delta n})}{1 - e^{-\delta}}$	
Uniformly over n periods	bn	n periods hence			$F = b\left[\dfrac{e^{\delta n} - 1}{\delta}\right]$	7
Uniformly over n periods	bn	now			$P = b\left[\dfrac{1 - e^{-\delta n}}{\delta}\right]$	8
At the end of each period $i = 0$ n	$b_j - c_j$	now	$P = \sum_{i=0}^{n}(b_j - c_j)v^j$		$P = \sum_{i=0}^{n}(b_j - c_j)e^{-\delta j}$	

since the instantaneous rate is denoted by δ. Appendix Table 7 gives values of $F(\delta, n)$ for $b = 1$ and various values of δ and n.

Similarly, the present value of an amount, bn, received uniformly over the next n periods and discounted continuously, when i is the interest per period, may be obtained by using the result for the case where b is received at the end of each of n periods, and discounted discretely. From (4), page 56,

$$P = \frac{b[1 - (1 + i)^{-n}]}{i}$$

Substituting b/m for b and i/m for i gives

$$P = \frac{b}{m}\left\{\frac{1 - [1 + (i/m)]^{-nm}}{i/m}\right\} = b\left\{\frac{1 - [1 + (i/m)]^{-nm}}{i}\right\}$$

The limit, as m goes to infinity, is

$$P(n, \delta) = b\left(\frac{1 - e^{-\delta n}}{\delta}\right) \tag{5}$$

Appendix Table 8 gives values of $P(\delta, n)$ for $b = 1$ and various values of δ and n.

Example 1. What is the value of $10 after one year compounded continuously with $\delta = 0.2$? From Appendix Table 5: $F(0.2, 1) = 1.2214$. Therefore, the value is $10(1.2214) = 12.21$. If $i = 0.2$ then

$$\delta = \ln(1 + 0.2) = 0.18232$$

and the value is $10(1.2000) = 12.00$.

Example 2. Find the value at the end of the period of $100 flowing uniformly during a two-year period if $i = 0.20$. From Appendix Table 7: $F(0.20, 2) = 2.4133$. The value is $(2.4133)(50) = \$120.67$. The solution, using formula (4), if $\delta = 0.2$, is:

$$\frac{50(e^{0.4} - 1)}{0.20} = \frac{(50)(0.4918)}{0.20} = \$122.95$$

Example 3. Find the present value of $150 to be received in ten years if $\delta = 0.10$. From Appendix Table 6: $P(0.10, 10) = 0.3679$. Therefore, the present value is $(150)(0.3679) = \$55.19$.

Example 4. Find the present value of $1,000 flowing uniformly over a five-year period, starting now, if i is 0.05 compounded continuously. If $1,000 is flowing in uniformly over a five-year period, then $200 is flowing in each year. From Appendix Table 8, $P(0.05, 5) = 4.4368$. Hence, the present value 200(4.4368) = \$887.37. The solution, using formula (5), if $\delta = 0.05$, is:

$$P = \frac{200(1 - e^{-0.25})}{0.05} = \frac{200(1 - 0.7788)}{0.05} = \frac{200(0.2212)}{0.05} = \$884.80$$

EXERCISES

1. What is the value, after two years, of \$100 deposited now if $\delta = 0.1$?

2. What is the present value of \$100, to be received five years hence, if $\delta = 0.05$? If $i = 0.05$?

3. What is the present value of a series of \$50 payments, to be made at the end of each year for ten years, beginning in one year, if $\delta = 0.05$?

4. What will be the value of the series in Exercise 3 at the end of the ten-year period?

5. In Exercise 5, p. 62, the formula for the present value of a series of payments constituting an arithmetic progression was developed. Suppose each payment flowed in uniformly during the period in which it was due, instead of being received as a lump sum at the end of the period. Develop the formula for present worth, assuming continuous compounding.

6. Using the formula developed in Exercise 5, find the present value of a series of payments:

$$\$100, \quad \$200, \quad \$300, \quad \$400, \quad \$500$$

where each payment flows uniformly throughout the year in which it is due if $i = 0.1$.

7. Appendix Table 8 can be used to check the answer to Exercise 6. Show how this can be done and verify your answer.

8. A company is considering a contract which will involve the immediate expenditure of \$10,000 and operating expenditure of \$24,000 uniformly spread over a three-year period thereafter. During the three years, revenues will flow in at a uniform rate; total revenues will be \$42,000. Salvage value of equipment, etc., remaining after completion of the contract will be \$4,000.

(a) What is the present value of the project if $\delta = 0.10$?

(b) What is the present value if i is 10%?

9. Show that $\dfrac{e^{\delta n} - 1}{e^{\delta} - 1} < \dfrac{e^{\delta n} - 1}{\delta}$ if $\delta > 0$. Interpret this result.

10. Show that $\dfrac{e^{-\delta}(1 - e^{-\delta n})}{1 - e^{-\delta}} < \dfrac{e^{\delta n} - 1}{\delta e^{\delta n}}$ if $\delta > 0$. Interpret this result.

11. Determine the percentage difference in the amount accumulated after n years if the interest rate i is used in place of the rate δ.

C. OPTIMIZATION DECISIONS IN THE SINGLE PROJECT PROBLEM WITH VARIABLE PROJECT LIFE

Implicit in the investment problems presented in Chapter 3 was the assumption that the length of the project is fixed. In Chapter 4, examples where the decision-maker can control the "length" of the project were discussed. The problem in this case becomes one of determining whether or not to undertake a project if it can be terminated at the "optimum" time. A simple example is the "replacement" problem, Chapter 4, in which a firm must decide on how frequently to replace a machine which, over time, has decreasing productivity and increasing repair costs.

To illustrate the problem in general terms, consider the following simple situation:

(a) An entrepreneur has available an amount of capital, C.
(b) There exists a bank which will pay interest continuously compounded at rate k and will accept any amount the entrepreneur wishes to deposit.
(c) The entrepreneur can also invest an amount C in a project now, and he can disinvest (or sell) at any time, $t(t \geq 0)$, for an amount $R(t, C)$. The function $R(t, C)$ has the properties
  (i) $R(t, C)$ is a monotonically increasing function of t; i.e, $R'(t, C) > 0$ or $R(t, C) < R(t_1, C)$ if $t < t_1$.
  (ii) The rate of increase of R as t increases is decreasing; i.e., $R''(t, C) < 0$ or $R(t, C)$ is a concave function of t.
  (iii) If the entrepreneur disinvests immediately, he suffers a loss; i.e., $0 \leq R(0, C) < C$.

One example of such a situation is a real estate investment where the value of the property increases with time. Another example in which the investor can invest and disinvest at will may be a distiller who owns a number of casks for aging liquor. The value of the liquor increases with age. The decision that must be made is when to disinvest. The criteria that were suggested in Chapter 3 were based on the present value and the internal rate of return. Let $P(\delta, t)$ denote the present value of the project if the continuous rate is δ and disinvestment occurs at time t. Then

$$P(\delta, t) = -C + R(t)e^{-\delta t} \qquad (1)$$

The present value approach is to choose the time of disinvestment t^* so as to maximize the present value of the project at rate k. The first derivative is:

$$\frac{dP(k, t)}{dt} = [-kR(t) + R'(t)]e^{-kt}$$

and t^* is the solution of

$$R'(t) = kR(t) \qquad (2)$$

$$\frac{d^2P}{dt} = e^{-kt}[k^2R(t) - 2kR'(t) + R''(t)]$$

for a maximum $d^2P/dt < 0$, i.e., $k^2R(t) - 2kR'(t) + R''(t) < 0$. Substituting $R'(t^*) = kR(t^*)$ from (2) gives the second order condition as

$$k^2R(t^*) - 2k^2R(t^*) + R''(t^*) < 0$$

which is satisfied since $R''(t)$ is negative. Therefore, there is a value of t for which the present value is maximized.

The internal rate of return approach is to choose the time of disinvestment t^* so as to maximize the internal rate of return. The solution of

$$P(\delta, t) = -C + R(t)e^{-\delta t} = 0$$

given by

$$\delta = \frac{1}{t} \ln \left[\frac{R(t)}{C} \right]$$

is the rate of return if disinvestment occurs at time t. The derivative is

$$\frac{d\delta}{dt} = -\frac{1}{t^2} \left[\ln \frac{R(t)}{C} \right] + \frac{1}{t} \frac{R'(t)}{R(t)}$$

The maximum value of δ^* occurs when t^* satisfies the equation

$$\frac{1}{t^*} \ln \left[\frac{R(t^*)}{C} \right] = \frac{R'(t^*)}{R(t^*)} \tag{3}$$

At this optimum

$$\delta^* = \frac{1}{t^*} \ln \frac{R(t^*)}{C} \tag{4}$$

and, therefore,

$$\delta^* = \frac{R'(t^*)}{R(t^*)} = \frac{d \ln R(t^*)}{dt} \tag{5}$$

Since $\ln R(t)$ is concave increasing, there is a single unique value of δ^*. However, the value of t^* obtained from (3) will not, in general, be equal to that obtained from (2). The reason for this can be clarified by illustrating a particular case graphically.

Example.   A distiller has a cask for aging liquor.   The value of liquor increases with age and the value of the liquor at time t is represented by $R(t) = 10,000\sqrt{1 + t}$ if the cask is filled now. Let the initial cost of the liquor $C = \$15,000$. The market rate of interest k is 0.05 compounded continuously. Therefore,

$$R(t) = 10,000\sqrt{1 + t}; \qquad C = 15,000; \qquad k = 0.05 \tag{6}$$

This situation is represented by Fig. 7.5. Time is plotted on the horizontal (x) axis on a linear scale, with the origin representing the time of initial investment. Present value, future value, and disinvestment value (in dollars) are plotted on the vertical (y) axis on a logarithmic scale. The point C on the y-axis represents the value of the initial investment and $R(t)$ represents the value of the liquor at time t.

The value of the initial investment C at any time in the future, when C is compounded continuously at a rate δ, is

$$S(t) = Ce^{\delta t}$$

or taking logarithms

$$\ln S(t) = \ln C + \delta t$$

This is the equation of a straight line passing through the point C with slope δ when a logarithmic scale is used on the y-axis, as in Fig. 7.5. Lines I, II, and III represent the future values of the initial investment C for rates $\delta_1 = 0.08$, $\delta_2 = 0.1$, $\delta_3 = 0.2$. In particular, if the rate is δ_2, the future value at time M is W. Similarly the future value of C at rate k is given by

$$S(t) = Ce^{kt}$$

and is represented in Fig. 7.5 by the line V. The value of the amount V_2 at any time is represented by the line IV. The present value of some amount, say, L, at some time in the future at rate k, is obtained graphically

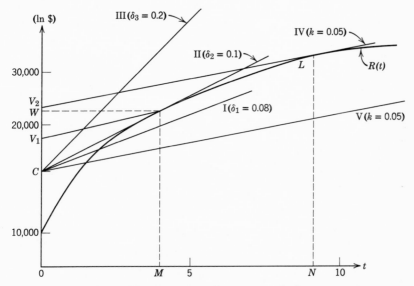

Figure 7.5   Illustration of investment criteria:

$$C = 15,000$$
$$R(t) = 10,000\sqrt{1 + t}$$

by drawing a line through L with slope k (i.e., parallel to lines IV and V). Since $R(t)$ is concave, there is one point on the curve at which a line of slope k will have a greater intercept than at any other point. In this case the point is in fact L. Disinvestment at time N will lead to a greater present value, V_2, than disinvestment at any other time.

From (2) the optimum value of t is the solution of

$$0.05\sqrt{1 + t} = \frac{1}{2\sqrt{1 + t}} \tag{7}$$

that is, $t^* = 9$ years.

The internal rate of return is maximized if the liquor is sold at time M for an amount W, because there is no line passing through point C and touching the curve $R(t)$ which has a greater slope than line II.

Substituting in (3) gives the equation for t^* as

$$\frac{1}{2t} \ln \left[\frac{1 + t}{1.5} \right] = \frac{1}{1 + t}$$

$$\ln 1.5 = 0.40547 = \tfrac{1}{2} \ln (1 + t) - \frac{t}{2(t + 1)} \tag{8}$$

This equation can be solved by computing the right-hand side for different values of t, and then determining the value of t which satisfies the equation

$$g(t) = \tfrac{1}{2} \ln (1 + t) - \frac{t}{2(t + 1)}$$

$g(1) = \tfrac{1}{2} \ln 2 - \tfrac{1}{4}$	$= 0.096574$	
$g(2) = \tfrac{1}{2} \ln 3 - \tfrac{1}{3}$	$= 0.215972$	
$g(3) = \tfrac{1}{2} \ln 4 - \tfrac{3}{8}$	$= 0.318145$	
$g(4) = \tfrac{1}{2} \ln 5 - \tfrac{2}{5}$	$= 0.404720$	
$g(5) = \tfrac{1}{2} \ln 6 - \tfrac{5}{12}$	$= 0.479213$	
$g(6) = \tfrac{1}{2} \ln 7 - \tfrac{3}{7}$	$= 0.544384$	

In this case t is just a little greater than 4 and, therefore, from (3):

$$\delta^* = \frac{1}{2(t + 1)} \simeq 0.1$$

The maximum internal rate of return is approximately 0.10 if the liquor is sold at the end of four years.

The present value is maximized (for rate 0.05) if the liquor is sold after nine years. The present values of the receipts at $t = 4$ and $t = 9$ are

$$W = 10{,}000\sqrt{1 + 4}\,(e^{0.1})^{-4} = 10{,}000(2.2361)(0.6703) = \$14{,}989$$

$$L = 10{,}000\sqrt{1 + 9}\,(e^{0.05})^{-9} = 10{,}000(3.1623)(0.6376) = \$20{,}163$$

Under the conditions assumed in this example, the distiller obtains a larger present value if he maximizes present value, than if he maximizes internal rate of return. However, if he sells at the end of four years, if he is able to reinvest in more liquor at that time, if the function $R(t)$ is unchanged, and if he is able to repeat this process indefinitely into the future, he will clearly be better off than if he sells every nine years. In practical problems, we must consider the alternative investment opportunities that will exist in the future. Some further cases are covered in the exercises.

EXERCISES

1. Develop (7) and (8) from first principles [i.e., without using (2) and (3)] and use second-order condition to verify that the maximum values have been obtained.

2. Determine the optimum time to disinvest if objective is to maximize the ratio of net present value (at rate k) to present cost; i.e.,

$$\frac{P(k, t)}{C}$$

3. (a) Determine the total value of the distiller at $t = 9$ if he disinvests at $t = 4$, invests (\$15,000) again in liquor, and deposits additional money in a bank, then repeats this procedure again at $t = 8$.

(b) Develop a general formula for the increase in value obtained by maximizing internal rate of return rather than present value if the initial investment can be repeated indefinitely and excess funds are invested in a bank.

4. Determine the optimum investment policy if the distiller has seven casks available but is limited by his capital. He starts with an amount C which he invests in liquor. Whenever he sells aged liquor he buys as many casksful of new liquor as his capital will allow. Any additional amount is deposited in a bank, and whenever he has enough to fill an additional cask he does so, if one is available.

D. MONOTONIC TRANSFORMATIONS

Let $y = f(x)$ denote the objective function defined for $a \leq x \leq b$ and let $\hat{x}$ denote the solution of

$$\frac{df(x)}{dx} = 0$$

Then f has a maximum at $x = \hat{x}$ if $f''(x) < 0$, and a minimum if $f''(x) > 0$. Let $g(y)$ be a strictly monotonic function of y, then

$$\frac{dg}{dy} > 0 \quad \text{or} \quad \frac{dg}{dy} < 0 \qquad \text{for } c \leq y \leq d$$

Let $\tilde{x}$ be the solution of

$$\frac{d}{dx} g[y(x)] = 0$$

Since

$$\frac{d}{dx} g(y) = \frac{dg}{dy} \frac{dy}{dx}$$

and dg/dy has the same sign through the interval, the solution of $\frac{dy}{dx} = 0$ is also the solution of $\frac{d}{dx} [g(y)] = 0$; i.e., $\tilde{x} = \hat{x}$.

The second derivative of g is

$$\frac{d^2}{dx^2} g(y) = \frac{d}{dx}\left[\left(\frac{dg}{dy}\right)\left(\frac{dy}{dx}\right) \right] = \left(\frac{dy}{dx}\right)\frac{d}{dx}\left(\frac{dg}{dy}\right) + \frac{dg}{dy}\left(\frac{d^2y}{dx^2}\right)$$

For the values of x which make $\frac{dy}{dx} = 0$,

$$\frac{d^2}{dx^2} g(y) = \left(\frac{dg}{dy}\right)\left(\frac{d^2y}{dx^2}\right)$$

and therefore $(d^2/dx^2)g(y)$ has the same sign as d^2y/dx^2 if $dg/dy > 0$, and the opposite sign if $dg/dy < 0$.

Example. Consider the function

$$f(x) = cxe^{ax^2+bx} \qquad \text{where a} < 0, \text{ b} > 0, \text{ c} > 0$$

Then

$$f'(x) = ce^{ax^2+bx} + cx(2ax + b)e^{ax^2+bx}$$

$$= ce^{ax^2+bx}(2ax^2 + bx + 1)$$

Since $c > 0$ and $e^{xa^2+bx} > 0$, the zeros of $f'(x)$ are given by

$$2ax^2 + bx + 1 = 0$$

The solutions to the quadratic are given by

$$x_1 = \frac{-b + \sqrt{b^2 - 8a}}{4a} \quad \text{and} \quad x_2 = \frac{-b - \sqrt{b^2 - 8a}}{4a}$$

The second derivative is

$$f''(x) = ce^{ax^2+bx}(4ax + b) + c(2ax + b)e^{ax^2+bx}(2ax^2 + bx + 1)$$

$$= ce^{ax^2+bx}[4a^2x^3 + 4abx^2 + (6a + b^2)x + 2b]$$

Substituting the values of x_1 and x_2 in $f''(x)$ will determine the nature of the extreme point for these values of x in terms of the given coefficients a, b, and c. If

$$a = -2, \quad b = 3, \quad c = 1$$

then

$$x_1 = \frac{-3 + \sqrt{9 + 16}}{-8} = -\frac{1}{4} \quad \text{and} \quad x_2 = \frac{-3 - \sqrt{25}}{-8} = 1$$

The second derivatives at these points are

$$f''(1) = e(16 - 24 - 3 + 6) = -5e < 0$$

$$f''(-\tfrac{1}{4}) = e^{-7/8}(-\tfrac{1}{4} - \tfrac{3}{2} + \tfrac{3}{4} + 6) = 5e^{-7/8} > 0$$

and hence the function has a maximum at $x = 1$ and a minimum at $x = -\frac{1}{4}$. Since $f(-\infty) = 0$ and $f(+\infty) = 0$, the function has the form shown in Fig. 7.6.

The logarithm of a monotonic function is a monotonic function, and the mathematics may be simplified by taking the logarithm of both sides of the equation. Ln y is defined only if $y > 0$ and since

$$f(x) > 0 \qquad \text{for } x > 0$$
and
$$f(x) < 0 \qquad \text{for } x < 0$$

the problem must be divided into two parts.

Consider, first, the case where $x > 0$. Then

$$\ln f(x) = \ln c + \ln x + (ax^2 + bx)$$

$$\frac{d}{dx} \ln f(x) = 0 + \frac{1}{x} + 2ax + b$$

Setting this $= 0$ gives $0 = 1 + bx + 2ax^2$

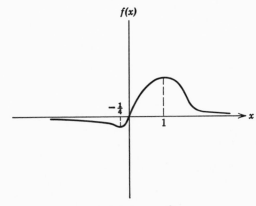

Figure 7.6 $f(x) = xe^{-x^2 + 3x}$.

and

$$x = \frac{-b \pm \sqrt{b^2 - 8a}}{4a}$$

The second derivative is

$$\frac{d^2 \ln f(x)}{dx^2} = -\frac{1}{x^2} + 2a \qquad >0 \text{ if } 2a > \frac{1}{x^2}$$

$$<0 \text{ if } 2a < \frac{1}{x^2}$$

For the particular values considered previously where

$$a = -2; \qquad b = 3; \qquad c = 1$$

the solutions to $\dfrac{d \ln f(x)}{dx} = 0$ are $x = 1$ and $x = -\frac{1}{4}$, but only $x = 1$ falls in the region $x > 0$. At this point

$$\frac{d^2 \ln f(x)}{dx^2} = \frac{-1}{1} + 2a = -5$$

which indicates that the objective function has a maximum at $x = 1$.

For the case where $f(x) < 0$, i.e., $x < 0$, the transformation that can be used is

$$\ln [-f(x)] = \ln c + \ln (-x) + ax^2 + bx$$

then

$$\frac{d \ln [-f(x)]}{dx} = \frac{1}{x} + 2ax + b$$

and the solution of $2ax^2 + bx + 1 = 0$ is

$$x = \frac{-b \pm \sqrt{b^2 - 8a}}{4a}$$

The second derivative is

$$\frac{d \ln [-f(x)]}{dx} = -\frac{1}{x^2} + 2a$$

For the numerical case

$$x = \frac{6 \pm \sqrt{9 + 16}}{-8}; \qquad x = 1 \quad \text{and} \quad -\frac{1}{4}$$

and the latter is the one that falls in the region under consideration.

The second derivative at this point is $-16 - 4 = -20$ and must be multiplied by -1 since

$$\frac{d^2g}{dx^2} = \frac{dg}{dy}\left(\frac{d^2g}{dy^2}\right)$$

$$\frac{dg}{dy} = -\frac{1}{4} = -\frac{1}{f(-\frac{1}{4})}$$

and therefore

$$\frac{d^2f(x)}{dx} > 0$$

which indicates that the function has a minimum at $x = -\frac{1}{4}$.

E. GROCERY STORE SALES MODEL

A department store has studied sales at a number of counters as a function of the number of brands of the product and of the number of boxes of each brand on display. The same number of boxes of each brand are carried on a counter and all the boxes on a counter are of equal size. This situation might exist, for example, where breakfast cereals are being sold. It was found that sales could be expressed by the following relationship:

$$S = kn^v v^n \tag{1}$$

where S = the sale in boxes per time period

n = the number of boxes of each brand on display

v = the number of brands on display

k = a constant

Determine the optimum number of brands which should be carried on a counter which can hold c boxes, assuming that management's goal is to maximize the total number of boxes sold. Apply the results to the case where $k = 10^{-22}$ and $c = 120$.

Solution. The situation described above requires n and v to be integers; however, in the analysis which follows it will be assumed that n and v do not have to be integers. The variables n, v, and c are subject to the constraint:

$$nv = c; \quad c > 0 \tag{2}$$

Therefore,

$$n = \frac{c}{v}$$

and

$$S(v) = k\left(\frac{c}{v}\right)^v v^{c/v} = kc^v v^{\frac{c}{v} - v} \qquad (3)$$

The problem is to find the value of v which, given c, maximizes S. The study of expression (3) can be made simpler by a logarithmic transformation. This transformation does not affect the optimization since the logarithmic function is a monotonically increasing function of the variable.

$$\ln S = \ln k + v \ln c + \left(\frac{c}{v} - v\right) \ln v \qquad (4)$$

The extreme points of this function occur for the zeros of the derivative; i.e., the solution of the equation

$$\frac{d \ln S}{dv} = \ln c - \left(1 + \frac{c}{v^2}\right) \ln v + \left(\frac{c}{v} - v\right)\frac{1}{v} = 0 \qquad (5)$$

This equation cannot be solved directly, but the number of solutions can be investigated by computing the second derivative after rewriting (5) as:

$$\frac{d \ln S}{dv} = [(\ln c) - 2] - \left(1 + \frac{c}{v^2}\right) \ln v + \left(\frac{c}{v^2} + 1\right) \qquad (6)$$

Let

$$y_3(v) = 1 + \frac{c}{v^2} \qquad \text{and} \qquad m = (\ln c) - 2$$

Then

$$\frac{d \ln S}{dv} = m - y_3 \ln v + y_3$$

and

$$\frac{d^2 \ln S}{dv^2} = -\left(y_3 \frac{1}{v} + y_3' \ln v\right) + y_3'$$

$$= \frac{1}{v^3} [2c \ln v - 3c] - \frac{1}{v} \qquad (7)$$

From equation (3) it can be seen that c/v and v play a symmetrical role:

$$S(v_0) = S\left(\frac{c}{v_0}\right)$$

Therefore, $v = \sqrt{c}$ must be either a maximum or a minimum of S, and it can easily be verified that $v = \sqrt{c}$ is always a zero of the derivative. Substituting in (5) gives

$$\frac{d \ln S}{dv} = \ln c - 2 \ln \sqrt{c} = 0$$

Substituting $v = \sqrt{c}$ in (7) gives

$$\frac{d^2 \ln S}{dv^2} = \frac{1}{\sqrt{c}}(2 \ln \sqrt{c} - 4) = \frac{1}{\sqrt{c}}(\ln c - 4)$$

which is positive if $\ln c > 4$. This proves that if $\ln c > 4$, $v = \sqrt{c}$ is a point at which S has a minimum, but if $\ln c < 4$, $v = \sqrt{c}$ is a point at which S has a maximum.

To compute the solutions of (5), let

$$y_1(v) = \ln v \quad \text{and} \quad y_2(v) = \frac{y_3 + m}{y_3}$$

Then the solution is the intersection of $y_1(v)$ and $y_2(v)$.

It is clear that y_1 is below y_2 at $v = 0$ and that at $v = \infty$, y_1 is above y_2. Therefore, they must cross an odd number of times, 1, 3, etc., since $dy_1/dv > 0$ for all $v > 0$. The derivative of y_2 is zero and becomes positive at $v = 0$, while as v approaches infinity the derivative of y_2 again approaches zero. In order to do this, the second derivative of y_2 must be zero somewhere in the interval between $v = 0$ and $v = \infty$. To compute the second derivative, write

$$y_2(v) = \frac{y_3 + m}{y_3} = 1 + \frac{m}{y_3}$$

Then

$$\frac{dy_2}{dv} = -my_3^{-2}\frac{dy_3}{dv}$$

and

$$\frac{d^2 y_2}{dv^2} = -m\left[-2y_3^{-3}\left(\frac{dy_3}{dv}\right)^2 + y_3^{-2}\frac{d^2 y_3}{dv^2}\right]$$

$$= -2cmv^{-6}y_3^{-3}[-4c + 3y_3 v^2] = -2cmv^{-6}y_3^{-3}[-c + 3v^2]$$

$$\frac{d^2 y_2}{dv^2} = 0$$

if $3v^2 - c = 0$, or $v = \pm\sqrt{c/3}$, or if $m = 0$.

This proves that y_2 has only one inflection point in the region $v > 0$, and hence there can be either one or three solutions to the equation $y_1 = y_2$.

Therefore, there is a single maximum and it occurs at $v = \sqrt{c}$, if $\ln c < 4$. However, if $\ln c > 4$, there are two values of v, say, v_1 and v_2, for which S is a maximum. The two values are related

$$v_2 = \frac{c}{v_1} \quad \text{and} \quad S(v_2) = S\left(\frac{c}{v_1}\right)$$

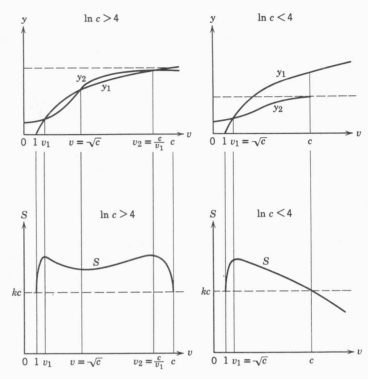

Figure 7.7 (*Top*) Graphs of y_1 and y_2 for different values of c. (*Bottom*) Graph of S for different values of c.

The functions y_1 and y_2 for the two cases are shown in Fig. 7.7. The function S for the two cases is also shown in Fig. 7.7.

Numerical Example ($k = 10^{-22}$, $c = 120$). Since $\ln c > 4$, there will be two possible values of v which will maximize S. The curves of y_1, y_2, and S are plotted on Fig. 7.8 from the accompanying table of

v	2	3	4	8	$\sqrt{c}$	15	30	40
n	60	40	30	15	$\sqrt{c}$	8	4	3
y_1	0.69	1.20	1.39	2.08	2.40	2.71	3.40	3.69
y_2	1.09	1.21	1.33	1.97	2.40	2.82	3.51	3.60
S	0.04134	77.63	92.98	9.022	8.143	9.022	92.98	77.63

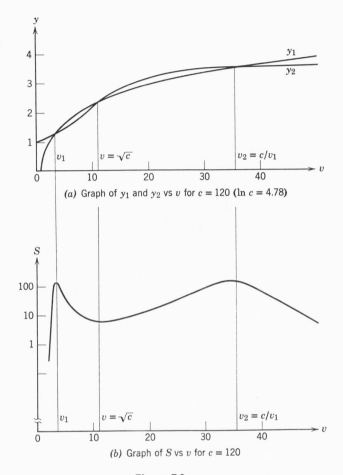

(a) Graph of y_1 and y_2 vs v for $c = 120$ (ln $c = 4.78$)

(b) Graph of S vs v for $c = 120$

Figure 7.8

values. It can be seen by inspection that the solutions occur for $v_1 \simeq 3.5$ and $v_2 \simeq 35$. By applying one of the methods of numerical approximation to the function $f = y_1 - y_2$, a more accurate result would be obtained:

$$v_1 = 3.64 \qquad \text{and} \qquad v_2 = 33$$

But since only integral values are acceptable, the combinations $v = 4$ and $n = 30$, or $v = 30$ and $n = 4$, are the only practical ones.

An upper or lower bound to a numerical solution can be obtained by noting that equation (5) may be written in the form

$$v^2 (\ln c - \ln v - 1) = c(\ln v - 1)$$

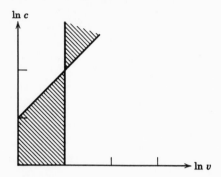

Figure 7.9 Equation (5) can have a solution for ln v and ln c in the shaded areas.

Both sides of this equation must have the same sign; therefore:

1. If ln v < 1, v cannot be a solution unless ln c − ln v < 1, or ln v > ln c − 1.
2. If ln v > 1, v cannot be a solution unless ln c − ln v > 1 or ln v < ln c − 1
3. $v = e$ is a solution if ln c = 2 because ln e = 1 and the right-hand side is equal to zero. The left-hand side becomes

$$e^2(\ln c - \ln e - 1) = e^2(2 - 1 - 1) = 0$$

Notes and References

Section B

Continuous interest tables are contained in most of the tables listed in Notes and References, Chapter 3. In using any of the tables, it is important to determine whether the rate used is i or $\delta = \ln(1 + i)$.

Section C

The model presented is based on:

Hildreth, C. (1946), "A note on maximization criteria," *Quarterly J. Economics,* **61,** pp. 157-164.

Lutz, F. (1945), "The criterion of maximum profits in the Theory of Investments," *Quarterly J. Economies,* **60,** pp. 56–77.

Lutz, F., and Lutz, V. L. (1951), *The Theory of Investment of the Firm*, Princeton University Press, Princeton, N.J.

CHAPTER EXERCISES

1. A utility firm is committed to meet a growing demand for its services for the next T years. Let $f(t)$ denote the demand at time to over and above that which presently existing facilities can accommodate. Additional facilities can

be installed at any time at a cost of b for equipment sufficient for one unit of demand plus an installation cost of a, independent of the number of units installed. The firm wishes to minimize the present value of all future investment costs discounted continuously at rate δ, while providing sufficient capacity for the T years.

(a) Show that if $f(t) = mt$, new equipment should be installed every x years where x is the solution of

$$e^{-\delta x} = \frac{1}{1 + (\delta a/mb) + x\delta}$$

(b) Verify that the solution in (a) is a minimum.

(c) Determine the optimum value of x if $T = 30$ years, $a = \$10,000$, $b = \$10,000$, $\delta = 0.06$, and $m = 2$.

2. Firm X and firm Y have each developed a revolutionary new video tape recording system. The market is limited and is known relatively precisely, namely: all television stations. However the total number of units that can be sold will depend entirely on the price. The total demand, $D(x)$, in units is given by

$$D(x) = b_0 + b_1 x + b_2 x^2$$

where x is the price per unit. The coefficients of $D(x)$ are such that $D(x)$ is concave for all non-negative x. The coefficients can be computed from the published income figures from all television stations.

Firm X's cost function is estimated by extrapolation from experience with a previous system to be

$$C(n) = a_0 + a_1 n + a_2 n^{3/4}$$

where n is the number of units manufactured and $C(n)$ is the total cost in producing n units. The coefficients in $C(n)$ are all positive.

Firm X knows that firm Y's prototype is almost at the same stage of development as that of firm X, the two final products are expected to be essentially equivalent. The Sales Department of firm X has concluded that firm X's share, say, p, of the total market will not depend on the price charged by firm X, because firm Y is likely to charge essentially the same price as A.

Determine the optimum selling price that firm X should charge to maximize its earnings from the system under the assumptions made above. Assume further that there will be no other competition; and note that $D(x)$ is the demand function for the whole industry. State the optimum decision in terms of the coefficients and parameters, verify that it is the optimum, and interpret the results.

3. As an example of the use of non-linear functions in business decision-making, consider the problem of how much to spend on advertising. As more money is spent, the number of people responding will tend to increase. The number of new responses per dollar spent will depend on many factors, including the type of advertising used, the period over which it is continued, etc. To make an optimum decision on how much to spend for advertising, the decision maker must have an estimate of the relationship between increasing expenditures and increasing response. He must also know the profit resulting from additional responses. As advertising expenses are increased, there usually comes a point at which the increasing expenses on advertising no longer result in an increase in profit.

Consider an isolated community in which a manufacturer attempts to elicit a response by a one-time air drop of leaflets. Assume that the response is a function only of the ratio of the number of leaflets dropped to the total population and that revenue is directly proportional to the number of responses. Let:

x = the intensity of advertising in terms of the number of leaflets dropped per person in the community, $0 < x < \infty$

$R(x)$ = the response measured in the proportion of persons in the community responding as a function of the intensity, x, $0 \leq R(x) < 1$

d = the fixed cost of dropping leaflets

s = the variable cost per unit for each leaflet

r = the unit revenue per response

N = the population of the town

The earnings are the difference between revenue and costs:

$$E(x) = \text{Revenue} - \text{Costs}$$

Revenue $= rNR(x)$:   the revenue is the unit revenue per response times the number of responses

Costs $= d + sxN$:   the cost is the fixed cost plus the variable cost

and

$$E(x) = rNR(x) - d - sxN$$

The optimum value of x is the solution of $E'(x) = 0$ for which $E''(x) < 0$.

$$\frac{dE(x)}{dx} = rN\frac{dR(x)}{dx} - sN$$

Therefore, x^* is the solution of $dR(x)/dx = s/r$ if, for the solution,

$$E''(x) = \frac{d^2R(x)}{dx} < 0$$

This problem can be solved if $R(x)$ is known. What form should $R(x)$ have?

Qualitatively, we would expect that the functional relationship between $R(x)$ and x would have the property that $R(x) = 0$ when $x = 0$, and that $R(x)$ increases as x increases. As x becomes very large, $R(x)$ approaches the value 1. Furthermore, $R(x)$ should increase relatively rapidly when x is small and less rapidly as x becomes large. This implies that $R'(x) > 0$; and $R''(x) < 0$ in the interval $0 < x < \infty$.

There are, of course, an infinite number of functions which will satisfy these requirements. Some of the more common ones are

Name	Function
Logarithm	$R_1(x) = a \ln x + b$
Exponential	$R_2(x) = c - de^{-hx-m}$
Rational	$R_3(x) = \dfrac{ax^2}{1 + bx + cx^2}$

(a) Discuss the implications of using each one of the three types of functions as response functions.

(b) Would a polynomial be a suitable response function?

(c) In any particular case where data are available, it may be possible to select the function which best "fits" the data. Assume that an experiment has been carried out and that the following represent the "best" fit to the empirical data:

$$R_1(x) = 0.12 \ln x + 0.43$$

$$R_2(x) = 1 - e^{-0.07x-0.4}$$

$$R_3(x) = \frac{0.83x^2}{1 + 1.8x + 0.8x^2}$$

Determine the optimum amount to be spent on advertising if the response is given by R_1, R_2, and R_3, respectively.

(d) Solve the general problem for the case where the revenue is an arbitrary function, say, $g(R)$, of the number of responses. What properties should this function have?

CHAPTER EIGHT

Models Involving Integration

and Differential Equations

The integral plays an important role in models of business operations. Many functions are most naturally interpreted as integrals. Integration is also essential in the solution of differential equations, and these are becoming increasingly common in management science models.

The mathematics in this chapter is limited to a review of elementary integral calculus and a discussion of some methods for solving differential equations of the first order and first degree. The examples and exercises illustrate the application to various problems: the machine replacement problem, learning curves, compound interest, advertising models, and diffusion models.

A. REVIEW OF INTEGRATION

Elementary Integration

The indefinite integral of a function $f(x)$ is denoted by

$$\int f(x)\, dx$$

and defined to be equal to

$$F(x) + C \qquad \text{where} \qquad DF(x) = f(x)$$

C is an arbitrary constant and the symbol D denotes d/dx.

The process of differentiation involves finding the derivatives of a given function; the process of integration is the inverse: it involves finding a function whose derivative is the given function. This is emphasized by writing:

$$\int f(x)\,dx = F(x) + C$$

as

$$\int f(x)\,dx = \int DF(x) = F(x) + C \tag{1}$$

The symbol used to denote the argument of the function, called the variable of integration, is immaterial; the form given in (1) is equivalent to

$$\int f(y)\,dy = F(y) + C$$

The basic rules for integration follow from the basic rules of differentiation. Let k be a constant and f and g be two functions of x. Then

$$\int kf(x)\,dx = k\int f(x)\,dx \tag{2}$$

$$\int [f(x) \pm g(x)]\,dx = \int f(x)\,dx \pm \int g(x)\,dx \tag{3}$$

The indefinite integrals of the elementary functions follow immediately from the rules for the differentiation of an elementary function:

$$\frac{Dx^{n+1}}{n+1} = x^n \qquad \int x^n\,dx = \frac{x^{n+1}}{n+1} + C; \quad n+1 \neq 0 \tag{4}$$

$$D\ln x = \frac{1}{x} \qquad \int \frac{dx}{x} = \ln x + C \qquad x > 0 \tag{5}$$

$$De^x = e^x \qquad \int e^x\,dx = e^x + C \tag{6}$$

From the chain rule for differentiation it follows that

$$\int f(g(x))\,Dg(x)\,dx = F(g(x)) + C \quad \text{where} \quad \int f(g)\,dg = F(g) + C \tag{7}$$

The integrals (4), (5), and (6) may be extended by use of (7) to

$$\int (ax+b)^n\,dx = \frac{(ax+b)^{n+1}}{a(n+1)} + C \qquad \text{if} \qquad n \neq -1 \tag{8}$$

Here $f = g^n$ and $g = ax + b$.

$$\int \frac{dx}{ax+b} = \frac{1}{a}\ln(ax+b) + C \qquad \text{if} \qquad (ax+b) > 0 \tag{9}$$

Here $f = \dfrac{1}{g}$ and $g = ax + b$.

$$\int (e^{ax+b}) \, dx = \frac{e^{ax+b}}{a} + C \qquad \text{if} \qquad a \neq 0 \tag{10}$$

Here $f = e^{g}$ and $g = ax + b$.

If u and v are functions of a single independent variable, the formula for the differentiation of a product states that

$$d(uv) = u \, dv + v \, du,$$

or

$$u \, dv = d(uv) - v \, du$$

Integrating gives the formula for *integration by parts*:

$$\int u \, dv = uv - \int v \, du \tag{11}$$

It is helpful in choosing the factors u and dv to remember that dx is always a part of dv and that dv must be integrable (i.e., the integral of dv must be available).

Example I.   To find $\int x \ln x \, dx$.   Let:

$$u = \ln x \qquad \text{and} \qquad dv = x \, dx$$

Then

$$du = \frac{dx}{x} \qquad\qquad v = \frac{x^2}{2},$$

and

$$\int x \ln x \, dx = (\ln x)\left(\frac{x^2}{2}\right) - \int \left(\frac{x^2}{2}\right)\frac{dx}{x}$$

$$= \frac{x^2}{2} \ln x - \int \frac{x}{2} \, dx$$

$$= \frac{x^2}{2} \ln x - \frac{x^2}{4} + C$$

Example 2.   To find $\int xe^{2x} \, dx$.   If

$$u = e^{2x} \qquad \text{and} \qquad dv = x \, dx$$

Then

$$du = 2e^{2x} \, dx \qquad\qquad v = \frac{x^2}{2},$$

Substitution gives

$$\int xe^{2x} \, dx = e^{2x} \frac{x^2}{2} - \int x^2 e^{2x} \, dx$$

Since $x^2 e^{2x}\, dx$ is more difficult to integrate than $x e^{2x}\, dx$, the need for a different choice of factors is indicated. Now let

$$u = x \qquad dv = e^{2x}\, dx$$

Then

$$du = dx \qquad v = \tfrac{1}{2} e^{2x}$$

Substitution gives

$$\int x e^{2x}\, dx = \frac{x}{2}\, e^{2x} - \left(\frac{1}{2}\right) \int e^{2x}\, dx$$

$$= \frac{x}{2}\, e^{2x} - \tfrac{1}{2} \cdot \tfrac{1}{2} e^{2x}$$

$$= \frac{e^{2x}}{2}\, (x - \tfrac{1}{2})$$

Integration of Rational Functions

The integration of rational functions of the form

$$f(x) = \frac{F(x)}{G(x)} \tag{12}$$

where F and G are polynomials can often be accomplished by dividing by $G(x)$, so that

$$f(x) = \frac{F(x)}{G(x)} = Q(x) + \frac{R(x)}{G(x)} \tag{13}$$

where the degree of $R(x)$ is less than that of $G(x)$. The last term can then be expanded in partial fractions, provided $G(x)$ has no common roots, in which the denominators are linear or quadratic. This is possible because any polynomial with real coefficients can be written as the product of factors which are either linear or quadratic. Hence,

$$\frac{R(x)}{G(x)} = t_1 + t_2 + \cdots + t_n \tag{14}$$

where t_i is of the form

$$\frac{A}{ax + b} \quad \text{or} \quad \frac{Bx + C}{ax^2 + bx + c} \tag{15}$$

and the number of terms, n is equal to the number of irreducible factors in $G(x)$. The lower case constants a, b, c, are obtained by factoring $G(x)$, while the upper case constants A, B, C, are obtained by equating co-efficients of like powers of x in (14) after multiplying through by $G(x)$, as illustrated in the following example.

Example 3. If

$$F(x) = x^4 + 2x^2 + 3$$
$$G(x) = x^3 + x$$

then the factors of $G(x)$ are

$$= x(x^2 + 1)$$

and rational function $F(x)/G(x)$ may be written as

$$\frac{x^4 + 2x^2 + 3}{x^3 + x} = x + \frac{x^2 + 3}{x^3 + x}$$

The last term can be written as

$$\frac{x^2 + 3}{x^3 + x} = \frac{A}{x} + \frac{Bx + C}{x^2 + 1} \tag{16}$$

Multiplying both sides of the equation (16) by $x(x^2 + 1)$ gives

$$x^2 + 3 = A(x^2 + 1) + (Bx + C)x$$
$$= x^2(A + B) + Cx + A$$

In order for this equality to hold, the polynomials on either side of the equals sign must have the same coefficients for the same power of x:

1. The coefficient of x^2 on the left-hand side must equal the coefficient of x^2 on the right hand side: $1 = A + B$.

2. The coefficient of x on the left-hand side must be equal to the coefficient of x on the right-hand side: $0 = C$

3. The constant term on the left-hand side must equal the constant term on the right-hand side: $3 = A$.

The three equations involving A, B, and C as unknowns are:

$$1 = A + B$$
$$0 = C$$
$$3 = A$$

Therefore, $A = 3$, $B = -2$, $C = 0$, and the indefinite integral of $F(x)/G(x)$ is:

$$\int \left(\frac{x^4 + 2x^2 + 3}{x^3 + x} \right) dx$$

$$= \int x\, dx + \int \frac{3}{x}\, dx - \int \frac{2x\, dx}{x^2 + 1}$$

$$= \frac{x^2}{2} + 3 \ln x - \ln (x^2 + 1) + C \qquad x > 0;$$

The Definite Integral

The symbol $\int_a^b f(x)\,dx$, called the definite integral of $f(x)$ from a to b, denotes the difference between the values of the indefinite integral at $x = b$ and $x = a$.

$$[F(b) + C] - [F(a) + C] = F(b) - F(a)$$

The word *definite* is appropriate because the result $F(b) - F(a)$ does not involve the arbitrary constant C and, therefore, has a definite value. Thus, by definition,

$$\int_a^b f(x)\,dx = F(b) - F(a) \tag{17}$$

In (17), a and b are called the *limits of integration*, a being the *lower* limit and b the *upper limit*. The variable x is called the variable of integration. However, x plays no essential role in this definition. Thus,

$$\int_a^b f(x)\,dx = \int_a^b f(y)\,dy = \int_a^b f(z)\,dz = F(b) - F(a)$$

The process of evaluating a definite integral is usually shown explicitly as:

$$\int_a^b f(x)\,dx = [F(x)]_a^b = F(b) - F(a)$$

The arbitrary constant C occurring in the indefinite integral is omitted because it does not appear in the value of the definite integral.

The following properties of definite integrals follow immediately from the definition:

$$\int_a^a f(x)\,dx = 0$$

$$\int_a^b f(x)\,dx = -\int_b^a f(x)\,dx$$

$$\int_a^b f(x)\,dx = \int_a^c f(x)\,dx + \int_c^b f(x)\,dx$$

Geometrically the definite integral can be interpetred as area under a curve. Let the curve be denoted by $f(t)$. Then the area under the curve and between the two ordinates a and x is given by the definite integral $\int_a^x f(t)\,dt$ as shown in Fig. 8.1. From this follows the basic result that

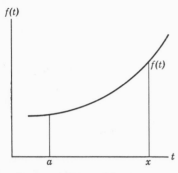

Figure 8.1

the derivative of an integral, with respect to the upper limit, is the integrand evaluated at the upper limit; more precisely, if

$$A(x) = \int_a^x f(t)\, dt$$

then

$$\frac{d}{dx}\, A(x) = f(x)$$

since by definition,

$$\frac{dA(x)}{dx} = \lim_{\Delta x \to 0} \left\{ \frac{A(x + \Delta x) - A(x)}{\Delta x} \right\}$$

$$= \lim_{\Delta x \to 0} \left\{ \frac{1}{\Delta x} \left[\int_a^{x+\Delta x} f(t)\, dt - \int_a^x f(t)\, dt \right] \right\}$$

$$= \lim_{\Delta x \to 0} \left\{ \frac{1}{\Delta x} \left[\int_a^x f(t)\, dt + \int_x^{x+\Delta x} f(t)\, dt - \int_a^x f(t)\, dt \right] \right\}$$

$$= \lim_{\Delta x \to 0} \frac{1}{\Delta x} \left[\int_x^{x+\Delta x} f(t)\, dt \right]$$

$$= \lim_{\Delta x \to 0} \frac{f(x)\, \Delta x}{\Delta x} \qquad \text{since } \int_x^{x+\Delta x} f(t)\, dt \sim f(x)\, \Delta x \text{ when } \Delta x \text{ is small}$$

$$= f(x)$$

Example 4.

$$\int_3^6 \left(\frac{1}{x^3} - \frac{1}{x} \right) dx = \int_3^6 \frac{dx}{x^3} - \int_3^6 \frac{dx}{x}$$

$$= \frac{-1}{2x^2} \bigg]_3^6 - \ln x \bigg]_3^6$$

$$= \frac{1}{24} - \ln 2$$

Example 5.   Find the area bounded by the curve $y = 2x^3 - 6x + 5$, the x axis, the local maximum and local minimum

$$\frac{dy}{dx} = 6x^2 - 6; \qquad \frac{dy}{dx} = 0 \text{ when } x = \pm 1$$

$$\frac{d^2y}{dx^2} = 12x \qquad \frac{d^2y}{dx^2} \text{ is positive when } x = +1$$

and negative when $x = -1$

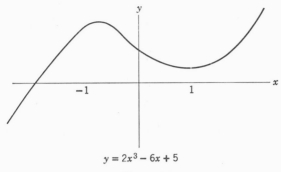

$$y = 2x^3 - 6x + 5$$

Figure 8.2

Therefore, $x = -1$ is a local maximum and $x = +1$ is a local minimum. The area under the curve between -1, 1 is

$$R = \int_{-1}^{+1} (2x^3 - 6x + 5)\, dx$$

$$= \left[\frac{x^4}{2} - 3x^2 + 5x \right]_{-1}^{+1}$$

$$= [\tfrac{1}{2} - 3 + 5] - [\tfrac{1}{2} - 3 - 5]$$

$$= 10$$

Example 6. Find the area of the region between the graphs of the function

$$y_1 = x - 2 \qquad \text{and} \qquad y_2 = 2x - x^2$$

The graphs will intersect in those points whose coordinates are the simultaneous solutions of the given equations:

$$x - 2 = 2x - x^2$$

$$x^2 - x - 2 = (x - 2)(x + 1) = 0$$

Thus, $x = 2$ or $x = -1$ and the common points of the two graphs are $(2, 0)$ and $(-1, -3)$. The region whose area is sought is shaded in Fig. 8.3. This area is given by

$$A = \int_{-1}^{2} [(2x - x^2) - (x - 2)]\, dx$$

$$= \int_{-1}^{2} (-x^2 + x + 2)\, dx = \left[-\frac{x^3}{3} + \frac{x^2}{2} + 2x \right]_{-1}^{2} = \frac{9}{2}$$

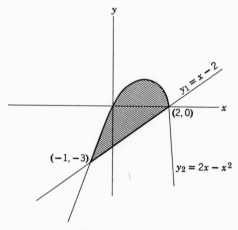

Figure 8.3

Example 7. A firm has purchased a machine which will produce gross earnings (revenue less cost of material and labor) at time t of

$$E(t) = 120 - \tfrac{1}{5}t^2$$

where $E(t)$ is in units of \$1,000 and t is in years. The repair and maintenance cost at time t is

$$R(t) = t^2$$

again measured in units of \$1,000. Suppose the firm can dispose of the machine at any time with no cost or salvage value. How long should the machine be operated?

The two functions $E(t)$ and $R(t)$ are shown in Fig. 8.4. $E(t)$ is a decreasing concave function for $t > 0$ and $R(t)$ is an increasing convex function. The value of t at which the curves cross is the solution of

$$E(t) = R(t)$$
$$120 - \tfrac{1}{5}t^2 = t^2 \qquad \text{or} \qquad t = \pm 10$$

Since after ten years the repair costs exceed the gross earnings, the firm will maximize net earnings if the machine is disposed of at the end of ten years. The total net earnings are

$$\int_0^{10} [E(t) - R(t)]\, dt = \int_0^{10} [120 - \tfrac{1}{5}t^2 - t^2]\, dt = \int_0^{10} [120 - \tfrac{6}{5}t^2]\, dt$$

$$= \left[120t - \frac{6}{5}\frac{t^3}{3} \right]_0^{10}$$

$$= 1{,}200 - \tfrac{6000}{15} = 1{,}200 - 400 = 800$$

or \$800,000.

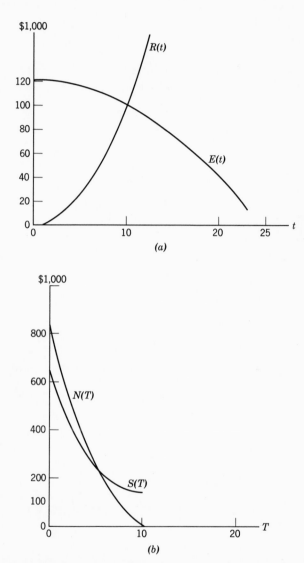

Figure 8.4 (a) Earnings function $E(t)$ and repair costs $R(t)$ for data in Example 7. (b) Total future earnings $N(T)$ and salvage values $S(T)$ for data in Example 7.

Suppose the machine has a salvage value $S(t)$ at time t where

$$S(t) = \frac{2,000}{3 + t}$$

in units of \$1,000. When should the firm sell the machine? The firm will maximize its total net earnings if it sells the machine at a time T when the salvage value just equals the net earnings obtainable after T; i.e., when

$$S(T) = \int_T^{10} [E(t) - R(t)] \, dt$$

$$\frac{2,000}{3 + T} = 800 - 120T + \frac{2T^3}{5}$$

The solution is $T = 5$. $S(T)$ is a monotonically decreasing function with $S(0) = 666.67$ and $S(10) = 153.84$. Similarly, the net earnings from year T to year 10; i.e.,

$$N(T) = 800 - 120T + \frac{2T^3}{5}$$

is a monotonically decreasing function with $N(0) = 800$ and $N(10) = 0$. Before five years the salvage value will be less than the potential future net earnings and after five years the salvage value will be greater. The optimum time to sell, therefore, is at the end of five years.

EXERCISES

Show that:

1. $\int \ln x \, dx = x(\ln x - 1) + C$

2. $\int te^{-\delta t} \, dt = \frac{e^{-\delta t}}{\delta^2} (\delta t - 1) + C$

3. $\int t^2 e^{-\delta t} \, dt = \left(-\frac{t^2}{\delta} - \frac{2t}{\delta^2} - \frac{2}{\delta^3} \right) e^{-\delta t} + C$

4. $\int \left(\frac{x + 1}{x^2 - x} \right) dx = \ln \left(\frac{(x - 1)^2}{x} \right) + C$

5. $\int \frac{\ln x}{(x + 1)^2} \, dx = -\frac{\ln x}{x + 1} + \ln x - \ln (x + 1) + C$

6. $\int \left(\frac{x^3 + 1}{x^3 - 4x} \right) dx = x - \frac{1}{4} \ln x + \frac{9}{8} \ln (x - 2) - \frac{7}{8} (x + 2) + C$

Find the following integrals:

7. $\int x2^x\, dx$

8. $\int \left(\dfrac{x^3}{x^2 - 2x - 3} \right) dx$

9. $\int \left(\dfrac{x^2 + 1}{x^3 + x^2 - 2x} \right) dx$

10. $\int \left(\dfrac{2x^2 - 3x - 2}{x^3 + x^2 - 2x} \right) dx$

11. $\int_0^1 xe^x\, dx$

12. $\int_0^2 x^2 e^{-x}\, dx$

13. In Example 6, Chapter 2, the formula for the production cost of the xth unit (incorporating learnings effects) was given as

$$U(x) = U(1) - xb$$

where b is the learning effect. Show that the total production cost for y units is given by

$$T(y) = U(1)y - \frac{y^2 b}{2}$$

Compare this result with that obtained in the example and explain the difference. Sketch a graph of $T(y)$ for values of y between 1 and 20 and $b = 0.8$.

14. Show that if $U(x) = U(1)x^b \qquad -1 < b < 0$,

$$T(y) = \frac{U(1)y^{b+1}}{b + 1}$$

15. Develop a general model for the problem presented in Example 7. Assume there is an activity which has an initial cost A, a decreasing gross earnings $E(t)$, an increasing repair cost $R(t)$ and a decreasing salvage value $S(t)$, and that future costs and benefits are discounted continuously at rate δ.

(a) Show that the present value of the activity, if it is terminated after x years, is

$$P(x) = -A + \int_0^x [E(t) - R(t)]e^{-\delta t}\, dt + S(x)e^{-\delta x}$$

(b) Show that optimum time to terminate the activity is x^* where x^* is the solution of the equation

$$E(x) - R(x) + \frac{dS(x)}{dx} - \delta S(x) = 0$$

(*c*) State the conditions on the functions which are necessary for a unique solution. Use second-order conditions.

(*d*) Verify the conclusion for the special case considered in the example.

B. DIFFERENTIAL EQUATIONS

Definition

An equation which contains the derivative of an unknown function is called a differential equation. Examples are:

$$\frac{dy}{dx} = cx \tag{1}$$

$$a\frac{d^2y}{dx^2} + b\frac{dy}{dx} = g(x) \tag{2}$$

$$\left(\frac{dy}{dx}\right)^2 + xy(x) = b(x) \tag{3}$$

Solving a differential means finding the function which satisfies the equation. For example, (1) can be solved by separating the variables and integrating

$$\int dy = c \int x \, dx$$

$$y = \frac{cx^2}{2} + C$$

In working with differential equations it is common practice to treat *dy* and *dx* as differentials and to manipulate them separately, as was done above. The unknown constant, C, can be determined if the value of the function $y(x)$ is known for some x; i.e., if $y(0)$ is known to be 5, then

$$y(x) = \frac{cx^2}{2} + 5$$

Differentiating gives

$$\frac{dy}{dx} = cx$$

which shows that the solution satisfies the differential equation (1).

Differential equations are commonly categorized by *order* and *degree*. The *order* of a differential equation is the order of the highest order derivative appearing in it. The largest exponent of the derivative of highest order in the equation is the *degree* of the equation. Thus the equation (1) is of first order and first degree, equation (2) is of second order and first degree, and equation (3) is of first order and second degree. All three are ordinary differential equations since they contain only one independent variable; a partial differential equation contains partial derivatives. In general, the problem of solving differential equations is very difficult; in this section only certain equations of the first order and first degree will be considered. For a comprehensive treatment, see the texts listed in Notes and References.

Separable Variables

One of the simplest differential equations is one in which the variables can be separated so that the equation can be written in the form

$$M(x) + N(y)\frac{dy}{dx} = 0 \tag{4}$$

The solution is given by

$$\int M(x)\,dx + \int N(y)\,dy = C \tag{5}$$

and can be evaluated if the integrals can be determined.

Example 1.   The differential equation

$$e^x + 3y^2\frac{dy}{dx} = 0$$

has the solution:

$$\int e^x\,dx + 3\int y^2\,dy = C$$

$$e^x + y^3 = C$$

Differentiating gives

$$e^x + 3y^2\frac{dy}{dx} = 0$$

Example 2.   The differential equation

$$kg(t) - \frac{1}{y}\frac{dy}{dt} = 0 \tag{6}$$

which may be written as

$$\frac{1}{y}\frac{dy}{dt} = kg(t) \qquad \text{or} \qquad \frac{dy}{dt} = kyg(t)$$

has the solution:

$$\int kg(t)\,dt - \int \frac{1}{y}\,dy = C$$

or

$$k \int g(t)\,dt - \ln y = C$$

$$y = C_1 e^{k\int g(t)\,dt} \qquad \text{where} \qquad C_1 = e^{-C} \tag{7}$$

Differentiating gives

$$\frac{dy}{dx} = [C_1 \, e^{k\int g(t)\,dt}]kg(t) = ykg(t)$$

Homogeneous Equations

A differential equation of the form:

$$M(x, y) + N(x, y)\frac{dy}{dx} = 0 \tag{8}$$

is said to be homogeneous if it can be written in the form

$$\frac{dy}{dx} = f\left(\frac{y}{x}\right)$$

Such equations may be solved by making the substitution

$$y = vx \qquad \text{or} \qquad \frac{y}{x} = v$$

thus obtaining an equation in which the variables are separable.

Example 3.   To solve the equation

$$y^2 + x^2 \frac{dy}{dx} = xy\frac{dy}{dx}$$

write it in the form

$$y^2 + (x^2 - xy)\frac{dy}{dx} = 0$$

$$\frac{dy}{dx} = \frac{y^2}{xy - x^2} = \frac{(y/x)^2}{(y/x) - 1}$$

Substituting $y = vx$ gives

$$x\frac{dv}{dx} + v = -\frac{v^2}{1 - v}$$

or

$$x(1 - v)\,dv + v\,dx = 0$$

The variables may be separated by dividing by vx to give

$$\frac{dx}{x} + \frac{(1-v)\,dv}{v} = 0$$

Thus,

$$\int \left(\frac{1}{x}\right) dx + \int \frac{dv}{v} - \int dv = C$$

$$\ln x + \ln v - v = C$$

$$\ln vx = C + v$$

$$vx = e^{C+v} = e^C e^v$$

since e^C is a constant $= C_1$

$$vx = C_1 e^v$$

Since $v = y/x$, the solution is

$$y = C_1 e^{y/x}$$

Differentiating gives

$$\frac{dy}{dx} = \frac{(y/x)^2}{(y/x) - 1}$$

Linear Equations

A differential equation of first order and first degree of the form

$$\frac{dy}{dx} + P(x)y = Q(x) \tag{9}$$

is said to be linear in y. Note that y appears to the first power only and that P and Q are not functions of y. The general method of solution consists of multiplying the equation by a function $I(x)$, known as the integrating factor, which makes the left-hand side of (9) the exact differential of the product

$$yI(x) \tag{10}$$

That is, $I(x)$ must satisfy the relation:

$$\frac{d}{dx}\left[y(x)I(x)\right] = I(x)\frac{dy}{dx} + y\frac{dI(x)}{dx} \tag{11}$$

Multiplying (9) by $I(x)$ gives

$$I(x)\frac{dy}{dx} + I(x)P(x)y = I(x)Q(x) \tag{12}$$

The left-hand side of (12) is the same as the right-hand side of (11) if

$$\frac{dI(x)}{dx} = I(x)P(x)$$

This differential equation has been solved in Example 2 (with $y = I$, $g = P$, and $k = 1$) and the solution therefore is

$$I(x) = e^{\int P(x)\, dx} \tag{13}$$

Hence (9) can be written as

$$\frac{d}{dx}[yI(x)] = I(x)Q(x)$$

where $I(x)$ is given by (13) and the solution to (9) is

$$y(x)I(x) = \int I(x)Q(x)\, dx + C$$

or

$$y(x) = \frac{1}{I(x)}\left[\int I(x)Q(x)\, dx + C\right]$$

$$= e^{-\int P(x)\, dx}\left[\int Q(x)(e^{\int P(x)\, dx})\, dx + C\right] \tag{14}$$

Example 4.   To solve

$$\frac{dy}{dx} + \frac{y}{x} = x^2 \tag{15}$$

compute the integrating factor by (13)

$$I(x) = e^{\int 1/x\, dx} = e^{\ln x} = x$$

The solution to (15) is given by

$$I(x)y(x) = \int x^3\, dx + C = \frac{x^4}{4} + C$$

or

$$y(x) = \frac{x^3}{4} + \frac{C}{x}$$

This result could also be obtained by substituting $P(x) = 1/x$ and $Q(x) = x^2$ in (14).

Differentiating gives

$$\frac{dy}{dx} = \frac{3x^2}{4} - \frac{C}{x^2} = -\frac{1}{x}\left[\frac{x^3}{4} + \frac{C}{x}\right] + x^2 = -\frac{y}{x} + x^2$$

Example 5. In Chapter 7 it was shown that the value at the end of n periods of receiving an amount b per period, uniformly over each period with continuous compounding at rate δ, is

$$S = \frac{b(e^{\delta n} - 1)}{\delta}$$

This result can also be obtained by stating the problem as a differential equation: the rate of growth of S is the sum of compounding rate, δ, applied to S plus the amount added each period, b, or

$$\frac{dS(t)}{dt} = \delta S(t) + b$$

$$\frac{dS(t)}{dt} - \delta S(t) = b$$

The integrating factor for this linear equation of first order and first degree is

$$I(t) = e^{\int -\delta dt} = e^{-\delta t}$$

$$e^{-\delta t}S(t) = \int be^{-\delta t}\, dt + C = -\frac{b}{\delta} e^{-\delta t} + C$$

$$S(t) = -\frac{b}{\delta} + Ce^{\delta t}$$

If $S(0) = 0$, then:

$$0 = -\frac{b}{\delta} + C; \qquad C = \frac{b}{\delta}$$

and

$$S(t) = \frac{b}{\delta}(e^{\delta t} - 1) \tag{16}$$

which is the same result as obtained earlier if $t = n$.

One advantage of this use of differential equations is that the amount added, b, which appears on the right-hand side, can be any arbitrary function of t, say, $b(t)$. In particular, consider the case where the amount added increases linearly with time; then

$$b(t) = \beta t$$

where β is a constant.

The differential equation becomes

$$\frac{dS(t)}{dt} - \delta S(t) = \beta t$$

The integrating factor is the same as before and

$$e^{-\delta t}S(t) = \int \beta t e^{-\delta t} + C$$

$$= \beta \left(\frac{t}{\delta} e^{-\delta t} - \frac{e^{-\delta t}}{\delta^2} \right) + C$$

$$S(t) = \frac{\beta t}{\delta} - \frac{\beta}{\delta^2} + C e^{\delta t}$$

At $t = 0$, $S = 0$; $0 = -\frac{\beta}{\delta^2} + C$ or $C = \frac{\beta}{\delta^2}$

$$S(t) = \frac{\beta}{\delta^2} [e^{\delta t} - 1] + \frac{\beta t}{\delta} \tag{17}$$

EXERCISES

Show that the following differential equations have the solution indicated:

1. $\dfrac{1}{x} + \dfrac{1}{y}\dfrac{dy}{dx} = 0$ $xy = C$

2. $\dfrac{dy}{dx} = \dfrac{1 + y^2}{(1 + x^2)xy}$ $\ln (1 + x^2)(1 + y^2) = 2 \ln x - C$

3. $\dfrac{dy}{dx} = \dfrac{1 - x}{1 - y}$ $y\left(1 - \dfrac{y}{2}\right) - x\left(1 - \dfrac{x}{2}\right) = C$

4. $(x + 2y) + (2x - 3y)\dfrac{dy}{dx} = 0$ $x^2 + 4xy - 3y^2 = C$

5. $\dfrac{dy}{dx} + 2xy = 2e^{-x^2}$ $y = (2x + C)e^{-x^2}$

6. $x \ln x \dfrac{dy}{dx} + y = 2 \ln x$ $y \ln x = (\ln x)^2 + C$

Solve the following differential equations and verify the solution:

7. $\dfrac{dy}{dx} = xy^2$

8. $(e^{x-y})\dfrac{dy}{dx} + 1 = 0$

9. $xy - (1 + x^2)\dfrac{dy}{dx} = 0$

10. $(2 + y) - (3 - x)\dfrac{dy}{dx} = 0$

11. $(1 - x)\dfrac{dy}{dx} - y^2 = 0$

12. $(2x + y) + (x + 3y)\dfrac{dy}{dx} = 0$

13. $\dfrac{dy}{dx} = \dfrac{1 + y^2}{1 + x^2}$

14. $\dfrac{dy}{dx} + 3y = e^{2x}$

15. $xy - \dfrac{dy}{dx} - y^3 e^{-x^2} = 0$

16. $(x + 2y^3)\dfrac{dy}{dx} = y$

17. $\dfrac{df}{dx} = af\left(1 - \dfrac{f}{be^{cx}}\right) - rf$ *Hint:* Let $f = ye^{cx}$.

18. Suppose a fund contains an amount a now. In the future amounts will be added at the rate $b(t)$ at time t. The value of the fund at time t with continuous compounding at the rate δ is given by

$$S(t) = ae^{\delta t} + \int_0^t b(t)e^{\delta(t-x)}\,dx$$

Develop this formula and use it to prove (16) and (17) in Example 5.

19. Use the differential equation method to determine $S(t)$ when the rate at which money is added is quadratic:

$$b(t) = \alpha + \beta t + \gamma t^2$$

20. The earnings of the Unbreakable Toy Co. increase linearly throughout each year:

$$b(t) = \alpha + \beta t \qquad 0 < t < 1$$

At the beginning of the next year, earnings again start at α and increase linearly, and so on. The value of α and β have not changed in the past several years and are not expected to change in the future. The International Motor Co. is considering diversification and is willing to purchase the Unbreakable Toy Co. from its owner for the present value of all future earnings, assuming continuous discounting at the rate δ. How much will the owner receive?

21. "Trading on the equity" has been defined by Hunt [1961] to be

$$g(s) = \dfrac{1}{s}\left[1 - \dfrac{C}{Y}(1 - s)i\right]$$

where g = "trading on the equity"
$\quad s$ = proportion of common stock in the total capitalization of the firm $(0 < s \le 1)$
$\quad C$ = total capitalization of the firm
$\quad Y$ = amount of earnings (before interest and taxes)
$\quad i$ = cost of debt expressed as an interest rate

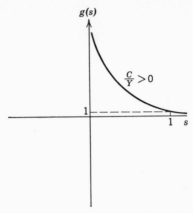

Figure 8.5 "Trading on the equity" $g(s)$ as a function of s.

If i is a constant, $g(s)$ has the form shown in Fig. 8.5. Use differential equations to determine the conditions under which $g(s)$ is a decreasing function of s, if i is assumed to be a function of s. Assume C/Y is positive.

C. DIFFERENTIAL EQUATION MODEL

A firm produces a single product and sells it in a market which can absorb no more than M dollars of the product per unit of time.

Assumption I

If the firm does no advertising, its rate of sales at any point in time will decrease at a rate proportional to the rate of sales at that time.
Let

$$S(t) = \text{rate of sales at time } t$$

$$\lambda = \text{a constant } (\lambda > 0)$$

The change in the rate of sales is given by $dS(t)/dt$, and by assumption 1

$$\frac{dS(t)}{dt} = -\lambda S(t) \tag{1}$$

This differential equation may be rewritten as

$$\frac{dS(t)}{S(t)} = -\lambda \, dt \tag{2}$$

and integrating both sides gives

$$\ln S(t) = -\lambda t + c$$

When $t = 0$, $S(t) = S_0$. Hence the constant is

$$\ln S_0 = 0 + c$$

and

$$\ln S(t) = -\lambda t + \ln S_0$$

Raising both sides to the power e gives

$$S(t) = S_0 e^{-\lambda t} \tag{3}$$

Thus under this assumption the sales decrease exponentially with time, depending on the value of λ.

Assumption 2

If the firm advertises, the rate of sales will increase at a rate proportional to the rate of advertising, but this increase affects only that proportion of the market that is not already purchasing the product. Assumption 1 controls the other part of the market.

Let

$$A = \text{rate of advertising}$$

$$\gamma = \text{a constant } (\gamma > 0)$$

Then

$$\left[1 - \frac{S(t)}{M} \right] = \text{part of the market affected by advertising}$$

Under assumption 2 the change in the rate of sales is

$$\frac{dS(t)}{dt} = -\lambda S(t) + \gamma A \left[1 - \frac{S(t)}{M} \right] \tag{4}$$

For simplicity the function of time, $S(t)$, will be written as S. The equation, after rearranging terms, becomes

$$\frac{dS}{dt} + \left(\lambda + \frac{\gamma A}{M} \right) S = \gamma A \tag{5}$$

In order to integrate the left-hand side, it is necessary to multiply the equation by the yet undetermined integrating factor, $I(t)$:

$$I \frac{dS}{dt} + \left(\lambda + \frac{\gamma A}{M} \right) I S = I \gamma A \tag{6}$$

The left-hand side will be of the form

$$vu' + v'u$$

where $u = S$ and $v = I$ if

$$\frac{dI}{dt} = \left(\lambda + \frac{\gamma A}{M}\right)I = \beta I \qquad \text{where} \qquad \beta = \lambda + \frac{\gamma A}{M} \tag{7}$$

The differential equation (7) is of the same form as (2); hence it has the solution

$$I = e^{\beta t} \tag{8}$$

provided A is a constant independent of t.

Since

$$\frac{d(uv)}{dt} = v\frac{du}{dt} + u\frac{dv}{dt} \tag{9}$$

integrating (6) with the value of I given by (8) gives

$$\int\left\{I\frac{dS}{dt} + S\frac{dI}{dt}\right\} dt = \int d\{Se^{\beta t}\} = \int \gamma A e^{\beta t} dt$$

$$Se^{\beta t} = \frac{\gamma A}{\beta} e^{\beta t} + C$$

$$S = \frac{\gamma A}{\beta} + Ce^{-\beta t} \tag{10}$$

At $t = 0$, $S(t) = S_0$,

$$S_0 = \frac{\gamma A}{\lambda + \gamma A/M} + C = \frac{M\gamma A}{M\lambda + \gamma A} + C$$

$$C = S_0 - \frac{M\gamma A}{M\lambda + \gamma A}$$

and

$$S(t) = \frac{M\gamma A}{M\lambda + \gamma A} + \left(S_0 - \frac{M\gamma A}{M\lambda + \gamma A}\right)e^{-(\lambda + \gamma A/M)t} \tag{11}$$

Several applications of this result will be described.

CASE I. *Constant advertising for a period, followed by no advertising.* To consider the case where advertising is constant for a given period and is then stopped, let a equal the total amount spent on advertising. Then

$$A(t) = \frac{a}{T} \qquad 0 \leq t \leq T$$

$$= 0 \qquad T < t \tag{12}$$

Then, from (11),

$$S(t) = \frac{M\gamma a}{TM\lambda + \gamma a} + \left[S_0 - \frac{M\gamma a}{TM\lambda + \gamma a}\right]e^{-(\lambda + \gamma a/TM)t} \qquad 0 \le t \le T$$

$$= S(T)e^{-\lambda(t-T)} \qquad\qquad\qquad\qquad T < t \qquad (13)$$

since (3) applies for $t > T$.

The form of $S(t)$ is shown in Fig. 8.6.

CASE II. *Single "pulse" campaign.* Suppose the amount a is spent in an extremely short period (such as one big TV program). The increase in the rate of sales is obtained by taking the limit of (13) as $T \to 0$:

$$S(0^+) = \lim_{T \to 0} S(T) = M + [S_0 - M]e^{-\gamma a/M} \qquad (14)$$

The immediate increase in sales is given by

$$S(0^+) - S_0 = M - S_0 + S_0 e^{-\gamma a/M} - Me^{-\gamma a/M}$$

$$= (M - S_0)(1 - e^{-\gamma a/M}) \qquad (15)$$

Thereafter the sales will decrease exponentially.

If there has been no advertising at all, the total sales from time $t = 0$ on are given by

$$\int_0^\infty S_0 e^{-\lambda t}\, dt \qquad (16)$$

The total sales from time $t = 0$ on, under a single advertising pulse, are given by

$$\int_0^\infty S(0^+)e^{-\lambda t}\, dt \qquad (17)$$

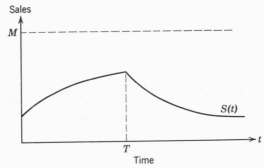

Figure 8.6 Sales as a function of time, with constant advertising up to time T and no advertising thereafter.

Hence the total additional sales from the advertising are

$$\int_0^\infty [S(0^+) - S_0] e^{-\lambda t} \, dt = \frac{(M - S_0)(1 - e^{-\gamma a/M})}{\lambda} \tag{18}$$

EXERCISES

Assuming that the parameters λ, γ are constant for all $t > 0$, and that in each period the amount $\$a$ is available for advertising, determine which of the following would maximize total sales for $0 \le t \le \infty$.

1. An advertising "pulse" once at the beginning of each period.
2. Constant advertising throughout each period.
3. Constant advertising at the beginning of each period for a kth part of the period ($0 < k < 1$) and then no advertising for the rest of the period.
4. Linear increase in advertising throughout each period starting with an amount $\$k$. (*Hint:* Note that $A(t)$ a function of t, hence (8) must be modified.)
5. If the maximum occurs for 3 or 4, determine the optimum value of k.

D. DIFFUSION MODELS

Basic Diffusion Model

Consider a group of people in which only certain members possesses a particular piece of information. Suppose that the total number of persons in the group under consideration remains constant and that diffusion of information only occurs through personal contact. The number of "contacts" made by an "average" person in an arbitrary unit of time is given by a "contact coefficient"; this coefficient is a *fixed* pure number which is the same for all members of the group. In a contact, the contactee receives the information if he does not already have it; if he already has it, the contact is wasted so far as increasing the number of people who have the information is concerned.

Let $K(0) \equiv K_0$ = number of informed participants in the group at time 0.

N = total number of participants in the group.

c = contact coefficient; the number of contacts made by one informed person per unit time, and

$K(t)$ = number of informed participants at time t

Then $\dfrac{K(t)}{N}$ = proportion of informed persons in the group at time t

$1 - \dfrac{K(t)}{N}$ = proportion of "uninformed" persons in the group at time t

$cK(t) \, dt$ = contacts made during a time interval dt

The increase in the total number of informed during a short interval of time dt is obtained by multiplying the number of contacts by the proportion of persons who do not possess the information, since only contacts with uninformed group members leads to an increase in informed members:

$$dK(t) = cK(t)\, dt \left(1 - \frac{K(t)}{N}\right)$$

This is the differential equation:

$$\frac{dK(t)}{dt} = cK(t)\left[1 - \frac{K(t)}{N}\right] \tag{1}$$

or, rearranging terms:

$$\frac{dK(t)}{K(t)[-(1/N)K(t) + 1]} = c\, dt \tag{2}$$

The left-hand side is of the form $\dfrac{dx}{x(\alpha x + \beta)}$ and can be integrated after being expanded into partial fractions. For example, suppose:

$$\frac{1}{x(\alpha x + \beta)} = \frac{A}{x} + \frac{B}{(\alpha x + \beta)}$$

or

$$1 = A(\alpha x + \beta) + Bx = (A\alpha + B)x + A\beta$$

then, equating coefficients of like powers of x gives:

$$\alpha A + B = 0$$
$$A\beta = 1$$

Thus:

$$A = \frac{1}{\beta} \qquad B = -\frac{\alpha}{\beta}$$

Returning to equation (2), let $\alpha = -\dfrac{1}{N} \qquad \beta = 1$

Substituting and writing (2) in terms of partial fractions gives

$$\left[\frac{1}{K} + \frac{1}{N}\left(\frac{1}{1 - K/N}\right)\right] dK = c\, dt$$

Integrating gives

$$\ln K - \ln \frac{(N - K)}{N} = ct + C'$$

$$\ln \frac{K}{1 - K/N} = ct + C'$$

or

$$\frac{K}{1 - K/N} = e^{ct+C'} = e^{ct} \cdot e^{C'} \tag{3}$$

The constant $e^{C'}$ can be obtained by using the fact that $K = K_0$ when $t = 0$; hence:

$$\frac{K_0}{1 - K_0/N} = e^{c0}e^{C'} = e^{C'}$$

and, substituting in (3) gives

$$\frac{K}{1 - K/N} = \frac{K_0}{1 - K_0/N} e^{ct}$$

Solving for K gives the number of informed participants as a function of t:

$$\frac{NK}{N - K} = e^{ct}\frac{NK_0}{N - K_0}$$

$$K\left[1 + e^{ct}\frac{K_0}{N - K_0}\right] = Ne^{ct}\frac{K_0}{N - K_0}$$

$$K(t) = \frac{Ne^{ct}K_0}{N - K_0 + K_0e^{ct}}$$

Dividing by N and dividing the denominator and numerator by $e^{ct}K_0$ gives

$$\frac{K(t)}{N} = \frac{1}{1 + (N/K_0 - 1)e^{-ct}} \tag{4}$$

From (4) it follows that as t approaches infinity, $K(t)/N$ approaches unity since the second term of the denominator goes to zero. Hence, eventually everyone in the group will be informed.

The rate at which all members of the group become informed is dependent on the value of the contact coefficient and on the number of informed participants at time $t = 0$. The larger the c is, the faster the factor $K(t)/N$ will approach one; and the more informed participants at t equal to zero, the faster all the participants will become informed.

Diffusion Model Incorporating Growth and Advertising

Suppose next that the "information" in the model given above is about the product of a firm, and assume that the firm can influence the number of contacts by spending money for "advertising." In particular, it can increase the number of contacts made by the informed people (above the ones included in c) by an additional number a per unit of time.

Suppose further that the number of members of the total group grows at a constant rate and that the number of members who are removed from the group is a certain fixed proportion of the total members of the group.

Let a = additional contact coefficient: the number of contacts by one informed person per unit time

N_0 = number of members in the group at $t = 0$

g = rate at which new members are added to the group

r = rate at which members are removed from the group

Then $aK(t)\, dt$ = number of additional contacts made in the time interval dt

e^{gt} = growth factor

$N(t) = N_0 e^{gt}$ number of members at time t

$rK(t)\, dt$ = informed persons removed from the group in time dt

The increase in the number of informed persons

$$= dK(t)/dt$$

is the increase due to normal contact,

$$cK(t)\left[1 - \frac{K(t)}{N(t)}\right]$$

plus the increase due to additional contacts,

$$aK(t)\left[1 - \frac{K(t)}{N(t)}\right]$$

less the number of persons removed, $rK(t)$.

Hence, the differential equation becomes:

$$\frac{dK(t)}{dt} = [cK(t) + aK(t)]\left[1 - \frac{K(t)}{N(t)}\right] - rK(t)$$

Substituting $N(t) = N_0 e^{gt}$ and dropping the function notation for K,

$$\frac{dK}{dt} = [c + a]K\left[1 - \frac{K}{N_0 e^{gt}}\right] - rK \tag{5}$$

To solve this differential equation let:

$$K(t) = y(t)e^{gt} \tag{6}$$

where $y(t)$ = an as yet undetermined function.

Differentiating (6) gives:

$$\frac{dK}{dt} = \left[\frac{dy}{dt} + gy\right]e^{gt} \tag{7}$$

Substituting (6) and (7) into (5) and dividing by e^{gt} gives:

$$\frac{dy}{dt} + gy = (c + a)y\left(1 - \frac{y}{N_0}\right) - ry$$

or

$$\frac{dy}{dt} = y\left[(c + a) - (g + r) - \frac{(c + a)}{N_0}y\right]$$

This differential equation can be written as

$$\frac{dy}{y(\alpha y + \beta)} = dt$$

$$\frac{dy}{\beta y} - \frac{\alpha \, dy}{\beta(\alpha y + \beta)} = dt$$

using partial fractions where

$$\beta = (c + a) - (g + r) \qquad \alpha = -\frac{c + a}{N_0} \tag{8}$$

Integrating gives:

$$\frac{1}{\beta} \ln y - \frac{1}{\beta} \ln (\alpha y + \beta) = t + C$$

where C is a constant

$$\ln \frac{y}{\alpha y + \beta} = \beta(t + C)$$

$$\frac{y}{\alpha y + \beta} = e^{\beta t} \cdot e^{\beta C}$$

Or, solving for y:

$$y[1 - \alpha e^{\beta t} e^{\beta C}] = \beta e^{\beta t} \cdot e^{\beta C}$$

Substituting for y in (6) gives K as:

$$K = \frac{\beta e^{\beta t} e^{\beta C} e^{gt}}{1 - \alpha e^{\beta t} e^{\beta c}} = \frac{\beta e^{\beta t} e^{gt}}{e^{-\beta C} - \alpha e^{\beta t}} \tag{9}$$

The constant C can be determined by noting that $t = 0$, $K = K(0) = K_0$; therefore

$$K_0 = \frac{\beta}{e^{-\beta C} - \alpha}, \qquad e^{-\beta C} = \frac{\beta + \alpha K_0}{K_0}$$

or

$$e^{\beta C} = \frac{K_0}{\alpha K_0 + \beta}$$

Substituting this value into (9) gives

$$K = \frac{\beta e^{\beta t + gt}}{\dfrac{\alpha K_0 + \beta}{K_0} - \alpha e^{\beta t}}$$

By multiplying numerator and denominator by $e^{-(\beta + g)t}$,

$$K = \frac{\beta}{\dfrac{(\alpha K_0 + \beta)}{K_0} e^{-(\beta + g)t} - \alpha e^{-gt}}$$

By substituting the values for α and β from (8), the expression becomes

$$K = \frac{(c + a) - (g + r)}{\dfrac{-(c + a)K_0 + \beta N_0}{K_0 N_0} e[^{-(c+a-r)t}] - \alpha e^{-gt}}$$

The final expression arrived at by suitable algebraic manipulation, noting that $N(t) = N_0 e^{gt}$, is

$$\frac{K(t)}{N(t)} = \frac{(c + a) - (g + r)}{(c + a) + \left[\left[\dfrac{N_0}{K_0} - 1\right](c + a) - \dfrac{N_0}{K_0}(g + r)\right]e^{-[(c+a)-(g+r)]t}} \tag{10}$$

The critical parameter in this model is the ratio

$$\frac{g + r}{c + a} = \frac{\text{growth rate} + \text{removal rate}}{\text{contact coefficient} + \text{additional contact coefficient}}$$

which will be denoted by ρ.

If $\rho \geq 1$, $\lim\limits_{t \to \infty} \dfrac{K(t)}{N(t)} = 0$

If the sum of the growth rate and removal rate equals or exceeds the sum of the contact and additional contact coefficients, the ratio of informed people to the total approaches zero and then stays there.

If $\rho < 1$, $\lim\limits_{t \to \infty} \dfrac{K(t)}{N(t)} = 1 - \dfrac{g + r}{c + a} = 1 - \rho$ \tag{11}

The "equilibrium" ratio of persons "informed" to the total members in a group is always less than one; never under the conditions of the model does the whole population become informed. The rate of informed people to the total number will approach $1 - \rho$ and then stay there. The greater the value of ρ, the faster will the equilibrium ratio be reached. As the additional contact coefficient a increases, ρ decreases, and hence the ratio of informed people to the total increases.

An Optimization Model

In the model discussed above, it was assumed that a firm could influence the value of a by its advertising expenditures. Let the cost to the firm of a single additional contact be p, assume that the firm cannot change its selling price, y, that each informed person buys k units of the firm's product per unit of time, and that the total production cost is a linear function of the quantity produced.

What is the optimum value of a to maximize the earnings for the firm at equilibrium? As the firm spends more on "advertising," the value of a will increase and the number of buyers will increase. However, as a increases the ratio K/N approaches 1 and a larger proportion of contacts is wasted because the contactees are already informed.

The Earnings function as a function of the quantity produced per period is given by

$$\text{Earnings} = \text{Revenue} - \text{Production Cost} - \text{Advertising Cost}$$

$$E(x) = yx - (u + vx) - apK \tag{12}$$

where x = number of units produced per unit of time
　　　= kK by assumption
　　k = number of units purchased by each informed person per unit of time
　　K = number of informed persons at equilibrium
　　u = fixed production cost
　　v = variable production cost
　　y = selling price per unit
　　a = number of additional contacts due to advertising made by each informed person per unit of time
　　p = cost of one additional contact

From (11), at equilibrium

$$K = N\left[1 - \frac{g+r}{c+a}\right] \quad \text{and, by assumption, } K = \frac{x}{k}$$

$$\frac{x}{kN} = 1 - \frac{g+r}{c+a} \tag{13}$$

$$a = (g+r)\left[1 - \frac{x}{kN}\right]^{-1} - c$$

and

$$\frac{da}{dx} = (g+r)\left(\frac{1}{kN}\right)\left[1 - \frac{x}{kN}\right]^{-2}$$

$$\frac{dK}{dx} = \frac{1}{k}$$

The optimum value of x is obtained by setting the derivative of $E(x)$, from (12), with respect to x equal to zero.

From (12),

$$\frac{dE(x)}{dx} = y - v - pK\frac{da}{dx} - pa\frac{dK}{dx}$$

$$= y - v - \frac{Kp(g+r)}{Nk\left(1 - \dfrac{x}{kN}\right)^2} - \frac{pa}{k}$$

$$= y - v - \frac{p(g+r)}{k\left(1 - \dfrac{x}{kN}\right)^2} + \frac{pc}{k}$$

$$= \frac{p}{k}\left\{\frac{k}{p}[y - v] + c - \frac{g+r}{\left(1 - \dfrac{x}{kN}\right)^2}\right\}$$

Let $m = \dfrac{k(y-v)}{p}$. Then m is the net revenue obtained from each informed person per unit expenditure of advertising.

$$\frac{dE(x)}{dx} = 0 \quad \text{if} \quad m + c = \frac{g+r}{\left(1 - \dfrac{x^*}{kN}\right)^2}$$

or

$$\left(1 - \frac{x^*}{kN}\right)^2 = \frac{g+r}{m+c}$$

$$x^* = kN\left[1 - \left(\frac{g+r}{m+c}\right)^{1/2}\right] \tag{14}$$

This value of x will result in maximum earnings since

$$\frac{d^2E(x)}{dx} = -\frac{2p}{k^2N}\frac{(g+r)}{\left(1 - \dfrac{x}{kN}\right)^3} < 0 \quad \text{if} \quad \frac{x}{kN} < 1$$

The value of a, which is necessary to sell the quantity x^*, is obtained by substituting (14) into (13) since the equilibrium condition (13) must hold:

$$a^* = \sqrt{(c+m)(g+r)} - c \tag{15}$$

The net revenues obtainable from each informed person per unit expenditure on advertising, m, is positive whenever selling price exceeds variable production cost. Therefore, the more informed people, the greater will be net revenue received by the firm. However, advertising costs rise and there is an optimum level of advertising expenditure. The important point is that this optimum level is reached before all the people in the group are informed. This represents an explanation for the empirically observed phenomenon that firms do not usually find capturing 100% of a market worthwhile.

Additional conclusions are also in accordance with practical experience.

1. As the variable cost, v, increases, the net revenue per person m decreases and the optimum output x^* (14) decreases.

2. As p, the cost of an additional contact, decreases, m increases and x^* increases.

3. "a^*" is directly proportional to the square root of the sum of growth and removal rates, $(g + r)$. Advertising is more effective if there are many "uninformed," and gets less and less effective as the number of "informed" persons grows.

EXERCISES

1. Compute the earnings if

$$g = 0.2; \quad r = 0.2; \quad c = 0.5; \quad k = 2; \quad y = 6; \quad q = 1; \quad v = 1.25$$

and show that the optimum value of x is such that $K/N = 0.8$.

2. Discuss more explicitly than was done in the text the effect of change in the parameters g, c, r, s, v, and y on the optimum value of the variables x^*, a^* and $E(x^*)$.

3. Dorfman and Steiner [1954] state "A firm which can influence the demand for its product by advertising will, in order to maximize its profits, choose the advertising budget and price such that the increase in gross revenue resulting from a one dollar increase in advertising expenditure is equal to the ordinary elasticity of demand for the firm's product," Show that this result holds for the model given above.

Notes and References

Section A

Integral calculus is covered in the basic texts on calculus or advanced calculus listed at the end of Chapter 5. A table of integrals is frequently helpful in practical problems. Many handbooks contain such tables; e.g.,

Dwight, H. B. (1955), *Table of Integrals and other mathematical data*. Macmillan, New York.
Gröbner, W. (1961), *Integraltafel*, Springer, Vienna.

Section B

For further study of differential equations, see:

Ford, L. R. (1955), *Differential Equations*, McGraw-Hill Book Co., New York.
Reddich, H. W., and Kibby, D. E. (1956), *Differential Equations*, 3rd ed., John Wiley and Sons, New York.

Exercise 21 was suggested by:
Hunt, P. (1961), "A Proposal for Precise Definitions of 'Trading on the Equity' and 'Leverage'," *J. Finance*, Vol. XVI, No. 3, pp. 377–386.

Section C

The model presented here is based on:
Vidale, M. L., and Wolfe, H. B. (1957), "An Operation-Research Study of Sales Response to Advertising," *Operations Research*, V, pp. 370–381. (Also reprinted in Bass, F. M., et al., Ed. (1961), *Mathematical Models and Methods in Marketing*, Richard D. Irwin, Homewood, Ill.)
It should be noted that the method of solution presented here assumes that the rate of advertising, A, is not a function of t. If it were, equation (8) would be changed.

Section D

The models presented are based on:
Ozya, S. A. (1960), "Imperfect Markets through Lack of Knowledge," *Quarterly J. Economics*, **74**, pp. 29–52.

The quotation in Exercise 3 is from
Dorfman, R., and Steiner, P. (1954), "Optimal Advertising and Optimal Quality," *American Economic Review*, XLIV, pp. 826–836. (Also reprinted in Bass, F. M. et al., Ed. (1961) *Mathematical Models and Methods in Marketing*, Richard D. Irwin, Homewood, Ill.)

Part Three

TWO-DECISION VARIABLE

OPTIMIZATION MODELS

Optimization of Functions

of Two-Decision Variables

The case of models with two-decision variables warrants separate treatment from the point of view of practical applications because problems with two-decision variables appear relatively frequently. Perhaps even more important is the fact that the techniques for dealing with many decision variables can best be explained and understood from a discussion of the two-variable case. Some aid is derived from geometrical intuition in three-dimensional space, and the notation is simpler.

This chapter discusses the theory of optimization of differentiable functions of two independent decision variables. Several examples are given in the next chapter. Chapter 11 is devoted to a study of optimization techniques when the decision variables are subject to constraints.

A. FUNCTIONS OF TWO VARIABLES

A function, u, is said to be a function of the variables x and y if a value of u can be determined for each set of values of x and y. The relationship is denoted, analogously to the notation used for functions of one variable, by

$$u = f(x, y)$$

The function may be defined for all possible values of x and y, or it may be defined only for certain values. The region of the x, y plane over which the function is defined is termed its domain of definition, R. A rectangular domain, for example, would be given by

$$a_1 \leq x \leq a_2 \qquad b_1 \leq y \leq b_2$$

Functions of one variable have been presented graphically in the previous chapters in a two-dimensional figure by a line or curve. The representation of a function of two variables requires a three-dimensional figure; the function is represented by a surface. Surfaces of three dimensions cannot be shown in a two-dimensional graph; some features of such surfaces, however, can be shown by the use of projective drawings or contour lines.

The particular functions which appear most frequently are generalizations of the ones studied in Chapters 5, 6, and 7.

The simplest function is the linear function of two variables

$$u(x, y) = a_{00} + a_{10}x + a_{01}y$$

The use of linear functions with only two variables, one independent and one dependent, was illustrated in Chapter 1. To represent business problems realistically, more variables and other functional relationships may be required. In this section several examples are considered.

Example I. Earnings Function for a Consulting Firm

Consider a consulting firm organized as shown in Fig. 9.1, with an executive office and two departments. The expenses associated with each are shown in parenthesis. The firm bills its customers for direct labor expended on a project plus a charge for overhead and profit which is directly proportional to the direct labor. For example, if the amount of direct labor on a project is \$100 and the charge rate is 0.5, the customer would be billed $100 + 0.50(100)$ or \$150.

The problem is to develop a general formula that gives the earnings of the firm in terms of the basic variables and parameters. Assuming that the revenues for any period can be associated with the costs incurred to produce them, the earnings for a given period are:

$$\text{Earnings} = \text{Revenues} - \text{Costs}$$

or

$$E = R - C$$

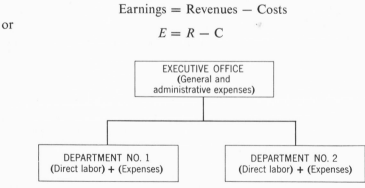

Figure 9.1

To express the revenue in functional form, let:

x_1 = the amount of direct labor expended in Department No. 1 (dollars)

r_1 = the charge rate for Department No. 1

R_1 = the total revenue due to Department No. 1 (dollars)

Then
$$R_1 = x_1 + r_1 x_1 = (1 + r_1)x_1 \qquad r_1 \geq 0; \quad x_1 \geq 0$$

If the subscript 2 is used to denote Department No. 2, then similarly
$$R_2 = (1 + r_2)x_2 \qquad r_2 \geq 0; \quad x_2 \geq 0$$

and
$$R = R_1 + R_1 = (1 + r_1)x_1 + (1 + r_2)x_2 = \sum_{i=1}^{2}(1 + r_i)x_i$$

The total cost, C, will be the sum of the costs incurred by the departments plus the cost incurred in the Executive Office. Assume studies have shown that in each department the total expenses can be expressed as a fixed expense independent of the amount of direct labor expended on projects, plus an additional expense which is directly proportional to the amount of direct labor. (If this could not be done, the firm would probably change the billing procedure to incorporate billing of unusual expenses.) To express the total cost for the ith department (where $i = 1$ or 2) let:

a_i = fixed expense in Department i (dollars)

b_i = proportion that variable expenses are of total direct labor in Department i

c_i = total cost of running Department i (dollars)

= fixed expense + variable (overhead) expense + direct labor expense

Then the total cost for the ith department is:
$$c_i = (a_i + b_i x_i) + x_i = a_i + (1 + b_i)x_i \qquad a_i \geq 0; \quad b_i \geq 0$$

The cost of running the Executive Office (General and Administrative Expenses) consists of a fixed cost plus costs proportional to the total costs in each of the departments, c_i; e.g.,
$$g = d_0 + d_1 c_1 + d_2 c_2 \qquad d_0 \geq 0; \quad d_1 \geq 0; \quad d_2 \geq 0$$

where g = General and Administrative Expenses, and d_0, d_1, and d_2 are parameters. The total cost of the firm, C, is then given by

$$\begin{aligned}
C = c_1 + c_2 + g &= a_1 + (b_1 + 1)x_1 + a_2 + (b_2 + 1)x_2 + d_0 \\
&\quad + d_1[a_1 + (b_1 + 1)x_1] + d_2[a_2 + (b_2 + 1)x_2] \\
&= [d_0 + a_1(d_1 + 1) + a_2(d_2 + 1)] + [(b_1 + 1)(d_1 + 1)]x_1 \\
&\quad + [(b_2 + 1)(d_2 + 1)]x_2
\end{aligned}$$

which is therefore a linear function of the two independent variables x_1 and x_2.

The earnings, $E = R - C$, are given by

$$E = [(1 + r_1) - (b_1 + 1)(d_1 + 1)]x_1 + [(1 + r_2) - (b_2 + 1)(d_2 + 1)]x_2$$
$$- [d_0 + a_1(d_1 + 1) + a_2(d_2 + 1)]$$

or, using the summation notation,

$$E = \sum_{i=1}^{2} [(1 + r_i) - (b_i + 1)(d_i + 1)]x_i - d_0 - \sum_{i=1}^{2} a_i(d_i + 1) \quad (1)$$

and this too is a linear function of the two variables x_1 and x_2.

If the parameters are

$$a_1 = 1,000 \qquad b_1 = 0.6$$
$$a_2 = 3,000 \qquad b_2 = 0.3$$
$$d_0 = 3,000 \qquad d_1 = 0.4 \qquad d_2 = 0.2$$
$$r_1 = 2 \qquad r_2 = 1.25$$

the Earnings function is

$$E(x_1, x_2) = [(1 + 2) - (0.6 + 1)(0.4 + 1)]x_1 + [(1 + 1.25) - (0.3 + 1)$$
$$\times (0.2 + 1)]x_2 - [3,000 + 1,000(0.4 + 1) + 3,000(0.2 + 1)]$$
$$= [3 - 2.24]x_1 + [2.25 - 1.56]x_2 - 8,000 \quad (2)$$
$$= 0.76x_1 + 0.69x_2 - 8,000 \quad (3)$$

Using this function the earnings can be computed for any set of values of the independent variables. For example, if

$$x_1 = 10,000 \qquad \text{and} \qquad x_2 = 5,000$$
$$E(10,000, 5,000) = 0.76(10,000) + 0.69(5,000) - 8,000 = 3,050$$

Since earnings are a function of two independent variables, there is no unique break-even point. Earnings will be zero whenever

$$0 = 0.76x_1 + 0.69x_2 - 8,000$$

or whenever

$$x_2 = \frac{8,000}{0.69} - \frac{0.76x_1}{0.69}$$

This is the equation of a line which is shown in Fig. 9.2 as the "break-even line." Any point on this line leads to zero earnings. The other lines shown

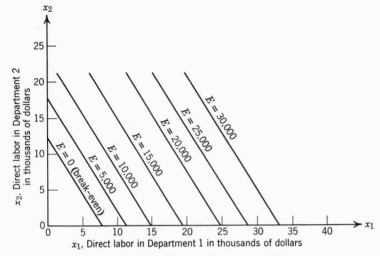

Figure 9.2 Constant earning lines.

in Fig. 9.2 are the solution to

$$E_0 = 0.76x_1 + 0.69x_2 - 8,000$$

where $E_0 = 5,000, 10,000, 15,000, 20,000$, etc. A manager can use Fig. 9.2 to determine earnings for any set of values x_1 and x_2.

In addition to serving as the basis for computing Fig. 9.2 the earnings function in the form given in (1) or (3) can be used as an aid in making decisions. Suppose a new project, which could be assigned to either department, is received. To which department should it be assigned if it can be assumed that the cost in direct labor will be the same in both departments?

The firm will try to make its earnings given by (3) as large as possible, and since $x_1 = x_2$ the numerical coefficients of the x terms are the critical measures of relative profitability. Department 1 will be chosen, since for every additional dollar of direct labor charge incurred, Dept. 1 earns $.76, whereas Dept. 2 earns $.69 for the firm.

Now suppose that, for competitive reasons, the firm bid K for the project. Does this affect the assignment?

The earnings function (2) can be written in the form

$$E(x_1, x_2) = 3x_1 - 2.24x_1 + 2.25x_2 - 1.56x_2 - 8,000$$

where $3x_1$ and $2.25x_2$ indicate revenues and $2.24x_1$ and $1.56x_2$ indicate costs in Departments 1 and 2, respectively. If the project is assigned to Dept. 1, the earnings will be

$$= K - 2.24x_1$$

since the revenue is K instead of $3x_1$; and if it is assigned to Dept. 2, earnings will be

$$= K - 1.56x_2$$

since the revenue in this case is K instead of $2.25x_2$.

Under the fixed fee arrangement, revenue is independent of the direct labor charge. Therefore, costs must be minimized in order to maximize earnings. The only cost figures pertinent are the costs which vary with the direct labor charge, since the fixed costs will be incurred in each department, regardless of whether or not that particular department gets the project. Since K is fixed, maximum earnings are achieved by minimizing the costs to be subtracted from K, and since $x_1 = x_2$, costs minimizing is achieved by selecting that department with smallest numerical coefficient of x_i; i.e., Dept. 2.

The important thing to note is that the charge rates r_1 and r_2 are not the only factors to be considered in making decisions in the firm. The final objective is to increase earnings which are affected by expenses as well as revenues. Formulas such as (1), (2), and (3), and much more complex ones which will be developed later, are useful to management because they summarize all the pertinent data.

Polynomials of Degree Two

The general polynomial of degree two in two variables is given by

$$u(x, y) = ax^2 + bxy + cy^2 + dx + ey + f$$

The use of polynomials is illustrated in Examples 2 and 3.

Example 2. The manager of a research and development division became interested in the cost of typing, reproducing, distributing, and filing reports. He asked a team to investigate this problem and they reported back as follows:

"Approximately 30 minutes per page is required to type the final draft, proofread it, and make the necessary corrections. Labor, including salary and overhead, is $4 an hour. The typing is done on a master which costs $0.10 per master (one master is required for each page of a report). The reproduction costs $0.50 per hundred sheets of paper plus 25¢ for inserting and removing the master from the reproducing machine. The collating and stapling is done by a machine which is amortized at $4 an hour and has an average rate of 2,000 sheets per hour. The addressing and mailing of the reports can be done at the rate of 50 copies per hour with labor worth $4 per hour. The cross-referencing and filing of the report can be done at the rate of 40 per hour at an average cost of $4 per hour."

Develop a relationship by which the manager can determine the cost of any given report, assuming that all copies of reports are mailed and all are filed. Sketch a graph showing the combination of independent variables yielding equal cost. Is this relationship linear?

Let t = typing and master costs/page = $\dfrac{\$4/\text{hr}}{2 \text{ pages/hr}}$ + \$0.10/page

$\qquad$ = \$2.10 page

$\quad r$ = reproducing costs/page = \$0.25/page + \$0.005/sheet

$$+ \dfrac{\$4/\text{hr}}{2,000 \text{ sheets/hr}}$$

$\qquad$ = \$0.25/page + \$0.007/sheet

$\qquad$ = \$0.25/page + \$0.007/copy/page

d = distribution costs/copy = $\dfrac{\$4/\text{hr}}{50 \text{ copies/hr}}$ = \$0.08/copy

f = filing costs/copy = $\dfrac{\$4/\text{hr}}{40 \text{ copies/hr}}$ = \$10/copy

x = No. of pages in a report

y = No. of copies of a report

T = total cost/report in dollars

Then $T = (t + r)x + (d + f)y$

$\qquad = (2.10 + 0.25 + 0.007y)x + (0.08 + 0.10)y$

$T(x, y) = 2.35x + 0.18y + 0.007xy \qquad\qquad\qquad (4)$

From (4) the manager can determine directly the cost of any report. $T(x, y)$ is a polynomial of second degree in x and y, and is not linear. The set of values of x and y which lead to a cost of \$10 is shown in Fig. 9.3.

Example 3.   The earnings of a certain store are given by

$$E(x, y) = 4x + 5y + xy - x^2 - y^2 + 5$$

where E = earnings in hundreds of thousands of dollars

$\qquad x$ = investment in inventory in hundreds of thousands of dollars

$\qquad y$ = floor space used for display in units of 10,000 square feet

The function $E(x, y)$ as a function of two variables is shown in Fig. 9.4. The contour lines $E(x, y) = C$ for several values of C are given in Fig. 9.5. Such contour lines are usually more useful, and much easier to draw, than the three dimensional figures such as Fig. 9.4. The method for

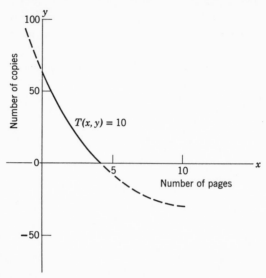

Figure 9.3 Values of x and y which lead to total cost of $10 for data in Example 2

drawing contour lines of f as a second-degree polynomial are described in standard texts in analytic geometry. A summary of the techniques is given in the Appendix C, page 690, for convenient reference.

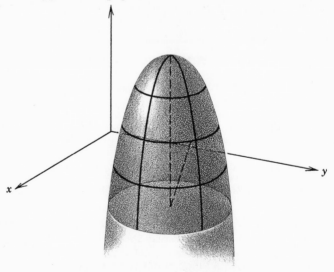

$$E(x, y) = 4x + 5y + xy - x^2 - y^2 + 5$$

Figure 9.4

Other Functions

Functions other than linear and second degree polynomials which also appear relatively frequently in business applications are the higher order polynomials and rational functions. Rational functions are quotients of

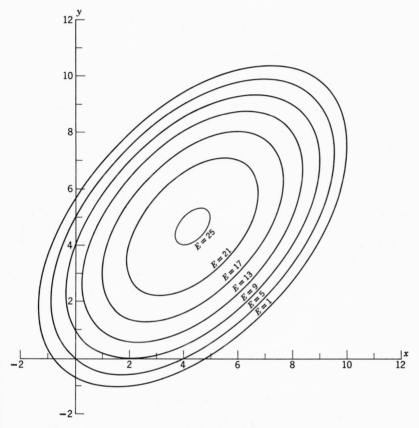

Figure 9.5   Contour lines for $E(x, y) = 4x + 5y + xy - x^2 - y^2 + 5$.

polynomials and are defined for all values except when the denominator is equal to zero. For example, the most general rational function of two variables with a second-degree polynomial in the denominator and a first-degree polynomial in the numerator is given by

$$u(x, y) = \frac{b_{10}x + b_{01}y + b_{00}}{a_{20}x^2 + a_{11}xy + a_{02}y^2 + a_{10}x + a_{01}y + a_{00}}$$

Example 4.   The future value of an investment with net cash flows

$$a_0, a_1, \ldots, a_n$$

was defined in Chapter 3, page 81, by the recurrence formula

$$
\begin{aligned}
F_0 &= a_0 \\
F_j(k, r) &= (1 + r)F_{j-1} + a_j &&\text{if } F_{j-1} \leq 0 \\
&= (1 + k)F_{j-1} + a_j &&\text{if } F_{j-1} > 0
\end{aligned}
\left.\rule{0pt}{3em}\right\} j = 1, \ldots, n
$$

If all $F_j(k, r)$ for $j < n$ are negative,

$$
\begin{aligned}
F_n(k, r) &= (1 + r)F_{n-1} + a_n \\
&= (1 + r)[(1 + r)F_{n-2} + a_{n-1}] + a_n \\
&= (1 + r)\{(1 + r)[(1 + r)F_{n-3} + a_{n-2}] + a_{n-1}\} + a_n \\
&\quad \cdot \quad \cdot \quad \cdot \quad \cdot \quad \cdot \quad \cdot \quad \cdot \quad \cdot \quad \cdot \quad \cdot \quad \cdot \\
&= (1 + r)^n a_0 + (1 + r)^{n-1} a_1 + \cdots + a_n
\end{aligned}
$$

In this case $F_n(k, r)$ is a polynomial of degree n in one variable $(1 + r)$. Similarly, if F_j for $j < n$ are all positive, $F_n(k, r)$ is a polynomial of degree n in one variable $(1 + k)$. However, if some F_j are positive and others are negative, $F_n(k, r)$ will be a polynomial of degree n in two variables $(1 + k)$ and $(1 + r)$ of the form

$$
\begin{aligned}
F_n(k, r) = a_0(1 + r)^{n-\alpha_0}(1 + k)^{\alpha_0} + a_1(1 + r)^{n-\alpha_1}(1 + k)^{\alpha_1} + \cdots \\
+ a_{n-1}(1 + r)^{n-\alpha_{n-1}}(1 + k)^{\alpha_{n-1}} + a_n
\end{aligned}
$$

where α_j is a non-negative integer and $\alpha_j \leq n - j$.

EXERCISES

1. Sketch constant earning lines for the firm in Example 1 if

$$
\begin{array}{ll}
a_1 = 1,000 & b_1 = 0.5 \\
a_2 = 3,000 & b_2 = 0.3 \\
d_0 = 3,000 & d_1 = 1.2 \qquad d_2 = 1.3 \\
r_1 = 2 & r_2 = 1.5
\end{array}
$$

2. The overhead rate of an organization is frequently defined as the expenses divided by the direct labor dollars. Develop the formulas for the overhead rate for each of the two departments and for the whole firm in Example 1. What are the relationships between the three rates?

3. The paint production of Eastern Paint Co. is given by

$$z = kx^\alpha y^{1-\alpha}$$

where z = number of gallons of paint produced per period
  x = labor cost per period ($)
  y = total value of equipment used ($)
  k = constant
  α = constant; $0 < \alpha < 1$
Sketch contour lines for different levels of production (z = a constant).
  4. Sketch contour lines for $F_n(k, r)$ defined in Example 4 where

$$a_0 = 24; \quad a_1 = -43; \quad a_2 = 35; \quad a_3 = -17; \quad a_4 = 1$$

for $r \geq -1, k \geq -1$.

B. CALCULUS OF FUNCTIONS OF TWO VARIABLES

Partial Derivatives

A function of two variables, $f(x, y)$, is said to approach a *limit*, L, at the point (a, b), if the difference between L and the value of the function in a very small region around the point (a, b) is arbitrarily small. This is symbolized by

$$\lim_{\substack{x \to a \\ y \to b}} f(x, y) = L$$

It is important to note that (x, y) can approach (a, b) through any sequence of points. For the function to be continuous, the limit must be L for any sequence.

A function $u = f(x, y)$ defined in a domain R is said to be continuous at a point (a, b) in R, if for all points (x, y) near (a, b) the value of the function is very close to $f(a, b)$ and if the difference becomes arbitrarily small if the point (x, y) is arbitrarily close enough to (a, b). This definition implies that (1) as (x, y) tends to (a, b) in R the function $f(x, y)$ must possess a limit L, and (2) the limit L must coincide with the value of the function at the point (a, b).

The essential difference between the concepts of limits and continuity for functions of two variables and those for functions of one variable is that the concepts refer to a small *region* around a point rather than to a small *interval* around a point.

As in the case of one variable, the sum, difference, and product of continuous functions of two variables are also continuous. The quotient of continuous functions is continuous except where the denominator vanishes. Continuous functions of continuous functions are themselves continuous. It follows that all polynomials are continuous and that all rational functions are continuous, except where the denominator vanishes.

The concepts of a limit and continuity at a point in the case of functions of one variable are generalized to functions of two variables by defining behavior of functions in a certain small region around the point. Derivatives, however, are generalized by using the definition of derivative with respect to each variable separately. Suppose y is a constant, $y = y_0$. The derivative of $u = f(x, y)$ with respect to the variable x is then defined since u is now a function of x only. This derivative is called the partial derivative of f with respect to x and is defined as

$$\lim_{h \to 0} \frac{f(x + h, y_0) - f(x, y_0)}{h}$$

and denoted by $\partial f / \partial x$ or f_x

Example I. If $f(x, y) = 4x + 5y + xy - x^2 - y^2 + 5$,

$$\frac{\partial f}{\partial x} = 4 + 0 + y - 2x - 0 + 0$$

Similarly, a partial derivative with respect to y is defined by

$$\lim_{k \to \infty} \frac{f(x_0, y + k) - f(x_0, y)}{k}$$

and denoted by $\partial f / \partial y$ or f_y

Example 2. For $f(x, y)$ defined in Example 1,

$$\frac{\partial f}{\partial y} = 0 + 5 + x - 0 - 2y + 0$$

The partial derivatives of f with respect to x, evaluated at the point x_0, y_0, gives the slope of the tangent to the surface $z = f(x, y)$ in the direction parallel to the x-axis. Similarly the partial derivative with respect to y gives the slope of the tangent in the direction parallel to the y-axis.

The rules for differentiation given for functions of one variable apply to obtaining partial derivatives.

Example 3. Let

$$u(x_1, x_2) = -60x_1{}^2 + 100x_1x_2 - 60x_2{}^2 + 1{,}760x_1 + 1{,}320x_2 - 50{,}000$$

Then

$$u_{x_1}(x_1, x_2) = -120x_1 + 100x_2 + 1{,}760$$
$$u_{x_2}(x_1, x_2) = 100x_1 - 120x_2 + 1{,}320$$

Example 4. Let

$$P(u, v) = -105{,}000 + 60{,}000u - 81v$$
$$+ 42uv + 0.004v^2 - 5{,}000u^2 - u^2v - 0.002v^2u$$

Then

$$P_u(u, v) = 60{,}000 + 42v - 10{,}000u - 2vu - 0.002v^2$$

$$P_v(u, v) = -81 + 42u + 0.008v - u^2 - 0.004vu$$

Example 5. Let

$$F(x, y) = e^{ax+by}$$

Then

$$F_x(x, y) = ae^{ax+by}$$

$$F_y(x, y) = be^{ax+by}$$

Example 6. Let

$$G(x_1, x_2) = \frac{a_1 x_1}{a_2 x_1 + a_3 x_2} = (a_1 x_1)(a_2 x_1 + a_3 x_2)^{-1}$$

Then

$$G_{x_1}(x_1, x_2) = a_1(a_2 x_1 + a_3 x_2)^{-1} - (a_1 x_1)(a_2 x_1 + a_3 x_2)^{-2}a_2$$

$$= a_1(a_2 x_1 + a_3 x_2)^{-2}(a_2 x_1 + a_3 x_2 - x_1 a_2)$$

$$= a_1(a_2 x_1 + a_3 x_2)^{-2}(a_3 x_2)$$

$$G_{x_2}(x_1, x_2) = -a_1 x_1(a_2 x_1 + a_3 x_2)^{-2}a_3$$

Higher-Order Derivatives

The partial derivatives are themselves functions of x and y, and this relationship may be stated explicitly by:

$$\frac{\partial f(x, y)}{\partial x} \quad \text{and} \quad \frac{\partial f(x, y)}{\partial y}$$

These functions may be differentiated again to yield the second derivatives

$$\frac{\partial}{\partial x}\left(\frac{\partial f(x, y)}{\partial x}\right) \quad \text{and} \quad \frac{\partial}{\partial y}\left(\frac{\partial f(x, y)}{\partial y}\right)$$

which are denoted by $\partial^2 f(x, y)/\partial x^2$ or $f_{xx}(x, y)$, and $\partial^2 f(x, y)/\partial y^2$ or $f_{yy}(x, y)$, respectively. The function $f_x(x, y)$ may also be differentiated with respect to y, and $f_y(x, y)$ may be differentiated with respect to x. These mixed partial derivatives are denoted by f_{xy} and f_{yx}, respectively.

If the mixed partial derivatives f_{xy} and f_{yx} of a function $f(x, y)$ are continuous in a domain R, then the equation

$$f_{yx} = f_{xy}$$

holds everywhere in the interior of this region. This is equivalent to saying that the order of differentiation with respect to x and y is immaterial. In repeated differentiation of a function of two variables the order of differentiation is immaterial if the derivatives in question are continuous functions.

Example 7.   The partial derivatives of

$$f(x, y) = x^2 + 4xy + y^3$$

are

$$\frac{\partial f}{\partial x} = 2x + 4y \qquad \frac{\partial f}{\partial y} = 4x + 3y^2$$

$$\frac{\partial^2 f}{\partial x^2} = 2 \qquad \frac{\partial^2 f}{\partial y^2} = 6y \qquad \frac{\partial^2 f}{\partial x \, \partial y} = \frac{\partial^2 f}{\partial y \, \partial x} = 4$$

The Total Differential

The increment in a function between two points is the difference in the values of the functions at the two points:

$$\Delta f = f(x + \Delta x, y + \Delta y) - f(x, y)$$
$$= f(x + \Delta x, y + \Delta y) - f(x, y + \Delta y) + f(x, y + \Delta y) - f(x, y)$$
$$= \left[\frac{f(x + \Delta x, y + \Delta y) - f(x, y + \Delta y)}{\Delta x} \right] \Delta x$$
$$+ \left[\frac{f(x, y + \Delta y) - f(x, y)}{\Delta y} \right] \Delta y$$

If the function possesses continuous partial derivatives at the point (x, y), the expressions in square brackets will approach

$$\frac{\partial f}{\partial x} \qquad \text{and} \qquad \frac{\partial f}{\partial y}$$

respectively, as Δx and Δy tend to zero. Hence, for very small increments in x and y, the increment in f is approximately

$$\Delta f \sim \frac{\partial f}{\partial x} \Delta x + \frac{\partial f}{\partial y} \Delta y$$

It is common practice to write this expression in the form

$$df = \frac{\partial f}{\partial x} dx + \frac{\partial f}{\partial y} dy \tag{1}$$

and call df the "*total differential*" of f. Note that df is a function of four variables: the coordinates of the point, x and y, and the increments in x and y, dx and dy.

One of the uses of the total differential is in determining the sensitivity of an objective function or decision rule to small changes in parameters.

Example 8. In Chapter 4 the decision rule for the economic lot size was found to be:

$$x = \left(\frac{c_c r}{2c_0}\right)^{1/2}$$

where c_c = carrying cost per period
$\quad c_0$ = ordering cost
$\quad r$ = demand per period

Determine the effect on x of small errors in c_c and c_0. From (1):

$$dx = \frac{\partial x}{\partial c_c}\, dc_c + \frac{\partial x}{\partial c_0}\, dc_0$$

$$= \frac{1}{2}\left(\frac{c_c r}{2c_0}\right)^{-1/2}\left(\frac{r}{2c_0}\right) dc_c + \left[\frac{1}{2}\left(\frac{c_c r}{2c_0}\right)^{-1/2}\left(\frac{c_c r}{2}\right)(-1)c_0^{-2}\right] dc_0$$

$$= \frac{1}{2c_c}\left(\frac{c_c r}{2c_0}\right)^{1/2}\left[dc_c - \left(\frac{c_c}{c_0}\right) dc_0\right] = \frac{x}{2}\left[\frac{dc_c}{c_c} - \frac{dc_0}{c_0}\right]$$

A small change of amount dc_c alone will cause a change in x of amount

$$dx = \frac{x}{2}\left(\frac{dc}{c_c}\right)$$

or

$$\frac{dx}{x} = \frac{1}{2}\frac{dc_c}{c_c}$$

A 1% error in c_c will cause a $\frac{1}{2}$% error in x in the same direction; i.e., if c_c is too large, x will be too large. Similarly, if dc_c is zero and the error in c_0 is dc_0,

$$\frac{dx}{x} = -\frac{1}{2}\frac{dc_0}{c_0}$$

and a 1% error in c_0 will cause a $\frac{1}{2}$% error in the opposite d irection. If the errors in c_c and c_0 are of the same sign, they counteract each other and if the ratio is

$$\frac{c_c}{c_0} = \frac{dc_c}{dc_0}$$

the term in square brackets will be zero and then there will be no error in x.

The total differential of a function can be obtained by determining the partial derivatives and substituting them into (1). However, it is frequently easier to use rules analogous to those used in obtaining derivatives; e.g., if u and v are two functions of x and y, then

$$d(u \pm v) = du \pm dv$$

$$d(uv) = u\, dv + v\, du$$

$$d\left(\frac{u}{v}\right) = \frac{v\, du - u\, dv}{v^2}$$

If w is a function of u, then $dw = w'(u)\, du$.

Example 9. Determine the total differential of

$$w = \ln\left(\frac{x}{x^2 + y^2}\right).$$

Let $u = \dfrac{x}{x^2 + y^2}$; then $w = \ln u$ and $dw = \dfrac{du}{u} = \dfrac{d\left[\dfrac{x}{x^2 + y^2}\right]}{\dfrac{x}{x^2 + y^2}}$

$$d\left[\frac{x}{x^2 + y^2}\right] = \frac{(x^2 + y^2)\, dx - x[d(x^2) + d(y^2)]}{(x^2 + y^2)^2}$$

$$= \frac{(x^2 + y^2)\, dx - x[2x\, dx + 2y\, dy]}{(x^2 + y^2)^2}$$

$$dw = \frac{(y^2 - x^2)\, dx - 2yx\, dy}{x(x^2 + y^2)}$$

If the function $f(x, y)$ possesses higher partial derivatives, it is possible to form higher differentials. The *second differential* is the total differential of the total differential:

$$d(df) = d^2f = \frac{\partial}{\partial x}\left(\frac{\partial f}{\partial x}\, dx + \frac{\partial f}{\partial y}\, dy\right) dx + \frac{\partial}{\partial y}\left(\frac{\partial f}{\partial x}\, dx + \frac{\partial f}{\partial y}\, dy\right) dy$$

$$= \frac{\partial^2 f}{\partial x^2}\, dx^2 + 2\frac{\partial^2 f}{\partial x\, \partial y}\, dx\, dy + \frac{\partial^2 f}{\partial y^2}\, dy^2 \qquad (2)$$

In this differentiation dx and dy are treated as constants ($dx \cdot dx = dx^2$). Similarly, the *third differential* is

$$d^3f = d(d^2f) = \frac{\partial^3 f}{\partial x^3}\, dx^3 + 3\frac{\partial^3 f}{\partial x^2\, \partial y}\, dx^2\, dy + 3\frac{\partial^3 f}{\partial x\, \partial y^2}\, dx\, dy^2 + \frac{\partial^3 f}{\partial y^3}\, dy^3$$

The *nth differential* may be denoted symbolically by:

$$d^n f = \left(\frac{\partial f}{\partial x} \, dx + \frac{\partial f}{\partial y} \, dy \right)^n$$

the expression on the right is expanded in a binomial series and terms

$$\frac{\partial^n f}{\partial x^n} \, dx^n \qquad \frac{\partial^n f}{\partial x^{n-1} \partial y} \, dx^{n-1} dy, \ldots, \frac{\partial^n f}{\partial y^n} \, dy^n$$

substituted for the products and powers of $(\partial f / \partial x) \, dx$ and $(\partial f / \partial y) \, dy$. These higher differentials are useful in the statement of the Taylor expansion for functions of two variables.

Differentiation of Functions of Functions

If f is a function of g, and g is a function of x, the chain rule for differentiation of functions of one variable states that

$$\frac{df}{dx} = \frac{df}{dg} \cdot \frac{dg}{dx}$$

The analogous result for functions of two variables may be derived from the basic formula for the total differential (1). Let $f(x, y)$ be a function of two variables x and y, which are both functions of two other variables, u and v; i.e., $x = x(u, v)$ and $y = y(u, v)$. From (1)

$$df = \frac{\partial f}{\partial x} \, dx + \frac{\partial f}{\partial y} \, dy \tag{3}$$

Since $x = x(u, v)$ and $y = y(u, v)$

$$dx = \frac{\partial x}{\partial u} \, du + \frac{\partial x}{\partial v} \, dv \qquad \text{and} \qquad dy = \frac{\partial y}{\partial u} \, du + \frac{\partial y}{\partial v} \, dv$$

Substituting and collecting terms give

$$df = \left[\frac{\partial f}{\partial x} \frac{\partial x}{\partial u} + \frac{\partial f}{\partial y} \frac{\partial y}{\partial u} \right] du + \left[\frac{\partial f}{\partial y} \frac{\partial y}{\partial v} + \frac{\partial f}{\partial y} \frac{\partial y}{\partial v} \right] dv$$

The terms in square brackets are the partial derivatives of f with respect to u and v, respectively:

$$\frac{\partial f}{\partial u} = \frac{\partial f}{\partial x} \frac{\partial x}{\partial u} + \frac{\partial f}{\partial y} \frac{\partial y}{\partial u} \qquad \text{and} \qquad \frac{\partial f}{\partial v} = \frac{\partial f}{\partial x} \frac{\partial x}{\partial v} + \frac{\partial f}{\partial y} \frac{\partial y}{\partial v} \tag{4}$$

A particular case of practical importance occurs when f is a function of

x and y, and x and y are both functions of one variable, t: $f = f(x, y)$; $x = x(t)$, $y = y(t)$. Then f is a function of one variable, t, and from (4) the ordinary derivative is

$$\frac{df}{dt} = \frac{\partial f}{\partial x}\frac{dx}{dt} + \frac{\partial f}{\partial y}\frac{dy}{dt} \tag{5}$$

Since f, x, and y are functions of one variable, their derivatives with respect to that variable are ordinary, rather than partial, derivatives.

Example 10. Let

x = number of units of a product produced and sold in a period
y = selling price per unit (\$)
z = marketing expenditures per period (\$)
$C(x)$ = cost of producing x units per period (\$)

In general, x will depend on y and z and the earnings of the firm per period are

$$\text{Earnings} = \text{Revenue} - \text{Cost}$$

$$E(y, z) = yx - C(x) - z$$

where $x = x(y, z)$. The partial derivatives of Earnings with respect to selling price and marketing expenditure may be obtained by using the chain rule (4):

$$\frac{\partial E}{\partial y} = x + y\frac{\partial x}{\partial y} - \frac{\partial C}{\partial x}\frac{\partial x}{\partial y}$$

$$\frac{\partial E}{\partial z} = y\frac{\partial x}{\partial z} - \frac{\partial C}{\partial x}\frac{\partial x}{\partial z} - 1$$

Implicit Functions

If two variables x and y are related by the equation $f(x, y) = 0$, then the function $x = x(y)$ and $y = y(x)$ are said to be defined implicitly. The contour lines shown in Fig. 9.2, Fig. 9.3, and Fig. 9.5 are examples of implicitly defined functions.

Example 11. The contour line in Fig. 9.3 is obtained from

$$2.35x + 0.18y + 0.007xy = c \tag{6}$$

where c is a constant. This equation can be solved for y:

$$y = \frac{c - 2.35x}{0.18 + 0.007x}$$

and the derivative computed by treating y as a function of x:

$$\frac{dy}{dx} = \frac{-2.35(0.18 + 0.007x) - (c - 2.35x)(0.007)}{(0.18 + 0.007x)^2}$$

$$= \frac{-0.423 - 0.007c}{(0.18 + 0.007x)^2}$$

The derivative could also be obtained by implicit differentiation:

$$2.35\frac{dx}{dx} + 0.18\frac{dy}{dx} + 0.007y\frac{dx}{dx} + 0.007x\frac{dy}{dx} = 0$$

and solving for dy/dx:

$$\frac{dy}{dx} = \frac{-2.35 - 0.007y}{0.18 + 0.007x}$$

In this form the derivative is expressed in terms of y and x and is correct only for values of x and y which satisfy the equation (6).

The derivative of y with respect to x can also be obtained by partial differentiation by treating $f = f(x, y)$ as a function of two variables. The total differential is

$$df = \frac{\partial f}{\partial x}\, dx + \frac{\partial f}{\partial y}\, dy$$

Since x and y must satisfy $f(x, y) = 0$, df must be identically zero. Solving $df = 0$ gives:

$$\frac{dy}{dx} = -\frac{\partial f/\partial x}{\partial f/\partial y} = -\frac{f_x}{f_y} \qquad \text{or} \qquad \frac{dx}{dy} = -\frac{f_y}{f_x} \tag{7}$$

Example II (*Continued*).   If $f(x, y) = 2.35x + 0.18y + 0.007xy - c$
Then $f_x = 2.35 + 0.007y$, $f_y = 0.007x$, and

$$\frac{dy}{dx} = -\frac{2.35 + 0.007y}{0.18 + 0.007x}$$

The use of partial differentiation gives the result in the same form as implicit differentiation, and is usually easier to apply.

Taylor Expansion

Taylor expansions for a function of two variables can be developed from the Taylor expansion for functions of one variable. If $F(t)$ is a function of one variable, an expansion for $F(t)$ is

$$F(t) = F(0) + tF'(0) + \frac{t^2}{2!} F''(0) + \frac{t^3}{3!} F'''(0) + \cdots + R_n \qquad (8)$$

Let $f(x, y)$ be a function of two variables with $x = a + ht$ and $y = b + kt$. Then $f(x, y)$ is a function of one variable t, say, $F(t)$.

From (5):

$$F'(t) = \frac{\partial f}{\partial x} \frac{dx}{dt} + \frac{\partial f}{\partial y} \frac{dy}{dt} = \frac{\partial f}{\partial x} h + \frac{\partial f}{\partial y} k \quad \text{since } \frac{dx}{dt} = h \text{ and } \frac{dy}{dt} = k$$

$$F''(t) = \frac{d}{dt} \left\{ h \frac{\partial f}{\partial x} + k \frac{\partial f}{\partial y} \right\}$$

$$= h \left\{ \frac{\partial^2 f}{\partial x^2} \frac{dx}{dt} + \frac{\partial^2 f}{\partial x \partial y} \frac{dy}{dt} \right\} + k \left\{ \frac{\partial^2 f}{\partial x \partial y} \frac{dx}{dt} + \frac{\partial^2 f}{\partial y^2} \frac{dy}{dt} \right\}$$

$$= h^2 \frac{\partial^2 f}{\partial x^2} + 2hk \frac{\partial^2 f}{\partial x \partial y} + k^2 \frac{\partial^2 f}{\partial y^2}$$

Setting $t = 1$ and substituting the values of F and its derivatives in (8) give

$$F(1) = f(a + h, b + k) = f(a, b) + \left\{ h \frac{\partial f}{\partial x} + k \frac{\partial f}{\partial y} \right\}$$

$$+ \frac{1}{2!} \left\{ h^2 \frac{\partial^2 f}{\partial x^2} + 2hk \frac{\partial^2 f}{\partial x \partial y} + h^2 \frac{\partial^2 f}{\partial y^2} \right\} + \cdots + R_n \qquad (9)$$

Each of the partial derivatives is assumed to exist at the point a, b and the values at this point are substituted in the expansion.

The terms in the braces are the total differentials defined by (1) and (2). The Taylor expansion may therefore be written more compactly as

$$f(a + h, b + k) = f(a, b) + df + \frac{1}{2} d^2 f + \frac{1}{3!} d^3 f + \cdots + R_n \qquad (10)$$

Example 12. Determine the Taylor expansion for the general polynomial:

$$f(x, y) = Ax^2 + Bxy + Cy^2 + Dx + Ey + F$$

Here $\quad f(x_0, y_0) = Ax_0^2 + Bx_0y_0 + Cy_0^2 + Dx_0 + Ey_0 + F$

$$f_x(x_0, y_0) = 2Ax_0 + By_0 + D$$

$$f_y(x_0, y_0) = Bx_0 + 2Cy_0 + E$$

$$f_{xx}(x_0, y_0) = 2A$$

$$f_{xy}(x_0, y_0) = B$$

$$f_{yy}(x_0, y_0) = 2C$$

All higher order derivatives are zero.

$$\begin{aligned} f(x_0 + h, y_0 + k) = f(x_0, y_0) + h(2Ax_0 + By_0 + D) \\ + k(Bx_0 + 2Cy_0 + E) + \tfrac{1}{2}\{2Ah^2 + 2Bhk + 2Ck^2\} \end{aligned}$$

(11)

In particular, if $x_0 = 0$, $y_0 = 0$,

$$f(h, k) = F + Dh + Ek + Ah^2 + Bhk + Ck^2$$

which is exactly the initial form. Since the Taylor Expansion after n terms gives an nth degree polynomial, the expansion in this case terminates after the second-order terms. The form (11) is useful for approximating the polynomial by a linear function in the neighborhood of a particular point, since the last term in (11) can be neglected if h and k are small.

EXERCISES

Find the first and second order partial derivatives of the functions given in Exercises 1 to 7.

1. $f(x, y) = \Sigma a_{ij}x^iy^j \quad i = 0, 1, 2; \quad j = 0, 1, 2; \quad i + j \leq 3.$

Verify the result in Example 4, p. 256.

2. $f(x, y) = (56x - 2x^2) - (x^2 - 4x + 100) + \dfrac{y}{1.2}[56 - 2y - 1.2(x - 3.5)]$

$$- \dfrac{1}{1.2}[y^2 - 4y + 100]$$

3. $f(x, y) = 1 - e^{-x} - x + \dfrac{xy}{2} - \dfrac{y^2}{2}$

4. $f(x, y) = (x + y)^4 + (y - 2)^3$

5. $f(x, y) = \ln(x + \sqrt{y})$

6. $f(x, y) = e^{x^2 + y^2 - 2xy}$

7. $f(c, s) = \dfrac{(1 - ac) + a(1 - 2ac)[1 + (a - 1)s] + a^2(1 - ac)[1 + (a - 1)s]}{1 + a + a^2}$

8. Show that the second derivative of y with respect to x, where $y(x)$ is defined implicitly by $f(x, y) = 0$, is

$$\frac{d^2y}{dx^2} = -\frac{1}{f_y{}^3} \left\{ f_{xx} f_y{}^2 - 2f_{xy} f_x f_y + f_{yy} f_x{}^2 \right\}$$

9. Verify the result in Exercise 8 for:

$$f(x, y) = 2.35x + 0.18y + 0.007xy - c$$

by deriving d^2y/dx^2 directly and by using the formula.

10. Compute dy/dx where $y(x)$ is defined by $f(x, y) = 0$, where

$$f(x, y) = 4x + 5y + xy - x^2 - y^2 + 5$$

by using partial differentiation. Verify, using Fig. 9.4, that the dy/dx is the slope of the contour line $x = 6$, $y = 0.75$ and $x = 2$, $y = 8$.

11. Derive dy/dx defined by $z = $ constant for z given in Exercise 3, p. 254.

12. Let $x = $ number of units of a product produced and sold in a period
$y = $ selling price per unit
$q = $ quality index
$A(x, q) = $ average manufacturing cost per unit when x units are produced per period at a quality index q.

Assume that x is a function of selling price and the quality index. Derive the partial derivatives of Earnings per period with respect to selling price and the quality index.

13. Develop the Taylor expansion for the $f(x, y)$ given in Exercise 3.

14. Show that the function $r(k)$ defined implicitly by $F_n(k, r) = 0$ in Example 4, p. 254, is monotonic non-decreasing for $k \geq -1$, $r \geq -1$. (*Hint*: Show first that $F_n(k, r)$ is a non-decreasing function of k and a non-increasing function of r.)

C. OPTIMIZATION

Conditions for Extreme Points

A function $u = f(x, y)$ of two independent variables, x and y, may be represented by a surface in xyu-space. This function has a local maximum at the point (x_0, y_0) if all the other values of u in a neighborhood around the point are less than $f(x_0, y_0)$. Geometrically, such a maximum corresponds to a "hill top" on a surface (Fig. 9.4). In the same way, the point (x_0, y_0) is a local minimum if all other values of the function in a certain neighborhood of the point are greater than $u_0 = f(x_0, y_0)$ (Fig. 9.6). Just as with functions of one variable, these definitions always refer only to a sufficiently small neighborhood of the point in question.

If $f(x)$ is a continuous function in one variable, the sign of the first derivative at a point x_0 indicates whether the function is increasing $(f' > 0)$ or decreasing $(f' < 0)$. If $f' = 0$, the function is stationary. Similarly, a function of two variables $f(x, y)$ is increasing (decreasing) at a

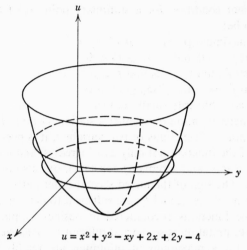

$$u = x^2 + y^2 - xy + 2x + 2y - 4$$

Figure 9.6

point (x_0, y_0), *as x increases* if $f_x(x_0, y_0) > 0 \ (<0)$. The function is stationary at x_0, y_0, *as x increases* if $f_x(x_0, y_0) = 0$. The function is increasing,
decreasing, or stationary, at a point (x_0, y_0) *as y increases* if $f_y(x_0, y_0)$ is
positive, negative, or zero, respectively.

A necessary condition that x_0 be a local extreme point for a function of
one variable $f(x)$ is that x_0 be a stationary point (i.e., $f'(x_0) = 0$). For a
function of two variables the two equations

$$f_x(x_0, y_0) = 0 \qquad f_y(x_0, y_0) = 0$$

are *necessary* conditions for the occurrence of a maximum or minimum of
a differentiable function $u = f(x, y)$ at the point (x_0, y_0). Suppose the
variable y is fixed at some value, say, y_0, and the function in the neighborhood of the point (x_0, y_0) is regarded as a function of the single variable x.
The necessary condition for this function to have an extreme value at a
point x_0 is that the derivative (with respect to x) be zero; i.e., $f_x(x_0, y_0)$
must be zero. The same argument applies if x is considered fixed; the
necessary condition is $f_y(x_0, y_0)$ equal to zero. Hence both partial derivatives must be zero at the point. A point at which $f_x = 0$ *and* $f_y = 0$ is
called a *stationary* point.

If $f(x)$ is a function of one variable, the sign of the second derivative
indicates whether the first derivative is increasing, decreasing. The
analogous results hold for functions of two variables. The derivative
$f_x(x_0, y_0)$ is increasing, decreasing, or stationary, at a point x_0, y_0, *as x
increases* if f_{xx} is positive, negative, or zero, respectively, and similarly for
$f_y(x_0, y_0)$ *as y increases*.

A sufficient condition for a stationary point x_0 of a function of one variable to be:

a local maximum point is that $f''(x_0) < 0$
   or that $f'' = 0$ and $f''(x_0 \pm \varepsilon) < 0$
a local minimum point is that $f''(x_0) > 0$
   or that $f'' = 0$ and $f''(x_0 \pm \varepsilon) > 0$

where ε is an arbitrarily small number.

For the determination of whether a stationary point is a maximum or a minimum point of functions of two variables, it is necessary to know the behavior of the function not only as x increases (and y remains constant), or as y increases (and x remains constant), but also as both x and y are increasing. The sign of the mixed second-order partial $f_{xy}(x_0, y_0)$ together with the signs of the f_{xx} and f_{yy} are sufficient to determine the behavior for most of the functions encountered in business applications. The geometrical interpretation is somewhat difficult to visualize, but the sufficient conditions for a maximum or minimum are readily derived from the Taylor expansion:

$$f(x_0 + h, y_0 + k) = f(x_0, y_0) + hf_x + kf_y + \frac{1}{2!}[h^2 f_{xx} + 2hk f_{xy} + k^2 f_{yy}] + R_2$$

All derivatives are evaluated at the point (x_0, y_0). At a stationary point (x_0, y_0) the first derivatives are zero and the behavior of the function in a small region around the stationary point is determined by the term containing the second derivatives. The function f will have a maximum value at a stationary point if

$$h^2 f_{xx} + 2hk f_{xy} + k^2 f_{yy} < 0$$

for any (small) h and k, since then $f(x_0 + h, y_0 + k) < f(x_0, y_0)$. The function will have a minimum value if the inequality is reversed. The expression on the left of the inequality sign is a function, say, g, of h and k:

$$g(h, k) = h^2 f_{xx} + 2hk f_{xy} + k^2 f_{yy}$$

since f_{xx}, f_{xy}, and f_{yy} have been evaluated at x_0, y_0 and now denote numerical quantities. The function $g(h, k)$ can be written as

$$g(h, k) = f_{xx}\left[h + \frac{f_{xy}}{f_{xx}} k \right]^2 - \frac{f_{xy}^2 k^2}{f_{xx}} + k^2 f_{yy}$$

$$= f_{xx}\left[h + \frac{f_{xy}}{f_{xx}} k \right]^2 + \left(\frac{f_{xx} f_{yy} - f_{xy}^2}{f_{xx}} \right) k^2$$

if $f_{xx} \neq 0$.

In this form, the variables h and k appear in only terms which are squared. It follows that

$$g(h, k) > 0 \quad \text{for any } h \text{ and } k \quad \text{if } f_{xx} > 0 \text{ and } f_{xx}f_{yy} - f_{xy}^2 > 0$$
$$< 0 \quad \text{for any } h \text{ and } k \quad \text{if } f_{xx} < 0 \text{ and } f_{xx}f_{yy} - f_{xy}^2 > 0$$
$$> 0 \quad \text{for some values of } h \text{ and } k \text{ and } < 0 \text{ for others if}$$
$$f_{xx}f_{yy} - f_{xy}^2 < 0$$

The results hold if $f_{xx} \neq 0$, or if $f_{yy} \neq 0$, since h and k appear symmetrically. More detailed statements can be obtained by considering the signs of f_{xx}, f_{xy}, and f_{yy}. If $f_{xy} = 0$, then $g(h, k)$ will always be positive (negative) if f_{xx} and f_{xy} are both positive (negative). If f_{xx} and f_{yy} have different signs, $g(h, k)$ will be positive for some values of h and k and negative for others. The situation where $g(h, k) = 0$ for all h and k can occur only where f_{xx}, f_{yy}, and f_{xy} are all zero.

To apply these results to sufficient conditions for an extremum, let

$$\Delta_1 = \Delta_1(x^*, y^*) = f_{xx}(x^*, y^*)$$

$$\Delta_2 = \Delta_2(x^*, y^*) = [f_{xx}(x^*, y^*)][f_{yy}(x^*, y^*)] - [f_{xy}(x^*, y^*)]^2$$

A stationary point (x^*, y^*):

> Is a local maximum point if $\Delta_1 < 0$ and $\Delta_2 > 0$
> Is a local minimum point if $\Delta_1 > 0$ and $\Delta_2 > 0$
> Is not a local extreme point if $\Delta_2 < 0$
> May or may not be a local extreme point if $\Delta_2 = 0$.

In particular, (x^*, y^*) is not an extreme point if both f_{xx} and f_{yy} are zero. It is a local extreme if f_{xy} is zero, and f_{xx} and f_{yy} have the same sign.

A stationary point is the solution of two simultaneous equations $f_x = 0$, $f_y = 0$. In the examples and exercises in this chapter the computation of the solutions is relatively simple. However, in practical problems considerable numerical computation may be required; an example is given in Section C in the next chapter. If the objective function is quadratic, the equations that must be solved are linear. Methods for solving systems of simultaneous linear equations are discussed in Chapter 12. More general techniques are given in numerical analysis textbooks.

Example I. Find the values of x and y for which the following function has an extreme value:

$$f(x, y) = x^2 - xy + y^2 + 2x + 2y - 4$$

Differentiating

$$\frac{\partial f}{\partial x} = 2x - y + 2 \qquad \frac{\partial f}{\partial y} = -x + 2y + 2$$

and setting the derivatives equal to zero gives

$$2x - y = -2 \qquad -x + 2y = -2$$

The solution to the two simultaneous equations is

$$x = -2; \qquad y = -2$$

Therefore, $(-2, -2)$ is a stationary point.
Since

$$\frac{\partial^2 f}{\partial x^2} = 2; \quad \frac{\partial^2 f}{\partial y^2} = 2; \quad \frac{\partial^2 f}{\partial x\,\partial y} = -1; \quad \Delta_2(-2, -2) = (2)(2) - (-1)^2 = 3$$

the conditions for a local minimum are satisfied at $(-2, -2)$ and $f(-2, -2) = -8$ is actually a minimum value. (Fig. 9.6)

Example 2. A function of two variables, possessing a stationary point which is not an extreme point, is $f(x, y) = y^2 - x^2$. Here

$$f_x = -2x = 0 \qquad f_y = 2y = 0$$

and hence there is one stationary point at $x = 0$, $y = 0$. The second derivatives are:

$$f_{xx} = -2$$
$$f_{yy} = 2$$
$$f_{xy} = f_{yx} = 0$$

and $\qquad \Delta_2(0, 0) = f_{xx}f_{yy} - (f_{xy})^2 = -2(2) - 0 = -4 < 0$

This stationary point is an example of a saddle point; the reason for the name is obvious from a three-dimensional graph of the function shown here in Fig. 9.7.

Example 3. A function which has Δ_2 equal to zero at a stationary point which is not an extreme point, is

$$f(x, y) = x^2 + y^2 + 2xy$$

For this function the stationary points are given by

$$f_x = 2x + 2y = 0 \qquad \text{and} \qquad f_y = 2x + 2y = 0$$

Any point which has its x coordinate equal to the negative of the y coordinate, i.e., all points of the form $(x = -y, y)$ e.g., $(-6, 6)$ or $(6, -6)$ are stationary points. The second derivatives are

$$f_{xx} = 2$$
$$f_{yy} = 2$$
$$f_{xy} = f_{yx} = 2$$

and $\qquad \Delta_2(x, y) = f_{xx}f_{yy} - (f_{xy})^2 = 0$

for all x and y.

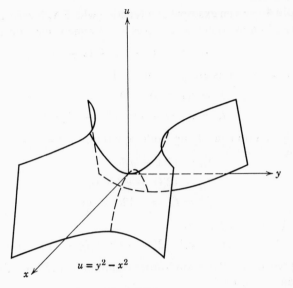

$$u = y^2 - x^2$$

Figure 9.7

From the last result it is apparent that additional analysis is necessary to determine the behavior of the function at the points $(x = -y, y)$. The function can be written as $(x + y)^2$, and hence the function is non-negative for all x and y. However, the function has the value 0 for all $x = -y$, and hence does not have a minimum at any particular (x^*, y^*). A sketch of the function is shown in Fig. 9.8.

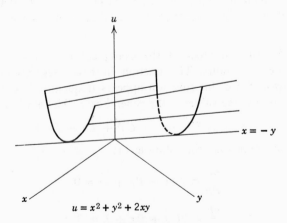

$$u = x^2 + y^2 + 2xy$$

Figure 9.8

Example 4. As an example of a function where Δ_2 is zero at a stationary point at which the function achieves an extreme value, consider

$$f(x, y) = (x - y)^4 + (y - 1)^4$$

The stationary points are given by

$$f_x = 4(x - y)^3 = 0$$

and $\quad f_y = 4[-(x - y)^3 + (y - 1)^3] = 0$

The only solution satisfying both equations is $x = y = 1$. The second derivatives give:

$$f_{xx} = 12(x - y)^2$$
$$f_{yy} = 12[(x - y)^2 + (y - 1)^2]$$
$$f_{yx} = f_{xy} = -12(x - y)^2$$

and $\quad \Delta_2(x, y) = f_{xx}f_{yy} - f_{xy}^2$
$$= 12(x - y)^2 \cdot 12[(x - y)^2 + (y - 1)^2] - [-12(x - y)^2]^2$$

The expression for the second-order condition depends on the values of x and y, and in particular, $\quad \Delta_2(1, 1) = 0 - 0 = 0$

However, by examining the behavior of $f(x, y)$ in a neighborhood of $(1, 1)$, it can be seen that the function attains a relative minimum at $(1, 1)$. Let h and k be arbitrarily small positive or negative numbers; then

$$f(1 + h, 1 + k) - f(1, 1)$$
$$= [(1 + h) - (1 + k)]^4 + (1 + k - 1)^4 - (0^4 + 0^4)$$
$$= (h - k)^4 + k^4$$

Clearly, the function is larger at any point $(1 + h, 1 + k)$ than at $(1, 1)$ and hence it has a minimum at $(1, 1)$ even though the Δ_2 is equal to zero at $(1, 1)$.

Example 5. In a number of the examples given above the second derivatives were constants. The functions in these cases were polynomials of degree two. Since this function appears frequently, it is worthwhile to examine its extreme values in the general case. The most general form is:

$$f(x, y) = Ax^2 + Bxy + Cy^2 + Dx + Ey + F$$

The stationary points are the solutions of:

$$\frac{\partial f}{\partial x} = 2Ax + By + D = 0$$

$$\frac{\partial f}{\partial y} = 2Cy + Bx + E = 0$$

Solving
$$2Ax + By = -D$$
$$Bx + 2Cy = -E$$

gives the stationary points x^*, y^*

$$x^* = \frac{2CD - EB}{B^2 - 4AC} \qquad y^* = \frac{2AE - BD}{B^2 - 4AC}$$

Since

$$\frac{\partial^2 f}{\partial x^2} = 2A; \qquad \frac{\partial^2 f}{\partial y^2} = 2C; \qquad \frac{\partial^2 f}{\partial x\, \partial y} = \frac{\partial^2 f}{\partial y\, \partial x} = B$$

$$\Delta_2 = \left(\frac{\partial^2 f}{\partial x^2}\right)\left(\frac{\partial^2 f}{\partial y^2}\right) - \left(\frac{\partial^2 f}{\partial x\, \partial y}\right)^2 = 4AC - B^2$$

If $4AC - B^2 > 0$, the function has a maximum if $A < 0$, and a minimum if $A > 0$; if $4AC - B^2 = 0$, further investigation is necessary; and if $4AC - B^2 < 0$, the stationary point is neither a maximum nor a minimum. These conclusions apply to the whole x, y plane since Δ_2 does not depend on x and y and because the function and its derivatives are continuous in the whole plane.

Concave and Convex Functions

Following the definitions of concavity and convexity given in Chapter 5, a function $f(x, y)$ is convex in a region if a line segment drawn through any two points on the surface never falls below the surface. The necessary and sufficient condition for a function of two variables to be convex is that

$$f[(1 - t)x_1 + tx_2, (1 - t)y_1 + ty_2]$$
$$\leq (1 - t)f(x_1, y_1) + tf(x_2, y_2) \quad \text{for} \quad 0 < t < 1$$

The function is strictly convex if the $\leq$ sign can be replaced everywhere in the interval by $<$ and concave (strictly concave) if the inequality is $\geq (>)$.

If a function is convex throughout a region and has a single stationary point, that point is a global minimum in the region. Similarly, if the function is concave and has a single stationary point, that point is a global maximum. Determining the global maximum of a convex function, or the global minimum of a concave function, or either if the function is both convex and concave in a region, is much more difficult than determining the minimum of a convex or the maximum of a concave. This problem will be discussed further in Chapter 11.

Example 6. Is a second-degree polynomial in two variables concave or convex? Let

$$f(x, y) = Ax^2 + Bxy + Cy^2 + Dx + Ey + F$$

and

$$X = (1 - t)x_1 + tx_2$$
$$Y = (1 - t)y_1 + ty_2$$

The polynomial will be convex if

$$f(X, Y) \leq (1 - t)f(x_1, y_1) + tf(x_2, y_2)$$

Both sides of the inequality will involve the coefficients, A, B, C, D, and E; the inequality can be written as

$$\alpha_1 A + \alpha_2 B + \alpha_3 C + \alpha_4 D + \alpha_5 E + \alpha_6 F$$
$$\leq \beta_1 A + \beta_2 B + \beta_3 C + \beta_4 D + \beta_5 E + \beta_6 F$$

$$\alpha_6 = 1 \text{ and } \beta_6 = (1 - t) + t = 1; \quad \text{therefore } \alpha_6 = \beta_6$$
$$\alpha_4 = (1 - t)x_1 + tx_2; \quad \beta_4 = (1 - t)x_1 + tx_2; \quad \alpha_4 = \beta_4$$

and similarly, $\alpha_5 = \beta_5$. Only the multipliers of A, B, and C are different and the inequality can be written as

$$A(\beta_1 - \alpha_1) + B(\beta_2 - \alpha_2) + C(\beta_3 - \alpha_3) \geq 0$$
$$\beta_1 = (1 - t)x_1^2 + tx_2^2$$
$$\alpha_1 = [(1 - t)x_1 + tx_2]^2 = (1 - t)^2 x_1^2 + 2t(1 - t)x_1 x_2 + t^2 x_2^2$$
$$\beta_1 - \alpha_1 = x_1^2[(1 - t) - (1 - t)^2] - 2t(1 - t)x_1 x_2 + x_2^2(t - t^2)$$
$$= t(1 - t)(x_1 - x_2)^2$$

Similarly,

$$\beta_2 - \alpha_2 = 2t(1 - t)(x_1 - x_2)(y_1 - y_2)$$
$$\beta_3 - \alpha_3 = t(1 - t)(y_1 - y_2)^2$$

and the inequality reduces to

$$t(1 - t)[A(x_1 - x_2)^2 + 2B(x_1 - x_2)(y_1 - y_2) + C(y_1 - y_2)] \geq 0$$

This is the same problem as that is examined on page 268 with $x_1 - x_2 = h$ and $y_1 - y_2 = k$. Hence, the term in square brackets is positive for any two points if

$$4AC - B^2 > 0 \quad \text{and} \quad A > 0 \text{ (and } C > 0)$$

negative, if

$$4AC - B^2 > 0 \quad \text{and} \quad A < 0 \text{ (and } C < 0)$$

It is zero if $4AC - B^2 = 0$ and is positive for some points and negative for others if $4AC - B^2 < 0$. A second-degree polynomial is therefore convex everywhere if $4AC - B^2 > 0$ and $A > 0$ $(C > 0)$; concave everywhere if $4AC - B^2 > 0$ and $A < 0$ $(C < 0)$, and is not convex or concave everywhere if $4AC - B^2 < 0$. This result is identical to the conclusion reached in Example 5: a polynomial of degree two has an extreme point if $4AC - B^2 > 0$ which is a maximum if $A < 0$ and a minimum if $A > 0$, and does not have an extreme point if $4AC - B^2 < 0$.

EXERCISES

For each of the functions in Exercises 1, 2, 3, and 4:
(a) Determine the stationary points and verify whether they are maxima or minima.
(b) Determine the global extrema.
(c) Give the regions in which the function is concave or convex.

1. $E(x, y) = 4x + 5y + xy - x^2 - y^2 + 5$
2. $f(x, y)$ given in Exercise 2, p. 265.
3. $f(x, y)$ given in Exercise 3, p. 265.
4. $f(c, s)$ given in Exercise 7, p. 265.
5. Determine the optimum values of y and z in Example 10, p. 262.
6. Discuss the problem of determining the global extrema of the general polynomial of degree three, (Exercise 1, p. 266).
7. Determine the global extrema of $e^{x^2+y^2-2xy}$

D. NONLINEAR EARNINGS FUNCTION OF TWO VARIABLES

In Chapter 5 the general earnings function was of the form

$$E(x) = R(x) - C(x)$$

where x represented the level of some activity, e.g., the number of units of a product to be produced or the price to be charged for a product. The general earnings function of two variables has the form

$$E(x, y) = R(x, y) - C(x, y)$$

There are now a number of interesting possibilities for different combinations of factors that x and y;

(i) They can represent for a single product in a single period, any two of the decision variables, price, quantity to be produced, advertising expenditure.

(ii) They can represent the production of two different products for a single period.

(*iii*) They can represent the production in two periods for a single product.

One of these possibilities is illustrated in the following example.

Example I. When production is between 4,000 and 14,000 units, a firm's total cost and demand in a period are, respectively,

$$C = x^2 - 4x + 100$$

$$x = 28 - \tfrac{1}{2}y$$

where y is unit selling price (in dollars), x is the number of units produced and sold (in thousands), and C is total cost (in thousands of dollars). The earnings are given by

$$E(x) = x(56 - 2x) - (x^2 - 4x + 100)$$

and the optimum production is $x^* = 10$. Then $y^* = 36$ and

$$E(x^*) = 200 \text{ is a maximum because}$$

$$E^2(x^*) = -6 < 0.$$

Next, suppose that the firm wishes to maximize profits over a longer horizon—specifically, over two periods. The cost of production in period two is the same as before, namely,

$$C_2(x_2) = x_2{}^2 - 4x_2 + 100$$

where the subscript 2 on the C and x indicates that this is the cost and quantity to be produced in the second period. The demand function for period two differs from that of period one because the demand in period two depends upon the amount sold in period one. In particular, the demand in period two satisfies the relation

$$y_2 = 56 - 2x_2 - 1.2(x_1 - \tfrac{7}{2})$$

If the firm uses an interest rate of 20% to discount the costs and revenues of period two, what will be the optimal selling price (and quantity) for each period?

Total Earnings = (Revenue in period 1) − (Costs in period 1)

$$+ \; [(\text{Revenue in period 2}) - (\text{Costs in period 2})]$$

$$\times \left(\frac{1}{1 + \text{interest rate}} \right)$$

$$E(x_1, x_2) = (56x_1 - 2x_1{}^2) - (x_1{}^2 - 4x_1 + 100)$$

$$+ \frac{x_2}{1.2}[56 - 2x_2 - 1.2(x_1 - \tfrac{7}{2})] - \frac{1}{1.2}[x_2{}^2 - 4x_2 + 100]$$

Set

$$\frac{\partial E}{\partial x_1} = 56 - 4x_1 - 2x_1 + 4 + \frac{x_2}{1.2}(-1.2) = 0$$

$$\frac{\partial E}{\partial x_2} = \frac{1}{1.2}[56 - 4x_2 - 1.2(x_1 - \tfrac{7}{2}) - 2x_2 + 4] = 0$$

$$60 - 6x_1 - x_2 = 0$$

$$\tfrac{7}{2}(1.2) + 60 - 6x_2 - 1.2x_1 = 0$$

and
$$x_1{}^* = 8\tfrac{1}{2} \qquad y_1{}^* = 39$$

$$x_2{}^* = 9 \qquad y_2{}^* = 32$$

$E(x_1{}^*, x_2{}^*) = 193\tfrac{1}{4} + \dfrac{143}{1.2} = 312.42$ if the second period costs are dis-

counted or $= 193\tfrac{1}{4} + 143 = 336\tfrac{1}{4}$ if they are not.

$$\frac{\partial^2 E}{\partial x_1{}^2} = -6; \qquad \frac{\partial^2 E}{\partial x_1 \partial x_2} = -1; \qquad \frac{\partial^2 E}{\partial x_2} = -5$$

$$\Delta_2 = (-6)(-5) - (-1)^2 = 29 > 0$$

Hence the second-order conditions are satisfied and the price and quantity do yield maximum profit.

If each period is optimized separately, the value of x_1 would be 10, as before, and x_2 would be obtained by optimizing:

$$E(x_2) = x_2[56 - 2x_2 - 1.2(\tfrac{13}{2})] - [x_2{}^2 - 4x_2 + 100]$$

$E' = 0$ gives $x_2{}^* = 8.7$ and

$$E(8.7) = 267.96 - 140.89 = 127.07$$

The total undiscounted earnings are $200 + 127.07 = 327.07$ which is less than the $336\tfrac{1}{4}$ obtainable if the optimum is based on earnings in both periods. The total discounted earnings are

$$200 + \frac{127.02}{1.2} \sim 305.90 \; (<312.42)$$

Optimizing each period separately, or using marginal analysis in each period, will not give maximum total earnings for the two periods if either demand or costs in the two periods are not independent.

EXERCISES

1. Develop and analyze a general model for the problem presented in Example 1. Assume that cost function $C(x)$ is an increasing quadratic function and the

same for both periods. The demand in the first period is a decreasing linear function of the price in the second period and the quantity produced in the first period. Use the solution to verify the numerical results in Example 1.

2. Dorfman and Steiner (1954) (Exercise 3, p. 246) state,

"A firm which can influence the demand for its product by advertising will, in order to maximize its profits, choose the advertising budget and price such that the increase in gross revenue resulting from a one-dollar increase in advertising expenditure is equal to the ordinary elasticity of demand for the firm's product."

Let η = ordinary elasticity of demand

$$= -\frac{y}{x}\frac{\partial x}{\partial y}$$

μ = increase in gross revenue resulting from a small increase in advertising expenditure

$$= y\frac{\partial x}{\partial z}$$

Use the model presented in Example 10, p. 262, to show that choosing y and z so that $\eta = \mu$ will maximize earnings (profit) if the second order conditions are satisfied.

3. For the model presented in Exercise 12, p. 266, let η_q be the elasticity of demand with respect to the quality index:

$$\eta_q = \frac{A}{x}\frac{\partial x/\partial q}{\partial A/\partial q}$$

Show that earnings are maximized if

$$\eta = \frac{y}{A}\eta_q$$

where η is as defined in Exercise 2.

Notes and References

Section A

Example 1 is based on:

Vazsonyi, A. (1956), *Operations Research and the Accountant*, Conference Handbook for AMA Special Finance Conference, October 3–5, New York.

Sections B and C

More detailed treatment of the calculus of functions of two variables appears in the textbooks mentioned in Chapter 5, p. 152. For detailed treatment of maxima and minima, see:

Hancock, H. (1917), *Theory of Maxima and Minima*, 1960 ed. Dover Publications New York.

Example 10, p. 262, and Exercise 12, p. 266, and 2 and 3, p. 278, are based on:

Dorfman, R., and Steiner, P. (1954), "Optimal Advertising and Optimal Quality," *American Economic Review*, XLIV, pp. 826–836. (Also reprinted in Bass, F. M. et al. (1961), *Mathematical Models and Methods in Marketing*, Richard D. Irwin, Homewood, Ill.)

Numerical analysis texts that discuss the solution of non-linear simultaneous equations are:

Hamming, R. W. (1962), *Numerical Methods for Scientists and Engineers*, McGraw-Hill Book Co., New York.

Householder, A. S. (1953), *Principles of Numerical Analysis*, McGraw-Hill Book Co., New York.

Milne, W. E. (1949), *Numerical Calculus*, Princeton University Press, Princeton, N.J.

CHAPTER TEN

Examples of Optimization
with Two-Decision Variables

Three examples of optimization of functions of two-decision variables are presented in this chapter. The first is a special case of a model originally developed by Holt, Modigliani, and others. The objective function is a polymonial of degree two. The second example is curve fitting by least squares. While this is not a business problem per se, it is a good example of optimizing functions of two variables and the result forms an important tool in the development of empirical relationships. The third example consists of a detailed study of an earnings function of two variables. The function is a polynomial of degree three; the example illustrates the close interrelationship between numerical computation and analytical investigation.

A. THE HOLT, MODIGLIANI, MUTH MODEL

A plant produces a single product which is measured in terms of a standard physical unit. The product might be paint, in which case the unit might be a gallon. The case where more than one product is produced can frequently be adequately treated under the one-product assumption, if the product mix is relatively constant and the quantities of the various products can all be measured in the same common unit.

In many plants, production decisions are made periodically; let the discrete periods be denoted by the subscripts $t = 1, 2, \ldots, n$. It is assumed that the requirement for the product is known exactly for the next n periods. The plant manager can meet these requirements by varying the level of production with a constant-size work force by working undertime or overtime, or by changing the size of the work force or by changing the amount in inventory or by some combination of these. Long range decisions, such as changing the capacity of the plants, will not be considered in this model.

The following notation will be used. Let

R_t = requirement for the product, in units, during period t

w_t = the number of productive workers employed at the beginning of the period t. It is assumed that there is no change in this number during the period and w_t is therefore the number of workers at the end of the period. Then

w_0 = number of productive workers at the beginning of period 1

I_t = "net" inventory in units at the end of period t (inventory minus unfilled orders). Then

I_0 = "net" inventory at the beginning of period 1,

p_t = number of units produced during period t. The production during a period is available to satisfy the requirements for that period. Therefore,

$$I_t = I_{t-1} + p_t - R_t$$

That is, the inventory at the end of a period is equal to the inventory at the beginning of the period plus the number of units produced less the number of units shipped.

The plant manager can control w_t and p_t. It will be assumed that decisions are implemented at the end of a period and are effective immediately. This would be strictly true only in situations where there is a ready pool of laborers, but may be a satisfactory initial assumption in other situations as well.

The objective of the plant manager is to minimize his cost in satisfying the requirements. The costs which vary with the decision variables w_t and p_t are the costs of paying the labor force, the costs associated with changing the size of the labor force, the cost of over- or under-production, and the cost of maintaining an inventory. These costs will be identified as follows:

C_1 = payroll costs

C_2 = hiring and firing costs

C_3 = payroll cost of over- or underproduction and other costs associated with changing the production rate

C_4 = costs of maintaining an inventory

The total cost in period t is then

$$C_t = C_{1t} + C_{2t} + C_{3t} + C_{4t}$$

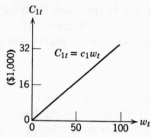

Figure 10.1 Payroll costs, $c_1 = 340$.

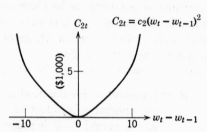

Figure 10.2 Hiring and firing costs, $c_2 = 64.3$.

Each cost term may be a function of p_t, w_t, and other variables. The relationship in practice may be fairly complex; for ease of analysis it will be assumed *that each cost term is a linear or quadratic function of the decision variables*, in particular:

1. Payroll costs are assumed to be directly proportional to the number of productive workers, i.e.,

$$C_{1t} = c_1 w_t \qquad c_1 > 0$$

where c_1 is the cost in dollars per period for one productive worker (Fig. 10.1).

2. Hiring and firing costs are assumed to be a quadratic function of the change in the number of workers, i.e.,

$$C_{2t} = c_2(w_t - w_{t-1})^2 \qquad c_2 > 0$$

(Fig. 10.2).

3. The costs associated with over- or underproduction are assumed to be a quadratic function of p_t and w_t

$$C_{3t} = c_3(p_t - c_4 w_t)^2 + c_5 p_t - c_6 w_t$$

where c_4 is the number of units produced by one worker per period and c_3, c_5 and c_6 are constants > 0 (Fig. 10.3).

4. The inventory costs are a quadratic function of the difference between actual inventory and a desired level, c_8.

$$C_{4t} = c_7(I_t - c_8)^2 \qquad c_7 > 0; \quad c_8 > 0$$

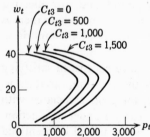

Figure 10.3 Over- and underproduction costs (for selected values of C_{t3}):

$$C_{t3} = c_3 p_t{}^2 - 2c_3 c_4 p_t w_t + c_3 c_4{}^2 w_t{}^2 + c_5 p_t - c_6 w_t$$

$c_3 = 0.2, \qquad c_4 = 5.67,$
$c_5 = 51.2, \qquad c_6 = 281$

The cost associated with $I_t > c_8$ are incremental inventory holding costs; the cost associated with $I_t < c_8$ are the costs of shortages (Fig. 10.4).

Consider the problem of deriving the optimum values of the decision variables in the case where costs in only one period are examined. Let this period be $t = 1$. Then the problem is to find p_1 and w_1 which minimize

$$C(w_1, p_1) = C_{11} + C_{21} + C_{31} + C_{41}$$

$$= c_1 w_1 + c_2(w_1 - w_0)^2 + c_3(p_1 - c_4 w_1)^2 + c_5 p_1 - c_6 w_1$$

$$+ c_7(I_1 - c_8)^2 \tag{1}$$

subject to

$$I_1 = I_0 + p_1 - R_1 \tag{2}$$

where c_1, c_2, c_3, c_4, c_5, c_6, c_7, and c_8 are constants and w_0, I_0, and R_1 are given.

$C(w_1, p_1)$ is a quadratic function of w_1 and p_1 and can be written in the form

$$C(w_1, p_1) = A w_1^2 + B w_1 p_1 + C p_1^2 + D w_1 + E p_1 + F \tag{3}$$

where $A = c_2 + c_3 c_4^2$

$$B = -2 c_3 c_4$$

$$C = c_3 + c_7$$

$$D = c_1 - 2 c_2 w_0 - c_6 \tag{4}$$

$$E = 2 c_7(I_0 - R_1 - c_8) + c_5$$

$$F = c_2 w_0^2 + c_7(I_0 - R_1 - c_8)^2$$

The optimum values are given by

$$w_1{}^* = \frac{2CD - EB}{B^2 - 4AC} \quad \text{and} \quad p_1{}^* = \frac{2AE - BD}{B^2 - 4AC} \tag{5}$$

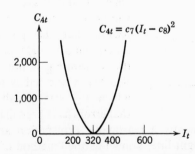

Figure 10.4 Inventory costs: $c_7 = 0.0825$, $c_8 = 320$.

Let the values of the parameters be given as:

$$
\begin{aligned}
c_1 &= 340 & c_5 &= 51.2 \\
c_2 &= 64.3 & c_6 &= 281 \\
c_3 &= 0.20 & c_7 &= 0.0825 \\
c_4 &= 5.67 & c_8 &= 320
\end{aligned}
\tag{6}
$$

Substituting these values gives the $w_1{}^*$ and $p_1{}^*$ in terms of the initial conditions, w_0, I_0, and R_1 as

$$
\begin{aligned}
w_1{}^* &= -0.397 + 0.972w_0 - 0.005I_0 + 0.005R_1 \\
p_1{}^* &= 1.237 + 3.900w_0 - 0.312I_0 + 0.312R_1
\end{aligned}
\tag{7}
$$

This set of equations can be used for any set of values of w_0, I_0, and R_1 as long as the parameters remain fixed.

EXERCISES

1. Verify (7) by substituting (6) into (1) and determining the minimum of $C(w_1, p_1)$.
2. Verify that (7) results in minimum cost.

B. CURVE FITTING BY LEAST SQUARES

Assume that a relationship exists between y and x. Thus it is possible to select a value of x and measure the corresponding value of y. The small circles in Fig. 10.5 represent the results of a number of such measurements. One glance at the figure shows that the circles tend to fall about a straight line:

$$
y = \alpha + \beta x
$$

where α and β are constants but the values of α and β are unknown. The reason that the points do not fall exactly on a straight line could be that the relationship is not really linear, or that the x selected is not the one for which a y was actually measured, or that errors have been made in measuring y. The latter is frequently a reasonable explanation and a method of "fitting" the best straight line, known as the "method of least squares," is based on that assumption.

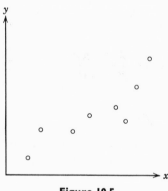

Figure 10.5

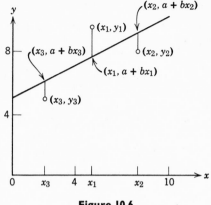

Figure 10.6

To illustrate the method, suppose three values, x_1, x_2 and x_3, have been selected. The x values and the corresponding measurements obtained are shown in Fig. 10.6. These points $(x_i,\ y_i)$ are called observed points. Note that the subscript on x denotes the order in which the x are selected, not their relative magnitude. The line that is to be drawn should pass as close to the points $(x_1,\ y_1)$, $(x_2,\ y_2)$ and $(x_3,\ y_3)$ as possible. Since it is assumed that a value of x can be selected without error and that errors can occur in measuring y, it is reasonable to minimize the vertical distance of an observed point from the line. If the line is $y = a + bx$, then the vertical distance from the first observed point to the line is

$$y_1 - (a + bx_1)$$

This distance may be either positive or negative, depending on whether the observed point falls above or below the line. Therefore, "closeness" must be expressed in such a way that distance from the line increases in either direction. Simple ways to do this are to use the absolute value or the square

$$|y_1 - (a + bx_1)| \qquad \text{or} \qquad [y_1 - (a + bx_1)]^2$$

Both of these have the property that the distance is zero, if the observed point falls on the line, and increases positively as the point falls further from the line in either direction. Minimizing of the square distance leads to simpler formulas and has other advantages; it is the one most commonly used and it is used here.

With the selection of the measure of closeness it is now possible to determine the values of the parameters for the straight line that best fits the observed points shown in Fig. 10.6. The closeness for any a and b

will be given by s where s is

$$s = [y_1 - (a + bx_1)]^2 + [y_2 - (a + bx_2)]^2 + [y_3 - (a + bx_3)]^2 \quad (1)$$

s is a quadratic function of the two "unknowns": a and b. To determine the values of a and b which minimize s, $\dfrac{\partial s}{\partial a}$ and $\dfrac{\partial s}{\partial b}$ must be set equal to zero.

$$\frac{\partial s}{\partial a} = -2[y_1 - (a + bx_1)] - 2[y_2 - (a + bx_2)]$$

$$- 2[y_3 - (a + bx_3)] = 0 \quad (2)$$

$$\frac{\partial s}{\partial b} = -2x_1[y_1 - (a + bx_1)] - 2x_2[y_2 - (a + bx_2)]$$

$$- 2x_3[y_3 - (a + bx_3)] = 0 \quad (3)$$

(2) and (3) are two simultaneous linear equations in two unknowns. Rewriting them in the more usual form, after dividing by -2, gives:

$$(1 + 1 + 1)a + (x_1 + x_2 + x_3)b = (y_1 + y_2 + y_3) \quad (4)$$

$$(x_1 + x_2 + x_3)a + (x_1^2 + x_2^2 + x_3^2)b = (x_1y_1 + x_2y_2 + x_3y_3) \quad (5)$$

The solution to (4) and (5) results in a minimum for s, because

$$\frac{\partial^2 s}{\partial a^2} = +2 + 2 + 2 \text{ is positive}$$

$$\frac{\partial^2 s}{\partial b^2} = 2x_1^2 + 2x_2^2 + 2x_3^2 \text{ is positive}$$

and

$$\Delta_2 = \left(\frac{\partial^2 s}{\partial a^2}\right)\left(\frac{\partial^2 s}{\partial b^2}\right) - \left(\frac{\partial^2 s}{\partial a\, \partial b}\right)^2$$

$$= 12(x_1^2 + x_2^2 + x_3^2) - [2(x_1 + x_2 + x_3)]^2 > 0 \quad (6)$$

Example. Suppose $x_1 = 5$, $x_2 = 8$, and $x_3 = 2$ are the chosen values of x, and the corresponding observed values of y are $y_1 = 9.5$, $y_2 = 8$, and $y_3 = 5$. Then

$$x_1 + x_2 + x_3 = 15, \quad x_1^2 + x_2^2 + x_3^2 = 93,$$
$$y_1 + y_2 + y_3 = 22.5, \quad \text{and } x_1y_1 + x_2y_2 + x_3y_3 = 121.5$$

and (4) and (5) become

$$3a + 15b = 22.5$$

$$15a + 93b = 121.5$$

The solution of this pair of equations in the two unknowns a and b is

$$a = \frac{(22.5)(93) - (121.5)(15)}{54} = 5$$

$$b = \frac{(3)(121.5) - 15(22.5)}{54} = \tfrac{1}{2}$$

Hence the "least squares" line from the three observations is

$$y = 5 + \tfrac{1}{2}x$$

The observations and the fitted straight line are shown in Fig. 10.6.

EXERCISES

1. Develop the method for fitting a straight line to a set of n observed points, using the method of least squares.
2. Verify that Δ_2 is positive.

C. EARNINGS FUNCTION: HIGHER-ORDER POLYNOMIALS IN TWO VARIABLES

As an example of a case where polynomials of higher order than the second are required, consider the problem of writing a general expression for the earnings of a manufacturing firm. In this simple example, it will be assumed that all units are sold in the period in which they are produced and that all revenues are matched against the costs of the same period.
The relationships which are to be included in the expression are:

(*a*) Earnings equals revenue minus costs
(*b*) Revenue equals number of units sold multiplied by the selling price per unit.
(*c*) Costs equal the production costs plus the money spent on marketing. (It is assumed that there are no other relevant costs.)

Assume further that the relationships have the following form: (illustrated in Fig. 10.7):

(*a*) The number sold is a linearly decreasing function of price and a concave function of amount spent on marketing (advertising).
(*b*) Production cost is a linearly increasing function of production volume plus a fixed cost.

The problem is to express the earnings for this firm by using the most

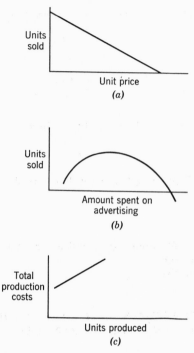

Figure 10.7 Functional forms used in the example.

general form of the relationships that is possible if the non-linear relationships are limited to quadratic functions. Let

$$E = \text{earnings}$$
$$x = \text{number of units sold} \qquad x \geq 0$$
$$y = \text{unit selling price} \qquad y \geq 0$$
$$z = \text{money spent for advertising} \qquad z \geq 0$$
$$g_2(x) = \text{production cost for } x \text{ units}$$

then the basic function may be written as follows:

$$\text{Earnings} = \text{revenue} - \text{Cost}$$
$$E = y \cdot x - (z + g_2)$$

The earnings function is a function of four variables, x, y, z, and g_2. However, from the assumptions made above, the number of units sold is a function of the unit selling price and the amount spent on advertising. This relationship may be written as:

$$x = g_1(y, z)$$

where g_1 is a linear function of y and a quadratic function of z.

The form of the function is illustrated in Fig. 10.7. The number sold, x, is a decreasing linear function of the unit price, y; and in Fig. 10.7b the number sold, x, is shown as a quadratic function of the amount spent for marketing, z. The statement of the relationship is not clear as to whether the two variables y and z interact; if they do not, the most general statement would be:

$$x = g_1(y, z)$$
$$= (a_1 + a_2 y) + (b_1 + b_2 z + b_3 z^2) \qquad a_1 \geq 0;\ a_2 \leq 0;\ b_3 < 0$$

If they do interact, the most general equation would be:

$$x = g_1(y, z) = a_1 + a_2 y + a_3 z + a_4 yz + a_5 z^2$$

The production cost is given by the equation

$$g_2(x) = e_1 + e_2 x \qquad \text{if } x > 0$$

Substituting into the earnings equation for g_2 gives as the general form for the earnings:

$$E = y \cdot x - z - e_1 - e_2 x = (y - e_2)x - z - e_1$$

Substituting $x = g_1(y, z)$ gives

$$E = (y - e_2)g_1(y, z) - z - e_1$$
$$= (y - e_2)[a_1 + a_2 y + a_3 z + a_4 yz + a_5 z^2] - e_1 - z \qquad (1)$$

Earnings, can be expressed as a third-degree polynomial of two variables: the unit price, y, and the money spent on advertising, z.

As an example, assume that the parameters have the following values:

$$a_1 = 50{,}000$$
$$a_2 = -5{,}000$$
$$a_3 = 40$$
$$a_4 = -1$$
$$a_5 = -0.002$$
$$e_1 = 100{,}000$$
$$e_2 = 2$$

The earnings are:

$$E(y, z) = -200{,}000 + 60{,}000y - 81z + 42yz + 0.004z^2 - 5{,}000y^2$$
$$- y^2 z - 0.002 z^2 y \qquad (2)$$

Figure 10.8 shows the values of y and z yielding constant earnings for selected values of the earnings.

The data for Fig. 10.8 would rarely be obtained if the computations had to be performed manually. However, electronic computers greatly simplify the preparation of the figure.

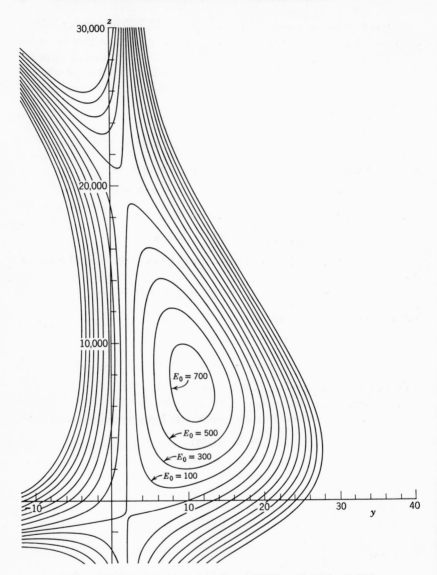

Figure 10.8   Constant earnings lines: $E(y, z) = E_0$ (E_0 in \$1,000).

From the figure it can be seen immediately that there is a maximum at approximately $y = 10$ and $z = 7,000$, and that there are two saddle points, one at (approximately) $y = 2$, $z = 20,000$ and the other at (approximately) $y = 2$, $z = -1,000$. From a practical viewpoint, all the data necessary for a decision is available from Fig. 10.8. However, it is usually advisable to support such a set of contour lines by a detailed analysis such as that presented next for this example.

The optimum values of y, z are given by the solutions of $E_y = 0$ and $E_z = 0$,

$$60,000 + 42z - 10,000y - 2yz - 0.002z^2 = 0 \tag{3}$$

$$-81 + 42y + 0.008z - y^2 - 0.004yz = 0 \tag{4}$$

Considerable computational effort may be saved if the existence of a maximum is demonstrated before the stationary points are computed numerically. The second derivatives are

$$\frac{\partial^2 E}{\partial y^2} = -2z - 10,000 \tag{5}$$

$$\frac{\partial^2 E}{\partial z^2} = 0.008 - 0.004y \tag{6}$$

$$\frac{\partial^2 E}{\partial y\, \partial z} = \frac{\partial^2 E}{\partial z\, \partial y} = 42 - 2y - 0.004z \tag{7}$$

For a maximum to exist, (5) and (6) must be negative. It follows from (5) that

$$\frac{\partial E^2}{\partial y^2} < 0 \text{ if } z > -5,000 \tag{8}$$

$$> 0 \text{ if } z < -5,000$$

and from (6) that

$$\frac{\partial E^2}{\partial z^2} < 0 \text{ if } y > 2 \tag{9}$$

$$> 0 \text{ if } y < 2$$

This analysis indicates that a local maximum may exist in the region $y > 2$, $z > -5,000$.

The second order condition for an extremum is that

$$\Delta_2(y, z) = \left(\frac{\partial^2 E}{\partial y^2}\right)\left(\frac{\partial^2 E}{\partial z^2}\right) - \left(\frac{\partial^2 E}{\partial y\, \partial z}\right)^2 > 0$$

or from (5), (6), and (7) that

$$(-2z - 10,000)(0.008 - 0.004y) - (42 - 2y - 0.004z)^2 > 0.$$

This is a quadratic function, and the equation derived by setting it equal to zero

$$-0.000016z^2 - 0.008yz - 4y^2 + 0.32z + 208y - 1,844 = 0 \tag{10}$$

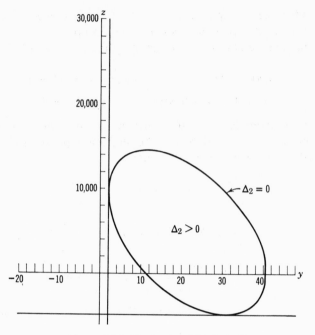

Figure 10.9   Region in which $\Delta_2 > 0$.

gives the boundary of the region of the y, z plane in which a maximum may occur. Applying the standard method (summarized in the appendix) shows that (10) in standard form is an ellipse

$$4.000008y''^2 + 0.000012z''^2 - 3{,}584 = 0 \tag{11}$$

The function (2) thus may have a maximum in the region defined by the equation (10). This region is the inside of the ellipse shown in Fig. 10.9.

Since it has now been shown that (2) may have a maximum, the next step is to solve (3) and (4) simultaneously. This pair of equations cannot be solved directly; one approach is to start with an estimate from a carefully drawn graph. Again applying the standard method (3) and (4) are reduced to the standard forms

$$-0.999y''^2 + 1.001z''^2 + 174{,}936.5 = 0 \tag{12}$$

$$1.000008y''^2 - 0.000004z''^2 + 1.003129 = 0 \tag{13}$$

respectively. Thus both (3) and (4) define hyperbolas. Both branches of (4) and a section of one branch of (3) are plotted in Fig. 10.10; only a section of (3) is plotted because the origin around which it is symmetric is considerably removed from the origin of the y, z axis when the variables are plotted in units most useful for this problem. Note that (4) is almost degenerate. From the graph it can be seen that (2) has stationary points at approximately $y = 10$, $z = 7,200$, $y = 2$, $z = -1,500$, and $y = 2$, $z = 20,000$. By comparing Figs. 10.9 and 10.10 it is obvious that the first point is a relative maximum while the second and third occur outside the region in which E can have a relative maximum. An examination of Fig. 10.8 reveals that these points are in fact saddle points. There may be two other stationary points that are not shown; these are not of interest because they occur outside the region in which a maximum may exist.

Numerical approximation of the point at which the acceptable relative maximum occurs, using a procedure analogous to the linear interpolation method of Chapter 5 and carrying four decimal places in the calculation, yields $y = 10.5594$, $z = 7330.794$. As a check, at this point

$$\frac{\partial E}{\partial y} = +0.6822 \simeq 0$$

$$\frac{\partial E}{\partial z} = +0.0051 \simeq 0$$

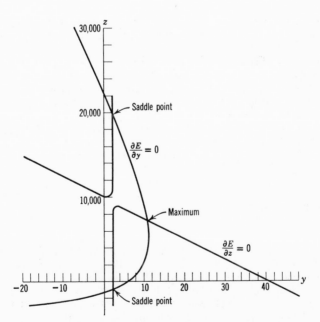

Figure 10.10 Stationary points of $E(y, z)$.

and

$$\Delta_2 = \left(\frac{\partial^2 E}{\partial y^2}\right)\left(\frac{\partial^2 E}{\partial z^2}\right) - \left(\frac{\partial^2 E}{\partial y\,\partial z}\right) = 733.0087 > 0$$

Hence the maximum attainable value of E is

$$E(10.5594,7330.794) = \$796,070.37$$

The function $E(y, z)$ may attain higher values, but not in the region in which it can be taken as a reasonably valid representation of practical situations.

EXERCISES

1. Develop equations (3) and (4) from the necessary conditions given in Example 10, p. 262.
2. Develop the formula for the necessary conditions in terms of η and μ as defined by the Dorfman and Steiner criteria (Exercise 2, p. 278). Verify that the condition is satisfied at the optimum.
3. Economists sometimes assume that the effect of advertising is to "tilt the demand curves." Increasing advertising is assumed to increase the intercept and decrease the slope. The parameters in the demand function

$$x = a_1 + a_2 y$$

then become functions of z. a_1 is an increasing function of z and a_2 is an increasing function of z. Develop the general model if a_1 and a_2 are linear functions of z.
4. Discuss the effect on the optimum decision if the production costs are convex (concave) functions of the number of units produced. Develop the general model incorporating the simplest form of such production functions.
5. Write the most general equation for the profit function for a firm using the same assumptions as in the above example, except that money may be spent on product improvement and the effect will be to increase the number of units sold in a quadratically increasing function, and will result in a linear decrease in the unit production cost. Give the physical interpretation of the various parameters and variables.

Notes and References

Section A

For the original work on the Holt, Modigliani, Muth Model, see:

Holt, C. C., Modigliani, F., and Simon, H. A. (1955), "A linear decision rule for production and employment scheduling," *Management Science*, 2, pp. 1–30.
Holt, C. C., Modigliani, F., and Muth, J. F. (1956), "Derivation of a linear decision rule for production and employment," *Management Science*, 2, pp. 159–177.
Holt, C. C., Modigliani, F., Muth, J. F., and Simon, H. A. (1960), *Planning Production, Inventories and Work Force*. Prentice-Hall, Inc., Englewood Cliffs, N. J.

CHAPTER ELEVEN

Optimization Subject

to Constraints

In one-decison variable models, the feasible values of the variable may be restricted to an interval. If this is the case, the end points have to be examined as possible extreme points.

In two-decision variable models, the problem is more complex. The feasible region may be limited in a number of different ways. Optimization techniques for three of the cases which occur most frequently are discussed in this chapter. The method of Lagrange multipliers (Section A) is used where the decision variables are subject to an equality constraint. The method is then generalized (Section B) to include the inequality constraints. The last case considered (Section C) is a special form of inequality constraints in which the variables are required to be non-negative.

A. EQUALITY CONSTRAINTS

Substitution

In Chapter 10, Section A, the model was of the form

$$C(w_1, p_1) = f(w_1, p_1, I_1; \ w_0, c_1, \ldots c_3) \tag{1}$$

where w_1 and p_1 are the decision variables, subject to the restriction that

$$I_1 = I_0 + p_1 - R_1 \tag{2}$$

and

$$I_0, R_1, w_0, \text{ and } c_1, \ldots c_8 \tag{3}$$

are parameters.

The inventory at the end of the period, I_1 is a function given by (2) of the decision variables work force, w_1, and production level, p_1. I_1 was eliminated from (1) by substitution. Problems in which the decision variables are subject to an equality constraint appear frequently. In theory the equality constraints can be solved for one of the decision variables, and the resulting expression substituted in the model.

Example I. Find among all rectangles with constant perimeter the one which has the maximum area. Let x be the length of one side and y the length of the other side. The problem is to maximize

$$A = xy \tag{4}$$

subject to

$$2x + 2y = c \tag{5}$$

where c is a constant. The variable y may be eliminated by solving (5):

$$y = \frac{c}{2} - x$$

and substituting in (4).

The problem can then be expressed as

$$\text{Maximize } A = \frac{xc}{2} - x^2$$

where x need only be non-negative. Setting the derivative

$$\frac{dA}{dx} = \frac{c}{2} - 2x$$

equal to zero and solving gives

$$x = \frac{c}{4} \quad \text{and} \quad y = \frac{c}{2} - \frac{c}{4} = \frac{c}{4}$$

The second derivative

$$\frac{d^2A}{dx^2} = -2$$

is negative and, therefore, the rectangle which has the maximum area for a given parameter is the one in which $x = y$, i.e., the square.

Lagrange Multipliers

In this example the constraining equation (5) could be solved rather easily, but not all equations are this simple. A general technique for the determination of optima when variables are subject to constraints, without necessarily solving the constraining equation explicitly, is the method of *Lagrange multipliers.* The necessary conditions for a point (x, y) to be an extremum of $f(x, y)$ subject to $g(x, y) = 0$ are obtained by defining a function $h(x, y, \lambda)$ of three variables, x, y, and the Lagrange multiplier λ:

$$h(x, y, \lambda) = f(x, y) - \lambda g(x, y)$$

and setting the partial derivatives of $h(x, y, \lambda)$ with respect to x, y, and λ equal to zero

$$\frac{\partial h}{\partial x} = 0; \qquad \frac{\partial f}{\partial x} - \lambda \frac{\partial g}{\partial x} = 0$$

$$\frac{\partial h}{\partial y} = 0; \qquad \frac{\partial f}{\partial y} - \lambda \frac{\partial g}{\partial y} = 0$$

$$\frac{\partial h}{\partial \lambda} = 0; \qquad g(x, y) = 0$$

Any point (x, y, λ) which satisfies these three necessary conditions is said to be a stationary point.

An intuitive feeling for why these conditions are necessary for an extremum can be obtained by examining Fig. 11.1. It shows the contour lines of a function $f(x, y)$ and the points which satisfy $g(x, y) = 0$. The extreme value of f, which satisfies $g(x, y) = 0$, is the one at which a contour line of f just touches $g(x, y) = 0$. At this point, say (x_0, y_0), the tangents to the two curves must have the same slope. The slope of the tangent is

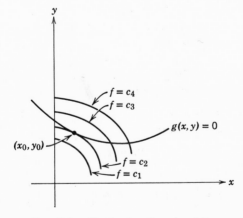

Figure 11.1   Contour line of the objective function, f, and the constraint, $g(x, y) = 0$, are tangent at (x_0, y_0).

given by the ratio of the two partial derivatives [Chapter 9, (7), page 263]. Therefore, at (x_0, y_0)

$$\frac{f_x}{f_y} = \frac{g_x}{g_y}$$

Let the common ratio be denoted by a constant λ. Then

$$\frac{f_x}{f_y} = \frac{g_x}{g_y} = \lambda; \qquad \frac{f_x}{g_x} = \frac{f_y}{g_y} = \lambda \qquad (6)$$

or

$$\frac{f_x}{g_x} = \lambda; \qquad \frac{f_y}{g_y} = \lambda$$

and

$$f_x - \lambda g_x = 0; \qquad f_y - \lambda g_y = 0$$

must be satisfied at the point x_0, y_0. Note that it has been assumed that both f and g are differentiable in the neighborhood of (x_0, y_0) and that f_y and g_y are not both zero at this point.

Example 2. For the problem in Example 1,

$$f(x, y) = xy$$

$$g(x, y) = 2x + 2y - c$$

and

$$h(x, y, \lambda) = xy - \lambda(2x + 2y - c)$$

A stationary point must satisfy the equations:

$$\frac{\partial h}{\partial x} = 0; \qquad y - 2\lambda = 0 \qquad (7)$$

$$\frac{\partial h}{\partial y} = 0; \qquad x - 2\lambda = 0 \qquad (8)$$

and

$$\frac{\partial h}{\partial \lambda} = 0; \qquad 2x + 2y - c = 0 \qquad (9)$$

Solving (7) for y gives $y = 2\lambda$, solving (8) for x gives $x = 2\lambda$, and substituting these results in (9) gives

$$8\lambda = c$$

Therefore,

$$\lambda = \frac{c}{8} \quad \text{and} \quad x = \frac{c}{4}, \quad y = \frac{c}{4}$$

A stationary point, obtained by the method of Lagrange multipliers, may be either a local maximum point, a local minimum point, or neither. The sufficient conditions may be obtained from those developed in Chapter 9 for a function of two variables when the variables are independent. The Taylor expansion for $f(x, y)$ of two variables [(10), page 264] is:

$$f(x + dx, y + dy) = f(x, y) + df + \frac{1}{2!} d^2f + \frac{1}{3!} d^3f + \cdots$$

The necessary conditions obtained above may be verified by using the fact that a necessary condition for an extreme point is that df is zero. Since x and y must satisfy the relation $g(x, y) = 0$, the differential dg must be zero and dx and dy must satisfy

$$g_x \, dx + g_y \, dy = 0 \qquad \text{or} \qquad dx = -\frac{g_y}{g_x} dy \qquad (10)$$

if $g_x \neq 0$.

Substituting (10) in the differential df

$$df = f_x \, dx + f_y \, dy$$

gives

$$df = \left[-\frac{f_x g_y}{g_x} + f_y \right] dy$$

Since dy is different from zero, a necessary condition for df to be zero is for the term in square brackets to be zero, or

$$\frac{f_x}{g_x} = \frac{f_y}{g_y} \qquad (11)$$

This is the same necessary condition obtained earlier (6).

The sufficient condition for the stationary point to be a maximum point is that d^2f be negative. The second differential was given in (2) page 260, for the case where x and y are independent. When x and y are not independent, the second differential contains two additional terms.

$$\begin{aligned} d^2f &= d(f_x \, dx + f_y \, dy) = d(f_x \, dx) + d(f_y \, dy) \\ &= d(f_x) \, dx + f_x \, d(dx) + d(f_y) \, dy + f_y \, d(dy) \\ &= (f_{xx} \, dx + f_{xy} \, dy) \, dx + f_x \, d^2x + (f_{yx} \, dx + f_{yy} \, dy) \, dy + f_y \, d^2y \\ &= f_{xx} \, dx^2 + 2f_{xy} \, dx \, dy + f_{yy} \, dy^2 + f_x \, d^2x + f_y \, d^2y \end{aligned} \qquad (12)$$

(dx^2 denotes $(dx)^2$ and d^2x the second total differential of x.)

The additional terms involve the second differentials of x and y which will be zero when x and y (and dx and dy) are independent, but are not zero when dx and dy must satisfy (10). Similarly, from (10)

$$g_{xx} \, dx^2 + 2g_{xy} \, dx \, dy + g_{yy} \, dy^2 + g_x \, d^2x + g_y \, d^2y = 0 \qquad (13)$$

Solving (13) for d^2x, substituting in (12), and collecting terms give

$$d^2f = \left[f_{xx} - \frac{f_x}{g_x} g_{xx} \right] dx^2 + 2\left[f_{xy} - \frac{f_x}{g_x} g_{xy} \right] dx\, dy$$

$$+ \left[f_{yy} - \frac{f_x}{g_x} g_{yy} \right] dy^2 + \left[f_y - \frac{f_x}{g_x} g_y \right] d^2y$$

The last term is zero because the factor in the square brackets is df. Substituting for dx from (10) and using λ as defined by (6) give

$$d^2f = \frac{dy^2}{dx^2} \cdot \Delta_3$$

$$\Delta_3 = -\{ g_y{}^2[f_{xx} - \lambda g_{xx}] - 2g_x g_y[f_{xy} - \lambda g_{xy}] + g_x{}^2[f_{yy} - \lambda g_{yy}] \} \quad (14)$$

The function $f(x, y)$ will have a maximum (minimum) subject to $g(x, y) = 0$ if Δ_3 is positive (negative). If Δ_3 is zero, higher differentials must be examined.

Example 3.   In Example 2,

$$f(x, y) = xy$$
$$g(x, y) = 2x + 2y - c$$

The stationary point is $x = y = \dfrac{c}{4}$; $\lambda = \dfrac{c}{8}$

$$
\begin{array}{llll}
f_x = y & f_{xx} = 0 & g_x = 2 & g_{xx} = 0 \\
f_y = x & f_{yy} = 0 & g_y = 2 & g_{yy} = 0 \\
& f_{xy} = 1 & & g_{xy} = 0
\end{array}
$$

$$\Delta_3 = -\{ 2^2[0] - 2(2)(2)[1] + 2^2[0] \} = 8$$

and therefore $x = y = \dfrac{c}{4}$ is a maximum point.

Remarks and Discussion

This method of Lagrange multipliers gives the same answer as that obtained by substituting for y before the differentiation. However, the Lagrange method also supplies a value of λ. The significance of the value of λ in Example 2 is that if c is increased by a small amount ε, then the new value of h, say, h_1, is given by

$$
\begin{aligned}
h_1(x^*, y^*, \lambda) &= f(x^*, y^*) - \lambda[2x^* + 2y^* - (c + \varepsilon)] \\
&= f(x^*, y^*) - \lambda[2x^* + 2y^* - c] + \lambda\varepsilon \\
&= h(x^*, y^*, \lambda) + \lambda\varepsilon
\end{aligned}
$$

The sign of λ indicates the direction of the effect, on h, of a small change in c. In this example, λ is positive and the value of h will increase if c is increased. Of course, this says nothing more than the obvious; if the perimeter is allowed to increase, the area will also increase. However, in more complicated problems, the sign of λ is useful in indicating the effect of small changes in the constraining equation where the sign of effect is not obvious.

In theory, the method of Lagrange multipliers can be generalized to two equality constraints. The necessary conditions for a point (x, y) to be an extremum of $f(x, y)$, subject to $g_1(x, y) = 0$ and $g_2(x, y) = 0$, are obtained by setting the partial derivatives of

$$h(x, y, \lambda_1, \lambda_2) = f(x, y) - \lambda_1 g_1(x, y) - \lambda_2 g_2(x, y)$$

with respect to x, y, λ_1, and λ_2 equal to zero. However, the two equations, $g_1(x, y) = 0$ and $g_2(x, y) = 0$, will normally have only one common point. Therefore, this particular case would not appear very frequently. The method would not be used with more than two equality constraints because it may not be possible to satisfy three or more equality constraints in two variables simultaneously.

One disadvantage of the method of Lagrange multipliers is that the number of variables has been increased and the number of equations which must be solved has also been increased. (The latter is the result of the added constraint—not of the method.) This disadvantage is usually offset by the elimination of the need to solve for the constraint directly. In practical two decision variable problems, however, the major reason for preferring the Lagrange multiplier method over the substitution method is the fact that it supplies a value of λ.

EXERCISES

1. Determine the stationary points of the function
$$f(x, y) = Ax^2 + Bxy + Cy^2 + Dx + Ey + F$$
subject to
$$ax + by - c = 0$$
by
   (a) Substitution.
   (b) Lagrange multipliers.
2. Determine the conditions under which the stationary points in Exercise 1 are maxima, minima, or neither.
3. Use the result in Exercise 1 to verify the solution in Example 2.
4. Among all rectangles with constant area, find the one with minimum perimeter by:
   (a) Substitution.
   (b) Lagrange multiplier.

5. A firm sells a single product in two districts, A and B. The number of units that can be sold in the ith district depends on the amount of money spent for marketing. In particular, the money that must be spent to sell the xth dollar's worth of product in District A is

$$m_A(x) = \alpha_A x^\beta$$

and the amount that must be spent to sell the yth dollar's worth of the product in District B is

$$m_B(y) = \alpha_B y^\beta$$

The total amount of money available for marketing in both districts is $\$K$.
(a) Show that the optimum allocation to maximize total sales is given by the x and y which satisfy:

$$m_A(x) = m_B(y)$$

and

$$x m_A(x) + y m_B(y) - (\beta + 1)K = 0$$

[*Hint*: Treat x and y as continuous variables and note that the total marketing expense in area A is given by the integral of $m_A(x)$.]
(b) Show that the solution is a maximum.

6. Use the Lagrange multiplier technique to show that the necessary condition for

$$S(n, v) = k n^v v^n \qquad n \geq 1; \qquad v \geq 1$$

to have an extreme point subject to

$$nv = c \qquad c \geq 0$$

is that

$$\ln v = \frac{c - v^2 + v^2 \ln c}{c + v^2}$$

7. A wholesaler sells two parts. Each part must be ordered separately and the cost of placing an order is C_0. The requirements for the parts are uniform and known, say, R_1 and R_2. The holding cost is a fixed percentage I of the cost. Let U_1 denote the cost of the first part and U_2 the cost of the second part. Determine the optimum ordering policy and the change in the optimum for small changes in K if the total value of the average inventory must be equal to a constant K.

8. The firm in Chapter 10, Section C, is using a policy of setting marketing expenditures equal to a fixed proportion, k, of revenues. Determine the optimum selling price and earnings as a function of k.

9. Discuss the problem of determining the optimum number of (1) levels and (2) span of control for an organization of fixed size for the model considered in Exercise 4, p. 52, using maximum average efficiency as the objective.

B. INEQUALITY CONSTRAINTS

In many business problems, the constraints are really limitations rather than equality constraints. It is not known in advance whether a constraint will be satisfied as an inequality or as an equality in the optimum solution. The sign of λ obtained in solving optimization problems involving

Lagrange multipliers is particularly useful in problems in which the constraints are really inequalities rather than equalities. In this section the Lagrange multiplier method is extended to the case of inequality constraints.

One Inequality Constraint

Example I. The earnings function for a certain store considered in Example 3, page 251, is given by:

$$E(x, y) = 4x + 5y + xy - x^2 - y^2 + 5$$

where E = earnings in hundreds of thousands of dollars

x = investment in inventory in hundreds of thousands of dollars

y = floor space used for display in units of 10,000 square feet

If there are no constraints on x and y, the maximum earnings are obtained by solving

$$\frac{\partial E}{\partial x} = 0 \quad \text{and} \quad \frac{\partial E}{\partial y} = 0$$

or

$$4 + y - 2x = 0$$
$$5 + x - 2y = 0$$

The solution is

$$x^* = \tfrac{13}{3} = 4\tfrac{1}{3} \qquad y^* = \tfrac{14}{3} = 4\tfrac{2}{3}$$

The second-order condition is

$$\Delta_1 = -2$$
$$\Delta_2(\tfrac{13}{3}, \tfrac{14}{3}) = E_{xx}E_{yy} - (E_{xy})^2 = (-2)(-2) - 1 = 3(>0)$$

Hence E has a maximum value at (x^*, y^*). The maximum earnings of $\$25\tfrac{1}{3}$ milllion are achieved when $\$433,333$ is invested in inventory and 46,667 square feet of floor space is used for display.

Suppose, next, that working capital is required to operate the store. Each dollar invested in inventory requires half a dollar in working capital, and each square foot of floor space requires ten dollars in working capital for furniture, rent, etc. The total working capital required for any x and y, in dollars is

$$(\tfrac{1}{2})(x)(100,000) + (10)(y)10,000 = 100,000\left(\frac{x}{2} + y\right)$$

For the maximum earnings, the working capital required is

$$(\tfrac{13}{6} + \tfrac{14}{3}) \, 100,000 = (\tfrac{41}{6})(100,000) \text{ dollars}$$

Assume the amount of working capital available is \$100,000 w. Thus $100,000 \left(\dfrac{x}{2} + y\right) \leq 100,000 \, w$. Then, assuming that *all* available capital will be used, the optimum x and y may be obtained by using Lagrange multipliers:

$$h(x, y, \lambda) = E(x, y) - \lambda\left(\frac{x}{2} + y - w\right) \tag{1}$$

$$\frac{\partial h}{\partial x} = 4 + y - 2x - \frac{\lambda}{2} = 0$$

$$\frac{\partial h}{\partial y} = 5 + x - 2y - \lambda = 0$$

$$\frac{\partial h}{\partial \lambda} = \frac{x}{2} + y - w = 0$$

The solution to this set of equations is:

$$x = \tfrac{3}{7} + \tfrac{4}{7}w; \qquad y = -\tfrac{3}{14} + \tfrac{5}{7}w; \qquad \lambda = -\tfrac{6}{7}w + (5 + \tfrac{6}{7}) \tag{2}$$

If $w > \tfrac{41}{6}$, then $\lambda < 0$, and $x^* = \tfrac{13}{3}$, $y^* = \tfrac{14}{3}$.

If $w = \tfrac{41}{6}$, then $\lambda = 0$

If $w < \tfrac{41}{6}$, then $\lambda > 0$ $\Bigg\}$ x^* and y^* are given by (2).

If the problem were initially stated as determining the maximum earnings with $w =$ say, 42/6, the sign of λ in the solution would indicate that the earnings could actually be increased by not using all the available working capital. If the problem had been stated as $w \leq 42/6$, the optimum solution would then require a $w < 42/6$. On the other hand, if the condition were stated as $w \leq 40/6$, then λ in the solution would be positive; this would indicate that the maximum earnings required $w = 40/6$.

The constraining equation

$$\frac{x}{2} + y \leq w$$

defines a region to the left of the line CB (Fig. 11.2) in which the points satisfy all the constraints. If the constraint is an equality, the stationary point will occur, by definition, at a point on the boundary of the region. If the constraint is an inequality, the stationary point can occur either on the boundary of the region or at an "interior" point. For the example given above, if the constraint were

$$\frac{x}{2} + y \leq \frac{40}{6}$$

λ will be positive, indicating that the stationary point occurs on the boundary, i.e., the unconstrained stationary point is outside the region.

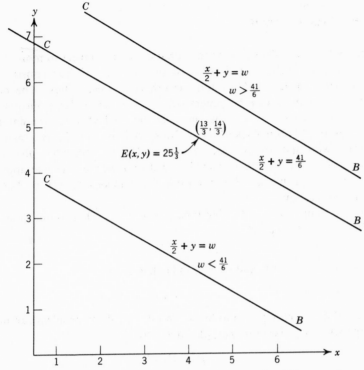

Figure 11.2 Working capital constraint $x/2 + y = w$ for different values of w.

On the other hand, if the constraint were

$$\frac{x}{2} + y \leq \frac{42}{6}$$

λ will be negative, indicating that the extreme point occurs inside the region.

The procedure for determining the maximum of a function of two variables subject to one inequality constraint, suggested above, consists of the following steps:

1. Determine the maximum by using a Lagrange multiplier, assuming the inequality holds as the equality.
2. If λ is non-negative, the maximum so obtained is also the maximum subject to the inequality constraint.
3. If λ is negative, determine the maximum without regard to the constraint. The resulting maximum will satisfy the constraint and be the solution of the problem.

306 OPTIMIZATION SUBJECT TO CONSTRAINTS

Kuhn-Tucker Conditions

The decision variables in a given problem may be subject to more than one inequality constraint and at the optimum, some of these constraints may be satisfied as equalities and the others as inequalities. The procedure given above can be generalized to include multiple inequality constraints. The conditions that must be satisfied at an extremum are known as the "Kuhn-Tucker" conditions, in honor of the two mathematicians who first formally stated them. [The essential idea, however, was well known to mathematicians long before Kuhn and Tucker applied it to business problems. See, for example, Hancock (1917), p. 149 in 1960 Dover edition.]

These conditions may be developed as follows: The problem is to maximize $f(x, y)$ subject to

$$g(x, y) \leq 0$$

Let z be a new variable and let $g(x, y)$ be defined by

$$z^2 = -g(x, y)$$

This condition forces $g(x, y)$ to be non-positive and the problem can now be expressed as: Maximize $f(x, y)$, subject to:

$$g(x, y) + z^2 = 0 \tag{3}$$

In this form the problem can be treated by the method of Lagrange multipliers, since the constraint is now an equality. Let

$$h(x, y, \lambda, z) = f(x, y) - \lambda[g(x, y) + z^2]$$

The necessary conditions for a stationary point are:

$$\frac{\partial h}{\partial x} = 0; \qquad \frac{\partial f}{\partial x} - \lambda \frac{\partial g}{\partial x} = 0 \tag{4}$$

$$\frac{\partial h}{\partial y} = 0; \qquad \frac{\partial f}{\partial y} - \lambda \frac{\partial g}{\partial y} = 0 \tag{5}$$

$$\frac{\partial h}{\partial \lambda} = 0; \qquad g(x, y) + z^2 = 0 \tag{6}$$

$$\frac{\partial h}{\partial z} = 0; \qquad 2\lambda z = 0 \tag{7}$$

(7) requires that either $\lambda = 0$ or $z = 0$; if $z = 0$, then from (6) $g(x, y)$ also equals zero. Equations (6) and (7) together therefore imply that

$$\lambda g(x, y) = 0 \tag{8}$$

at a stationary point. Since (6) merely restates the requirement that $g(x, y)$ be non-positive, the necessary conditions for a local extremum are (4), (5), (8), and $g(x, y) \leq 0$. From the discussion given above it follows that the extremum will be a local maximum if $\lambda \geq 0$. The variable z can now be discarded because it was merely an artificiality and the Kuhn-Tucker conditions may be stated as follows:

The necessary condition for a point (x, y) to be a local maximum of $f(x, y)$ subject to $g(x, y) \leq 0$ is that a non-negative λ exists such that λ and (x, y) satisfy the following:

$$\frac{\partial f}{\partial x} - \lambda \frac{\partial g}{\partial x} = 0 \qquad (9)$$

$$\frac{\partial f}{\partial y} - \lambda \frac{\partial g}{\partial y} = 0$$

$$\lambda g(x, y) = 0$$

$$g(x, y) \leq 0$$

These conditions are also sufficient if f is concave and the constraints are concave. The result is directly applicable to minimizing a convex function, since a maximum point of f is a minimum point of $-f$.

Example 2. In the problem in Example 1, the objective is to maximize

$$E(x, y) = 4x + 5y + xy - x^2 - y^2 + 5$$

subject to

$$\frac{x}{2} + y \leq w$$

$E(x, y)$ is a concave function since $B^2 - 4AC = 1 - 4 = -3$. (See page 275.) Let

$$g(x, y) = \frac{x}{2} + y - w$$

Then the necessary conditions for a maximum from (9) are

$$\frac{\partial E}{\partial x} - \lambda \frac{\partial g}{\partial x} = 4 + y - 2x - \frac{\lambda}{2} = 0 \qquad (10)$$

$$\frac{\partial E}{\partial y} - \lambda \frac{\partial g}{\partial y} = 5 + x - 2y - \lambda = 0 \qquad (11)$$

$$\lambda\left(\frac{x}{2} + y - w\right) = 0 \qquad (12)$$

$$\frac{x}{2} + y - w \leq 0 \qquad (13)$$

$$\lambda \geq 0 \qquad (14)$$

A stationary point (x, y, λ) must satisfy (10) — (14). From (12) it follows that either $\lambda = 0$ or $x/2 + y - w = 0$.

If $\lambda = 0$, then (10) and (11) reduce to

$$4 + y - 2x = 0$$

$$5 + x - 2y = 0$$

which have the solution obtained earlier:

$$x = \tfrac{13}{3}; \qquad y = \tfrac{14}{3}$$

This solution will also satisfy (12), (13), and (14) if $w \geq \tfrac{41}{6}$, but will not satisfy (13) if $w < \tfrac{41}{6}$.

If $\lambda \neq 0$, then to satisfy (12):

$$\frac{x}{2} + y - w = 0 \qquad \text{or} \qquad y = w - \frac{x}{2}$$

Substitution in (10) and (11) gives

$\qquad\qquad and \quad 2x - \lambda = 2w - 5$

$$-\frac{5}{2}x + \frac{\lambda}{2} = -4 - w$$

The solution to these equations is

$$x = \tfrac{3}{7} + \tfrac{4}{7}w \qquad y = -\tfrac{3}{14} + \tfrac{5}{7}w \qquad \lambda = \tfrac{41}{7} - \tfrac{6}{7}w$$

If

$$w < \tfrac{41}{6}, \text{ then } \lambda > 0; \qquad w = \tfrac{41}{6}, \text{ then } \lambda = 0; \qquad w > \tfrac{41}{6}, \text{ then } \lambda < 0$$

Only the case $w \leq 41/6$ satisfies condition (14); (13) is then also satisfied.

The solution may be summarized as follows:

If $w \geq \tfrac{41}{6}$ the optimum solution is

$$x = \tfrac{13}{3}; \qquad y = \tfrac{14}{3}; \qquad \lambda = 0$$

If $w < \tfrac{41}{6}$ the optimum solution is

$$x = \tfrac{3}{7} + \tfrac{4}{7}w; \qquad y = -\tfrac{3}{14} + \tfrac{5}{7}w; \qquad \lambda = \tfrac{41}{7} - \tfrac{6}{7}w \ (> 0)$$

This solution is of course exactly the same as that obtained in (2). From the solution in (2) it was argued that, if λ turned out to be positive ($w < 41/6$ in this case), the constraint is binding and $g(x, y) = 0$ at the optimum solution. On the other hand, if λ turned out to be negative ($w > 41/6$ in this case), the constraint is not binding and may be disregarded. The advantage of the formulation in this section is that it is immediately applicable to more than one constraint.

Kuhn-Tucker Conditions for More than One Inequality Constraint

To generalize the Kuhn-Tucker conditions to more than one inequality constraint, consider next the case of two inequality constraints. The problem is to maximize $f(x, y)$ subject to $g_1(x, y) \leq 0$ and $g_2(x, y) \leq 0$. Two new variables z_1 and z_2 are defined and the constraints set equal to z_1^2 and z_2^2; e.g.,

$$-g_1(x, y) = z_1^2; \qquad -g_2(x, y) = z_2^2$$

Two Lagrange multipliers, λ_1 and λ_2, are defined and the function to be maximized is now a function of six variables.

$$h(x, y, \lambda_1, \lambda_2, z_1, z_2) = f(x, y) - \lambda_1[g_1(x, y) + z_1^2] - \lambda_2[g_2(x, y) + z_2^2]$$

Following the method used above and eliminating z_1 and z_2 leads to the following statement:

The necessary condition for a point (x, y) to be a maximum of $f(x, y)$, subject to $g_1(x, y) \leq 0$ and $g_2(x, y) \leq 0$, is that non-negative values of λ_1 and λ_2 exist such that $\lambda_1, \lambda_2, x,$ and y satisfy the equations:

$$\frac{\partial f}{\partial x} - \lambda_1 \frac{\partial g_1}{\partial x} - \lambda_2 \frac{\partial g_2}{\partial x} = 0 \tag{15}$$

$$\frac{\partial f}{\partial y} - \lambda_1 \frac{\partial g_1}{\partial y} - \lambda_2 \frac{\partial g_2}{\partial y} = 0 \tag{16}$$

$$g_1(x, y) \leq 0; \qquad g_2(x, y) \leq 0 \tag{17}$$

$$\lambda_1 g_1(x, y) = 0; \qquad \lambda_2 g_2(x, y) = 0 \tag{18}$$

Again these conditions are sufficient if f, g_1, and g_2 are concave.

Example 3. Suppose that in addition to the constraint on working capital, there is another constraint in that only v clerks are available. For the purposes of this illustration, it will be assumed that the number of clerks required increases with floor space used and with the amount invested in inventory. In particular, one clerk is required for each \$25,000 invested in inventory and each 10,000 square feet of floor space used; the total number of clerks required is:

$$\frac{x}{4} + y$$

Also for illustrative purposes it will be assumed that the number of clerks does not have to be an integer; a fraction merely represents a part of a clerk's time.

The problem then is to:

maximize $E(x, y)$ subject to $g_1(x, y) \leq 0$ and $g_2(x, y) \leq 0$

where $E(x, y) = 4x + 5y + xy - x^2 - y^2 + 5$

$$g_1(x, y) = \frac{x}{2} + y - w$$

$$g_2(x, y) = \frac{x}{4} + y - v$$

The necessary conditions for an optimum are:

$$4 + y - 2x - \tfrac{1}{2}\lambda_1 - \tfrac{1}{4}\lambda_2 = 0$$
$$5 + x - 2y - \lambda_1 - \lambda_2 = 0$$
$$\frac{x}{2} + y - w \leq 0$$
$$\frac{x}{4} + y - v \leq 0$$
$$\lambda_1\left(\frac{x}{2} + y - w\right) = 0$$
$$\lambda_2\left(\frac{x}{4} + y - v\right) = 0$$
$$\lambda_1 \geq 0 \qquad \lambda_2 \geq 0$$

The solutions for the four possible combinations of λ_1 and λ_2, equal to or different from zero, are given in the accompanying table.

	λ_1	λ_2	g_1	g_2	λ_1	λ_2	x	y	g_1	g_2
(a)	0	0	$\neq 0$	$\neq 0$	0	0	$\frac{13}{3}$	$\frac{14}{3}$	$\frac{41}{6} - w$	$\frac{23}{4} - v$
(b)	$\neq 0$	0	0	$\neq 0$	$-\frac{6}{7}w + \frac{41}{7}$	0	$\frac{4}{7}w + \frac{3}{7}$	$\frac{5}{7}w - \frac{3}{14}$	0	$\frac{6}{7}w - \frac{3}{28} - v$
(c)	0	$\neq 0$	$\neq 0$	0	0	$-\frac{8}{7}v + \frac{46}{7}$	$\frac{4}{7}v + \frac{22}{21}$	$\frac{6}{7}v - \frac{11}{42}$	$\frac{8}{7}v + \frac{11}{42} - w$	0
(d)	$\neq 0$	$\neq 0$	0	0	$-42w + 48v + 11$	$+24w - 28v - 3$	$4(w - v)$	$-w + 2v$	0	0

Generally speaking, three cases can occur:

1. Neither of the two constraints is binding (case a in the table). In this case the constrained optimum is the same as the unconstrained optimum and could be obtained by determining the optimum of the objective function without regard to the constraints. From the table it can be seen that this occurs when $w \geq \frac{41}{6}$ and $v \geq \frac{23}{4}$. The optimum is $x^* = \frac{13}{3}$; $y^* = \frac{14}{3}$.

2. One of the constraints is binding and the other is not; say, $g_i(x, y)$ is binding (cases b and c in the table). Then the constrained optimum will satisfy $g_i(x, y) = 0$ and the solution could be obtained by optimizing the objective function subject to this equality constraint; the other constraint can be disregarded.

From the table (case b) it can be seen that the first constraint is binding and all the conditions are satisfied if:

$$\lambda_1 \geq 0 \quad \text{or} \quad -\frac{6w}{7} + \frac{41}{7} \geq 0 \quad \text{or} \quad w \leq \frac{41}{6}$$

and

$$g_2 \leq 0 \quad \text{or} \quad \frac{6w}{7} - \frac{3}{28} - v \leq 0 \quad \text{or} \quad 24w - 28v - 3 \leq 0$$

The optimum is $x^* = \frac{1}{7}(4w + 3)$; $y^* = \frac{1}{14}(10w - 3)$. The second constraint (case c) will be binding and all the conditions will be satisfied if:

$$\lambda_2 \geq 0 \quad \text{or} \quad -\frac{8}{7}v + \frac{46}{7} \geq 0 \quad \text{or} \quad v \leq \frac{23}{4}$$

and

$$g_1 \leq 0 \quad \text{or} \quad \frac{8v}{7} + \frac{11}{42} - w \leq 0 \quad \text{or} \quad -42w + 48v + 11 \leq 0$$

The optimum is $x^* = \frac{1}{21}(12v + 22)$; $y^* = \frac{1}{42}(36v - 11)$.

3. Both constraints are binding. Here the constrained optimum must satisfy both constraints as equalities. In the case being considered in this chapter (two-decision variables), the two constraints normally will have only one solution and this will be the constrained optimum. From the table it can be seen that both constraints will be binding and all conditions will be satisfied if:

$$-42w + 48v + 11 \geq 0$$

and

$$24w - 28v - 3 \geq 0$$

The optimum is $x^* = 4w - 4v$; $y^* = -w + 2v$.

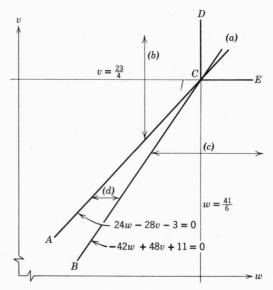

Figure II.3 Regions of parameter values (w, v) for which neither constraint is binding (a), only the capital constraint is binding (b), only the clerk constraint is binding (c), and both are binding (d).

The four regions are shown in Fig. 11.3. In the rectangle bounded by DCE, labeled (a), neither constraint is binding. In the region labeled (b), bounded by ACD, the capital constraint is binding. In the region labeled (c), bounded by BCE, the clerk constraint is binding; and in the region labeled (d), bounded by ACB, both constraints are binding.

The conditions (15)-(18) are sufficient in this example because E, g_1, and g_2 are concave.

EXERCISES

In each exercise, verify the sufficient condition for global extrema whenever appropriate.

1. (a) Determine the maximum value of the function

$$f(x, y) = Ax^2 + Bxy + Cy^2 + Dx + Ey + F$$

subject to

$$ax + by - c \leq 0$$

(b) Verify the solution obtained in Example 1.

2. (a) Determine the maximum value of the function

$$f(x, y) = Ax^2 + Bxy + Cy^2 + Dx + Ey + F$$

subject to

$$a_1 x + b_1 y - c_1 \le 0$$
$$a_2 x + b_2 y - c_2 \le 0$$

(b) Verify the solution to Example 2.

3. Determine the conditions under which

$$f(x, y) = Bxy + Dx + Ey + F$$

has a local maximum subject to

$$ax + by - c \le 0$$

4. Answer Exercise 8, p. 302, if the constraint is treated as an inequality.

5. Answer Exercise 9, p. 302, if the total administrator cost must not exceed K. Assume the salary ratio, b, is constant.

6. Formulate as an optimization problem and solve (if possible) the problem in Exercise 1, p. 204, if $f(t) = e^{mt}$ and if new equipment cannot be installed more than twice during the period.

7. Develop necessary conditions for an extreme point of $f(x, y)$ subject to $g_1(x, y) \le 0$ and $g_2(x, y) = 0$.

C. LINEAR OBJECTIVE, LINEAR, AND NON-NEGATIVE CONSTRAINTS

The previous section has dealt with examples in which non-linear objective functions were optimized, subject to one or more inequality constraints. In many problems, the objective function is linear and in this section the Kuhn-Tucker conditions will be applied to such problems. The method will also be extended to cover the case where the decision variables must be non-negative.

Linear Objective Function

Example I. A firm produces two types of precision screws, wood screws and metal screws, and can sell all the screws produced for 10¢ per box of wood screws and 11¢ per box of metal screws. Raw material is available in unlimited quantities and costs 5¢ for a box of wood screws and 7¢ for a box of metal screws. Fixed costs per week are $50, including labor, since operators are guaranteed a weekly wage.

Production of either type of screws requires the use of two machines: a slotting machine (I) and a threading machine (II). A box of wood screws requires four minutes on machine I and two minutes on machine II. A box of metal screws requires two minutes on machine I and 13 minutes on machine II. Both machines can be used up to 4,800 minutes per week and are idle when not used to produce screws. The objective is to maximize earnings:

$$\text{Earnings} = \text{Revenue} - \text{Cost}$$

Let x_1 = number of boxes of wood screws produced, and
$\quad\;\; x_2$ = number of boxes of metal screws produced

$$\text{Revenue} = 10x_1 + 11x_2 \text{ (in cents)}$$
$$\text{Costs} = 5x_1 + 7x_2 + 5{,}000 \text{ (in cents)}$$
$$\text{Earnings} = 10x_1 + 11x_2 - 5x_1 - 7x_2 - 5{,}000$$
$$= 5x_1 + 4x_2 - 5{,}000$$

The constraints are:

$$4x_1 + 2x_2 \leq 4{,}800 \qquad \text{Machine I restriction}$$
$$2x_1 + 13x_2 \leq 4{,}800 \qquad \text{Machine II restriction}$$

To use the Kuhn-Tucker conditions, let

$$f(x_1, x_2) = 5x_1 + 4x_2 - 5{,}000$$
$$g_1(x_1, x_2) = 4x_1 + 2x_2 - 4{,}800$$
$$g_2(x_1, x_2) = 2x_1 + 13x_2 - 4{,}800$$

The necessary conditions are:

$$5 - 4\lambda_1 - 2\lambda_2 = 0$$
$$4 - 2\lambda_1 - 13\lambda_2 = 0$$
$$4x_1 + 2x_2 - 4{,}800 \leq 0$$
$$2x_1 + 13x_2 - 4{,}800 \leq 0$$
$$\lambda_1(4x_1 + 2x_2 - 4{,}800) = 0$$
$$\lambda_2(2x_1 + 13x_2 - 4{,}800) = 0$$
$$\lambda_1 \geq 0 \qquad \lambda_2 \geq 0$$

In this case an attempt to solve the different cases shows that the equations cannot be satisfied if $\lambda_1 = \lambda_2 = 0$, or if $\lambda_1 = 0$, or if $\lambda_2 = 0$. Only one combination, $\lambda_1 \neq 0$, $\lambda_2 \neq 0$, satisfies the conditions.

λ_1	λ_2	g_1	g_2	λ_1	λ_2	x_1	x_2	g_1	g_2
0	0	$\neq 0$	$\neq 0$						
0	$\neq 0$	$\neq 0$	0						
$\neq 0$	0	0	$\neq 0$						
$\neq 0$	$\neq 0$	0	0	$+\frac{19}{16}$	$+\frac{1}{8}$	1,100	200	0	0

In this case all the conditions are satisfied by the solution

$$x_1 = 1{,}100; \qquad x_2 = 200; \qquad \lambda_1 = +\tfrac{19}{16}; \qquad \lambda_2 = +\tfrac{1}{8}$$

indicating that both constraints are binding.

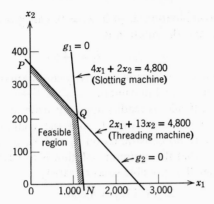

Figure 11.4   Values of x_1 and x_2 satisfy the constraints in Example 1.

The result may be interpreted graphically using Fig. 11.4. The inequality $g_1 \leq 0$ is satisfied by all points to the left of line $g_1 = 0$ and the inequality $g_2 \leq 0$ is satisfied by all points to the left and below line $g_2 = 0$. By setting $\lambda_1 = \lambda_2 = 0$, interior points are examined; by setting $\lambda_1 = 0$, feasible points on line QP are examined and by setting $\lambda_2 = 0$, feasible points on the line segment QN are examined. In no case is there a stationary point and hence the only other possibility is the point at which both λ_1 and λ_2 are not zero, namely, Q.

Non-Negativity Constraints

In the examples considered so far, the critical points have always been in the positive quadrant. However, in practical problems, it may be necessary to ensure this by adding additional constraints.

Example 2.   Suppose that the objective in Example 1 is to maximize

$$1x_1 + 8x_2$$

subject to the same conditions. The necessary conditions are:

$$1 - 4\lambda_1 - 2\lambda_2 = 0$$
$$8 - 2\lambda_1 - 13\lambda_2 = 0$$
$$4x_1 + 2x_2 - 4{,}800 \leq 0$$
$$2x_1 + 13x_2 - 4{,}800 \leq 0$$
$$\lambda_1(4x_1 + 2x_2 - 4{,}800) = 0$$
$$\lambda_2(2x_1 + 13x_2 - 4{,}800) = 0$$
$$\lambda_1 \geq 0 \qquad \lambda_2 \geq 0$$

Again, only one combination $\lambda_1 \neq 0$, $\lambda_2 \neq 0$, can possibly satisfy the necessary conditions and the solution is:

$$\lambda_1 = -\tfrac{1}{16}; \qquad \lambda_2 = +\tfrac{5}{8}$$

This solution does not satisfy the non-negativity condition on λ_1, indicating that the solution is not a local maximum.

The source of the difficulty is readily apparent from an examination of Fig. 11.5, which shows the constraints and the contour lines of the objective. If there were no constraints on x_1 and x_2, other than $g_1 \leq 0$ and $g_2 \leq 0$, it is clear that the optimum solution is to have x_2 as large as possible (and x_1 as small as possible so as to satisfy

$$2x_1 + 13x_2 = 4{,}800$$

as an equality). If $x_2 = K$, then

$$x_1 = \frac{4{,}800}{2} - \frac{13K}{2}$$

$$= 2{,}400 - \frac{13}{2}K$$

and the objective function is

$$2{,}400 - \tfrac{13}{2}K + 8K = 2{,}400 + \tfrac{3}{2}K$$

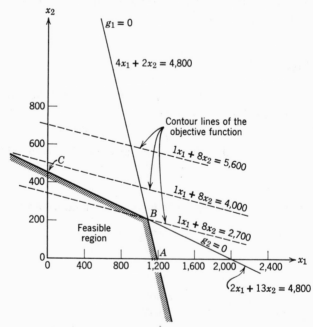

Figure 11.5 Feasible region and contour lines of the objective function, Example 2.

The other constraint, $g_1 \leq 0$, is satisfied since

$$4[2,400 - \tfrac{13}{2}K] + 2K = 9,600 - 24K < 4,800$$

if K is a large positive number. The optimum solution is to make K as large as possible, in particular

$$x_2 = +\infty$$
$$x_1 = -\infty$$
$$\lambda_1 = 0$$
$$\lambda_2 = +\tfrac{8}{13}$$

This solution is not feasible in practice because the decision variables are usually constrained to be not less than some minimum value; without loss of generality the minimum value can be taken to be zero. This requirement can be introduced by adding two more constraints:

$$g_3(x_1, x_2) \leq 0 \qquad g_3(x_1, x_2) = -x_1$$
$$g_4(x_1, x_2) \leq 0 \qquad g_4(x_1, x_2) = -x_2$$

and two more λ's, λ_3, and λ_4.

The problem now is:

maximize $\qquad\qquad f(x_1, x_2)$

subject to

$$g_j(x_1, x_2) \leq 0 \qquad j = 1, 2, 3, 4$$
$$f(x_1, x_2) = x_1 + 8x_2$$
$$g_1(x_1, x_2) = 4x_1 + 2x_2 - 4,800$$
$$g_2(x_1, x_2) = 2x_1 + 13x_2 - 4,800$$
$$g_3(x_1, x_2) = -x_1$$
$$g_4(x_1, x_2) = -x_2.$$

The necessary conditions are:

$$1 - 4\lambda_1 - 2\lambda_2 + \lambda_3 = 0$$
$$8 - 2\lambda_1 - 13\lambda_2 + \lambda_4 = 0$$
$$4x_1 + 2x_2 - 4,800 \leq 0$$
$$2x_1 + 13x_2 - 4,800 \leq 0$$
$$-x_1 \leq 0$$
$$-x_2 \leq 0$$
$$\lambda_1(4x_1 + 2x_2 - 4,800) = 0$$
$$\lambda_2(2x_1 + 13x_2 - 4,800) = 0$$
$$-\lambda_3 x_1 = 0$$
$$-\lambda_4 x_2 = 0$$
$$\lambda_j \geq 0 \qquad j = 1, 2, 3, 4$$

There are now sixteen possibilities which must be examined; each of the four λ's can be zero or different from zero. A table such as that used above could be constructed; it would show that the only solution satisfying the necessary conditions arises from

$$\lambda_1 = 0; \qquad \lambda_2 \neq 0; \qquad \lambda_3 \neq 0; \qquad \lambda_4 = 0$$

In this case

$$g_2 = 0 \qquad \text{gives} \qquad 2x_1 + 13x_2 = 4{,}800$$

$$g_3 = 0 \qquad \text{gives} \qquad x_1 = 0$$

and therefore,

$$x_2 = \frac{4{,}800}{13}$$

The solution $x_1 = 0$; $x_2 = 4{,}800/13$ satisfies $g_1 = 4x_1 + 2x_2 - 4{,}800 \leq 0$ and $g_4 = -x_2 \leq 0$. The values of λ_2 and λ_3, obtained by solving

$$1 - 2\lambda_2 + \lambda_3 = 0$$

$$8 - 13\lambda_2 = 0$$

are $\lambda_2 = +\frac{8}{13}$; $\lambda_3 = +\frac{3}{13}$

The solution obtained is therefore a local maximum and since the functions are concave it is the global maximum.

This method requires one λ for each decision variable; the value of λ gives the cost of the constraint. If this value is not required, the necessary conditions (15), (16), (17), and (19) in Section B for an extremum value of $f(x, y)$ subject to

$$g_j(x, y) \leq 0 \qquad j = 1, 2, \ldots m$$

can be generalized for the case where x and y must be non-negative without including any additional λ's. The necessary conditions for this case are:

$$\frac{\partial f}{\partial x} - \Sigma \lambda_j \frac{\partial g_j}{\partial x} \leq 0; \qquad \frac{\partial f}{\partial y} - \Sigma \lambda_j \frac{\partial g_j}{\partial y} \leq 0$$

$$x \left[\frac{\partial f}{\partial x} - \Sigma \lambda_j \frac{\partial g_j}{\partial x} \right] + y \left[\frac{\partial f}{\partial y} - \Sigma \lambda_j \frac{\partial g_j}{\partial y_j} \right] = 0$$

$$\lambda_j g_j = 0$$

$$g_j(x, y) \leq 0 \qquad j = 1, 2, \ldots m$$

$$\lambda_j \geq 0$$

$$x \geq 0, \qquad y \geq 0$$

For the example given above, the solution

$$\lambda_1 = 0; \qquad \lambda_2 = +\tfrac{8}{13}; \qquad x_1 = 0; \qquad x_2 = \tfrac{4800}{13}$$

satisfies all the requirements:

$$1 - 0(4) - \tfrac{8}{13}(2) = -\tfrac{3}{13} < 0$$

$$8 - 0(2) - \tfrac{8}{13}(13) = 0 \le 0$$

$$0[-\tfrac{3}{13}] + \tfrac{1}{13}(4{,}800)[0] = 0$$

$$g_1(x_1, x_2) = 0 + \tfrac{2}{13}(4{,}800) - 4{,}800 \le 0$$

$$g_2(x_1, x_2) = 0 + \tfrac{13}{13}(4{,}800) - 4{,}800 = 0$$

$$\lambda_1 \ge 0; \qquad \lambda_2 \ge 0; \qquad x_1 \ge 0; \qquad x_2 \ge 0$$

EXERCISES

In each exercise, verify the sufficient condition for a global extremum, whenever appropriate.

1. Determine the maximum value of the function

$$f(x, y) = Ax^2 + Bxy + Cy^2 + Dx + Ey + F$$

subject to

$$ax + by - c \le 0$$

$$x \ge 0, \qquad y \ge 0$$

2. Determine the maximum value of the function $f(x, y)$ in Exercise 1 subject to

$$a_1 x + b_1 y - c_1 \le 0$$

$$a_2 x + b_2 y - c_2 \le 0$$

$$x \ge 0; \qquad y \ge 0$$

3. Use the result of Exercise 2 to verify the solution to Example 1.
4. Use the result of Exercise 2 to verify the solution to Example 2.
5. Solve the problem in Example 1 if an additional machine is required. On this machine 3 minutes are needed for each box of wood screws and 2 minutes for each box of metal screws. Machine available for 4,800 minutes.
6. Answer Exercise 5 if the times are 0.1 and 4 minutes, respectively.
7. Answer Exercise 5 if the objective function is the one given in Example 2.
8. Formulate as an optimization problem and determine the values of c and s which maximize the average efficiency in the model presented in (6), p. 49, if the time spent on contacts must not exceed the total time available.
9. Formulate the model presented in Chapter 6, Section C, p. 165, as a two-variable optimization problem and discuss the solution.

SUMMARY

Optimization techniques have been extended in this chapter to cases in which the model can be expressed as a function of two variables subject to equality constraints or inequality constraints. Throughout the chapter it has always been assumed that the objective function and the constraints were continuous and differentiable functions.

The analytical or numerical computation of optimum values becomes more complicated as the problem becomes more complicated.

(a) If there are no constraints, the critical points are obtained by solving two simultaneous equations in two unknowns. The sufficient conditions for a local extreme point involve a relatively simple function of the second derivatives.

(b) If there are m equality constraints ($m = 1$ or 2), the determination of critical points involves either solving the constraints simultaneously for $2 - m$ variables and substituting to reduce the problem to optimization of $2 - m$ variables, or by using Lagrange multipliers and solving $2 + m$ simultaneous equations in $2 + m$ unknowns. The sufficient conditions involve a more complicated expression of the second derivatives.

(c) If there are m inequality constraints, the Kuhn-Tucker conditions isolate 2^m "stationary" points. The examination of each point may require as much effort as step (a).

All points satisfying necessary conditions must be examined to determine whether there are local extreme points, and then the global extreme points must be chosen. If the function is convex when a minimum is desired or concave when a maximum is desired, there will be one local extreme point.

What remains now is the generalization of these techniques to functions of n variables. This could be done at this point, but the algebra would become cumbersome. Hence, the next few chapters will be devoted to developing more powerful notation.

Notes and References

This chapter has dealt with the general problem of optimizing a function of two variables with continuous second-order partial derivatives where the variables may be subject to one or more of the following types of constraints:

Equality	$g(x, y) = 0$	
Inequality	$g(x, y) \leq 0$	or $\quad g(x, y) \geq 0$
Non-negativity	$x \geq 0, y \geq 0$	

The general approach to the problem is to express the objective in the form:

$$h(x, y, \lambda) = f(x, y) - \lambda g(x, y)$$

and then determine the necessary and sufficient condition that must be satisfied if f has an extreme value at point (x, y) subject to the constraints.

It should be recognized that there are three major arbitrary choices that can be made in the formulation of this problem:

1. The problem can be stated as one requiring maximization or requiring minimization.
2. The second term in h can be either $+$ or $-$. In other words, the term λg may be either added or subtracted.
3. The inequality constraints can be stated as either $g \leq 0$ or as $g \geq 0$.

There is no standard convention in the literature. (See Table 18.1 for selected examples for the case of n variables.) The choices that have been made were based on the following reasoning. The most logical way to look at business problems is to examine the earnings; and, naturally, the objective is to maximize. The problem then is specified to this extent:

$$\text{maximize } f(x, y) \pm \lambda g(x, y)$$

where $f(x, y)$ represents earnings and the term $\pm \lambda g(x, y)$ represents the change in earnings due to the restriction g greater than or less than zero. If the constraint is binding, $g(x, y)$ will be equal to zero and λ will then denote the marginal cost of the constraint. However, since f represents earnings and the constraints will usually reduce earnings, it is reasonable to have λ also represent the cost of the constraint. The "cost due the constraint" is the decrease in earnings resulting if the constraint (resources) are decreased by a small amount. The constraints can usually be expressed most naturally in the form

$$G(x, y) \leq b$$

where G represents the amount of the resource "used" by the decision (x, y) and b is the available amount of the resource. Let ε be a small negative change in b; then if the term λg is subtracted,

$$f(x, y) - \lambda g(x, y) = f(x, y) - \lambda[G(x, y) - (b + \varepsilon)]$$
$$= f(X) - \lambda[G(X) - b] + \lambda \varepsilon$$

If the constraint had been binding $[G(X) - b = 0]$ at the maximum, λ would have been positive and hence a negative change in b, of amount ε, would have decreased earnings approximately by the positive amount $\lambda \varepsilon$. If the constraint were not binding, λ would have been zero and there would be no change in earnings. The natural choice, therefore, is to use the minus sign and define $g(x, y)$ as the amount of resources used less the amount available; i.e.,

$$g(x, y) = G(x, y) - b$$

The inequality will then be $g(x, y) \leq 0$.

A general proof of the Lagrange multiplier method is given by Everett III, H. (1963), "Generalized Lagrange Multiplier Method for Solving Problems of Optimum Allocation of Resources," *Operations Research*, **11**, pp. 399–417.

Part Four

LINEAR SYSTEMS

CHAPTER TWELVE

Introduction to Matrices
and Linear Systems

The variables in many business problems are related by systems of linear equations. Matrices are invaluable in the formulation and solution of such problems. Matrices and the basic operations of addition, subtraction, and multiplication are defined and illustrated in the first section. The second section is devoted to methods for the solution of systems of linear equations in two variables.

A. MATRICES

Example of Matrices

Much of the data used in business organizations can conveniently be thought of as being arranged in rectangular arrays. For example, suppose a business firm sells four products I, II, III, and IV in each of two geographical areas U and V to three classes of customers: consumers, retailers, and wholesalers. Sales, in units, for a certain period might appear as follows:

Sales in Units: Geographical Area U

Sold to	Product			
	I	II	III	IV
Consumers	3	4	6	3
Retailers	6	2	5	3
Wholesalers	7	1	4	1
Total	16	7	15	7

Sales in Units: Geographical Area V

Sold to	Product			
	I	II	III	IV
Consumers	4	5	3	6
Retailers	7	2	8	0
Wholesalers	7	2	4	1
Total	18	9	15	7

The total sales, by product, could be arranged as follows:

	Product			
	I	II	III	IV
Total Sales	34	16	30	14

The firm pays a commission or bonus to salesmen, territory managers, and division managers. The rates vary by geographical areas as follows:

	Salesmen	Territory Managers	Division Managers
Area U	0.06	0.05	0.02
Area V	0.04	0.03	0.03

The selling price is:

Product	Selling Price, in Dollars per Unit
I	2.00
II	10.00
III	5.00
IV	7.00

Rectangular arrays of numbers appear so frequently both in business problems and elsewhere that mathematicians have given them the special name of "matrix." Furthermore, mathematicians have discovered a number of algebraic operations, analogous to the arithmetical operations (addition, subtraction, multiplication, and division) on numbers, which can be defined for matrices. Many of these operations turn out to be meaningful and useful in business problems and will be illustrated here, using the example given above. The firm might wish to compute:

(a) Total sales in units by product and customer type.
(b) Difference between geographical areas in sales in units by product and customer type.
(c) Sales for the next period by geographical area, product, and customer type based on a forecast of 10% increase in sales.
(d) Total sales in dollars by geographical area.
(e) Sales in dollars by customer type for each geographical area.
(f) Total amount of commission to be paid by type of commission and type of customer.

As will be shown below, the computations required can be represented in terms of matrix operations.

Definitions

A rectangular array of numbers is called a *matrix*. A symbol, usually a capital letter in bold face, is used to denote the entire matrix. The firm mentioned above would identify the following matrices.

Let U = matrix of unit sales by type of customer and product in geographical area U. Then

$$U = \begin{bmatrix} 3 & 4 & 6 & 3 \\ 6 & 2 & 5 & 3 \\ 7 & 1 & 4 & 1 \end{bmatrix}$$

Let V = matrix of unit sales by type of customer and product in geographical area V. Then

$$V = \begin{bmatrix} 4 & 5 & 3 & 6 \\ 7 & 2 & 8 & 0 \\ 7 & 2 & 4 & 1 \end{bmatrix}$$

Let R = matrix of commission rates by geographical area and type of employee. Then

$$R = \begin{bmatrix} 0.06 & 0.05 & 0.02 \\ 0.04 & 0.03 & 0.03 \end{bmatrix}$$

Let P = matrix of selling price per unit by product. Then

$$P = \begin{bmatrix} 2 \\ 10 \\ 5 \\ 7 \end{bmatrix}$$

Let S = matrix of total unit sales by product. Then

$$S = \begin{bmatrix} 34 & 16 & 30 & 14 \end{bmatrix}$$

The numbers in a matrix are called *elements* and are identified by their position in the matrix; i.e., the row and column in which they appear. A matrix A may be represented generally by

$$\begin{bmatrix} a_{11} & a_{12} \\ a_{21} & a_{22} \\ a_{31} & a_{32} \end{bmatrix} = [a_{ij}]$$

where the subscripts identify the position of the element:

a_{32} is the element in the third row and second column.
a_{ij} is the element in the ith row and jth column.
$a_{11,10}$ is the element in the 11th row and 10th column.

If the number of rows or columns is greater than 10, a comma is used to separate the two subscripts. A comma may also be used in other cases to avoid possible confusion.

The *size* of a matrix is specified by two numbers: the number of rows, denoted by m, and the number of columns, denoted by n. The number of elements in a matrix is then mn. Of the matrices defined above U and V are 3×4; i.e., three rows and four columns. R is 2×3, P is 4×1, and S is 1×4. It is frequently convenient to be able to show the size of a matrix. This can be done by writing A_{mn} or $(a_{ij})_{mn}$ to denote a matrix with m rows and n columns.

Special names are given to matrices where m and n have particular values or when the elements within the matrix have certain values.

Square Matrix. A square matrix is one in which $m = n$; i.e., the number of rows is equal to the number of columns. For example,

$$\begin{bmatrix} 2 & 3 \\ 1 & 6 \end{bmatrix}, \quad \begin{bmatrix} 1 & 4 & 2 \\ 6 & 7 & 1 \\ 8 & 3 & 9 \end{bmatrix}, \quad \text{and} \quad \begin{bmatrix} a_{11} & a_{12} & a_{13} \\ a_{21} & a_{22} & a_{23} \\ a_{31} & a_{32} & a_{33} \end{bmatrix}$$

are square matrices of size 2×2, 3×3, and 3×3, respectively. **U, V, R**, and **P** are not square matrices. The elements of a square matrix which lie on the main diagonal (from the top left to the lower right) of the matrix are called the *diagonal elements*; e.g., a_{11}, a_{22}, and a_{33} are the diagonal elements of

$$\begin{bmatrix} a_{11} & a_{12} & a_{13} \\ a_{21} & a_{22} & a_{23} \\ a_{31} & a_{32} & a_{33} \end{bmatrix}$$

Symmetrical Matrix.   A square matrix is said to be symmetrical if $a_{ij} = a_{ji}$ for all i and j. For example, if

$$\mathbf{A} = \begin{bmatrix} 1 & 2 & 3 \\ 2 & 4 & 7 \\ 3 & 7 & 6 \end{bmatrix} \quad \text{and} \quad \mathbf{B} = \begin{bmatrix} 1 & 4 \\ 7 & 3 \end{bmatrix}$$

then **A** is a symmetrical matrix but **B** is not.

Row Vector.   A row vector is a matrix with one row and more than one column. For example,

$$[1 \ \ 1 \ \ 1], \quad [1 \ \ 2 \ \ 3], \quad \text{and} \quad [a_1 \ \ a_2]$$

are row vectors of size 1×3, 1×3, and 1×2, respectively, but **R** and **P** are not row vectors. The elements of a $1 \times n$ row vector $[a_j]$ have a single subscript denoting the column number.

Column Vector.   A column vector is a matrix with one column and more than one row.

$$\begin{bmatrix} 1 \\ 2 \end{bmatrix}, \quad \begin{bmatrix} a_1 \\ a_2 \\ a_3 \end{bmatrix}, \quad \begin{bmatrix} x_1 \\ x_2 \\ x_3 \\ x_4 \end{bmatrix}, \quad \text{and} \quad \mathbf{P} = \begin{bmatrix} 2 \\ 10 \\ 5 \\ 7 \end{bmatrix}$$

are column vectors of size 2×1, 3×1, 4×1, and 4×1, respectively. The elements of a column vector have a single subscript denoting the row number.

Scalar.   A scalar is a matrix with one row and one column; i.e., an ordinary number. It is convenient to distinguish scalars from matrices in many problems, and here the convention will be to denote scalars by lower case letters, and matrices and vectors by capital letters in bold face.

There are two particular matrices which play important roles in the theory and application:

Null or Zero Matrix. A null or zero matrix of size $m \times n$ is an $m \times n$ matrix with every element equal to zero. If, for example,

$$A = \begin{bmatrix} 0 & 0 \\ 0 & 0 \end{bmatrix} \qquad B = \begin{bmatrix} 0 & 0 \\ 0 & 0 \\ 0 & 0 \end{bmatrix}$$

then A is a null matrix of size 2×2 and B is a null matrix of size 3×2.

Diagonal Matrix. A diagonal matrix is a square matrix in which all non-diagonal elements are zero. For example,

$$\begin{bmatrix} 3 & 0 & 0 \\ 0 & 1 & 0 \\ 0 & 0 & 2 \end{bmatrix}$$

is a diagonal matrix but

$$\begin{bmatrix} 3 & 1 & 0 \\ 0 & 1 & 0 \\ 0 & 0 & 2 \end{bmatrix}$$

is not.

The Identity Matrix I. A square matrix in which all diagonal elements are equal to 1 and all non-diagonal elements are equal to zero is called the identity or unit matrix and is usually denoted by the letter I. For example,

$$I = \begin{bmatrix} 1 & 0 & 0 & 0 \\ 0 & 1 & 0 & 0 \\ 0 & 0 & 1 & 0 \\ 0 & 0 & 0 & 1 \end{bmatrix}$$

is the identity matrix with four rows and four columns. The identity matrix is a special case of the diagonal matrix.

Comparison of Matrices. Two matrices can be compared only if they have the same dimensions; i.e., the same number of rows and columns. Two such matrices, having the same number of rows and the same number of columns, are *equal;* if each $a_{ij} = b_{ij}$.

Example. $A = B$ where

$$A = \begin{bmatrix} 1 & 2 \\ 4 & 7 \end{bmatrix} \qquad B = \begin{bmatrix} 1 & 2 \\ 4 & 7 \end{bmatrix};$$

Example

$$A = \begin{bmatrix} 1 & 2 \\ 4 & 7 \end{bmatrix} \qquad B = \begin{bmatrix} 5 \\ 6 \end{bmatrix};$$

These matrices cannot be compared because they do not have the same dimensions.

The matrix A is *greater* than the matrix B if every a_{ij} is greater than every b_{ij}.

Example

$$\begin{bmatrix} 1 & 2 \\ 4 & 7 \end{bmatrix} > \begin{bmatrix} 0 & 1 \\ 3 & 5 \end{bmatrix}$$

but $\begin{bmatrix} 1 & 2 \\ 4 & 7 \end{bmatrix}$ is not greater than $\begin{bmatrix} 0 & 1 \\ 5 & 5 \end{bmatrix}$

because the element a_{21} is not greater than the element b_{21}'. The expression $A \geq B$ is used to indicate that each $a_{ij} \geq b_{ij}$. This includes the case where all $a_{ij} = b_{ij}$; i.e., $A = B$ or where one or more $a_{ij} = b_{ij}$ and the others satisfy $a_{ij} > b_{ij}$, as well as where all $a_{ij} > b_{ij}$.

Example

$$\begin{bmatrix} 3 & 6 \\ 7 & 2 \end{bmatrix} \geq \begin{bmatrix} 2 & 4 \\ 1 & 0 \end{bmatrix} \quad \text{and} \quad \begin{bmatrix} 3 & 6 \\ 7 & 2 \end{bmatrix} \geq \begin{bmatrix} 3 & 6 \\ 7 & 2 \end{bmatrix}$$

In comparing real numbers, $\not\geq$ implies $<$, but this is not true in the comparison of matrices, because only one a_{ij} less than the corresponding b_{ij} is enough to make $A \not\geq B$, while all a_{ij} must be less than the corresponding b_{ij} in order that $A < B$; e.g.,

$$\begin{bmatrix} 5 & 10 \\ 1 & -1 \end{bmatrix} \not\geq \begin{bmatrix} 1 & 1 \\ 2 & -6 \end{bmatrix} \quad \text{but} \quad \begin{bmatrix} 5 & 10 \\ 1 & -1 \end{bmatrix} \text{ is not } < \begin{bmatrix} 1 & 1 \\ 2 & -6 \end{bmatrix}$$

Matrix Operations

A matrix is a rectangular array of numbers; in this section certain operations on such rectangular arrays will be defined. These are analogous to operations defined for real numbers. It will be recalled that if a and b are real numbers, the operations of $+$, $-$, and $\times$, result in other real numbers.

(a) *Addition:* $a + b = c_1$; where c_1 is a real number. Furthermore there exists a particular real number called 0 such that $a + 0 = a$.

(b) *Subtraction:* $a - b = c_2$; where c_2 is a real number and $a - 0 = a$.

(c) *Multiplication:* $a \times b = ab = c_3$; where c_3 is a real number and, furthermore, there exists a particular real number called 1 such that $a \cdot 1 = 1 \cdot a = a$.

Operations on matrices analogous to addition, subtraction, and multiplication will be defined in this section. Since a matrix is an array of numbers rather than a single number, the operations will not be exactly identical and will not possess all the properties of operations on real numbers. Each operation is introduced as an example of a sequence of computations on numbers which the firm described earlier might require. A numerical illustration will be given. This will be followed by the rule for the operation expressed verbally and symbolically. Finally, a number of exercises and problems are given.

Transpose. The matrix **U** gives the sales in units for each type of customer for each product. The sales to the first type of customer (consumers) are given in row one, the sales to the second type (retailers) in row two, and the sales to the third type (wholesalers) in row three. Similarly, the columns represent the different products; column one gives sales for Product I, column two gives sales for Product II, etc. The same sales data could have been presented in the form in which the rows gave sales for the different products and columns gave sales to the different type of customers, e.g.,

Sales in Geographical Area U

Product	Consumers	Retailers	Wholesalers
I	3	6	7
II	4	2	1
III	6	5	4
IV	3	3	1

and the sales matrix would have been defined as, say U′, where

$$\mathbf{U}' = \begin{bmatrix} 3 & 6 & 7 \\ 4 & 2 & 1 \\ 6 & 5 & 4 \\ 3 & 3 & 1 \end{bmatrix}$$

This matrix is closely related to the matrix U defined before; the columns of U are rows of U′ and vice versa. This leads to the definition of the operation of transposition:

RULE. *The transpose of an $m \times n$ matrix, A, is an $n \times m$ matrix obtained by replacing the ith row with the ith column, and is denoted by a prime;* e.g., the transpose of A is written A'. If $A = (a_{ij})$, then $A' = (a_{ji})$. The operation is defined for a matrix of any size. For example,

if
$$A = \begin{bmatrix} a_{11} & a_{12} & a_{13} \\ a_{21} & a_{22} & a_{23} \end{bmatrix} \qquad \text{then} \qquad A' = \begin{bmatrix} a_{11} & a_{21} \\ a_{12} & a_{22} \\ a_{13} & a_{23} \end{bmatrix}$$

The diagonal elements of a square matrix are the same as those of its transpose.

$$A = \begin{bmatrix} 2 & 4 \\ 5 & 6 \end{bmatrix} \qquad A' = \begin{bmatrix} 2 & 5 \\ 4 & 6 \end{bmatrix}$$

The transpose of a symmetric matrix is equal to that matrix, i.e., $A = A'$, if A is symmetric.

$$A = \begin{bmatrix} 2 & 4 \\ 4 & 6 \end{bmatrix} \qquad A' = \begin{bmatrix} 2 & 4 \\ 4 & 6 \end{bmatrix}$$

The transpose of a column vector is a row vector and the transpose of a row vector is a column vector.

$$A = \begin{bmatrix} a_1 \\ a_2 \end{bmatrix} \qquad A' = [a_1 \quad a_2]$$

$$B = [b_1 \quad b_2] \qquad B' = \begin{bmatrix} b_1 \\ b_2 \end{bmatrix}$$

EXERCISES

1. Show that $(A')' = A$.

Addition. The business firm will be interested in computing the total sales in units for both geographical areas by type of customer and product.

Geographical Area

Product	U				V				Total			
	I	II	III	IV	I	II	III	IV	I	II	III	IV
Consumers	3	4	6	3	4	5	3	6	7	9	9	9
Retailers	6	2	5	3	7	2	8	0	13	4	13	3
Wholesalers	7	1	4	1	7	2	4	1	14	3	8	2

The total is obtained by adding the sales for each of the areas in each of the categories. The matrices $\mathbf{U}$ and $\mathbf{V}$ were defined to represent the sales in each geographical area. A new matrix $\mathbf{T}$ can be defined to be the total sales; $\mathbf{T}$ is the sum of the matrices $\mathbf{U}$ and $\mathbf{V}$:

$$\mathbf{T} = \mathbf{U} + \mathbf{V}$$

RULE. *The sum of an $m \times n$ matrix $\mathbf{A}$ and an $m \times n$ matrix $\mathbf{B}$ is a new $m \times n$ matrix, $\mathbf{C}$, the elements of which are the sum of the corresponding elements of the matrices $\mathbf{A}$ and $\mathbf{B}$.*

If $\mathbf{C} = \mathbf{A} + \mathbf{B}$, then $c_{ij} = a_{ij} + b_{ij}$, $i = 1, 2, \ldots, m$; $j = 1, 2, \ldots, n$. For example,

$$\begin{bmatrix} a_{11} & a_{12} \\ a_{21} & a_{22} \\ a_{31} & a_{32} \end{bmatrix} + \begin{bmatrix} b_{11} & b_{12} \\ b_{21} & b_{22} \\ b_{31} & b_{32} \end{bmatrix} = \begin{bmatrix} a_{11} + b_{11} & a_{12} + b_{12} \\ a_{21} + b_{21} & a_{22} + b_{22} \\ a_{31} + b_{31} & a_{32} + b_{32} \end{bmatrix}$$

The sum of two matrices is defined only if they are of the same size; i.e., if they have both the same number of rows and the same number of columns.

EXERCISES (Continued)

2. Show that

$$\begin{bmatrix} 25 & 5 & 26 \\ 1 & 3 & 0 \\ 35 & 10 & 40 \end{bmatrix} + \begin{bmatrix} 12 & 1 & 9 \\ 1 & 3 & 2 \\ 13 & 0 & 14 \end{bmatrix} = \begin{bmatrix} 37 & 6 & 35 \\ 2 & 6 & 2 \\ 48 & 10 & 54 \end{bmatrix}$$

3. Compute $\mathbf{A} + \mathbf{B}$ where

$$\mathbf{A} = \begin{bmatrix} 1 & -1 & 0 & 0 \\ 0 & 1 & 0 & 0 \\ 1 & 0 & 1 & 0 \\ 3 & -4 & 0 & 1 \end{bmatrix} \qquad \mathbf{B} = \begin{bmatrix} 1 & 1 & 0 & 0 \\ 0 & 1 & 0 & 0 \\ 1 & 1 & 1 & 0 \\ 3 & 7 & 0 & 1 \end{bmatrix}$$

4. The firm wishes to compute the total sales in units by product for sales to consumers in both areas. Define appropriate matrices and carry out the addition to obtain the desired total.

5. Show that $(\mathbf{A} + \mathbf{B})' = \mathbf{A}' + \mathbf{B}'$.

6. Show that $\mathbf{A} + \mathbf{B} = \mathbf{B} + \mathbf{A}$ and that $(\mathbf{A} + \mathbf{B}) + \mathbf{C} = \mathbf{A} + (\mathbf{B} + \mathbf{C})$.

Subtraction. The business firm might be interested in computing the difference in sales between the two geographical areas by type of customer and product. This array could be represented by a new matrix, **D**, which would be obtained by subtracting **V** from **U**.

$$\mathbf{D} = \mathbf{U} - \mathbf{V}$$

Then

$$\mathbf{D} = \begin{bmatrix} 3 & 4 & 6 & 3 \\ 6 & 2 & 5 & 3 \\ 7 & 1 & 4 & 1 \end{bmatrix} - \begin{bmatrix} 4 & 5 & 3 & 6 \\ 7 & 2 & 8 & 0 \\ 7 & 2 & 4 & 1 \end{bmatrix}$$

$$= \begin{bmatrix} 3-4 & 4-5 & 6-3 & 3-6 \\ 6-7 & 2-2 & 5-8 & 3-0 \\ 7-7 & 1-2 & 4-4 & 1-1 \end{bmatrix} = \begin{bmatrix} -1 & -1 & 3 & -3 \\ -1 & 0 & -3 & 3 \\ 0 & -1 & 0 & 0 \end{bmatrix}$$

RULE. *The difference between an $m \times n$ matrix, **A**, and an $m \times n$ matrix, **B**, is an $m \times n$ matrix, **C**, the elements of which are the differences of the corresponding elements of the two matrices.*

If $\mathbf{C} = \mathbf{A} - \mathbf{B}$, then $c_{ij} = a_{ij} - b_{ij}$, $i = 1, 2, \ldots, m$; $j = 1, 2, \ldots, n$. For example,

$$\begin{bmatrix} a_{11} & a_{12} & a_{13} \\ a_{21} & a_{22} & a_{23} \end{bmatrix} - \begin{bmatrix} b_{11} & b_{12} & b_{13} \\ b_{21} & b_{22} & b_{23} \end{bmatrix} = \begin{bmatrix} a_{11} - b_{11} & a_{12} - b_{12} & a_{13} - b_{13} \\ a_{21} - b_{21} & a_{22} - b_{22} & a_{23} - b_{23} \end{bmatrix}$$

The difference of two matrices is defined only if both are of the same size; i.e., if both have the same number of rows and the same number of columns.

EXERCISES (Continued)

7. Show that

$$\begin{bmatrix} 25 & 5 \\ 1 & 3 \\ 35 & 10 \end{bmatrix} - \begin{bmatrix} 12 & 1 \\ 1 & 3 \\ 13 & 0 \end{bmatrix} = \begin{bmatrix} 13 & 4 \\ 0 & 0 \\ 22 & 10 \end{bmatrix}$$

8. Compute $\mathbf{A}' - \mathbf{B}'$ where

$$\mathbf{A} = \begin{bmatrix} 12 & 1 & 9 \\ 1 & 3 & 2 \\ 13 & 0 & 14 \end{bmatrix} \qquad \mathbf{B} = \begin{bmatrix} 6 & 2 & 16 \\ 1 & 0 & 2 \\ 0 & 1 & 2 \end{bmatrix}$$

9. The firm wishes to compute the difference between sales in units by product to retailers and wholesalers in each of the two geographical areas. Define

appropriate matrices and carry out the subtraction to obtain the desired difference by product and by type of distributor.

10. Show that $(A - B)' = A' - B'$, that $A - 0 = A$, and that $0 - A = -A$.

Product of a Scalar Times a Matrix. Assume that a 10% increase in sales has been forecast and the firm is interested in the predicted sales by type of customer and product. For area U these sales can be represented by a new matrix, F, in which each element has been multiplied by a constant 1.1. Therefore,

$$F = 1.1U = 1.1 \begin{bmatrix} 3 & 4 & 6 & 3 \\ 6 & 2 & 5 & 3 \\ 7 & 1 & 4 & 1 \end{bmatrix} = \begin{bmatrix} 3.3 & 4.4 & 6.6 & 3.3 \\ 6.6 & 2.2 & 5.5 & 3.3 \\ 7.7 & 1.1 & 4.4 & 1.1 \end{bmatrix}$$

RULE. *The product of a scalar, d, times an m × n matrix A is an m × n matrix, C, each element of which is obtained by multiplying the corresponding element of A by d.*

If $C = dA$, then $c_{ij} = da_{ij}$, $i = 1, 2, \ldots, m$; $j = 1, 2, \ldots, n$. For example, if

$$A = \begin{bmatrix} a_{11} & a_{12} \\ a_{21} & a_{22} \\ a_{31} & a_{32} \end{bmatrix} \quad \text{then} \quad C = dA = \begin{bmatrix} da_{11} & da_{12} \\ da_{21} & da_{22} \\ da_{31} & da_{32} \end{bmatrix}$$

EXERCISES (Continued)

11. From past experience, the firm expects 5% of all units sold to be returned in the next period. Compute, using matrices, the returns expected in area V by type of customer and product.

Product of a Row Vector Times a Column Vector. The row vector, S, gives the sales in units by product while the column vector P gives the selling price in dollars per unit by product; e.g.,

$$S = [34 \quad 16 \quad 30 \quad 14] \quad \text{and} \quad P = \begin{bmatrix} 2 \\ 10 \\ 5 \\ 7 \end{bmatrix}$$

The total sales, in dollars, is

$$34 \times 2 + 16 \times 10 + 30 \times 5 + 14 \times 7 = 476.$$

To obtain this result by matrices the operation of multiplication of a row vector times a column vector is defined.

RULE. *The product of an* $1 \times n$ *row vector,* **A**, *times an* $n \times 1$ *column vector* **B** *is a scalar obtained by summing the product of the corresponding elements,*

$$c = \mathbf{AB} \qquad c = \sum_{i=1}^{n} a_i b_i$$

For example,

$$\mathbf{A} = [a_1 \quad a_2 \quad a_3], \quad \mathbf{B} = \begin{bmatrix} b_1 \\ b_2 \\ b_3 \end{bmatrix} \quad \text{then } c = \mathbf{AB} \text{ is}$$

$$c = a_1 b_1 + a_2 b_2 + a_3 b_3$$

EXERCISES (Continued)

12. Show that

$$[8 \quad 4] \begin{bmatrix} 3 \\ 2 \end{bmatrix} = 32$$

13. Compute **AX** where $\mathbf{A} = [a_1 \quad a_2]$; $\mathbf{X}' = [x_1 \quad x_2]$.

14. Define appropriate vectors and perform a row vector by column vector mutliplication to obtain the total sales in dollars to wholesalers in area V.

Product of a Matrix Times a Column Vector. The matrix **U** gives unit sales by type of customer and product; the vector **P** gives the price in dollars per unit by product. Suppose the firm wishes to compute the sales in dollars by type of customer; there will be three numbers, one for each type of customer, and each will be obtained by summing the product of unit sales by price per unit. Let **Y** be the column vector of dollar sales by type of customer. Then

$$\mathbf{UP} = \mathbf{Y}$$

For example,

$$\begin{bmatrix} 3 & 4 & 6 & 3 \\ 6 & 2 & 5 & 3 \\ 7 & 1 & 4 & 1 \end{bmatrix} \begin{bmatrix} 2 \\ 10 \\ 5 \\ 7 \end{bmatrix} = \begin{bmatrix} 3 \times 2 + 4 \times 10 + 6 \times 5 + 3 \times 7 \\ 6 \times 2 + 2 \times 10 + 5 \times 5 + 3 \times 7 \\ 7 \times 2 + 1 \times 10 + 4 \times 5 + 1 \times 7 \end{bmatrix} = \begin{bmatrix} 97 \\ 78 \\ 51 \end{bmatrix}$$

RULE. *The product of an* $m \times n$ *matrix,* **A**, *and a* $n \times 1$ *column vector,* **B**, *is an* $m \times 1$ *column vector,* **C**.

$$\mathbf{C} = \mathbf{AB} \quad \text{where} \quad c_i = \sum_{k=1}^{n} a_{ik} b_k \qquad i = 1, \ldots, m$$

That is, the element in the ith row of the product vector is the sum of the products of the corresponding elements in the ith row of the matrix **A** and the vector **B**.

For example:

$$\begin{bmatrix} a_{11} & a_{12} \\ a_{21} & a_{22} \end{bmatrix} \begin{bmatrix} b_1 \\ b_2 \end{bmatrix} = \begin{bmatrix} a_{11}b_1 + a_{12}b_2 \\ a_{21}b_1 + a_{22}b_2 \end{bmatrix}$$

This product is defined only if the number of columns of **A** is equal to the number of rows in **B**.

EXERCISES (Continued)

15. What is the product of an identity matrix by a vector?

16. $\mathbf{A} = \begin{bmatrix} 1 & 2 \\ 6 & 4 \end{bmatrix}$ $\mathbf{B} = \begin{bmatrix} x_1 \\ x_2 \end{bmatrix}$ $\mathbf{C} = \mathbf{AB} = ?$

17. $\mathbf{A} = \begin{bmatrix} 3 & 6 & 9 \\ 6 & 4 & 2 \\ 2 & 5 & 8 \end{bmatrix}$ $\mathbf{B} = \begin{bmatrix} 2 \\ 4 \\ 3 \end{bmatrix}$ $\mathbf{C} = \mathbf{AB} = ?$

18. $\mathbf{A} = \begin{bmatrix} 1 & 3 & 6 & 7 \\ 5 & 4 & 1 & 0 \\ 9 & 3 & 2 & 5 \end{bmatrix}$ $\mathbf{B} = \begin{bmatrix} 4 \\ 1 \\ 5 \end{bmatrix}$ $\mathbf{C} = \mathbf{AB} = ?$

19. $\mathbf{A} = \begin{bmatrix} 0 & 6 & 2 \\ 3 & 4 & 1 \end{bmatrix}$ $\mathbf{B} = \begin{bmatrix} 6 \\ 5 \end{bmatrix}$ $\mathbf{C} = \mathbf{A'B} = ?$

20. Compute **Z**, the column vector giving sales in area V in dollars by type of customer.

Multiplication of a Matrix by a Matrix. The vectors **Y** and **Z** give the sales in dollars by type of customer for each geographic area, e.g.,

$$\mathbf{Y} = \begin{bmatrix} 97 \\ 78 \\ 51 \end{bmatrix} \quad \text{and} \quad \mathbf{Z} = \begin{bmatrix} 115 \\ 74 \\ 61 \end{bmatrix}$$

Let **W** be a 3×2 matrix in which rows represent types of customer and columns represent geographical areas, e.g.,

$$\mathbf{W} = \begin{bmatrix} 97 & 115 \\ 78 & 74 \\ 51 & 61 \end{bmatrix} = [\mathbf{Y} \quad \mathbf{Z}]$$

The column vector **Y** is the first column of **W** and the column vector **Z** is the second column of **Y**.

The matrix **R** gives the rate for each of three types of commission for each of the two geographical areas. Let **E** be the amount of commission to be paid for each type of customer by type of commission, e.g.,

E = **WR**

$$\mathbf{E} = \begin{bmatrix} 97 & 115 \\ 78 & 74 \\ 51 & 61 \end{bmatrix} \begin{bmatrix} 0.06 & 0.05 & 0.02 \\ 0.04 & 0.03 & 0.03 \end{bmatrix}$$

$$= \begin{bmatrix} 97(0.06) + 115(0.04) & 97(0.05) + 115(0.03) & 97(0.02) + 115(0.03) \\ 78(0.06) + 74(0.04) & 78(0.05) + 74(0.03) & 78(0.02) + 74(0.03) \\ 51(0.06) + 61(0.04) & 51(0.05) + 61(0.03) & 51(0.02) + 61(0.03) \end{bmatrix}$$

$$= \begin{bmatrix} 10.42 & 8.30 & 5.39 \\ 7.64 & 6.12 & 3.78 \\ 5.50 & 4.38 & 2.85 \end{bmatrix}$$

This leads to the definition of the multiplication of a matrix by a matrix.

RULE. *The product of an $m \times q$ matrix, **A**, and a $q \times n$ matrix, **B**, is an $m \times n$ matrix, **C**.*

$$\mathbf{C} = \mathbf{AB} \quad \text{where} \quad c_{ij} = \sum_{k=1}^{q} a_{ik}b_{kj} \quad i = 1, 2, \ldots, m, j = 1, 2, \ldots, n$$

That is, the element in the ith row and the jth column of the product matrix is the sum of the products of the corresponding element in the ith row of the first matrix **A** and the jth column of the second matrix **B**. For example:

$$\begin{bmatrix} a_{11} & a_{12} & a_{13} \\ a_{21} & a_{22} & a_{23} \end{bmatrix} \begin{bmatrix} b_{11} & b_{12} \\ b_{21} & b_{22} \\ b_{31} & b_{32} \end{bmatrix}$$

$$= \begin{bmatrix} a_{11}b_{11} + a_{12}b_{21} + a_{13}b_{31} & a_{11}b_{12} + a_{12}b_{22} + a_{13}b_{32} \\ a_{21}b_{11} + a_{22}b_{21} + a_{23}b_{31} & a_{21}b_{12} + a_{22}b_{22} + a_{23}b_{32} \end{bmatrix}$$

The product of two matrices is defined only if the number of columns in the first matrix is equal to the number of rows in the second.

The order of multiplication must be specified; in the product **AB**, **A** is post multiplied by **B**, or **B** is premultiplied by **A**.

Example. Suppose the firm wanted to compute total sales to consumers, wholesalers and retailers in region V. The sales are, by product:

	Consumers	Retailers	Wholesalers
I	4	7	7
II	5	2	2
III	3	8	4
IV	6	0	1

The totals are the sums of the columns and summing the columns is equivalent to post multiplying the row vector $\mathbf{K} = [1 \quad 1 \quad 1 \quad 1]$ by the matrix of sales in units; e.g.,

$$[1 \quad 1 \quad 1 \quad 1] \begin{bmatrix} 4 & 7 & 7 \\ 5 & 2 & 2 \\ 3 & 8 & 4 \\ 6 & 0 & 1 \end{bmatrix} = \begin{bmatrix} 4+5+3+6 \\ 7+2+8+0 \\ 7+2+4+1 \end{bmatrix}' = \begin{bmatrix} 18 \\ 17 \\ 14 \end{bmatrix}'$$

EXERCISES (Continued)

21. If $\mathbf{A} = \begin{bmatrix} 4 & 2 \\ 2 & 13 \end{bmatrix}$ $\mathbf{B} = \begin{bmatrix} \dfrac{13}{48} & -\dfrac{1}{24} \\ \dfrac{-1}{24} & \dfrac{1}{12} \end{bmatrix}$

show that $\mathbf{AB} = \mathbf{BA} = \mathbf{I}$.

22. Show that

$$\mathbf{M} = \begin{bmatrix} 31 & 4 & 19 \\ 1 & 6 & 0 \\ 48 & 9 & 52 \end{bmatrix} \quad \text{where} \quad \mathbf{M} = \mathbf{ABC} + \mathbf{CB} - \mathbf{DE}'$$

$$\mathbf{A} = \begin{bmatrix} 2 & 1 & 0 \\ 0 & 1 & 0 \\ 2 & 2 & 1 \end{bmatrix} \quad \mathbf{B} = \begin{bmatrix} 1 & 0 & 2 \\ 0 & 1 & 0 \\ 2 & 0 & 1 \end{bmatrix} \quad \mathbf{C} = \begin{bmatrix} 2 & 1 & 5 \\ 1 & 3 & 0 \\ 5 & 0 & 4 \end{bmatrix}$$

$$\mathbf{D} = \begin{bmatrix} 6 & 2 \\ 1 & 0 \\ 0 & 1 \end{bmatrix} \quad \mathbf{E} = \begin{bmatrix} 1 & 0 \\ 0 & 1 \\ 2 & 2 \end{bmatrix}$$

23. Compute **AB** where

$$\mathbf{A} = \begin{bmatrix} 1 & -1 & 0 & 0 \\ 0 & 1 & 0 & 0 \\ -1 & 0 & 1 & 0 \\ -3 & -4 & 0 & 1 \end{bmatrix} \qquad \mathbf{B} = \begin{bmatrix} 1 & 1 & 0 & 0 \\ 0 & 1 & 0 & 0 \\ 1 & 1 & 1 & 0 \\ 3 & 7 & 0 & 1 \end{bmatrix}$$

24. If **A** is a matrix with p rows and q columns, and **B** is a matrix with q rows and r columns, the product **AB** is a matrix **C**—a matrix with p rows and r columns. Using this result and the formula for matrix multiplication given above, develop the rule for post multiplying a vector by a matrix and use it to compute **AB** where

$$\mathbf{A} = [x_1 \quad x_2] \qquad \mathbf{B} = \begin{bmatrix} a_{11} & a_{12} \\ a_{21} & a_{22} \end{bmatrix}$$

25. Using the rule developed in Exercise 24 and the row vector **K**, compute the row vector which gives sales in units for area **U** by product.

26. Develop the formula for post multiplying a column vector by a row vector and use it to compute **AB** where

$$\mathbf{A'} = [a_1 \quad a_2] \qquad \text{and} \qquad \mathbf{B} = [b_1 \quad b_2]$$

27. Show that $\mathbf{A(BC)} = \mathbf{(AB)C}$ where **A**, **B**, and **C** are 2×2 matrices.
28. Show that $\mathbf{(BA)'} = \mathbf{A'B'}$ where **A** and **B** are 2×2 matrices.
29. Show that $\mathbf{AO} = \mathbf{OA} = \mathbf{O}$.
30. Show that $\mathbf{IA} = \mathbf{AI} = \mathbf{A}$.

Properties of Matrix Operations

The operation of *addition* of matrices of the same size satisfies the *Commutative Law:*

$$\mathbf{A} + \mathbf{B} = \mathbf{B} + \mathbf{A}$$

and the *Associative Law:*

$$\mathbf{(A + B)} + \mathbf{C} = \mathbf{A} + \mathbf{(B + C)} = \mathbf{A} + \mathbf{B} + \mathbf{C}$$

The order in which matrices are added has no effect on the resulting sum.

The operation of *multiplication* of two matrices which are compatible, i.e., the number of columns in the first matrix is equal to the number of rows in the second matrix, satisfies the *Distributive Law:*

$$\mathbf{A[B + C]} = \mathbf{AB} + \mathbf{AC}$$

if **B** and **C** are of the same order or size, but does not satisfy the *Commutative Law.*

AB need not be equal to **BA**, even if both products are defined.

These properties of matrix operations are summarized in Table 12.1.

Table 12-1

Operation	Addition $C = A + B$	Multiplication $C = AB$
Defined	If A and B are of the same size	If A and B are compatible
Associative	Yes	Yes
Commutative	Yes	No
Distributive	Yes	

EXERCISES (*Continued*)

31. (*a*) Verify that $AB = BA$ where

$$A = \begin{bmatrix} 2 & 1 \\ 1 & 2 \end{bmatrix} \quad \text{and} \quad B = \begin{bmatrix} 3 & -1 \\ -1 & 3 \end{bmatrix}$$

(*b*) Determine the conditions under which $AB = BA$, for the 2×2 matrices:

$$A = \begin{bmatrix} a_{11} & a_{12} \\ a_{21} & a_{22} \end{bmatrix} \quad \text{and} \quad B = \begin{bmatrix} b_{11} & b_{12} \\ b_{21} & b_{22} \end{bmatrix}$$

32. Verify that $AB = 0$ where

$$A = \begin{bmatrix} 1 & 2 & 0 \\ 1 & 1 & 0 \\ -1 & 4 & 0 \end{bmatrix} \quad \text{and} \quad B = \begin{bmatrix} 0 & 0 & 0 \\ 0 & 0 & 0 \\ 1 & 4 & 9 \end{bmatrix}$$

33. Verify that $AB = AC$ even though $B \neq C$ where

$$A = \begin{bmatrix} 1 & 2 & 0 \\ 1 & 1 & 0 \\ 1 & 4 & 0 \end{bmatrix} \quad B = \begin{bmatrix} 2 & 2 & 3 \\ 2 & 1 & -1 \\ 2 & 1 & 2 \end{bmatrix} \quad \text{and} \quad C = \begin{bmatrix} 2 & 2 & 3 \\ 2 & 1 & -1 \\ 1 & 3 & 1 \end{bmatrix}$$

34. The costs of manufacturing washing machines at two plants are given by:

	Plant I	Plant II
Direct labor	2	4
Materials	1	2
Indirect labor	3	1

and the costs of manufacturing dryers are:

	Plant I	Plant II
Direct labor	3	5
Materials	2	2
Indirect labor	4	2

The production rates for the two types at the plants are:

	Plant I	Plant II
Number of washing machines	1,000	500
Number of dryers	6,000	7,000

Define appropriate matrices and use matrix operations to find:

(*a*). The cost of each of the three categories for the total production of washing machines.

(*b*). The cost of each of the three categories for the total production of dryers.

(*c*). The cost of each of the three categories for the total production of all appliances.

(*d*). The total costs of production of all appliances for the manufacturing firm.

(*Hint:* It may be helpful to use the vector [1, 1, 1] or its transpose.)

B. SYSTEMS OF LINEAR EQUATIONS IN TWO UNKNOWNS

Relationships between variables have been represented by one linear equation in several of the examples treated in the previous chapters. In many business problems, variables may have to satisfy more than one linear equation simultaneously. Any set of values which *simultaneously* satisfies a set of linear equations is said to be a *solution* to that set of equations. This section, and the next chapter, are concerned with the problem of determining how many different solutions (if any) exist for a given set of linear equations, and with techniques for obtaining numerical values for the solutions when they exist.

The "product-mix" problem is an example in which a number of linear equations must be satisfied. A firm produces a number of products, each of which requires processing on some or all of several different machines. The order in which the machines are used is immaterial. The maximum amount of time each one of the machines can be used, the amount of time each product requires on each machine, and the profit per unit of each product are given. The objective is to *determine the amount of each product to be produced so that the machines will not be idle.*

As a simple example of a product-mix problem, assume that two operations, slotting and threading, are required in the manufacture of two products: wood screws and metal screws. The first operation is slotting the heads of the screws and during an operating period 4,800 minutes are available on the "slotter:" Four minutes are required to slot a box of wood screws and 2 minutes to slot a box of metal screws. If

x_1 = the number of boxes of wood screws produced

x_2 = the number of boxes of metal screws produced

the total time required on the slotter is $4x_1 + 2x_2$. Since 4,800 minutes are available, the variables must satisfy the equation

$$4x_1 + 2x_2 = 4,800$$

In the second process—threading—it takes 2 minutes to thread a box of wood screws and 13 minutes to thread a box of metal screws. The relationship that x_1 and x_2 must satisfy, if 4,800 minutes per period are available, is given by

$$2x_1 + 13x_2 = 4,800$$

The system of equations

$$4x_1 + 2x_2 = 4,800 \tag{1}$$

$$2x_1 + 13x_2 = 4,800 \tag{2}$$

can be written in matrix notation as

$$AX = B$$

where

$$A = \begin{bmatrix} 4 & 2 \\ 2 & 13 \end{bmatrix} \qquad X = \begin{bmatrix} x_1 \\ x_2 \end{bmatrix} \qquad B = \begin{bmatrix} 4,800 \\ 4,800 \end{bmatrix}$$

Solution by Algebraic Elimination

The solution to a set of two simultaneous linear equations in two unknowns can be obtained algebraically by using the facts that an equality is unchanged if (1) equal quantities are added to, or subtracted from, both sides of the equality, or (2) if both sides are multiplied or divided by the same (non-zero) number. For example, Equation (2), multiplied by -2, becomes:

$$-4x_1 - 26x_2 = -9,600 \tag{3}$$

Next, the right-hand side of (3) can be added to the right-hand side of (1) and the left-hand side of (3) can be added to the left-hand side of (1). This operation will not change the solution, since the two sides of (3) are equal:

$$4x_1 + 2x_2 + (-4x_1 - 26x_2) = 4,800 + (-9,600) \tag{4}$$

Collecting terms, (4) reduces to

$$x_1(4 - 4) + x_2(2 - 26) = -4,800$$
$$-24x_2 = -4,800$$
$$x_2 = 200$$

Next, x_1 can be obtained by substituting the value obtained for x_2 into either one of the equations and solving for the one unknown, since either equation then becomes one equation in one unknown. In this case, substituting $x_2 = 200$ into (1) gives

$$4x_1 + 2(200) = 4,800$$
$$x_1 = 1,100$$

The set $x_1 = 1,100$, $x_2 = 200$ is the solution since

$$\begin{bmatrix} 4 & 2 \\ 2 & 13 \end{bmatrix} \begin{bmatrix} 1,100 \\ 200 \end{bmatrix} = \begin{bmatrix} 4,800 \\ 4,800 \end{bmatrix}$$

Solution by Determinants

Two equations in two unknowns with general coefficients are:

$$a_{11}x_1 + a_{12}x_2 = b_1$$
$$a_{21}x_1 + a_{22}x_2 = b_2$$

Suppose neither a_{11} nor a_{22} is zero. Then since a_{11} is not zero,

$$x_1 = \frac{b_1 - a_{12}x_2}{a_{11}} \tag{5}$$

from the first equation.

And similarly, since a_{22} is not zero,

$$x_2 = \frac{b_2 - a_{21}x_1}{a_{22}} \tag{6}$$

from the second equation.

Substituting (6) into (5), collecting terms, and simplifying give

$$x_1 = \frac{a_{22}b_1 - a_{12}b_2}{a_{11}a_{22} - a_{21}a_{12}} \tag{7}$$

provided $a_{11}a_{22} - a_{21}a_{12} \neq 0$.

Substituting (5) into (6), collecting terms, and simplifying give

$$x_2 = \frac{a_{11}b_2 - a_{21}b_1}{a_{11}a_{22} - a_{21}a_{12}} \tag{8}$$

provided the denominator is not zero.

The formulas for the solutions (7) and (8) can be presented more symmetrically and more compactly through the use of determinants.

The Symbols

$$|\mathbf{A}| \equiv \begin{vmatrix} a_{11} & a_{12} \\ a_{21} & a_{22} \end{vmatrix}$$

denote the determinant of the system of equations; its value is defined as:

$$a_{11}a_{22} - a_{12}a_{21}$$

The determinant in this case is said to be of order two because the matrix **A** has two rows and two columns.

The solutions to the system of equations can now be written as the ratio of two determinants:

$$x_1 = \frac{\begin{vmatrix} b_1 & a_{12} \\ b_2 & a_{22} \end{vmatrix}}{|\mathbf{A}|} \tag{9} \qquad\qquad x_2 = \frac{\begin{vmatrix} a_{11} & b_1 \\ a_{21} & b_2 \end{vmatrix}}{|\mathbf{A}|} \tag{10}$$

Equation (9) is merely another way of writing (7), and (10) is another way of writing (8). The solution to the example is:

$$x_1 = \frac{\begin{vmatrix} 4{,}800 & 2 \\ 4{,}800 & 13 \end{vmatrix}}{\begin{vmatrix} 4 & 2 \\ 2 & 13 \end{vmatrix}} = \frac{13(4{,}800) - 2(4{,}800)}{13(4) - 2(2)} = \frac{11(4{,}800)}{48} = 1{,}100$$

$$x_2 = \frac{\begin{vmatrix} 4 & 4{,}800 \\ 2 & 4{,}800 \end{vmatrix}}{48} = \frac{4(4{,}800) - 2(4{,}800)}{48} = 200$$

The expression of the solution to a system of linear equations as a ratio of two determinants is known as Cramer's rule.

It was assumed that $a_{11} \neq 0$, $a_{22} \neq 0$, and $|\mathbf{A}| \neq 0$. The case where either a_{11} or a_{22} is zero causes no difficulty. Suppose $a_{11} = 0$; then

$$x_2 = -\frac{b_1}{a_{12}}$$

if $a_{12} \neq 0$, and

$$x_1 = \frac{1}{a_{21}}\left(b_2 - \frac{a_{22}b_1}{a_{12}}\right)$$

The case $|\mathbf{A}| = 0$ is of more interest.

If the set of equations is

$$4x_1 + 2x_2 = 4{,}800$$

$$8x_1 + 4x_2 = 16{,}400$$

a solution, by elimination, can be attempted by multiplying the first equation by -2 and adding it to the second. However, when this is done, both x_1 and x_2 disappear. Figure 12.1 shows why; the two lines are parallel and, therefore, a point which lies on one line cannot also lie on the other.

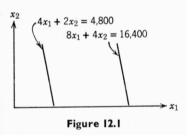

Figure 12.1

Another special case is illustrated by the set

$$4x_1 + 2x_2 = 4{,}800$$

$$8x_1 + 4x_2 = 9{,}600$$

If the first equation is multiplied by -2 and added to the second, both sides of the equation become zero. All points which lie on one line also lie on the other.

The determinant of the system for both of the above sets of equations is

$$\begin{vmatrix} a_{11} & a_{12} \\ a_{21} & a_{22} \end{vmatrix} = \begin{vmatrix} 4 & 2 \\ 8 & 4 \end{vmatrix} = 16 - 16 = 0$$

A system of 2 linear equations in 2 unknowns will have a single unique solution if the determinant is different from zero and, conversely, if the determinant is zero, there will be either no solution or an infinite number of solutions, depending on the right-hand side.

Linear Independence

Let the first equation in the system of simultaneous linear equations of two equations in two unknowns be denoted by L_1 and the second by L_2.

$$L_1: \ a_{11}x_1 + a_{12}x_2 = b_1$$
$$L_2: \ a_{21}x_1 + a_{22}x_2 = b_2 \tag{11}$$

A *linear combination* L_3 of L_1 and L_2 is given by

$$L_3 = c_1L_1 + c_2L_2$$

where c_1 and c_2 are constants. L_3 is

$$c_1[a_{11}x_1 + a_{12}x_2] + c_2[a_{21}x_1 + a_{22}x_2] = c_1b_1 + c_2b_2$$
$$(c_1a_{11} + c_2a_{21})x_1 + (c_1a_{12} + c_2a_{22})x_2 = c_1b_1 + c_2b_2 \tag{12}$$

Equations (11) are said to be *linearly independent* if there exists no set of numbers (c_1, c_2), other than $(0, 0)$, such that the coefficients of x_1 and x_2 in (12) are identically zero and are said to be *linearly dependent* if such numbers exist. The coefficients of x_1 and x_2 in (12) will both be zero if

$$c_1a_{11} + c_2a_{21} = 0 \tag{13}$$

$$c_1a_{12} + c_2a_{22} = 0 \tag{14}$$

Solving these equations gives, from (13),

$$c_1 = -c_2\frac{a_{21}}{a_{11}}$$

and from (14),

$$c_1 = -c_2\frac{a_{22}}{a_{12}}$$

A non-trivial solution for c_1 and c_2 will exist if

$$\frac{a_{22}}{a_{12}} = \frac{a_{21}}{a_{11}}$$

or if

$$a_{11}a_{22} - a_{12}a_{21} = \begin{vmatrix} a_{11} & a_{12} \\ a_{21} & a_{22} \end{vmatrix} = 0$$

A system of two linear equations in two unknowns is linearly independent if and only if the determinant is different from zero, and is linearly dependent if and only if the determinant of the system is equal to zero.

The solution to a set of two simultaneous linearly independent linear equations in two unknowns (11) is not changed if the equations are replaced by two independent linear combinations. Let

$$c_1 L_1 + c_2 L_2 = L_3$$

$$c_3 L_1 + c_4 L_2 = L_4$$

L_3 is given by (12). Similarly, L_4 is

$$(c_3 a_{11} + c_4 a_{21})x_1 + (c_3 a_{12} + c_4 a_{22})x_2 = c_3 b_1 + c_4 b_2 \tag{15}$$

By Cramer's rule, the solution to (12) and (15) will be given by the ratio of two determinants; in particular,

$$x_1 = \frac{\begin{vmatrix} c_1 b_1 + c_2 b_2 & c_1 a_{12} + c_2 a_{22} \\ c_3 b_1 + c_4 b_2 & c_3 a_{12} + c_4 a_{22} \end{vmatrix}}{\begin{vmatrix} c_1 a_{11} + c_2 a_{21} & c_1 a_{12} + c_2 a_{22} \\ c_3 a_{11} + c_4 a_{21} & c_3 a_{12} + c_4 a_{22} \end{vmatrix}}$$

The determinant in the denominator is

$$(c_1 a_{11} + c_2 a_{21})(c_3 a_{12} + c_4 a_{22}) - (c_1 a_{12} + c_2 a_{22})(c_3 a_{11} + c_4 a_{21})$$

$$= c_1 c_3 a_{11} a_{12} + c_1 a_{11} c_4 a_{22} + c_2 a_{21} c_3 a_{12} + c_2 a_{21} c_4 a_{22}$$

$$- c_1 a_{12} c_3 a_{11} - c_1 a_{12} c_4 a_{21} - c_2 a_{22} c_3 a_{11} - c_2 a_{22} c_4 a_{21}$$

$$= c_1 c_4 (a_{11} a_{22} - a_{12} a_{21}) - c_2 c_3 (-a_{21} a_{12} + a_{11} a_{22})$$

$$= \begin{vmatrix} c_1 & c_2 \\ c_3 & c_4 \end{vmatrix} \begin{vmatrix} a_{11} & a_{12} \\ a_{21} & a_{22} \end{vmatrix}$$

The analogous result can be obtained for the numerator and

$$x_1 = \frac{\begin{vmatrix} c_1 & c_2 \\ c_3 & c_4 \end{vmatrix} \begin{vmatrix} b_1 & a_{12} \\ b_2 & a_{22} \end{vmatrix}}{\begin{vmatrix} c_1 & c_2 \\ c_3 & c_4 \end{vmatrix} \begin{vmatrix} a_{11} & a_{12} \\ a_{21} & a_{22} \end{vmatrix}}$$

This is the same result as (9), provided

$$\begin{vmatrix} c_1 & c_2 \\ c_3 & c_4 \end{vmatrix} \neq 0$$

Solution by Systematic Elimination

The method of solving equations by systematic elimination consists in finding some linear combination of the given equations such that one of the unknowns has a zero coefficient in each linear combination. To illustrate the application of this method, let

$$L_1: \ 4x_1 + 2x_2 = 4{,}800$$

$$L_2: \ 2x_1 + 13x_2 = 4{,}800$$

If we choose $L_3 = \frac{1}{4}(L_1) - \frac{1}{2}(L_2)$, then

$$\tfrac{1}{4}[4x_1 + 2x_2] - \tfrac{1}{2}[2x_1 + 13x_2] = \tfrac{1}{4}[4{,}800] - \tfrac{1}{2}[4{,}800]$$

$$0 \cdot x_1 - 6x_2 = -1{,}200$$

Therefore,

$$x_2 = 200$$

Similarly, if we choose $L_4 = \frac{1}{2}(L_1) - \frac{1}{13}(L_2)$, then

$$L_4 = \tfrac{1}{2}[4x_1 + 2x_2] - \tfrac{1}{13}[2x_1 + 13x_2] = \tfrac{1}{2}[4{,}800] - \tfrac{1}{13}[4{,}800]$$

$$\tfrac{48}{26}x_1 + 0 \cdot x_2 = \frac{11 \times 4{,}800}{26}$$

Therefore,

$$x_1 = 1{,}100$$

For numerical computation, particularly when the number of unknowns is large, it is desirable to have a more systematic procedure. The procedure is illustrated in Table 12-2; the rules are:

1. The coefficients of the two unknowns x_1 and x_2 and the right-hand sides of the equations b_1 and b_2, are entered in the table as shown by lines I and II. A final column contains the sum of the coefficients and the right-hand side of the equation. It is used in verifying that the numerical calculations are correct.

2. An iteration consists of replacing every equation with an "appropriate" linear combination of the other equations. A pivot element is selected for each iteration. The linear combinations are chosen so that the pivot element becomes one and the other element in the same column as the pivot element becomes zero.

3. In the first iteration (which produces lines III and IV), the pivot element is a_{11}. Line III is the linear combination (a_{11}^{-1}) (line I). In the next linear combination IV, the coefficient of x_1 must be zero. This can be done by defining line IV as the linear combination of line

Table 12-2 Systematic Elimination Method for Solving Two Equations in Two Unknowns

Order of Solution	Line	Linear Combination	x_1	x_2	b	Sum*
L_1	I		a_{11}	a_{12}	b_1	$a_{11} + a_{21} + b_1 = s_{1,0}$
L_2	II		a_{21}	a_{22}	b_2	$a_{21} + a_{22} + b_2 = s_{2,0}$
1	III $= a_{11}^{-1}$I	1	$\dfrac{a_{12}}{a_{11}}$	$\dfrac{b_1}{a_{11}}$	$a_{11}^{-1}s_{1,0}\,(= s_{1,1}) \stackrel{?}{=} 1 + \dfrac{a_{12}}{a_{11}} + \dfrac{b_1}{a_{11}}$
2	IV $=$ II $- a_{21}$III	0	$a_{22} - \dfrac{a_{21}a_{12}}{a_{11}}$	$b_2 - \dfrac{a_{21}b_1}{a_{11}}$	$s_{2,0} - a_{21}s_{1,1}(= s_{2,1}) \stackrel{?}{=} a_{22} - \dfrac{a_{21}a_{12}}{a_{11}} + b_2 - \dfrac{a_{21}b_1}{a_{11}}$
4	V $=$ III $- \dfrac{a_{12}}{a_{11}}$VI	1	0	$\dfrac{b_1}{a_{11}} - \dfrac{a_{12}}{a_{11}}\left[\dfrac{a_{11}b_2 - a_{21}b_1}{a_{11}a_{22} - a_{21}a_{12}}\right]$	$s_{1,1} - \dfrac{a_{12}}{a_{11}} s_{2,2}(= s_{1,2}) \stackrel{?}{=} 1 + \dfrac{b_1}{a_{11}} - \dfrac{a_{12}}{a_{11}}\left(\dfrac{a_{11}b_2 - a_{21}b_1}{a_{11}a_{22} - a_{21}a_{12}}\right)$
3	VI $= \left[a_{22} - \dfrac{a_{21}a_{12}}{a_{11}}\right]^{-1}$IV	0	1	$\dfrac{a_{11}b_2 - a_{21}b_1}{a_{11}a_{22} - a_{21}a_{12}}$	$\left[a_{22} - \dfrac{a_{21}a_{12}}{a_{11}}\right]s_{2,1}(= s_{2,2}) \stackrel{?}{=} 1 + \dfrac{a_{11}b_2 - a_{21}b_1}{a_{11}a_{22} - a_{21}a_{12}}$

* After each row is computed, numerical accuracy is verified by adding the coefficients in each row. The question mark above the equality sign indicates that the equality should be so verified.

II $-$ (a_{21}) (line III). In the first column the result will be

$$1 \cdot a_{21} - a_{21} \cdot 1 = 0.$$

The first iteration is now complete.

4. The sum is considered part of the equation for the computation of the linear combination and the same operations are applied to numbers in the Sum column as in the other columns. Then all the numbers already in the line are totaled. An error has been made if they do not equal the computed sum.

For example, in the first iteration the sum of line III,

$$1 + \frac{a_{12}}{a_{11}} + \frac{b_1}{a_{11}}$$

must equal $1/a_{11}$ times the value of the sum column for line I, $a_{11} + a_{12} + b_1$. The fact that the line total should be verified against the value of the sum computed from the operations of the linear combinations is shown by the symbol $\stackrel{?}{=}$.

5. In the second iteration (which produces V and VI), the pivot element is the coefficient of x_2 in IV. Line VI is obtained by dividing IV by this coefficient. Then line V is produced by the linear combination

$$V = III - \frac{a_{12}}{a_{11}} VI$$

The coefficient of x_2 in V is zero. The coefficients of x_1 are not changed. Note that the solution is identical with that obtained by the use of determinants.

6. The number of iterations necessary to achieve a solution is equal to the number of unknowns—two, in this example. The iterations are separated by a set of double solid lines in the table. In the example, a_{12} could have been chosen as the pivot elements for the first iteration. Then the coefficient of x_1 in IV would have been selected for the second iteration.

7. Other linear combinations could also be used. However, the particular ones chosen are the easiest to remember.

Table 12-2 may be presented in a condensed form by the use of a third subscript to designate the number of the iteration. For example, $a_{12.0}$ is the original coefficient of x_2 in equation 1, $a_{12.1}$ is the coefficient of x_2 in equation 1 after the first iteration: $a_{12.1} = a_{12}/a_{11}$. The same notation used in the other columns greatly simplifies the presentation of the operations of this method in Table 12-3.

Note that the order of generation of the lines does not follow the order of listing. Line VI is generated before line V. The reason for this becomes

Table 12-3   Systematic Elimination Method for Solving Two Equations in Two Unknowns—Abbreviated Notation

Line		x_1	x_2	b	Sum
	I	$a_{11.0}$	$a_{12.0}$	$b_{1.0}$	$s_{1.0}$
	II	$a_{21.0}$	$a_{22.0}$	$b_{2.0}$	$s_{2.0}$
1	III $= a_{11.0}^{-1}$I	1	$a_{12.1}$	$b_{1.1}$	$s_{1.1}$
2	IV $=$ II $- a_{21.0}$III	0	$a_{22.1}$	$b_{2.1}$	$s_{2.1}$
4	V $=$ III $- a_{12.1}$VI	1	0	$b_{1.2}$	$s_{1.2}$
3	VI $= a_{22.1}^{-1}$IV	0	1	$b_{2.2}$	$s_{2.2}$

obvious if we remember that the general method is *first* to set one of the coefficients of the unknowns in a column equal to one, and *then* use that equation in setting all other coefficients of the same unknown equal to zero.

Example. The procedure applied to the product-mix problem is given in Table 12-4.

(a) Lines I and II are a statement of the equations in tabular form. The + and = signs are omitted. The sum is obtained by adding the coefficients in each row, e.g.,

$$4 + 2 + 4{,}800 = 4{,}806$$

$$2 + 13 + 4{,}800 = 4{,}815$$

(b) Line III is a linear combination of lines I and II and the coefficients chosen so that the coefficient of x_1 will be 1 e.g.,

$$\text{III} = \tfrac{1}{4}(\text{I})$$

Table 12-4   Example of Systematic Elimination Method

Order	Line		Linear Combination	x_1	x_2	b	Sum
	I			4	2	4,800	4,806
	II			2	13	4,800	4,815
1	III	$=$	$\tfrac{1}{4}$(I)	1	0.5	1,200	1,201.5
2	IV	$=$	II $-$ 2(III)	0	12	2,400	2,412
4	V	$=$	III $- \tfrac{1}{2}$(VI)	1	0	1,100	1,101
3	VI	$=$	$\tfrac{1}{12}$(IV)	0	1	200	201

The linear combination, applied to the Sum column, gives

$$\tfrac{1}{4}(4{,}806) + 0(4{,}815) = 1{,}201.5$$

The check consists of computing the horizontal sum

$$1 + 0.5 + 1{,}200 = 1{,}201.5$$

and comparing it with the previous result.

(c) Line IV is a linear combination of lines III and II in which the coefficient of II is one and the coefficient of III is chosen so that the coefficient x_1 will be zero.

$$\text{IV} = 1(\text{II}) - 2(\text{III})$$

(d) One iteration has been completed, since the coefficients in the x_1 column are now 1 and 0. The next iteration must result in a zero for the coefficient of x_2 in the first equation and a one for the coefficient of x_2 in the second equation. Therefore, line VI is obtained by dividing IV by 12.

(e) V is then obtained by subtracting $\tfrac{1}{2}$ of VI from III.

The method of systematic elimination is a procedure by which all but one of the coefficients of the unknowns in each equation are successively reduced to zero; i.e., eliminated, so that each linear equation results in only one non-zero unknown and each unknown appears in one linear combination with a coefficient of one and in all the others with a coefficient of zero. The method requires the same set of computations as the method of algebraic elimination, but is more systematic and hence more useful for numerical work.

EXERCISES

1. Show that $x = 4$, $y = 2$ is the solution of

$$6x + 5y = 34$$
$$2x + 17y = 42$$

2. Show that the system

$$x_1 + 3 = 4x_2$$
$$2x_1 - 5 = 8x_2$$

has no solution.

Solve the following sets of simultaneous equations by each of the three methods. Verify the correctness of your solutions by substitution in the equations.

3. $\dfrac{3u}{2} + \dfrac{5v}{3} = 2$

$5u + \dfrac{2v}{9} = -\dfrac{4}{3}$

4. $4a - 9 = 8b$

   $2a - 4b = 6$

5. $1.923077x_1 + 1.538462x_2 = 2$

   $1.153846x_1 + 1.923077x_2 = 3$

SUMMARY

A rectangular array of numbers is called a matrix; the numbers within the array are called elements of the matrix. A matrix with m rows and n columns is of size $m \times n$. A matrix having one row and one colum (i.e., a single number) is called a scalar; a matrix with m rows and one column is a column vector; a matrix with one row and n colums is a row vector.

A matrix with 1's down the main diagonal, and all other elements zero, is called the identity matrix, and is denoted by $\mathbf{I}$. $\mathbf{I}$ must necessarily be a square matrix—a matrix having the same number of rows as columns. If $\mathbf{I}$ and $\mathbf{A}$ are $n \times n$ matrices, the identity matrix has the property that $\mathbf{IA} = \mathbf{AI} = \mathbf{A}$. A matrix consisting entirely of elements equal to zero is called a null matrix. If $\mathbf{A}$ is an $n \times n$ matrix, $\mathbf{0}$ the $n \times n$ null matrix then $\mathbf{0A} = \mathbf{A0} = \mathbf{0}$.

Matrix operations that have been defined are:

1. Transposition: the ith row becomes the ith column and the jth row becomes the jth column.
2. Addition (subtraction) of matrices: each element of one matrix is added to (subtracted from) the corresponding element of the second matrix; the operations can be performed only when the matrices are of the same size.
3. Multiplication: element c_{ij} in the product of $\mathbf{AB}$ is the sum of the products of the elements in the ith row of $\mathbf{A}$ and the corresponding elements in the jth column of $\mathbf{B}$. The number of columns in $\mathbf{A}$ must be equal to the number of rows in $\mathbf{B}$. Multiplication is associative but unlike ordinary multiplication, is not commutative; that is, $\mathbf{A(BC)} = \mathbf{(AB)C}$, but in general $\mathbf{AB} \neq \mathbf{BA}$.

Two linear equations in two unknowns can be written as a matrix equation $\mathbf{AX} = \mathbf{B}$. The equation will have a unique solution if the determinant of the system, $|\mathbf{A}|$, is not zero. The value of the determinant of a 2×2 matrix is the product of the elements on main diagonal less the product of the elements on the other diagonal. The two equations are said to be linearly independent if $|\mathbf{A}|$ is not zero. The solution to the system of equations is not changed if the system is replaced by a linear combination of the original equations, provided the determinant of the constants in the linear combination is not zero.

Three methods of solving systems of two linear equations in two unknowns are discussed:

1. *Algebraic elimination.* Equal quantities are added or subtracted on both sides of an equation, or both sides are multiplied or divided by the same non-zero number, in such a way as to eliminate one of the variables.
2. *Determinants.* Cramer's rule states the solution is the ratio of two determinants.
3. *Systematic elimination.* All but one of the coefficients of the unknowns in each equation are successively reduced to zero, so that each original equation is finally transformed into an expression involving only one variable. The procedure consists of a series of iterations, each iteration incorporating the replacement of every equation by an appropriate linear combination of other equations. This method is a form of the method of algebraic elimination.

Notes and References

Some texts in the field of matrices and systems of linear equations are:

Birkoff, G., and McLane, S. (1947), *A Survey of Modern Algebra*, Macmillan, New York.

Hohn, F. E. (1958), *Elementary Matrix Algebra*, Macmillan, New York.

Murdoch, D. C. (1957), *Linear Algebra for Undergraduates*, John Wiley and Sons, New York.

Nering, E. D. (1963), *Linear Algebra and Matrix Theory*, John Wiley and Sons, New York.

CHAPTER THIRTEEN

Matrix Inversion

and Linear Systems

In the previous chapter the operations of matrix addition, subtraction, and multiplication have been defined. The definitions were motivated partly for ease in presentation and manipulation of arrays of numbers and partly for dealing with systems of simultaneous linear equations in many unknowns.

In this chapter matrix inversion is defined; this operation is analogous to ordinary division. In Section A the operation is applied to 2×2 matrices. It is then extended to 3×3 matrices in Section B, and to $n \times n$ matrices in Section C. In each section the relationship between matrix inversion and solution of systems of linear equations is stressed.

Section D is devoted to partitioning of matrices; particularly to its use in matrix inversion. The general case of m linear equations in n unknowns is discussed briefly in Section E. This section is an introduction to the optimization models in Chapter 15.

A. MATRIX INVERSION

Definition of the Inverse

The equation $ax = g$, where a and g are real numbers, can be solved by division; dividing both sides by a gives

$$x = \frac{1}{a} \times g = a^{-1}g$$

The symbol a^{-1} represents the reciprocal of a; i.e., $= 1/a$. Note that $1/a \times a = a^{-1} \times a = 1 \quad \left(= a \times a^{-1} = a \times \dfrac{1}{a} \right)$.

For each square matrix, **A**, size of $m \times m$, there may exist another matrix, $\mathbf{A}^{-1}$, also of size $m \times m$, called the inverse of **A**, which has the property that

$$\mathbf{AA}^{-1} = \mathbf{A}^{-1}\mathbf{A} = \mathbf{I}$$

where **I** denotes the identity matrix of size $m \times m$.

Example I.   The two equations

$$4x_1 + 2x_2 = 4{,}800$$

$$2x_1 + 13x_2 = 4{,}800$$

can be represented as a single matrix equation $\mathbf{AX} = \mathbf{G}$ where

$$\mathbf{A} = \begin{bmatrix} 4 & 2 \\ 2 & 13 \end{bmatrix} \quad \mathbf{X} = \begin{bmatrix} x_1 \\ x_2 \end{bmatrix} \quad \mathbf{G} = \begin{bmatrix} 4{,}800 \\ 4{,}800 \end{bmatrix}$$

Provided $\mathbf{A}^{-1}$ exists, the equation $\mathbf{AX} = \mathbf{G}$ can be multiplied on both sides by the matrix $\mathbf{A}^{-1}$ which formally gives the solution

$$\mathbf{A}^{-1}\mathbf{AX} = \mathbf{A}^{-1}\mathbf{G}$$

$$\mathbf{X} = \mathbf{A}^{-1}\mathbf{G}$$

since $\mathbf{A}^{-1}\mathbf{A} = \mathbf{I}$ and $\mathbf{IX} = \mathbf{X}$.

In this example, if

$$\mathbf{A} = \begin{bmatrix} 4 & 2 \\ 2 & 13 \end{bmatrix}$$

then

$$\mathbf{A}^{-1} = \begin{bmatrix} \frac{13}{48} & -\frac{1}{24} \\ -\frac{1}{24} & \frac{1}{12} \end{bmatrix}$$

(since $\mathbf{AA}^{-1} = \mathbf{I}$) and, therefore,

$$\mathbf{X} = \mathbf{A}^{-1}\mathbf{G} = \begin{bmatrix} \frac{13}{48} & -\frac{1}{24} \\ -\frac{1}{24} & \frac{1}{12} \end{bmatrix}\begin{bmatrix} 4{,}800 \\ 4{,}800 \end{bmatrix} = \begin{bmatrix} \frac{13}{48}(4{,}800) - \frac{1}{24}(4{,}800) \\ -\frac{1}{24}(4{,}800) + \frac{1}{12}(4{,}800) \end{bmatrix}$$

$$= \begin{bmatrix} 1{,}100 \\ 200 \end{bmatrix}$$

Computation of the Inverse by Solving of Linear Equations

If $\mathbf{A}^{-1}$ exists and is known, 2 simultaneous linear equations in 2 unknowns may be solved by premultiplying a vector by the inverse matrix.

If the inverse (A^{-1}) is not known, it must first be computed. There are a number of different ways to compute the inverse of a matrix A. One straightforward way is to let the unknown inverse matrix be C and use the definition, $AC = I$, to solve equations for the elements of the inverse, C, one column at a time. If $AC = I$, i.e., if

$$\begin{bmatrix} a_{11} & a_{12} \\ a_{21} & a_{22} \end{bmatrix} \begin{bmatrix} c_{11} & c_{12} \\ c_{21} & c_{22} \end{bmatrix} = \begin{bmatrix} 1 & 0 \\ 0 & 1 \end{bmatrix}$$

then the following sets of equations must hold:

and

$$\begin{bmatrix} a_{11} & a_{12} \\ a_{21} & a_{22} \end{bmatrix} \begin{bmatrix} c_{11} \\ c_{21} \end{bmatrix} = \begin{bmatrix} 1 \\ 0 \end{bmatrix} : \quad \begin{aligned} a_{11}c_{11} + a_{12}c_{21} &= 1 \\ a_{21}c_{11} + a_{22}c_{21} &= 0 \end{aligned}$$

$$\begin{bmatrix} a_{11} & a_{12} \\ a_{21} & a_{22} \end{bmatrix} \begin{bmatrix} c_{11} \\ c_{22} \end{bmatrix} = \begin{bmatrix} 0 \\ 1 \end{bmatrix} : \quad \begin{aligned} a_{11}c_{12} + a_{12}c_{22} &= 0 \\ a_{21}c_{12} + a_{22}c_{22} &= 1 \end{aligned}$$

The first set is a set of two equations in two unknowns c_{11} and c_{21}, while the second is a set of two equations in two unknowns c_{12} and c_{22}. Since the a_{ij} are known, we can attempt to solve these equations.

Example 2. To compute the inverse of the matrix A defined in Example 1, let $C = A^{-1}$. Then the equations from

$$\begin{bmatrix} 4 & 2 \\ 2 & 13 \end{bmatrix} \begin{bmatrix} c_{11} & c_{12} \\ c_{21} & c_{22} \end{bmatrix} = \begin{bmatrix} 1 & 0 \\ 0 & 1 \end{bmatrix}$$

are

$$4c_{11} + 2c_{21} = 1$$
$$2c_{11} + 13c_{21} = 0$$

and

$$4c_{12} + 2c_{22} = 0$$
$$2c_{12} + 13c_{22} = 1$$

Using the elimination procedure on the first set gives

$$c_{11} = \tfrac{13}{48}, \qquad c_{21} = -\tfrac{1}{24}$$

and using it on the second set gives

$$c_{12} = -\tfrac{1}{24}, \qquad c_{22} = \tfrac{1}{12}$$

so that

$$C = A^{-1} = \begin{bmatrix} \tfrac{13}{48} & -\tfrac{1}{24} \\ -\tfrac{1}{24} & \tfrac{1}{12} \end{bmatrix}$$

Again it is convenient to have a systematic procedure and the one described in Chapter 12, Section B (page 350) for solving systems of linear equations, can be expanded to yield the inverse of a matrix. The computations for the above example are shown in Table 13-1. Two additional right-hand sides have been added in the columns labelled c_1 and c_2. In two iterations the original equations are solved and the inverse appears in the two additional columns. Since the solution to the system of two equations in two unknowns is available in the column labelled b, there is

Table 13-1 Computation of the Inverse of a 2 × 2 Matrix

Order	Number	x_1	x_2	b	c_1	c_2	Sum
I		4	2	4,800	1	0	4,807
II		2	13	4,800	0	1	4,816
1	III $= \frac{1}{4}$(I)	1	0.5	1,200	$\frac{1}{4}$	0	1,201.75
2	IV $= 1$(II) $- 2$(III)	0	12	2,400	$-\frac{1}{2}$	1	2,412.5
4	V $= 1$(III) $- \frac{1}{2}$(VI)	1	0	1,100	$\frac{13}{48}$	$-\frac{1}{24}$	$1,101\frac{11}{48}$
3	VI $=$ $\quad + \frac{1}{12}$(IV)	0	1	200	$-\frac{1}{24}$	$\frac{1}{12}$	$201\frac{1}{24}$

no point in calculating the inverse just to solve the equations. However, frequently the inverse is useful for other purposes. For example, if the system of equations is to be solved for many values of the right-hand side, the computation of the inverse reduces the solution of the other sets to a matrix multiplication.

Computation of the Inverse by Determinants

A convenient way to compute the inverse of a 2 × 2 matrix is by the use of determinants. If $\mathbf{A}$ is

$$\mathbf{A} = \begin{bmatrix} a_{11} & a_{12} \\ a_{21} & a_{22} \end{bmatrix}$$

and $\mathbf{C}$ is the inverse of $\mathbf{A}$, then

$$\mathbf{C} = \begin{bmatrix} \dfrac{a_{22}}{|\mathbf{A}|} & -\dfrac{a_{12}}{|\mathbf{A}|} \\ -\dfrac{a_{21}}{|\mathbf{A}|} & \dfrac{a_{11}}{|\mathbf{A}|} \end{bmatrix}$$

Since $\mathbf{AC} = \mathbf{I}$,

$$\mathbf{AC} = \begin{bmatrix} a_{11} & a_{12} \\ a_{21} & a_{22} \end{bmatrix} \begin{bmatrix} \dfrac{a_{22}}{|\mathbf{A}|} & -\dfrac{a_{12}}{|\mathbf{A}|} \\ -\dfrac{a_{21}}{|\mathbf{A}|} & \dfrac{a_{11}}{|\mathbf{A}|} \end{bmatrix}$$

$$= \begin{bmatrix} \dfrac{a_{11}a_{22} - a_{12}a_{21}}{|\mathbf{A}|} & \dfrac{-a_{11}a_{12} + a_{12}a_{11}}{|\mathbf{A}|} \\ \dfrac{a_{21}a_{22} - a_{22}a_{21}}{|\mathbf{A}|} & \dfrac{-a_{21}a_{12} + a_{22}a_{11}}{|\mathbf{A}|} \end{bmatrix}$$

$$= \begin{bmatrix} 1 & 0 \\ 0 & 1 \end{bmatrix}$$

The Existence of an Inverse. A square matrix $\mathbf{A}$ is said to be *singular* if it does not have an inverse and *non-singular* if $\mathbf{A}^{-1}$ exists. From the formula for the computation of the inverse by determinants given above it follows that if $\mathbf{A}$ is a 2×2 matrix, $\mathbf{A}$ is singular if $|\mathbf{A}| = 0$ since division by zero is not defined. The converse can also be proved: $\mathbf{A}$ is non-singular if $|\mathbf{A}| \neq 0$.

EXERCISES

1. Show that if

$$\mathbf{A} = \begin{bmatrix} 4 & 2 \\ 1 & 13 \end{bmatrix} \quad \text{then} \quad \mathbf{A}^{-1} = \begin{bmatrix} \frac{13}{50} & -\frac{1}{25} \\ -\frac{1}{50} & \frac{2}{25} \end{bmatrix}$$

2. Show that if

$$\mathbf{L} = \begin{bmatrix} 1 & -0.8 \\ -0.6 & 1 \end{bmatrix} \quad \text{then} \quad \mathbf{L}^{-1} = \begin{bmatrix} 1.923077 & 1.538462 \\ 1.153846 & 1.923077 \end{bmatrix}$$

3. Show that $(\mathbf{AB})^{-1} = \mathbf{B}^{-1}\mathbf{A}^{-1}$ and that $(\mathbf{A}')^{-1} = (\mathbf{A}^{-1})'$ where

$$\mathbf{A} = \begin{bmatrix} 4 & 1 \\ 2 & 1 \end{bmatrix} \quad \text{and} \quad \mathbf{B} = \begin{bmatrix} 2 & 1 \\ 2 & 3 \end{bmatrix}$$

4. Compute $\mathbf{A}^{-1}$ where

$$\mathbf{A} = \begin{bmatrix} \frac{520}{1000} & \frac{300}{800} \\ \frac{350}{1000} & \frac{400}{800} \end{bmatrix}$$

5. Show that $|\mathbf{AB}| = |\mathbf{A}|\,|\mathbf{B}|$ where $\mathbf{A}$ and $\mathbf{B}$ are 2×2 matrices.
6. Show that if $\mathbf{A}$ and $\mathbf{B}$ are 2×2 matrices, and $\mathbf{AB} = \mathbf{0}$, then either
(a) $\mathbf{A} = \mathbf{0}$ or $\mathbf{B} = \mathbf{0}$ or
(b) $\mathbf{A}$ and $\mathbf{B}$ are both singular.

B. THREE EQUATIONS IN THREE UNKNOWNS

The problem of solving two simultaneous equations in two unknowns was discussed in the previous chapter. The system has a solution if and only if the determinant of the system is different from zero. Several methods for finding solutions were illustrated. Most practical business problems involve more than two unknowns, and in this section the theory and methods for three equations and three unknowns are considered.

The system of three equations and three unknowns:

$$a_{11}x_1 + a_{12}x_2 + a_{13}x_3 = b_1$$

$$a_{21}x_1 + a_{22}x_2 + a_{23}x_3 = b_2$$

$$a_{31}x_1 + a_{32}x_2 + a_{33}x_3 = b_3$$

may be written as

$$\sum_{j=1}^{3} a_{ij}x_j = b_i \qquad i = 1, 2, 3$$

or as

$$AX = B$$

where

$$A = \begin{bmatrix} a_{11} & a_{12} & a_{13} \\ a_{21} & a_{22} & a_{23} \\ a_{31} & a_{32} & a_{33} \end{bmatrix} \qquad X = \begin{bmatrix} x_1 \\ x_2 \\ x_3 \end{bmatrix} \qquad B = \begin{bmatrix} b_1 \\ b_2 \\ b_3 \end{bmatrix}$$

Formally, the solution is given by

$$X = A^{-1}B$$

and hence, if A^{-1} is known, the solution can be obtained by a matrix multiplication.

The problem of computing the inverse can be considered as the problem of solving three sets of simultaneous equations in three unknowns. Let C be the inverse of A and let C_1, C_2, and C_3 denote the three columns of C:

$$C_1 = \begin{bmatrix} c_{11} \\ c_{21} \\ c_{31} \end{bmatrix} \qquad C_2 = \begin{bmatrix} c_{12} \\ c_{22} \\ c_{32} \end{bmatrix} \qquad C_3 = \begin{bmatrix} c_{13} \\ c_{23} \\ c_{33} \end{bmatrix}$$

Then the three sets of equations that must be solved are:

$$AC_1 = \begin{bmatrix} 1 \\ 0 \\ 0 \end{bmatrix} \qquad AC_2 = \begin{bmatrix} 0 \\ 1 \\ 0 \end{bmatrix} \qquad AC_3 = \begin{bmatrix} 0 \\ 0 \\ 1 \end{bmatrix}$$

Any method for solving systems of linear equations is also a method for computing the inverse of a matrix.

Solution by Determinants

Cramer's rule gives the solution as the ratio of two determinants.

$$
x_1 = \frac{\begin{vmatrix} b_1 & a_{12} & a_{13} \\ b_2 & a_{22} & a_{23} \\ b_3 & a_{32} & a_{33} \end{vmatrix}}{|A|}
\qquad
x_2 = \frac{\begin{vmatrix} a_{11} & b_1 & a_{13} \\ a_{21} & b_2 & a_{23} \\ a_{31} & b_3 & a_{33} \end{vmatrix}}{|A|}
\qquad
x_3 = \frac{\begin{vmatrix} a_{11} & a_{12} & b_1 \\ a_{21} & a_{22} & b_2 \\ a_{31} & a_{32} & b_3 \end{vmatrix}}{|A|}
$$

This formula can be obtained by the same method as that used for two equations in two unknowns.

The determinant in each denominator is the determinant of the coefficients of the variables, and the determinant in the numerator for x_i is obtained by replacing the ith column with the right-hand side of the determinant of the system.

The value of a third-order determinant (the order of a determinant is equal to the number of rows or columns) may be conveniently computed by writing the determinant, repeating the first two columns,

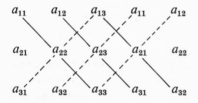

adding the three products of the three terms linked by solid lines, and subtracting the sum of the three products of the three terms linked by broken lines. The value of the determinant shown above is

$$
D = (a_{11}a_{22}a_{33} + a_{12}a_{23}a_{31} + a_{13}a_{21}a_{32})
$$
$$
-(a_{13}a_{22}a_{31} + a_{11}a_{23}a_{32} + a_{12}a_{21}a_{33})
$$

The value is equal to the sum of six (three-element) terms, where no two elements come from the same row or the same column

Example I.   The determinant

$$\begin{vmatrix} 2 & 0 & 4 \\ 2 & 1 & 0 \\ 3 & 1 & 3 \end{vmatrix}$$

has the value:

$$(2)(1)(3) + (0)(0)(3) + (4)(2)(1) - (4)(1)(3) - (2)(0)(1) - (0)(2)(3)$$
$$6 + 0 + 8 - 12 - 0 - 0 = 2$$

Inverse of a 3 × 3 Matrix by Determinants

The formula for computing the inverse of a 3 × 3 matrix may be expressed conveniently in terms of *cofactors*.

The determinant of the order 2 obtained by deleting the row and the column in which any particular element lies in a 3 × 3 determinant is defined as the *minor* of that particular element. The minor of the a_{ik} element will be denoted by $|A_{ik}|$. Thus the minor $|A_{22}|$ of the determinant

$$\begin{vmatrix} a_{11} & a_{12} & a_{13} \\ a_{21} & a_{22} & a_{23} \\ a_{31} & a_{32} & a_{33} \end{vmatrix} \quad \text{is} \quad \begin{vmatrix} a_{11} & a_{13} \\ a_{31} & a_{33} \end{vmatrix}$$

Similarly,

$$|A_{31}| = \begin{vmatrix} a_{12} & a_{13} \\ a_{22} & a_{23} \end{vmatrix}$$

The minor of a_{ik} prefixed by its sign is called the *cofactor* of a_{ik}. The sign of a minor is positive if the sum of the subscript of the column and the subscript of the row in which the particular element appears is even, and negative if the sum is odd. Thus,

$$(-1)^{(i+k)} |A_{ik}| = \text{the cofactor of the element } a_{ik}$$

For example, the sign of the cofactor of a_{23} element would be negative because $2 + 3$ is odd.

Example 2.   If

$$A = \begin{bmatrix} 2 & 0 & 4 \\ 2 & 1 & 0 \\ 3 & 1 & 3 \end{bmatrix}$$

the cofactors are

$$(-)^2 \begin{vmatrix} 1 & 0 \\ 1 & 3 \end{vmatrix} = 3 \qquad (-)^3 \begin{vmatrix} 2 & 0 \\ 3 & 3 \end{vmatrix} = -6 \qquad (-)^4 \begin{vmatrix} 2 & 1 \\ 3 & 1 \end{vmatrix} = -1$$

$$(-)^3 \begin{vmatrix} 0 & 4 \\ 1 & 3 \end{vmatrix} = 4 \qquad (-)^4 \begin{vmatrix} 2 & 4 \\ 3 & 3 \end{vmatrix} = -6 \qquad (-)^5 \begin{vmatrix} 2 & 0 \\ 3 & 1 \end{vmatrix} = -2$$

$$(-)^4 \begin{vmatrix} 0 & 4 \\ 1 & 0 \end{vmatrix} = -4 \qquad (-)^5 \begin{vmatrix} 2 & 4 \\ 2 & 0 \end{vmatrix} = 8 \qquad (-)^6 \begin{vmatrix} 2 & 0 \\ 2 & 1 \end{vmatrix} = 2$$

If A is a 3×3 matrix and C is its inverse, an element of the inverse, c_{ik}, is equal to the cofactor of a_{ki} divided by the determinant of A:

$$c_{ik} = \left[\frac{1}{|A|} (-1)^{k+i} |A_{ki}| \right] \qquad \text{for } i = 1, 2, 3 \text{ and } k = 1, 2, 3$$

Note that the subscripts on a and c are interchanged; another form of the statement is that c_{ik} is the cofactor of a_{ik} in A' divided by $|A|$.

Example 3.   Calculate the inverse of A in Example 1 by determinants. The cofactors are given in Example 2.

The value of A^{-1} is

$$A^{-1} = \begin{vmatrix} \frac{3}{2} & \frac{4}{2} & -\frac{4}{2} \\ -\frac{6}{2} & -\frac{6}{2} & \frac{8}{2} \\ -\frac{1}{2} & -\frac{2}{2} & \frac{2}{2} \end{vmatrix}$$

$$= \begin{vmatrix} 1.5 & 2 & -2 \\ -3 & -3 & 4 \\ -0.5 & -1 & 1 \end{vmatrix}$$

The answer may be verified directly

$$\begin{matrix} (A) & (A^{-1}) & = & I \end{matrix}$$

$$\begin{bmatrix} 2 & 0 & 4 \\ 2 & 1 & 0 \\ 3 & 1 & 3 \end{bmatrix} \begin{bmatrix} 1.5 & 2 & -2 \\ -3 & -3 & 4 \\ -0.5 & -1 & 1 \end{bmatrix} = \begin{bmatrix} 1 & 0 & 0 \\ 0 & 1 & 0 \\ 0 & 0 & 1 \end{bmatrix}$$

Systematic Elimination

The procedure and notation described in Chapter 12, Section B, can be extended to solve systems of three equations in three unknowns. The procedure in symbolic form is shown in Table 13-2.

Table 13-2 Systematic Elimination Procedure for Three Equations in Three Unknowns

Order	Line	Linear Combinations	x_1	x_2	x_3	b	Sum
1	I		$a_{11.0}$	$a_{12.0}$	$a_{13.0}$	$b_{1.0}$	$s_{1.0}$
2	II		$a_{21.0}$	$a_{22.0}$	$a_{23.0}$	$b_{2.0}$	$s_{2.0}$
3	III		$a_{31.0}$	$a_{32.0}$	$a_{33.0}$	$b_{3.0}$	$s_{3.0}$
4	$IV = \dfrac{1}{a_{11.0}} I$		1	$a_{12.1}$	$a_{13.1}$	$b_{1.1}$	$s_{1.1}$
5	$V = II - a_{21.0}IV$		0	$a_{22.1}$	$a_{23.1}$	$b_{2.1}$	$s_{2.1}$
6	$VI = III - a_{31.0}IV$		0	$a_{32.1}$	$a_{33.1}$	$b_{3.1}$	$s_{3.1}$
8	$VII = IV - a_{12.1}VIII$		1	0	$a_{13.2}$	$b_{1.2}$	$s_{1.2}$
7	$VIII = \dfrac{1}{a_{22.1}} V$		0	1	$a_{23.2}$	$b_{2.2}$	$s_{2.2}$
9	$IX = VI - a_{32.1}VIII$		0	0	$a_{33.2}$	$b_{3.2}$	$s_{3.2}$
11	$X = VII - a_{13.2}XII$		1	0	0	$b_{1.3}$	$s_{1.3}$
12	$XI = VIII - a_{23.2}XII$		0	1	0	$b_{2.3}$	$s_{2.3}$
10	$XII = \dfrac{1}{a_{33.2}} IX$		0	0	1	$b_{3.3}$	$s_{3.3}$

An iteration consists of three lines. In each iteration one column is reduced to two 0's and one 1, and three iterations are required. The pivot elements are $a_{11.0}$, $a_{22.1}$ and $a_{33.2}$ in the first, second, and third iterations, respectively. Any number of right-hand sides may be used. Table 13-3 shows three right-hand sides; in this case the identity matrix. The result is the inverse matrix.

Table 13-3 Example of the Inversion of a 3 × 3 Matrix

Line	Linear Combination	x_1	x_2	x_3	c_1	c_2	c_3	s
I		60	30	20	1	0	0	111
II		30	20	15	0	1	0	66
III		20	15	12	0	0	1	48
IV	$\frac{1}{60}$I	1	$\frac{1}{2}$	$\frac{1}{3}$	$\frac{1}{60}$	0	0	$\frac{111}{60}$
V	II − 30(IV)	0	5	5	$-\frac{1}{2}$	1	0	$\frac{21}{2}$
VI	III − 20(IV)	0	5	$\frac{16}{3}$	$-\frac{1}{3}$	0	1	11
VII	IV − $\frac{1}{2}$(VIII)	1	0	$-\frac{1}{6}$	$\frac{1}{15}$	$-\frac{1}{10}$	0	$\frac{4}{5}$
VIII	$\frac{1}{5}$V	0	1	1	$-\frac{1}{10}$	$\frac{1}{5}$	0	$\frac{21}{10}$
IX	VI − 5(VIII)	0	0	$\frac{1}{3}$	$\frac{1}{6}$	−1	1	$\frac{1}{2}$
X	VII + $\frac{1}{6}$(XII)	1	0	0	$\frac{3}{20}$	$-\frac{3}{5}$	$\frac{1}{2}$	$\frac{21}{10}$
XI	VIII − XII	0	1	0	$-\frac{3}{5}$	$\frac{16}{5}$	−3	$\frac{3}{5}$
XII	3(IX)	0	0	1	$\frac{1}{2}$	−3	3	$\frac{3}{2}$

Therefore, the inverse of

$$A = \begin{bmatrix} 60 & 30 & 20 \\ 30 & 20 & 15 \\ 20 & 15 & 12 \end{bmatrix} \quad \text{is} \quad A^{-1} = \begin{bmatrix} \frac{3}{20} & -\frac{3}{5} & \frac{1}{2} \\ -\frac{3}{5} & \frac{16}{5} & -3 \\ \frac{1}{2} & -3 & 3 \end{bmatrix}$$

To verify, compute AA^{-1}, e.g.,

$$\begin{bmatrix} \frac{180}{20} - \frac{90}{5} + \frac{20}{2} & -\frac{180}{5} + \frac{480}{5} - 60 & \frac{60}{2} - 90 + 60 \\ \frac{90}{20} - \frac{60}{5} + \frac{15}{2} & -\frac{90}{5} + \frac{320}{5} - 45 & \frac{30}{2} - 60 + 45 \\ 3 - \frac{45}{5} + \frac{12}{2} & -\frac{60}{5} + \frac{240}{5} - 36 & \frac{20}{2} - 45 + 36 \end{bmatrix} = \begin{bmatrix} 1 & 0 & 0 \\ 0 & 1 & 0 \\ 0 & 0 & 1 \end{bmatrix}$$

EXERCISES

1. Show by determinants and by systematic elimination that if

$$A = \begin{bmatrix} 2 & 0 & 1 \\ 2 & 1 & 1 \\ 3 & 1 & 1 \end{bmatrix} \quad \text{then} \quad A^{-1} = \begin{bmatrix} 0 & -1 & 1 \\ -1 & 1 & 0 \\ 1 & 2 & -2 \end{bmatrix}$$

2. Show by determinants and by systematic elimination that if

$$L = \begin{bmatrix} 1 & 0 & -0.5 \\ -0.1 & 1 & -0.3 \\ -0.2 & -0.6 & 1 \end{bmatrix}$$

then $$L^{-1} = \begin{bmatrix} 1.188406 & 0.434783 & 0.724638 \\ 0.231884 & 1.304348 & 0.507246 \\ 0.376812 & 0.869565 & 1.449275 \end{bmatrix}$$

3. Compute the inverse of

$$\begin{bmatrix} 3 & -2 & 4 \\ 1 & 1 & 1 \\ 2 & 1 & 0 \end{bmatrix}$$

by determinants and by systematic elimination. Verify the answer.

C. n EQUATIONS IN n UNKNOWNS

The general system of n linear equations in n unknowns is:

$$a_{11}x_1 + a_{12}x_2 + \cdots + a_{1n}x_n = b_1$$
$$a_{21}x_1 + a_{22}x_2 + \cdots + a_{2n}x_n = b_2$$
$$\cdot \qquad\qquad\qquad \cdot$$
$$\cdot \qquad\qquad\qquad \cdot \qquad\qquad (1)$$
$$\cdot \qquad\qquad\qquad \cdot$$
$$a_{n1}x_1 + a_{n2}x_2 + \cdots + a_{nn}x_n = b_n$$

The system may be expressed more concisely as

$$\sum_{j=1}^{n} a_{ij}x_j = b_i \qquad i = 1, \ldots, n$$

or as

$$AX = B$$

where A is the $n \times n$ matrix (a_{ij}) and X and B are the $n \times 1$ vectors (x_j) and (b_j), respectively.

Solution by Determinants

The solution to the system is given formally by

$$X = A^{-1}B$$

or from Cramer's rule as

$$x_j = \frac{|A_j|}{|A|}$$

where $|A|$ is the determinant of the system and $|A_j|$ is the determinant obtained by replacing the jth column of $|A|$ by the column of the b's. The solution will exist and be unique if $|A| \neq 0$.

The method of computing the numerical value of a determinant [shown in the previous section for three equations in three unknowns], will not work in cases where n is greater than 3. In general, the value of the determinant of **A** is given by

$$\sum_{j_1,\ldots,j_n} \pm a_{1j_1} a_{2j_2} \cdots a_{nj_n}$$

where $j_1, \ldots, j_n$ runs through all permutations of the numbers $1, \ldots, n$. The $+$ sign is given to a term when the permutation is even, the $-$ sign when it is odd. A permutation is even if the number of inversions (a larger number preceding a smaller number) of the integers from their natural order is even; e.g., 1, 2, 5, 3, 4 is even and 1, 2, 3, 5, 4 is odd. The value of $|A|$ is, however, rarely computed from this definition; it is usually more practical to expand a determinant of order n in terms of determinants of smaller orders.

A determinant, $|A|$, may be expressed as the sum of the n products of the elements and corresponding cofactors of *any* row *or* column, e.g., the value of the determinant

$$\begin{vmatrix} a_{11} & a_{12} & a_{13} \\ a_{21} & a_{22} & a_{23} \\ a_{31} & a_{32} & a_{33} \end{vmatrix}$$

is given by

$$|A| = a_{11}|A_{11}| - a_{12}|A_{12}| + a_{13}|A_{13}|$$

or

$$|A| = a_{11}\begin{vmatrix} a_{22} & a_{23} \\ a_{32} & a_{33} \end{vmatrix} - a_{12}\begin{vmatrix} a_{21} & a_{23} \\ a_{31} & a_{33} \end{vmatrix} + a_{13}\begin{vmatrix} a_{21} & a_{22} \\ a_{31} & a_{32} \end{vmatrix}$$

and also by

$$|A| = -a_{12}|A_{12}| + a_{22}|A_{22}| - a_{32}|A_{32}|$$

The general expression for finding determinants by expansion by minors is:

$$|A| = \sum_{k=1}^{n} (-1)^{i+k} a_{ik}|A_{ik}| \tag{2}$$

In practical problems the numerical computations for $n \geq 4$ will usually be performed on electronic computers using available programs. Several different algorithms are in general use; the most frequent are variations of the systematic elimination method. The details are given in numerical analyses texts and program descriptions available from computer manufacturers. Determinants are not very convenient or efficient for numerical computation. However, they are of considerable value in theoretical work in that they provide a useful criterion for the existence of solutions. Some properties, useful in evaluating determinants, are given here for reference.

Properties of Determinants

The following properties can frequently be used to reduce the amount of computation:

1. If two rows (or columns) of a determinant are interchanged, the *sign* of the determinant is changed; e.g.,

$$\begin{vmatrix} a_{11} & a_{12} & a_{13} \\ a_{21} & a_{22} & a_{23} \\ a_{31} & a_{32} & a_{33} \end{vmatrix} = (-1) \begin{vmatrix} a_{31} & a_{32} & a_{33} \\ a_{21} & a_{22} & a_{23} \\ a_{11} & a_{12} & a_{13} \end{vmatrix}$$

Example I.

$$\begin{vmatrix} a_{11} & a_{12} \\ a_{21} & a_{22} \end{vmatrix} = (-1) \begin{vmatrix} a_{21} & a_{22} \\ a_{11} & a_{12} \end{vmatrix}$$

$$a_{11}a_{22} - a_{12}a_{21} = -1(a_{12}a_{21} - a_{11}a_{22})$$

2. If two rows (or columns) of a determinant are equal, the value of the determinant is zero.

   This property is a consequence of the previous one.

Example 2.

$$\begin{vmatrix} a_{11} & a_{12} & a_{13} \\ a_{21} & a_{22} & a_{23} \\ a_{11} & a_{12} & a_{13} \end{vmatrix} = 0$$

$$a_{11}a_{22}a_{13} + a_{12}a_{23}a_{11} + a_{13}a_{21}a_{12} - a_{13}a_{22}a_{11} - a_{11}a_{23}a_{12} - a_{12}a_{21}a_{13} = 0$$

3. If each of the elements of a row (or column) of a determinant is zero, the value of the determinant is zero.

   This property follows immediately from expansion by minors.

Example 3.

$$\begin{vmatrix} a_{11} & a_{12} & a_{13} \\ a_{21} & a_{22} & a_{23} \\ 0 & 0 & 0 \end{vmatrix} = 0$$

$$a_{11}a_{22} \cdot 0 + a_{12}a_{23} \cdot 0 + a_{13}a_{21} \cdot 0 - a_{13}a_{22} \cdot 0 - a_{11}a_{23} \cdot 0 - a_{12}a_{21} \cdot 0 = 0$$

4. The value of a determinant is not changed if a multiple of one row is added to another row.

$$\begin{vmatrix} a_{11} & a_{12} & a_{13} \\ a_{21} + ca_{31} & a_{22} + ca_{32} & a_{23} + ca_{33} \\ a_{31} & a_{32} & a_{33} \end{vmatrix} = \begin{vmatrix} a_{11} & a_{12} & a_{13} \\ a_{21} & a_{22} & a_{23} \\ a_{31} & a_{32} & a_{33} \end{vmatrix}$$

The row whose elements are each multiplied by the constant c remains the same, and only the elements of the augmented row are changed.

Example 4.

$$\begin{vmatrix} a_{11} & a_{12} \\ a_{21} & a_{22} \end{vmatrix} = \begin{vmatrix} a_{11} + ca_{21} & a_{12} + ca_{22} \\ a_{21} & a_{22} \end{vmatrix}$$

$$a_{11}a_{22} - a_{12}a_{21} = a_{22}(a_{11} + ca_{21}) - a_{21}(a_{12} + ca_{22})$$
$$= a_{11}a_{22} + ca_{21}a_{22} - ca_{21}a_{22} - a_{12}a_{21}$$

5. If all the elements of a row (or column) are multiplied by a constant c, then the determinant is multiplied by the same constant c.

This property also follows immediately from expansion by minors.

Example 5.

$$c\begin{vmatrix} a_{11} & a_{12} & a_{13} \\ a_{21} & a_{22} & a_{23} \\ a_{31} & a_{32} & a_{33} \end{vmatrix} = \begin{vmatrix} ca_{11} & ca_{12} & ca_{13} \\ a_{21} & a_{22} & a_{23} \\ a_{31} & a_{32} & a_{33} \end{vmatrix}$$

$$c(a_{11}a_{22}a_{33} + a_{12}a_{23}a_{31} + a_{13}a_{21}a_{32} - a_{13}a_{22}a_{31} - a_{11}a_{23}a_{32} - a_{12}a_{21}a_{33})$$
$$= ca_{11}a_{22}a_{33} + ca_{12}a_{23}a_{31} + ca_{13}a_{21}a_{32} - ca_{11}a_{23}a_{32} - ca_{12}a_{21}a_{33} - ca_{13}a_{22}a_{31}$$

6. The value of a determinant is *not* changed if corresponding rows and columns are interchanged.

$$\begin{vmatrix} a_{11} & a_{12} & a_{13} \\ a_{21} & a_{22} & a_{23} \\ a_{31} & a_{32} & a_{33} \end{vmatrix} = \begin{vmatrix} a_{11} & a_{21} & a_{31} \\ a_{12} & a_{22} & a_{32} \\ a_{13} & a_{23} & a_{33} \end{vmatrix}$$

This property follows from 1 because an even number of interchanges is required to change corresponding rows and columns.

Example 6.

$$\begin{vmatrix} a_{11} & a_{12} \\ a_{21} & a_{22} \end{vmatrix} = \begin{vmatrix} a_{11} & a_{21} \\ a_{12} & a_{22} \end{vmatrix}$$

$$a_{11}a_{22} - a_{12}a_{21} = a_{11}a_{22} - a_{21}a_{12}$$

It follows from property 6 that for every result concerning the rows of a determinant, there is a corresponding result concerning the columns.

EXERCISES

1. Show by determinants and by systematic elimination that if

$$A = \begin{bmatrix} 1 & 1 & 1 & 1 \\ 1 & 2 & 3 & 4 \\ 1 & 3 & 6 & 10 \\ 1 & 4 & 10 & 20 \end{bmatrix} \quad \text{then } A^{-1} = \begin{bmatrix} 4 & -6 & 4 & -1 \\ -6 & 14 & -11 & 3 \\ 4 & -11 & 10 & -3 \\ 1 & 3 & -3 & 1 \end{bmatrix}$$

2. Find the inverse of A where

$$A = \begin{bmatrix} 1 & 0 & 0 & 0 & 0 \\ 0 & 1 & 0 & 0 & 0 \\ 0 & 0 & 1 & 0 & 0 \\ -1 & -3 & -1 & 1 & 0 \\ -2 & -3 & -1 & -2 & 1 \end{bmatrix}$$

3. Compute the inverse of:

$$\begin{bmatrix} 1 & -1 & -1 & -1 \\ 2 & 4 & 3 & 0 \\ 0 & 3 & -4 & -2 \\ -2 & 0 & 4 & 3 \end{bmatrix}$$

4. Formulate the product mix problem for the case where n machines are used to produce n products. State the physical meaning of the symbols used. Give the general solution.

5. (a) Show that

$$\begin{bmatrix} 2 & -1 & 0 \\ -1 & 2 & -1 \\ 0 & -1 & 1 \end{bmatrix} \begin{bmatrix} 1 & 1 & 1 \\ 1 & 2 & 2 \\ 1 & 2 & 3 \end{bmatrix} = \begin{bmatrix} 1 & 0 & 0 \\ 0 & 1 & 0 \\ 0 & 0 & 1 \end{bmatrix}$$

(*b*) Also that

$$
\begin{bmatrix}
2 & -1 & 0 & 0 \\
-1 & 2 & -1 & 0 \\
0 & -1 & 2 & -1 \\
0 & 0 & -1 & 1
\end{bmatrix}
\begin{bmatrix}
1 & 1 & 1 & 1 \\
1 & 2 & 2 & 2 \\
1 & 2 & 3 & 3 \\
1 & 2 & 3 & 4
\end{bmatrix}
=
\begin{bmatrix}
1 & 0 & 0 & 0 \\
0 & 1 & 0 & 0 \\
0 & 0 & 1 & 0 \\
0 & 0 & 0 & 1
\end{bmatrix}
$$

(*c*) Determine the inverse of the $n \times n$ matrix of the form:

$$
\begin{bmatrix}
2 & -1 & 0 & 0 & \cdots & 0 & 0 & 0 & 0 \\
-1 & 2 & -1 & 0 & \cdots & 0 & 0 & 0 & 0 \\
0 & -1 & 2 & -1 & \cdots & 0 & 0 & 0 & 0 \\
\cdot & \cdot & \cdot & \cdot & \cdots & \cdot & \cdot & \cdot & \cdot \\
\cdot & \cdot & \cdot & \cdot & \cdots & \cdot & \cdot & \cdot & \cdot \\
\cdot & \cdot & \cdot & \cdot & \cdots & \cdot & \cdot & \cdot & \cdot \\
0 & 0 & 0 & 0 & \cdots & -1 & 2 & -1 & 0 \\
0 & 0 & 0 & 0 & \cdots & 0 & -1 & 2 & -1 \\
0 & 0 & 0 & 0 & \cdots & 0 & 0 & -1 & 1
\end{bmatrix}
$$

D. PARTITIONING OF MATRICES

Up to this point matrices have been rectangular arrays of elements, each of which is a number. However, the notation and results are also valid if each element is itself a matrix. For example, the matrix

$$
\mathbf{A} = \begin{bmatrix} a_{11} & a_{12} & a_{13} \\ a_{21} & a_{22} & a_{23} \end{bmatrix}
$$

may be written as

$$
\mathbf{A} = [\mathbf{C}_1 \quad \mathbf{C}_2 \quad \mathbf{C}_3] \quad \text{where} \quad \mathbf{C}_1 = \begin{bmatrix} a_{11} \\ a_{21} \end{bmatrix} \quad \mathbf{C}_2 = \begin{bmatrix} a_{12} \\ a_{22} \end{bmatrix}
$$

$$
\text{and} \quad \mathbf{C}_3 = \begin{bmatrix} a_{13} \\ a_{23} \end{bmatrix}
$$

or as

$$
\mathbf{A} = \begin{bmatrix} \mathbf{R}_1 \\ \mathbf{R}_2 \end{bmatrix} \quad \text{where} \quad \mathbf{R}_1 = [a_{11} \quad a_{12} \quad a_{13}] \quad \text{and} \quad \mathbf{R}_2 = [a_{21} \quad a_{22} \quad a_{23}]
$$

or as

$$
\mathbf{A} = [\mathbf{A}_1 \quad \mathbf{A}_2]
$$

where

$$A_1 = \begin{bmatrix} a_{11} & a_{12} \\ a_{21} & a_{22} \end{bmatrix} \quad \text{and} \quad A_2 = \begin{bmatrix} a_{13} \\ a_{23} \end{bmatrix}$$

or where

$$A_1 = \begin{bmatrix} a_{11} \\ a_{21} \end{bmatrix} \quad \text{and} \quad A_2 = \begin{bmatrix} a_{12} & a_{13} \\ a_{22} & a_{23} \end{bmatrix}$$

The process of dividing a matrix into smaller matrices, or submatrices, is called partitioning and is usually denoted by a dotted line. The four partitions described would be denoted respectively as follows:

$$\left[\begin{array}{c|c|c} a_{11} & a_{12} & a_{13} \\ a_{21} & a_{22} & a_{23} \end{array}\right]; \quad \left[\begin{array}{ccc} a_{11} & a_{12} & a_{13} \\ \hline a_{21} & a_{22} & a_{23} \end{array}\right]$$

$$\left[\begin{array}{cc|c} a_{11} & a_{12} & a_{13} \\ a_{21} & a_{22} & a_{23} \end{array}\right] \quad \text{and} \quad \left[\begin{array}{c|cc} a_{11} & a_{12} & a_{13} \\ a_{21} & a_{22} & a_{23} \end{array}\right]$$

Matrix operations can then be performed with matrices whose elements are matrices, provided the rules of operation are valid for the given matrix and for the resulting submatrices.

Example I. Calculate **AB**, given

$$A = \begin{bmatrix} 6 & 0 & 1 \\ 2 & 1 & 0 \end{bmatrix} \quad \text{and} \quad B = \begin{bmatrix} 4 & 3 \\ 0 & 1 \\ 1 & 0 \end{bmatrix}$$

Solution. Partition the two matrices:

$$A = \left[\begin{array}{c|cc} 6 & 0 & 1 \\ 2 & 1 & 0 \end{array}\right] = [A_1 \quad A_2] \quad \text{and} \quad B = \left[\begin{array}{cc} 4 & 3 \\ \hline 0 & 1 \\ 1 & 0 \end{array}\right] = \begin{bmatrix} B_1 \\ B_2 \end{bmatrix}$$

where

$$A_1 = \begin{bmatrix} 6 \\ 2 \end{bmatrix}, \quad A_2 = \begin{bmatrix} 0 & 1 \\ 1 & 0 \end{bmatrix}, \quad B_1 = [4 \quad 3], \quad \text{and} \quad B_2 = \begin{bmatrix} 0 & 1 \\ 1 & 0 \end{bmatrix}$$

then

$$AB = [A_1 \quad A_2] \begin{bmatrix} B_1 \\ B_2 \end{bmatrix} = A_1 B_1 + A_2 B_2$$

and

$$AB = \left[\begin{bmatrix} 6 \\ 2 \end{bmatrix} [4 \quad 3] + \begin{bmatrix} 0 & 1 \\ 1 & 0 \end{bmatrix} \begin{bmatrix} 0 & 1 \\ 1 & 0 \end{bmatrix} \right] = \left[\begin{bmatrix} 24 & 18 \\ 8 & 6 \end{bmatrix} + \begin{bmatrix} 1 & 0 \\ 0 & 1 \end{bmatrix} \right]$$

$$AB = \begin{bmatrix} 25 & 18 \\ 8 & 7 \end{bmatrix}$$

Partitioning a matrix can be especially helpful when some of the submatrices are of a special type, such as the identity matrix $\mathbf{I}$ or the null matrix $\mathbf{O}$.

Example 2. Compute $\mathbf{AB}$ where $\mathbf{A}$ and $\mathbf{B}$ can be partitioned as follows:

$$\mathbf{A} = \left[\begin{array}{c|c} \mathbf{N} & \mathbf{I} \\ \hline \mathbf{O} & \mathbf{M} \end{array}\right] \quad \text{and} \quad \mathbf{B} = \left[\begin{array}{c} \mathbf{P} \\ \hline \mathbf{Q} \end{array}\right]$$

then

$$\mathbf{AB} = \left[\begin{array}{c} \mathbf{NP} + \mathbf{IQ} \\ \hline \mathbf{OP} + \mathbf{MQ} \end{array}\right] = \left[\begin{array}{c} \mathbf{NP} + \mathbf{Q} \\ \hline \mathbf{MQ} \end{array}\right]$$

provided the rules of multiplication and addition for the submatrices are valid.

Suppose $\mathbf{A}$ is $m \times n$ and $\mathbf{B}$ is $n \times p$; then $\mathbf{AB}$ is defined and is $m \times p$. Suppose further that the identity submatrix in $\mathbf{A}$ is $r \times r$; then

$$\mathbf{A} = \begin{array}{c} {\scriptstyle n-r \quad r} \\ \left[\begin{array}{c|c} \mathbf{N} & \mathbf{I} \\ \hline \mathbf{O} & \mathbf{M} \end{array}\right] \begin{array}{l} {\scriptstyle r} \\ {\scriptstyle m-r} \end{array} \end{array} \qquad \mathbf{B} = \begin{array}{c} {\scriptstyle p} \\ \left[\begin{array}{c} \mathbf{P} \\ \hline \mathbf{Q} \end{array}\right] \begin{array}{l} {\scriptstyle n-r} \\ {\scriptstyle r} \end{array} \end{array}$$

$$\mathbf{AB} = \left[\begin{array}{ccc|c} \overbrace{\mathbf{NP}}^{(r \times n-r)(n-r \times p)} + & \overbrace{\mathbf{IQ}}^{(r \times r)(r \times p)} & \overbrace{\mathbf{NP} + \mathbf{Q}}^{r \times p \quad r \times p} \\ \hline \underbrace{\mathbf{OP}}_{(m-r \times n-r)(n-r \times p)} + & \underbrace{\mathbf{MQ}}_{(m-r \times r)(r \times p)} & \underbrace{\mathbf{MQ}}_{m-r \times p} \end{array}\right] \begin{array}{l} {\scriptstyle r} \\ {\scriptstyle m-r} \end{array}$$

The original matrix multiplication requires the computation of mp elements, each of which requires n multiplications and additions. In the partitioned form the number of elements is still the same; but the number of multiplications and additions per element is reduced.

Frequently the inversion of matrices can also be simplified by partitioning. Suppose $\mathbf{A}$ is $m \times m$ and $\mathbf{C} = \mathbf{A}^{-1}$ exists, and $\mathbf{A}$ and $\mathbf{C}$ are partitioned:

$$\mathbf{A} = \begin{array}{c} {\scriptstyle r \quad m-r} \\ \left[\begin{array}{cc} \mathbf{A}_1 & \mathbf{A}_2 \\ \mathbf{A}_3 & \mathbf{A}_4 \end{array}\right] \begin{array}{l} {\scriptstyle r} \\ {\scriptstyle m-r} \end{array} \end{array} \qquad \text{and} \qquad \mathbf{C} = \begin{array}{c} {\scriptstyle r \quad m-r} \\ \left[\begin{array}{cc} \mathbf{C}_1 & \mathbf{C}_2 \\ \mathbf{C}_3 & \mathbf{C}_4 \end{array}\right] \begin{array}{l} {\scriptstyle r} \\ {\scriptstyle m-r} \end{array} \end{array}$$

so that $\mathbf{A}_1$ and $\mathbf{C}_1$ are $r \times r$, $\mathbf{A}_4$ and $\mathbf{C}_4$ are $m - r \times m - r$, and $\mathbf{A}^{-1}$ exists.

Since $\mathbf{AC} = \mathbf{I}$

$$\begin{bmatrix} A_1 & A_2 \\ A_3 & A_4 \end{bmatrix} \begin{bmatrix} C_1 & C_2 \\ C_3 & C_4 \end{bmatrix} = \begin{bmatrix} A_1C_1 + A_2C_3 & A_1C_2 + A_2C_4 \\ A_3C_1 + A_4C_3 & A_3C_2 + A_4C_4 \end{bmatrix} = \begin{bmatrix} I & O \\ O & I \end{bmatrix}$$

where the $m \times m$ is identity matrix is partitioned appropriately.

Equating submatrices of AC and I gives the following set of matrix equations:

$$(a) \quad A_1C_1 + A_2C_3 = I$$

$$(b) \quad A_1C_2 + A_2C_4 = O$$

$$(c) \quad A_3C_1 + A_4C_3 = O$$

$$(d) \quad A_3C_2 + A_4C_4 = I$$

From (b)

$$A_1C_2 = O - A_2C_4$$

or since A_1^{-1} is assumed to exist,

$$A_1^{-1}A_1C_2 = C_2 = -A_1^{-1}A_2C_4$$

Substituting this result into (d) gives

$$A_3(-A_1^{-1}A_2C_4) + A_4C_4 = I$$

or

$$(A_4 - A_3A_1^{-1}A_2)C_4 = I$$

which gives

$$C_4 = (A_4 - A_3A_1^{-1}A_2)^{-1}$$

From (a)

$$A_1C_1 = I - A_2C_3$$

or

$$A_1^{-1}A_1C_1 = C_1 = A_1^{-1} - A_1^{-1}A_2C_3$$

Substituting this result in (c) gives

$$A_3(A_1^{-1} - A_1^{-1}A_2C_3) + A_4C_3 = 0$$

or

$$A_3A_1^{-1} = (A_3A_1^{-1}A_2 - A_4)C_3$$

Noting that the expression in the parenthesis on the right-hand side is equivalent to $-C_4^{-1}$, upon substitution

$$A_3A_1^{-1} = -C_4^{-1}C_3 \qquad \text{or} \qquad C_3 = -C_4A_3A_1^{-1}$$

In summary, the submatrices C_i can be expressed in terms of the submatrices A_i as:

$$C_4 = (A_4 - A_3A_1^{-1}A_2)^{-1}$$

$$C_3 = -C_4A_3A_1^{-1}$$

$$C_2 = -A_1^{-1}A_2C_4$$

$$C_1 = A_1^{-1} - A_1^{-1}A_2C_3$$

It can be seen that computing the inverse is greatly simplified because only matrices of order $r \times r$ and $m - r \times m - r$ have to be inverted. Further simplification results if $\mathbf{A}$ can be partitioned so that $\mathbf{A}_1^{-1}$ is known or easily determined. Then $\mathbf{A}_4 - \mathbf{A}_3\mathbf{A}_1^{-1}\mathbf{A}_2$ which must be inverted to find $\mathbf{C}_4$, may be considerably smaller than $\mathbf{A}$.

Example 3. To invert

$$\mathbf{A} = \begin{bmatrix} 3 & -2 & 4 \\ 1 & 1 & 1 \\ 2 & 1 & 0 \end{bmatrix}$$

partition it in the form

$$\begin{bmatrix} 3 & -2 & \vdots & 4 \\ 1 & 1 & \vdots & 1 \\ \cdots & \cdots & & \cdots \\ 2 & 1 & \vdots & 0 \end{bmatrix}$$

Here

$$\mathbf{A}_1 = \begin{bmatrix} 3 & -2 \\ 1 & 1 \end{bmatrix} \quad \text{and} \quad \mathbf{A}_1^{-1} = \begin{bmatrix} \frac{1}{5} & \frac{2}{5} \\ -\frac{1}{5} & \frac{3}{5} \end{bmatrix}$$

Then

$$\mathbf{A}_3\mathbf{A}_1^{-1}\mathbf{A}_2 = [2 \quad 1]\begin{bmatrix} \frac{1}{5} & \frac{2}{5} \\ -\frac{1}{5} & \frac{3}{5} \end{bmatrix}\begin{bmatrix} 4 \\ 1 \end{bmatrix} = [\frac{1}{5} \quad \frac{7}{5}]\begin{bmatrix} 4 \\ 1 \end{bmatrix} = \frac{4}{5} + \frac{7}{5} = \frac{11}{5}$$

and

$$\mathbf{A}_4 - \mathbf{A}_3\mathbf{A}_1^{-1}\mathbf{A}_2 = \mathbf{O} - \tfrac{11}{5}$$

Further,

$$\mathbf{C}_4 = (\mathbf{A}_4 - \mathbf{A}_3\mathbf{A}_1^{-1}\mathbf{A}_2)^{-1} = [-\tfrac{11}{5}]^{-1} = -\tfrac{5}{11}$$

$$\mathbf{C}_3 = -\mathbf{C}_4\mathbf{A}_3\mathbf{A}_1^{-1} = \tfrac{5}{11}[2 \quad 1]\begin{bmatrix} \frac{1}{5} & \frac{2}{5} \\ -\frac{1}{5} & \frac{3}{5} \end{bmatrix} = \tfrac{5}{11}[\frac{1}{5} \quad \frac{7}{5}]$$

$$= [\tfrac{1}{11} \quad \tfrac{7}{11}]$$

$$\mathbf{C}_2 = -\mathbf{A}_1^{-1}\mathbf{A}_2\mathbf{C}_4 = -\begin{bmatrix} \frac{1}{5} & \frac{2}{5} \\ -\frac{1}{5} & \frac{3}{5} \end{bmatrix}\begin{bmatrix} 4 \\ 1 \end{bmatrix}[-\tfrac{5}{11}] = -\begin{bmatrix} \frac{6}{5} \\ -\frac{1}{5} \end{bmatrix}[\tfrac{5}{11}] = \begin{bmatrix} \frac{6}{11} \\ -\frac{1}{11} \end{bmatrix}$$

and

$$\mathbf{C}_1 = \mathbf{A}_1^{-1} - \mathbf{A}_1^{-1}\mathbf{A}_2\mathbf{C}_3 = \begin{bmatrix} \frac{1}{5} & \frac{2}{5} \\ -\frac{1}{5} & \frac{3}{5} \end{bmatrix} - \begin{bmatrix} \frac{6}{5} \\ -\frac{1}{5} \end{bmatrix}[\tfrac{1}{11} \quad \tfrac{7}{11}]$$

$$= \begin{bmatrix} \frac{1}{5} & \frac{2}{5} \\ -\frac{1}{5} & \frac{3}{5} \end{bmatrix} - \begin{bmatrix} \frac{6}{55} & \frac{42}{55} \\ -\frac{1}{55} & -\frac{7}{55} \end{bmatrix} = \begin{bmatrix} \frac{1}{11} & -\frac{4}{11} \\ -\frac{2}{11} & \frac{8}{11} \end{bmatrix}$$

Finally,

$$\mathbf{A}^{-1} = \begin{bmatrix} \frac{1}{11} & -\frac{4}{11} & \frac{6}{11} \\ -\frac{2}{11} & \frac{8}{11} & -\frac{1}{11} \\ \frac{1}{11} & \frac{7}{11} & -\frac{5}{11} \end{bmatrix} = \frac{1}{11} \begin{bmatrix} 1 & -4 & 6 \\ -2 & 8 & 1 \\ 1 & 7 & -5 \end{bmatrix}$$

To verify, compute

$$\frac{1}{11} \begin{bmatrix} 3 & -2 & 4 \\ 1 & 1 & 1 \\ 2 & 1 & 0 \end{bmatrix} \begin{bmatrix} 1 & -4 & 6 \\ -2 & 8 & -1 \\ 1 & 7 & -5 \end{bmatrix}$$

$$= \frac{1}{11} \begin{bmatrix} 3+4+4 & -12-16+28 & 18+2-20 \\ 1-2+1 & -4+8+7 & 6-1-5 \\ 2-2+0 & -8+8+0 & 12-1+0 \end{bmatrix}$$

$$= \begin{bmatrix} 1 & 0 & 0 \\ 0 & 1 & 0 \\ 0 & 0 & 1 \end{bmatrix}$$

EXERCISES

1. Verify the result in Example 1 by matrix multiplication, using unpartitioned matrices.

2. Compute the inverse of A where

$$\mathbf{A} = \begin{bmatrix} 1 & 0 & 0 & 0 & 0 \\ -6 & 1 & 0 & 0 & 0 \\ -2 & -1 & 1 & 0 & 0 \\ 0 & -4 & -2 & 1 & 0 \\ -1 & 0 & -3 & 0 & 1 \end{bmatrix}$$

by partitioning $\mathbf{A}$ in the form

$$\begin{bmatrix} \mathbf{A}_1 & \mathbf{A}_2 \\ \mathbf{A}_3 & \mathbf{A}_4 \end{bmatrix}$$

where $\mathbf{A}_1$ is a 3×3 and $\mathbf{A}_4$ is a 2×2.

E. m EQUATIONS IN n UNKNOWNS

When business problems are formulated as systems of m linear equations in n unknowns, m and n frequently will not be equal.

More Equations than Unknowns ($m > n$)

In many product-mix problems of the type described earlier, the number of machines will not be the same as the number of products. Suppose, for example, that three machines are required to produce the screws, with the third machine being used to plate the screws.

Let

a_1 = the number of minutes required to plate a box of wood screws

a_2 = the number of minutes required to plate a box of machine screws

b_1 = the number of minutes the plating machine is available

and, as before,

x_1 = the number of boxes of wood screws

x_2 = the number of boxes of metal screws

The equations then become:

$$4x_1 + 2x_2 = 4,800 \tag{I}$$

$$2x_1 + 13x_2 = 4,800 \tag{II}$$

$$a_1x_1 + a_1x_2 = b_1 \tag{III}$$

Assume, as before, that the problem is to determine the number of wood screws and the number of metal screws whose production will use all of the available machine time.

Each pair of 2 equations will have a unique solution provided their determinant is not zero. There are three such pairs (I, II), (I, III), and (II, III), and it is possible that the three sets of solutions are identical; e.g., if (III) is $3x_1 + 2x_2 = 3,700$. The lines are shown in Fig. 13.1. All three meet at the point $x_1 = 1,100$, $x_2 = 200$. However, this situation is

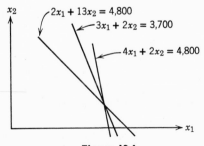

Figure 13.1

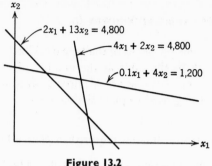

Figure 13.2

rather unlikely; a more representative problem is one where the three sets of solutions are different, as in Fig. 13.2. In such a situation it will be impossible to keep all machines busy all the time. The choice of which machine is to be idle must be based on other considerations.

More Unknowns than Equations $(n > m)$

Another case occurs when the number of products is greater than the number of machines. Suppose, for example, that the manufacturer can produce a third product, say aluminum screws. Each box requires 1 minute of machine I time and 2 minutes of machine II time.

This problem can be formulated as follows:
Find values of

$$x_1 = \text{number of boxes of wood screws}$$

$$x_2 = \text{number of boxes of metal screws}$$

$$x_3 = \text{number of boxes of aluminum screws}$$

which satisfy the equations

$$4x_1 + 2x_2 + x_3 = 4,800$$

$$2x_1 + 13x_2 + 2x_3 = 4,800$$

Since there are three variables and only two equations, there will in general be an infinite number of solutions. (If the equations are linearly dependent, there may be no solution.) If one of the variables can be set equal to a constant, the system reduces to a set of two equations in two unknowns which will have a unique solution if their determinant is not zero.

The possible sets of equations which may have unique solutions are

$$\left.\begin{array}{l} 2x_2 + x_3 = 4{,}800 - 4c_1 \\ 13x_2 + 2x_3 = 4{,}800 - 2c_1 \end{array}\right\}\text{I}$$

$$\left.\begin{array}{l} 4x_1 + x_3 = 4{,}800 - 2c_2 \\ 2x_1 + 2x_3 = 4{,}800 - 13c_2 \end{array}\right\}\text{II}$$

$$\left.\begin{array}{l} 4x_1 + 2x_2 = 4{,}800 - c_3 \\ 2x_1 + 13x_2 = 4{,}800 - 2c_3 \end{array}\right\}\text{III}$$

in which the constants c_1, c_2, and c_3 can have any values. For any value of c_1, c_2, or c_3, the solution would require all the available machine time.

To illustrate the computation of all possible solutions to the three-product two-machine product-mix problem, suppose one of the products is not produced at all. There will be $3!/2!\,1! = 3$ possible solution sets in which one x_j is equal to zero. These can be found by solving the set of simultaneous linear equations for two of the variables, i.e., sets I, II and III above with $c_1 = 0$, $c_2 = 0$, $c_3 = 0$, respectively.

For example, if x_3 is set $= 0$, the solution for x_1 and x_2 could be obtained as follows:

Order	Line	Linear Combination	x_1	x_2	x_3	b
1	I		4	2	1	4,800
2	II		2	13	2	4,800
3	III	(I/4)	1	$\frac{1}{2}$	$\frac{1}{4}$	1,200
4	IV	(II $-$ (2 · III))	0	12	$\frac{3}{2}$	2,400
6	V	(III $-$ VI/2)	1	0	$\frac{3}{16}$	1,100
5	VI	(IV/12)	0	1	$\frac{1}{8}$	200

Because the set of equations in each iteration is a linear combination of the equation in the previous iteration, the set V, VI is equivalent to the set I, II. However, the set V, VI is said to be in *basic form* because one variable in each equation has a coefficient of "1" and zero coefficients in the other equation. Variables x_1 and x_2 in V and VI are called *basic variables*, and x_3 is a non-basic variable.

When a set of equations is in basic form, values of the basic variables can be read off directly by setting the non-basic variables equal to zero. Here, if $x_3 = 0$, then $x_1 = 1{,}100$ and $x_2 = 200$.

Next, suppose the set to be examined is x_2 and x_3, with $x_1 = 0$. Then continuing the row operation gives:

Order	Line	Linear Combination	x_1	x_2	x_3	b
7	VII	$(16/3 \cdot V)$	$\dfrac{16}{3}$	0	1	$\dfrac{17,600}{3}$
8	VIII	$(VI - VII/8)$	$-\dfrac{2}{3}$	1	0	$-\dfrac{1,600}{3}$

It follows that if $x_1 = 0$, then $x_2 = -1,600/3$ and $x_3 = 17,600/3$. Of course, this is not a practical or feasible solution, since negative amounts of product cannot be produced.

The operation that was performed to get VII and VIII from V and VI is systematic elimination with the pivot element in row V and column x_3. Pivoting around the intersection of the chosen row and column and involves the following steps:

1. Choosing a column, j' (a variable to become basic).
2. Choosing a row, i' (a variable to become non-basic).
3. Forming a new, equivalent set of equations by:
   (a) Dividing the row i' by the coefficient of the variable becoming basic to form a new row i'.
   (b) For all other rows $i \neq i'$, multiplying the new row i' by the coefficient in row i of the variable (j') becoming basic and subtracting the product from row i to form a new row i.

To obtain a solution for the set x_1, x_3, with $x_2 = 0$, the pivoting is carried out with x_1, the new basic variable, and x_2, the new non-basic variable, as shown in:

Order	Line	Linear Combination	x_1	x_2	x_3	b
10	IX	$(V - 3/16X)$	1	$-\frac{3}{2}$	0	800
9	X	$(8VI)$	0	8	1	1,600

Hence if $x_2 = 0$, then $x_1 = 800$ and $x_3 = 1,600$.

How should we choose among these several product mixes? If we knew the profit per unit of x_1, x_2, and x_3, the mix that would maximize profit could be chosen. Suppose that profits were 5 cents per x_1, 4 cents per x_2, and 2 cents per x_3. Then the total profit is given by:

$$Z = 5x_1 + 4x_2 + 2x_3$$

This function is the *objective function*.

For the three sets of equations examined here, the values of Z are:

$$x_1 = 1{,}100 \qquad x_2 = 200 \qquad x_3 = 0 \qquad Z = 6{,}300$$

$$x_1 = 800 \qquad x_2 = 0 \qquad x_3 = 1{,}600 \qquad Z = 7{,}200$$

$$x_1 = 0 \qquad x_2 = -533 \qquad x_3 = 5{,}866 \qquad \text{Infeasible}$$

In the case where x_2 and x_3 are basic variables, the product mix that uses all the machine time is infeasible because we cannot produce a negative amount of a product. A solution which is feasible is:

$$x_1 = 0 \qquad x_2 = 0 \qquad x_3 = 2{,}400 \qquad Z = 4{,}800$$

The product mix which gives the greatest profit among the possible ones considered here is to produce 800 boxes of wood screws and 1,600 boxes of aluminum screws. However, there are other possible product mixes which have not been considered.

The analysis carried out here is a very simple example of a class of optimization models, known as linear programming, which will be studied in more detail in Chapter 15.

General Procedure

A procedure for formulating systems of equations is illustrated in Fig. 13.3. After the problem is initially formulated, the formulation should be checked to see whether all pertinent equations and variables are included and no extraneous equations or variables are present. Three different cases may arise. The number of equations may be less than, equal to, or greater than the number of variables. If the number of equations is less than the number of variables, any set of $m - n$ of the variables can be set equal to arbitrary values; the number of equations then becomes equal to the number of variables. If there are more equations than unknowns, any set of n equations can be selected.

Once the number of equations is equal to the number of variables, a numerical solution can be obtained, provided the determinant of the system is not equal to zero. If the determinant is equal to zero, we can either remove one equation or set one variable equal to an arbitrary value and try again until a unique solution is obtained. If the determinant is again equal to zero, this procedure is repeated until the determinant at some point is not equal to zero.

Mathematically, there will in general be considerable flexibility in which variables are set equal to arbitrary values, what arbitrary values are

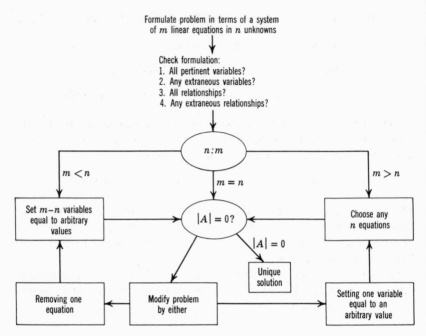

Figure 13.3 Procedure for reducing a general linear system to one which has a unique solution.

selected, or which equations are selected if there are more equations than unknowns. The choices here must be taken on the basis of other factors in the problem.

EXERCISES

1. Determine all possible solutions to the 3-machine 2-product product-mix problem, if the equations are:

$$2x_1 + 13x_2 = 4,800$$
$$4x_1 + 2x_2 = 4,800$$
$$x_1 + 2x_2 = 2,000$$

2. Determine all possible solutions to the 2-machine 3-product product-mix problem in which the equations are:

$$4x_1 + 2x_2 + x_3 = 4,800$$
$$2x_1 + 13x_2 + 2x_3 = 4,800$$

and where one or two products are produced. Determine the optimum product mix if profit is 5 cents per unit for x_1, 4 cents for x_2, and 2 cents for x_3.

3. Formulate and solve the general product-mix problem in matrix notation for the case

$$(i) \; n > m$$

$$(ii) \; n < m$$

State the number of possible solutions in each case.

SUMMARY

A *non-singular matrix* is a square matrix which can be multiplied by another matrix such that the product is equal to the identity matrix. The second matrix is defined as the *inverse* of the first; i.e., $\mathbf{A^{-1}A} = \mathbf{AA^{-1}} = \mathbf{I}$. Furthermore, if $\mathbf{AB} = \mathbf{I}$, then $\mathbf{B} = \mathbf{A^{-1}}$; if the inverse exists, it is unique. A *singular matrix* is a matrix which cannot be multiplied by another matrix such that the product is the identity matrix; that is, the inverse does not exist. A matrix is singular if and only if its determinant is zero.

A system of n linear equations in n unknowns may be written as

$$\mathbf{AX = B}$$

where $\mathbf{A}$ is $n \times n$ and $\mathbf{X}$ and $\mathbf{B}$ are $n \times 1$. The formal solution is

$$\mathbf{X = A^{-1}B}$$

The solution can be obtained by matrix multiplication if $\mathbf{A^{-1}}$ is known.

The computation of an inverse is essentially equivalent to the solution of n systems of n equations in n unknowns, because, if $\mathbf{B}$ is one column of the identity, the solution $\mathbf{X}$ is the corresponding column of the inverse. Any method for solving systems of equations may be used to compute an inverse. Two methods are presented:

(a) *Determinants.* An element in the inverse of $\mathbf{A}$ is the cofactor of the element in $\mathbf{A'}$, divided by $|\mathbf{A}|$. This method is convenient if $\mathbf{A}$ is 2×2 or 3×3, but, in general, it is impractical for larger matrices.

(b) *Systematic Elimination.* This method is an extension of the procedure presented in the previous chapter for $n = 2$. It is relatively practical for computations with desk calculators for n up to 5 or 6.

In general, m equations and n unknowns with $m \neq n$, do not have a single unique solution. If $m > n$ (more equations than unknowns), any set of n equations will have a unique solution if the equations are linearly independent. If $n > m$ (more unknowns than equations), values for any set of $n - m$ variables can be arbitrarily specified. The remaining m variables will then have a unique solution if the m equations are linearly independent. In other words, if there are more equations than unknowns, some equations are eliminated; if there are more unknowns than equations the values of certain variables are fixed to obtain a unique solution. Which equations should be discarded, or which variables should be fixed, must be determined from the statement of the particular problem.

CHAPTER EXERCISES

1. Let A be an $n \times n$ matrix with an inverse, C, and let B be a matrix obtained by replacing the kth column of A with another vector, X:

$$b_{ij} = a_{ij} \quad \text{if} \quad j \neq k$$

$$= x_j \quad \text{if} \quad j = k$$

$$B = \begin{bmatrix} a_{11} & \cdots & a_{1,k-1} & x_1 & a_{1,k+1} & \cdots & a_{1n} \\ \cdots & & & & & & \cdots \\ \cdots & & & & & & \cdots \\ a_{nn} & \cdots & a_{njk-1} & x_n & a_{n,k+1} & \cdots & a_{nn} \end{bmatrix}$$

Show that if D is the inverse of B, then

$$d_{ij} = c_{ij} - \left(\frac{y_i}{y_k}\right) c_{kj} \quad \text{if } i \neq k$$

$$= \frac{c_{kj}}{y_k} \quad \text{if } i = k$$

where the vector Y is defined by

$$Y = A^{-1}X$$

[*Hint:* Define a new matrix E which differs from the identity only in that the kth column is replaced by the vector Y, and show that $B = AE$. Then $B^{-1} \equiv D = E^{-1}A^{-1}$ and, since E^{-1} differs from the identity only in the kth column, the d_{ij} are as given.]

2. Use the result to compute the inverse of:

$$\begin{bmatrix} 2 & 0 & 1 \\ 2 & 1 & 1 \\ 3 & 1 & 1 \end{bmatrix} \quad \text{if} \quad \begin{bmatrix} 2 & 0 & 4 \\ 2 & 1 & 0 \\ 3 & 1 & 3 \end{bmatrix}^{-1} = \begin{bmatrix} 1.5 & 2 & -2 \\ -3 & -3 & 4 \\ -0.5 & -1 & 1 \end{bmatrix}$$

Verify the result by multiplication.

CHAPTER FOURTEEN

Examples of the Use of Matrices in Business Problems

Matrices are a convenient system of notation for many problems in business and in other fields. In fact, the statement of many problems would be cumbersome without matrices. This chapter presents two examples of their use in business problems. The first is a statement of the computations required in parts "explosion" in a manufacturing process. The second is a statement of the computations required in cost allocation in production processes involving joint products and by-products.

Both examples may be considered as special cases of a general model known in economics literature as the Input-Output model. A brief introduction to this model is given in Section *C*.

A. MATRICES IN A PRODUCTION PROBLEM

A manufacturer sells five products which will be denoted by *A*, *B*, *C*, *D*, and *E*. *B* and *E* are parts fabricated directly from raw material, and *A*, *C*, and *D* are subassemblies:

> *C* requires 2 *B* parts and 3 *E* parts;
> *A* requires 4 *B* parts and 1 *C* assembly;
> *D* requires 6 *A* assemblies, 2 *C* assemblies, and 1 *E* part.

Suppose that the sales forecast calls for 16 *A* assemblies, 3 *C* assemblies, 5 *D* assemblies, and 6 *E* parts. The manufacturer wants to compute:

The raw material requirements.
The total number of assemblies and parts required.
The total cost of production.

Graphical Solution

The sales forecast can be "exploded" graphically as in Fig. 14.1a. The top line represents one unit of each point or assembly. In the first explosion, each assembly is exploded in its subassemblies and parts; e.g., 1 A is exploded in 4 B and 1 C. Then, in the second explosion, the subassemblies are in turn exploded and so on until only parts are required. For example, a total of 6 B and 3 E are needed to build 1 A, but 2 B and 3 E of these will go into one subassembly C. In the usual terminology:

B and E are called parts.
C is a first-level assembly because it requires only parts.
A is a second-level assembly because it requires a first-level assembly.
D is a third-level assembly because it requires a second-level assembly.

Note that the "levels" shown in Fig. 14.1a are "levels of explosion" and that, for example, to reduce a third-level assembly, D, into its basic parts, three successive explosions are needed. The explosion process is the reverse of the assembly process shown in Fig. 14.1b. The lines and numbers

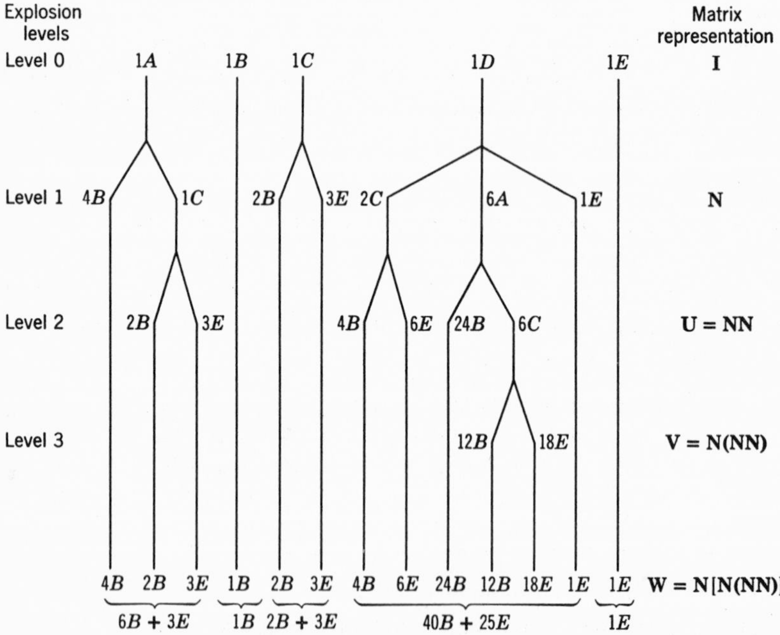

Figure 14.1a Graph of the explosion process.

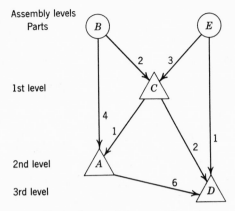

Figure 14.1b   Graph of the assembly process.

beside them in Fig. 14.1b indicate the subassemblies required; e.g., to produce 1 A requires 4 B and 1 C.

To determine the requirements for building more than one assembly, it is necessary to multiply the requirements for one by the appropriate constant. To build 16 A, for example, will require:

$$16(4B + 1C) = 64B + 16C \text{ in basic parts and assemblies; or}$$
$$= 16[4B + (2B + 3E)]$$
$$= 96B + 48E \text{ in basic parts.}$$

If C_{TP} is the total cost of production to meet the original sales forecast,

$$= \text{Assembly cost} + \text{Fabrication cost} + \text{Raw material cost}$$

If C_A is the cost to assemble 1 A from 4 B and 1 C,
C_B is the cost of producing part B from raw material,
K_B is the cost of the raw material required for a B, etc.

The total cost of producing 16 A will be:

$$= [16C_A + 16C_C] + [96C_B + 48C_E] + [96K_B + 48K_E]$$

The same method can be applied to products B, C, D, and E, and all the partial results can be added to give total requirements and total costs. In this example the following will be required to satisfy the sales forecast:

> 302 B and 188 E parts
> 59 C assemblies
> 46 A assemblies
> 5 D assemblies

Solution by Matrix Multiplication

The matrix notation permits a simple statement of the computations required. The accompanying table shows the inputs in parts and assemblies (rows) that go into an output assembly (columns).

Output: Parts and assemblies

		A	B	C	D	E
	A				6	
Input: Parts and assemblies	B	4		2		
	C	1			2	
	D					
	E			3	1	

The columns represent the requirements to assemble each product; for example, the assembly of 1 A requires 4 B and 1 C; B requires no assembly since it is a part. The elements in the row show how many of a given assembly are needed to produce one each of the other assemblies; for example, 4 B are needed to produce 1 A, and 2 B to produce 1 C.

If the empty spaces are filled with zeros, the result is a square array of numbers which may be considered to be a matrix. Let this matrix be denoted by **N**. Then

$$\mathbf{N} = \begin{bmatrix} 0 & 0 & 0 & 6 & 0 \\ 4 & 0 & 2 & 0 & 0 \\ 1 & 0 & 0 & 2 & 0 \\ 0 & 0 & 0 & 0 & 0 \\ 0 & 0 & 3 & 1 & 0 \end{bmatrix}$$

where $\mathbf{N} = (n_{ij})$,

n_{ij} = number of i assemblies required to produce one j assembly,

$i, j = A, B, C, D, E,$

and **N** may be termed the assembly matrix since it states what must be assembled to produce a given assembly. The definition implies that to assemble 1 A, we need to assemble 0 A, 4 B, 1 C, 0 D, and 0 E. The diagonal elements by convention are all zeros. (This could be interpreted as stating that to assemble an A there is nothing to assemble if an A is available already assembled.)

The assembly matrix N represents the first explosion process (level 1) shown in Fig. 14.1a and, in fact, is merely the requirements to assemble one of each assembly stated in a different form. The next step in developing a formula for the explosion process is to represent the second explosion level by a matrix expression.

Consider, for example, the question of how many B's will be required at level 2 to obtain 1 D at level 0. B's will be required to produce A's which go into a D, and B's are also required to produce C's which go into a D. For this particular problem the number required can be computed as follows:

(number of B's required for 1 A)(number of A's required for a D)

$+$ (number of B's required for 1 C)(number of C's required for 1 D)

$= (4)(6) + (2)(2) = 28$

The formula could be stated more generally as:

(number of B's required for 1 A)(number of A's required for 1 D)

$+$ (number of B's required for 1 B)(number of B's required for 1 D)

$+$ (number of B's required for 1 C)(number of C's required for 1 D)

$+$ (number of B's required for 1 D)(number of D's required for 1 D)

$+$ (number of B's required for 1 E)(number of E's required for 1 D)

since (number of y's required for a z) is zero if a z requires no y's.

The formula can be expressed more compactly as

$$u_{B,D} = \sum_{K=A}^{E} n_{BK} n_{KD}, \qquad K = A, B, C, D, E \qquad (1)$$

since n_{BK} is defined as the number of B's required to assemble 1 K. This formula will be recognized immediately as the formula for an element in the product of two matrices. Therefore, u_{ij} gives the number of i assemblies needed at level 2 to produce one j at level 0; i.e.,

$$U = NN =
\begin{bmatrix}
0 & 0 & 0 & 6 & 0 \\
4 & 0 & 2 & 0 & 0 \\
1 & 0 & 0 & 2 & 0 \\
0 & 0 & 0 & 0 & 0 \\
0 & 0 & 3 & 1 & 0
\end{bmatrix}
\begin{bmatrix}
0 & 0 & 0 & 6 & 0 \\
4 & 0 & 2 & 0 & 0 \\
1 & 0 & 0 & 2 & 0 \\
0 & 0 & 0 & 0 & 0 \\
0 & 0 & 3 & 1 & 0
\end{bmatrix}
=
\begin{bmatrix}
0 & 0 & 0 & 0 & 0 \\
2 & 0 & 0 & 28 & 0 \\
0 & 0 & 0 & 6 & 0 \\
0 & 0 & 0 & 0 & 0 \\
3 & 0 & 0 & 6 & 0
\end{bmatrix}$$

By referring to Fig. 14.1a, it can be verified that to produce an A eventually (i.e., at level 0) requires 2 B's and 3 E's at level 2. Furthermore, the A row now consists entirely of zeros, indicating that the A's needed have been completely exploded.

By following the argument we can easily verify that v_{ij} gives the number of i assemblies needed at level 3 to produce one j assembly at level 0, where

$$V = NU = \begin{bmatrix} 0 & 0 & 0 & 6 & 0 \\ 4 & 0 & 2 & 0 & 0 \\ 1 & 0 & 0 & 2 & 0 \\ 0 & 0 & 0 & 0 & 0 \\ 0 & 0 & 3 & 1 & 0 \end{bmatrix} \begin{bmatrix} 0 & 0 & 0 & 0 & 0 \\ 2 & 0 & 0 & 28 & 0 \\ 0 & 0 & 0 & 6 & 0 \\ 0 & 0 & 0 & 0 & 0 \\ 3 & 0 & 0 & 6 & 0 \end{bmatrix}$$

$$= \begin{bmatrix} 0 & 0 & 0 & 0 & 0 \\ 0 & 0 & 0 & 12 & 0 \\ 0 & 0 & 0 & 0 & 0 \\ 0 & 0 & 0 & 0 & 0 \\ 0 & 0 & 0 & 18 & 0 \end{bmatrix}$$

Again, it may be verified by inspection that 12 B's and 18 E's are required at this level to produce 1 D eventually, and that the C assemblies have been exploded.

The next step in the process leads to a matrix in which all elements are zero,

$$W = NV = \begin{bmatrix} 0 & 0 & 0 & 6 & 0 \\ 4 & 0 & 2 & 0 & 0 \\ 1 & 0 & 0 & 2 & 0 \\ 0 & 0 & 0 & 0 & 0 \\ 0 & 0 & 3 & 1 & 0 \end{bmatrix} \begin{bmatrix} 0 & 0 & 0 & 0 & 0 \\ 0 & 0 & 0 & 12 & 0 \\ 0 & 0 & 0 & 0 & 0 \\ 0 & 0 & 0 & 0 & 0 \\ 0 & 0 & 0 & 18 & 0 \end{bmatrix}$$

$$= \begin{bmatrix} 0 & 0 & 0 & 0 & 0 \\ 0 & 0 & 0 & 0 & 0 \\ 0 & 0 & 0 & 0 & 0 \\ 0 & 0 & 0 & 0 & 0 \\ 0 & 0 & 0 & 0 & 0 \end{bmatrix}$$

This shows that no further explosion is required.

Each successive explosion is represented by a higher power of the matrix; level 1 by N, level 2 by NN ($\equiv N^2$), level 3 by N^3, etc. Therefore, if the graph of the assembly process (Fig. 14.1*b* in this example) has n levels, N^n will be the null matrix.

A total requirement matrix, T, is the sum of the requirements at each level of explosion. For this problem then,

$$T = I + N + U + V = I + N + N(N) + N(NN) \tag{2}$$

$$T = \begin{bmatrix} 1 & 0 & 0 & 0 & 0 \\ 0 & 1 & 0 & 0 & 0 \\ 0 & 0 & 1 & 0 & 0 \\ 0 & 0 & 0 & 1 & 0 \\ 0 & 0 & 0 & 0 & 1 \end{bmatrix} + \begin{bmatrix} 0 & 0 & 0 & 6 & 0 \\ 4 & 0 & 2 & 0 & 0 \\ 1 & 0 & 0 & 2 & 0 \\ 0 & 0 & 0 & 0 & 0 \\ 0 & 0 & 3 & 1 & 0 \end{bmatrix}$$

$$+ \begin{bmatrix} 0 & 0 & 0 & 0 & 0 \\ 2 & 0 & 0 & 28 & 0 \\ 0 & 0 & 0 & 6 & 0 \\ 0 & 0 & 0 & 0 & 0 \\ 3 & 0 & 0 & 6 & 0 \end{bmatrix} + \begin{bmatrix} 0 & 0 & 0 & 0 & 0 \\ 0 & 0 & 0 & 12 & 0 \\ 0 & 0 & 0 & 0 & 0 \\ 0 & 0 & 0 & 0 & 0 \\ 0 & 0 & 0 & 18 & 0 \end{bmatrix}$$

$$= \begin{bmatrix} 1 & 0 & 0 & 6 & 0 \\ 6 & 1 & 2 & 40 & 0 \\ 1 & 0 & 1 & 8 & 0 \\ 0 & 0 & 0 & 1 & 0 \\ 3 & 0 & 3 & 25 & 1 \end{bmatrix}$$

where t_{ij} is the number of i assemblies that must be assembled to have eventually one j assembly.

An element, t_{ij} in the total requirements matrix, T, gives the *total* number of i assemblies or parts that have to be assembled or fabricated in order to produce one j assembly. The matrix operations in (2) are therefore equivalent to the graphical explosion shown in Fig. 14.1*a*; the values of t_{ij} can be verified directly by comparison with Fig. 14.1*a*. By definition $t_{ii} = 1$ because an i assembly must be assembled to "produce" one i assembly.

Production Requirements and Costs

The sales forecast, as stated previously, calls for 16 A, 0 B, 3 C, 5 D, and 6 E. It can be represented by the vector **S** where

$$\mathbf{S} = \begin{bmatrix} 16 \\ 0 \\ 3 \\ 5 \\ 6 \end{bmatrix}$$

and the total production requirement will be given by the product

$$\mathbf{X} = \mathbf{TS} = \begin{bmatrix} 1 & 0 & 0 & 6 & 0 \\ 6 & 1 & 2 & 40 & 0 \\ 1 & 0 & 1 & 8 & 0 \\ 0 & 0 & 0 & 1 & 0 \\ 3 & 0 & 3 & 25 & 1 \end{bmatrix} \begin{bmatrix} 16 \\ 0 \\ 3 \\ 5 \\ 6 \end{bmatrix} = \begin{bmatrix} 46 \\ 302 \\ 59 \\ 5 \\ 188 \end{bmatrix}$$

which states that in order to meet the forecast, 46 A, 302 B, 59 C, 5 D, and 188 E will have to be produced and assembled.

To determine the cost of production, let

C_A denote the cost of assembling 1 A from B and already-assembled C's

C_B denote the cost of producing 1 B from raw material, etc.

and define the assembly cost vector, **C**, to be

$$\mathbf{C} = [C_A \ C_B \ C_C \ C_D \ C_E]$$

Using equation (2), the total cost of fabricating and assembling parts and subassemblies to meet the sales forecast will be given by:

$$C_{TA} = \mathbf{CX} = \mathbf{C(TS)} = \mathbf{CS} + \mathbf{CNS} + \mathbf{CN(NS)} + \mathbf{CN[N(NS)]} \quad (3)$$

that is, the sum of the cost of assembly at each level of explosion.

The total production cost is obtained by adding the cost of raw material:

$$C_{RM} = 302K_B + 188K_E$$

where K_B is the cost of raw material for 1 B

K_E is the cost of raw material for 1 E

The total cost of production becomes

$$C_{TP} = C_{TA} + C_{RM}$$

Solution by Matrix Inversion

From the previous section it is clear that the total production requirement and the total cost of production can be computed once the total
requirements matrix **T** is determined. One approach to compute **T** was
shown above. However, it can also be obtained by a different approach.
Consider the two matrices **N** and **T**:

$$\mathbf{N} = \begin{bmatrix} 0 & 0 & 0 & 6 & 0 \\ 4 & 0 & 2 & 0 & 0 \\ 1 & 0 & 0 & 2 & 0 \\ 0 & 0 & 0 & 0 & 0 \\ 0 & 0 & 3 & 1 & 0 \end{bmatrix} \qquad \mathbf{T} = \begin{bmatrix} 1 & 0 & 0 & 6 & 0 \\ 6 & 1 & 2 & 40 & 0 \\ 1 & 0 & 1 & 8 & 0 \\ 0 & 0 & 0 & 1 & 0 \\ 3 & 0 & 3 & 25 & 1 \end{bmatrix}$$

and, for example, the element t_{BD}. This is the number of assemblies B
needed to assemble $1D$. It can also be interpreted as

(number of B's required for 1 A)(the *total number* of A's in 1 D)

+ (number of B's required for 1 B)(the *total number* of B's in 1 D)

+ (number of B's required for 1 C)(the *total number* of C's in 1 D)

+ (number of B's required for 1 D)(the *total number* of D's in 1 D)

+ (number of B's required for 1 E)(the *total number* of E's in 1 D)

In particular,

$$t_{B,D} = (4)(6) + (0)(40) + (2)(8) + (0)(1) + (0)(25) = 40$$

The formula may be expressed more compactly as

$$t_{ij} = \sum_{k=A}^{E} n_{ik} t_{kj} \qquad i, j, k = A, B, C, D, E$$

which is the formula for the product **NT**. However, the diagonal elements
of **NT** are zero, for example.

$$\sum_{k=A}^{E} n_{Ak} t_{kA} = (0)(1) + (0)(6) + (0)(1) + (6)(0) + (0)(3) = 0,$$

By definition $t_{AA} = 1$ and, therefore, the diagonal elements must be
added and the formula becomes:

$$\mathbf{T} = \mathbf{NT} + \mathbf{I}$$

The diagonal elements of **T** represent the zero level, i.e., the finished product, which is not taken into account in matrix **N**. The product **NT** will give a zero in a diagonal element because the finished product is not assembled from itself. **T** contains ones in the diagonal element because the finished products are part of the total requirement.

From the simple relation $\mathbf{T} = \mathbf{NT} + \mathbf{I}$, a method for calculating **T** when **N** is given can be derived:

$$\mathbf{T} - \mathbf{NT} = \mathbf{I}, \quad \mathbf{IT} - \mathbf{NT} = \mathbf{I}, \quad (\mathbf{I} - \mathbf{N})\mathbf{T} = \mathbf{I},$$

$$(\mathbf{I} - \mathbf{N})^{-1}(\mathbf{I} - \mathbf{N})\mathbf{T} = (\mathbf{I} - \mathbf{N})^{-1}\mathbf{I}$$

and therefore $\mathbf{T} = (\mathbf{I} - \mathbf{N})^{-1}$, provided $(\mathbf{I} - \mathbf{N})^{-1}$ exists.

Generalization

The assemblies are denoted by A_1, A_2, ..., A_n, and the assembly matrix **N** will be a square matrix with n rows and n columns, each element a_{ij} being the number of subassemblies A_i needed to produce one assembly A_j.

The total requirement matrix, T, can be obtained as

$$\mathbf{T} = (\mathbf{I} - \mathbf{N})^{-1}$$

or as

$$\mathbf{T} = \mathbf{I} + \mathbf{N} + \mathbf{NN} + \mathbf{N}(\mathbf{NN}) + \mathbf{N}[\mathbf{N}(\mathbf{NN})] + \cdots$$

where the last matrix of this sum is obtained when its product by **N** is a matrix whose elements are all zeros.

The sales forecast is denoted by the vector **S** which has n rows. The ith element of this vector is the forecast of the number of A_i to be sold.

$$\mathbf{S} = \begin{bmatrix} S_1 \\ S_2 \\ \cdot \\ \cdot \\ \cdot \\ S_n \end{bmatrix}$$

The total number of assemblies, subassemblies and parts is given by the matrix **X**, where

$$\mathbf{X} = \mathbf{TS}$$

If C_i is the cost of assembling assembly A_i from already-assembled subassemblies, an assembly cost vector $\mathbf{C}_A$ can be defined as:

$$\mathbf{C} = [C_1 \, C_2 \ldots C_n]$$

where C_i is the cost of fabricating A_i if A_i is a part

C_i is the cost of assembling A_i if A_i is an assembly,

and the total cost of assembly will be:

$$C_{TA} = \mathbf{CX}$$

If K_i is the cost of raw material included in the basic part A_i, a raw material cost vector $\mathbf{K}_{RM}$ can be defined:

$$\mathbf{K}_{RM} = [K_1 \, K_2 \ldots K_n]$$

where $K_i = 0$ if A_i is not a basic part

$K_i \neq 0$ if A_i is a part fabricated from raw material

Then the total cost of raw material will be:

$$C_{RM} = \mathbf{K}_{RM}\mathbf{X}$$

and the total cost of production will be:

$$C_{TP} = C_{TA} + C_{RM} = [\mathbf{C} + \mathbf{K}_{RM}]\mathbf{X}$$

EXERCISES

1. Verify with the numerical values of the example that $\mathbf{NT} + \mathbf{I} = \mathbf{T}$ and that $\mathbf{T} = (\mathbf{I} - \mathbf{N})^{-1}$.

2. What simplifications can be made in the computation of $\mathbf{T}$ and $\mathbf{C}_{TP}$ if the rows and columns of $\mathbf{N}$ are rearranged so that the parts appear last, then the first-order assemblies next to last, then the second-order assemblies, etc. (*Hint:* Compare the matrix $\mathbf{I} - \mathbf{N}$ in the example above with that given in Exercise 2, p. 378).

3. A manufacturer produces 7 products, $A_1, A_2, \ldots, A_7$; these products are made up as follows:

A_1 requires 3 A_2, 2 A_6 and 1 A_3
A_2 requires only raw material
A_3 requires 1 A_7 and 2 A_6
A_4 requires 3 A_6, 1 A_2 and 3 A_3
A_5 requires 1 A_3 and 1 A_6
A_6 requires 1 A_2 and 3 A_7
A_7 requires only raw material

Compute the requirement matrix and use it to *compute* the requirements to meet a sales forecast which calls for:

$$15A_1, 1A_2, 0A_3, 6A_4, 1A_5, 7A_6, 0A_7$$

Verify your results by a graphical explosion and also verify that the assembly matrix N and the requirements matrix T satisfy the relation

$$T = (I - N)^{-1}$$

4. A matrix A which has the property that A^n ($\equiv A \cdot A \cdots A$) for some n is the zero matrix is said to be nil potent. What characteristics must a production process possess to ensure that its assembly matrix be nil potent?

5. Suppose that the sales forecast is given for the next t periods in the form of an $n \times t$ matrix. The first column is the sales forecast L periods from now, the second for $L + 1$ periods from now, ..., and the last $L + t$ periods from now. L is the lead time, the number of periods required to produce the final assemblies from parts. Derive the formula for the number of assemblies of each type to be assembled each period, and the work load for each period. Make simplifying assumptions such as (a) initial inventory is zero, (b) no setup time is required, etc.

6. Indicate how formulas in Exercise 5 could be extended to the case where there is an initial inventory and where there are setup costs, and how results analogous to the optimum ordering size formula developed in Chapter 4 could be used to minimize production costs.

B. REQUIREMENTS AND COST ALLOCATION IN JOINT PRODUCTION

The Problem

In the example in the previous section total requirements were computed to meet the sales forecast for a production process which consisted of a sequence of fabrication and assembly operations. Each part and assembly could be produced independently of the others. More complex problems arise in production processes known as joint production where one product cannot be obtained without obtaining at the same time a certain amount of one or more other products. Frequently the process will yield some outputs known as by-products which are economically unimportant as far as the process is concerned. In many cases of joint production the proportion of inputs to, and the resulting proportion of outputs from, any process are fixed. If these proportions of different products from each process are controllable, the problem becomes one of optimizing the product mix. This requires the programming techniques that will be discussed in the next chapter.

A classic example of joint production is the use of cattle in the meat

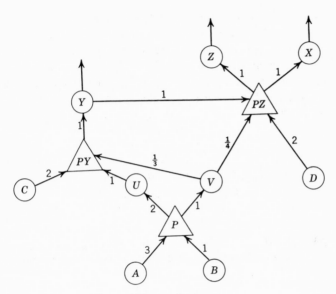

Figure 14.2 Production system.

packing business for two products: hides and beef. For all practical purposes, the proportion of hides to beef is not under the control of the rancher. Joint production also occurs in other industries and is particularly common in the chemical and oil industries.

Suppose, for example, a firm has the production system shown in Fig. 14.2. The final products or outputs X, Y, and Z are produced by three processes, PY, PZ, and P, from the four inputs, A, B, C, and D. Product X is considered a by-product. There are two intermediary products, U and V. Part of V is used to produce Z and X and part to produce Y. The numbers beside the arrows indicate the amounts of output which go to the next process. If the input to P is 1 unit of B and 3 units of A, then the output will be 2 units of U and 1 unit of V.

A sales forecast giving the demand for each of the primary outputs Y and Z is given and the cost per unit of each of the inputs is known. Management wishes (*a*) to determine the input requirements to satisfy the sales forecast and (*b*) to allocate the costs of the inputs to the outputs.

Fictitious Processes

Figure 14.2 is similar to Fig. 14.1*b*; the inputs A, B, C, and D in Fig. 14.2 correspond to the parts B and E in Fig. 14.1*b*, and the processes P,

PY, and *PZ* correspond to the assembly operations *C*, *A*, and *D*. It is therefore reasonable to try to apply the procedures used in Section A here. A comparison shows that there is one very important difference between Fig. 14.1*b* and Fig. 14.2. In Fig. 14.1*b* each process has only a single output and hence the process could be identified by its output, whereas in Fig. 14.2, a process may have more than one output. The equations governing the processes in Fig. 14.1*b* are:

Process	Equation
C	$C = 2B + 3E$
A	$A = C + 4B$
D	$D = 6A + 2C + E$

The outputs are written at the left of the equal signs and the inputs on the right. Analogous equations governing the processes in Fig. 14.2 are:

Process	Equation
P	$2U + V = 3A + B$
PY	$Y = 2C + U + \frac{1}{3}V$
PZ	$Z + X = Y + \frac{1}{4}V + 2D$

Since the technique developed in Section *A* depended on each process having a single output, it cannot be applied to this problem unless the production system can be represented by processes having single outputs. It will now be shown that this can be done by introducing the concept of fictitious products.

Suppose the process *P* is replaced by two processes: *PU* which produces *U* only, and *PV* which produces *V* only. The equation for process *PU* can be obtained from that for *P*. The equation for *P* was

$$2U + V = 3A + B$$

If the process *PU* is to produce *U* only, *V* must be considered an input and moved to the input side; then

$$2U = 3A + B - V$$

This can also be written as

$$2U = 2A + A + B - V \quad \text{or}$$
$$= 2A - F$$

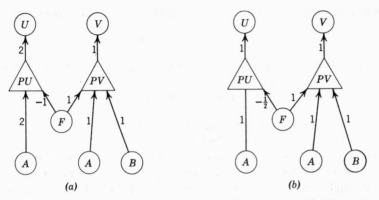

(a)   *(b)*

Figure 14.3 Schematic of two production processes equivalent to *P* in Figure 14.2.

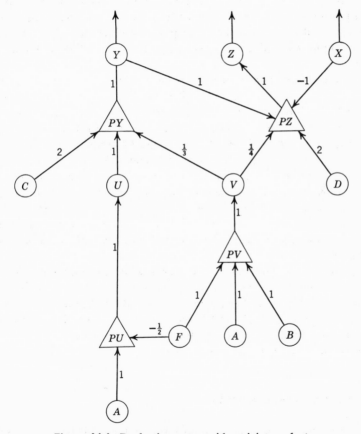

Figure 14.4 Production system without joint products.

where F is a fictitious product; its production must satisfy the equation:

$$-F = A + B - V$$

The process PV produces V only. Hence, moving V to the output and F to the input side gives

$$V = A + B + F$$

as the equation governing the fictitious process PV. The two processes PU and PV are shown in Fig. 14.3.

The two versions shown in Fig. 14.3 are equivalent since a process is unchanged if all the numbers on arrows going into and out of one process are multiplied by a constant. The schematic (b) has F appearing as an input to PU with a negative sign. Physically, of course, an input cannot be negative, but the concept of negative inputs can be used for computational purposes. Thus the two processes in (b) are physically equivalent to process P, if and only if the net required production of F is zero; the negative input required to PU must be equal to the positive input required by PV.

The equivalence of the process P in Fig. 14.2 and the processes in Fig. 14.3 may be verified by noting that if a sales forecast is compatible with Fig. 14.2, it will result in zero balance for F, the fictitious by-product, in Fig. 14.3. A sales forecast is compatible with 14.2 if it requires U and V in the ratio which P produces. For example, 200 units of U and 100 units of V can be produced, but 200 units of U and 150 units of V cannot; if 150 units of V are produced, then 300 units of U will be obtained. The table at top of p. 403 shows the two forecasts, amounts of input required, and the outputs. The first column under the second forecast shows an excess of -50 for F. The second column shows that if net requirements for F are set equal to zero, 100 units of U in excess of the forecast will be produced.

It is readily apparent from the manner in which the equation governing PU was derived that the processes PU and PV are not unique. The implication will be considered below under cost allocation.

Using the processes PU and PV, the production system in Fig. 14.2 can be replaced by the one shown in Fig. 14.4. Since X is a by-product, it can be treated as a negative input to PZ.

Production Requirements

The problem is now stated in a form that is amenable to the techniques developed in Section A. The total requirements for a given sales forecast

FORECAST

		1	2	
	U	200	200	
	V	100	150	
P	Input A	300	450	
	Input B	100	150	
	Output U	200	300	
	Output V	100	150	
PU	Input A	200	200	300
	Input F	-100	-100	-150
	Output U	200	200	300
PV	Input A	100	150	150
	Input B	100	150	150
	Input F	100	150	150
	Output V	100	150	150
	Excess F	0	-50	0
	Excess U	0	0	100

can be computed by arranging the information in the form of an input output table, defining the process matrix N, computing the total requirement matrix T from it, and multiplying the sales forecast vector by T.

The accompanying table summarizes the information contained in Fig. 14.4. The first column states that there is a process, PY, which requires 1 unit of U, $\frac{1}{3}$ unit of V, and 2 units of C, etc., for each unit of

				Process	
Outputs		Y	Z	U	V
Inputs:	Product	PY	PZ	PU	PV
Y			1		
Z					
U		1			
V		$\frac{1}{3}$	$\frac{1}{4}$		
D			2		
C		2			
A				1	1
B					1
X			-1		
F				$-\frac{1}{2}$	1

Y produced. Since each process produces one output and each output is produced by a single process, the columns of the table represent the processes unambiguously.

The information from this array can be presented in the form of a square matrix, $\mathbf{N}$, called the process matrix, by adding one column for each input and placing zeros in the empty spaces.

Outputs	Y	Z	U	V	D	C	A	B	X	F
Inputs										
Y	0	1	0	0	0	0	0	0	0	0
Z	0	0	0	0	0	0	0	0	0	0
U	1	0	0	0	0	0	0	0	0	0
V	$\frac{1}{3}$	$\frac{1}{4}$	0	0	0	0	0	0	0	0
$\mathbf{N} = D$	0	2	0	0	0	0	0	0	0	0
C	2	0	0	0	0	0	0	0	0	0
A	0	0	1	1	0	0	0	0	0	0
B	0	0	0	1	0	0	0	0	0	0
X	0	−1	0	0	0	0	0	0	0	0
F	0	0	$-\frac{1}{2}$	1	0	0	0	0	0	0

The elements of the last six columns are all zero because the products A, B, etc., are all inputs; hence, none will be produced. These products correspond to the parts B and E in the example in Section A.

The total requirement matrix is $\mathbf{T} = (t_{ij})$ where t_{ij} = total number of units of product i needed to produce eventually one unit of product j. By analogy with the assembly matrix in Section A, it follows that $\mathbf{T}$ can be computed by the formula:

$$\mathbf{T} = \mathbf{I} + \mathbf{N} + \mathbf{NN} + \mathbf{N(NN)} \cdots$$

$$= \mathbf{I} + \mathbf{N} + \mathbf{N}^2 + \mathbf{N}^3 + \cdots$$

provided that some power of $\mathbf{N}$ is the null matrix.

$\mathbf{T}$ can also be computed as

$$\mathbf{T} = (\mathbf{I} - \mathbf{N})^{-1}$$

provided $|\mathbf{I} - \mathbf{N}| \neq 0$.

A straightforward calculation in this case shows that

Outputs	Y	Z	U	V	D	C	A	B	X	F
Inputs										
Y	1	1	0	0	0	0	0	0	0	0
Z	0	1	0	0	0	0	0	0	0	0
U	1	1	1	0	0	0	0	0	0	0
V	$\frac{1}{3}$	$\frac{7}{12}$	0	1	0	0	0	0	0	0
T = D	0	2	0	0	1	0	0	0	0	0
C	2	2	0	0	0	1	0	0	0	0
A	$\frac{4}{3}$	$\frac{19}{12}$	1	1	0	0	1	0	0	0
B	$\frac{1}{3}$	$\frac{7}{12}$	0	1	0	0	0	1	0	0
X	0	−1	0	0	0	0	0	0	1	0
F	$-\frac{1}{6}$	$\frac{1}{12}$	$-\frac{1}{2}$	1	0	0	0	0	0	1

The procedure used in Section A will lead to the requirements needed to meet any given sales forecast exactly. In this case there is the constraint that $F = 0$ which was not present in Section A. Therefore, the procedure must be modified to take account of the constraints which are inherent in the process.

Suppose the sales forecast, **S**, in the example is given by:

$$
S = \begin{bmatrix}
100 \\
50 \\
0 \\
0 \\
0 \\
0 \\
0 \\
0 \\
0 \\
0
\end{bmatrix}
$$

The elements of the vector $\mathbf{R} = \mathbf{TS}$ will give the requirements of each input to meet this sales forecast.

$$\mathbf{R} = \begin{array}{c} Y \\ Z \\ U \\ V \\ D \\ C \\ A \\ B \\ X \\ F \end{array} \begin{bmatrix} 150 \\ 50 \\ 150 \\ 62.5 \\ 100 \\ 300 \\ 212.5 \\ 62.5 \\ -50 \\ -12.5 \end{bmatrix}$$

To produce 100 units of Y and 50 units of Z will require 100, 300, 212.5, and 62.5 units of D, C, A, and B, respectively. As intermediate products, 150 units of U and 62.5 units of V will be produced, and -50 units of the by-product X are required as input, i.e., 50 units, will be produced. Also -12.5 units of the fictitious product, F, are produced.

Since the requirements for F must be zero; the sales forecast is not compatible with the physical process.

By definition, the process is balanced in the matrix $\mathbf{T}$ because $\mathbf{T}$ describes exactly what is required to produce one unit of each of the outputs. An imbalance occurs when the sales forecast is inconsistent with the constraints of the process. The way in which the production is modified to correct the imbalance depends on whether or not the sales forecast is regarded as a minimum requirement.

Suppose the sales forecast calls for y units of Y and z units of Z. The matrix multiplication $\mathbf{TS}$ will then yield

$$-\tfrac{1}{6}y + \tfrac{1}{12}z$$

as the production of F. Since this must be zero,

$$-\tfrac{1}{6}y + \tfrac{1}{12}z = 0$$
$$z = 2y$$

A forecast must call for production of half as much Y as Z to be compatible with the physical process.

Cost Allocation

The procedure used in Section A to allocate the costs of the inputs to the outputs was to define a unit cost vector and then multiply the vector by **T**. Let the unit cost of the basic inputs be given by the column vector $\mathbf{C}_I$ (I for input) with ten components:

$$Y \quad Z \quad U \quad V \quad D \quad C \quad A \quad B \quad X \quad F$$
$$\mathbf{C}_I' = [0 \quad 0 \quad 0 \quad 0 \quad c_D \quad c_E \quad c_A \quad c_B \quad c_X \quad 0]$$

The cost of the outputs Y and Z, the intermediary products U and V, and the fictitious by-product, F, are zero. The cost of the by-product c_X, is the market price of this product. Since by-products are considered as negative inputs, the minus sign in the **N** matrix corresponds to crediting this cost to the main output, Z. If the disposal of the by-product involves a cost, c_X would be negative.

The total cost of the outputs is given by the column vector $\mathbf{C}_0'$

$$\mathbf{C}_0' = \mathbf{C}_I' \mathbf{T}$$

If, for example,

$$\mathbf{C}_I' = [0 \quad 0 \quad 0 \quad 0 \quad 2 \quad 3.5 \quad 5 \quad 2 \quad 2.5 \quad 0]$$

then

$$\mathbf{C}_0' = [14\tfrac{1}{3} \quad 34\tfrac{7}{12} \quad 5 \quad 7 \quad 2 \quad 3.5 \quad 5 \quad 2 \quad 2.5 \quad 0]$$

The cost per unit is $14\tfrac{1}{3}$ for Y and $34\tfrac{7}{12}$ for Z.

It is important to note that allocation of costs depends on the particular fictitious process that was introduced.

In the process shown in Fig. 14.5 the physical flow is governed by the equation

$$2U + 1V = 3A + 1B$$

which states that (in whatever units the products are being measured) 3 units of A and 1 unit of B must be used as inputs to produce 2 units of U and 1 unit of V. This description does not contain any information about the allocation of the costs of the inputs to the cost of the outputs. In fact the rule for the allocation has not been stated. *Various rules could be used:* e.g.,

Rule 1: The cost of 2 units of A is to be charged to the 2 units of U and the cost of 1 unit of A and 1 unit of B to V.

Rule 2: The costs are to be allocated on the basis of units of output; in this case one-third of the cost of the inputs would be charged to V and two-thirds to U.

Once a rule has been specified, the fictitious process can be defined.

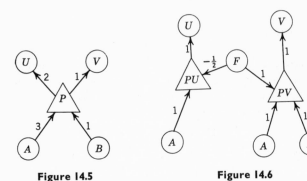

Figure 14.5   Figure 14.6

For Rule I. The equation for the process P, can be rewritten as:

$$2U = 2A + A + B - V$$

$$2U = A - F$$

$$U = A - \tfrac{1}{2}F$$

then

$$-F = A + B - V$$

or

$$V = A + B - F$$

The system shown in Fig. 14.6 is equivalent to the process in Fig. 14.5 and it allocates costs according to Rule 1. For every 3 units of A and 1 unit of B as input, 1 unit of V and 2 units of U will be produced. If the input is in the ratio of 3 units of A to 1 unit of B, the process will be balanced; i.e., PV will produce as much F as PU requires. If the system is balanced, the cost of 1 unit of V is the cost of 1 unit of A plus the cost of 1 unit of B, and the cost of 1 unit of U is the cost of 1 unit of A as required by Rule I. This is, in fact, the rule used to compute the **T** matrix developed above. These are the costs shown in $\mathbf{C}_0$.

For Rule 2. The equation for the process P can also be rewritten as:

$$V = A + \tfrac{1}{3}B + 2A + \tfrac{2}{3}B - U$$

$$V = A + \tfrac{1}{3}B + F$$

$$F = 2A + \tfrac{2}{3}B - 2U$$

$$U = A + \tfrac{1}{3}B - \tfrac{1}{2}F$$

The system shown in Fig. 14.7 is also equivalent to the process in Fig. 14.5, but it allocates costs as required by Rule 2.

Joint production involves processes which produce two or more outputs in fixed proportions. The analysis presented here has shown that such a production system can be represented by another system in which each process produces a single output. Each joint process is replaced by one or more fictitious processes and some ficititious products are produced. Once this is done, the system can be completely described by an input-output matrix, **N**. The requirements, **R**, to meet any sales forecast can be computed as

$$R = TS$$

where **T** is the total requirements matrix $T = (I - N)^{-1}$. In general **R** will call for production of one or more fictitious products; this indicates that the sales forecase is not compatible with the fixed proportions in which outputs are produced. The system is "balanced in the **T** matrix and from it the production to meet the sales forecast as a minimum can be computed.

The representation of the actual process by a set of fictitious processes is not unique; this fact can be used to select the fictitious processes in a manner that allocates costs according to some *previously stated* rule. The representation of a process by the matrix N does not state what rule should be used. It merely provides a systematic procedure for computing the cost allocations once the rule is given. Cost allocation computation for complex systems can be reduced to a routine procedure or programmed for a computer.

The representation of the system by the **T** matrix embodies the allocation rule that has been selected. In itself the **T** matrix does not state what rule should be used and in fact no representation can do this. The selection of the rule must be based on the objectives of the cost allocation system. Once these objectives are specified, the representation can be used to determine whether a particular **T** matrix (or, equivalently, the allocation rule on which it is based) will accomplish the objectives.

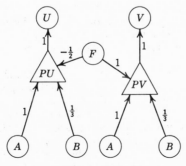

Figure 14.7

EXERCISES

1. The N and T matrices contain a large number of zeros. Show that by partitioning the N matrix in the following form

$$
N = \begin{bmatrix}
0 & 1 & 0 & 0 & 0 & 0 & 0 & 0 & 0 & 0 \\
0 & 0 & 0 & 0 & 0 & 0 & 0 & 0 & 0 & 0 \\
1 & 0 & 0 & 0 & 0 & 0 & 0 & 0 & 0 & 0 \\
\frac{1}{3} & \frac{1}{4} & 0 & 0 & 0 & 0 & 0 & 0 & 0 & 0 \\
0 & 2 & 0 & 0 & 0 & 0 & 0 & 0 & 0 & 0 \\
2 & 0 & 0 & 0 & 0 & 0 & 0 & 0 & 0 & 0 \\
0 & 0 & 1 & 1 & 0 & 0 & 0 & 0 & 0 & 0 \\
0 & 0 & 0 & 1 & 0 & 0 & 0 & 0 & 0 & 0 \\
0 & -1 & 0 & 0 & 0 & 0 & 0 & 0 & 0 & 0 \\
0 & 0 & -\frac{1}{2} & 1 & 0 & 0 & 0 & 0 & 0 & 0
\end{bmatrix}
$$

where
$$
I - N = \begin{bmatrix} I - N^u & -M^u \\ -N^L & I - M^L \end{bmatrix}
$$

The T matrix can be defined as

$$
T = \begin{bmatrix} T^U & V^U \\ T^L & V^L \end{bmatrix}
$$

where the partitioning is analogous to that of the N matrix, and

$$
T^U = (I - N^U)^{-1} \qquad V^U = O
$$
$$
T^L = N^L T^U \qquad V^L = I
$$

Show that if S is defined in the example as a vector with a number of rows equal to the number of output products, then

$$
R = \begin{bmatrix} T^U \\ T^L \end{bmatrix} [S]
$$

2. Young, Inc., has perfected a process for producing two chemical compounds, *YIP* and *ZIP*, from three raw materials, *A*, *B*, and *C*. The three raw materials are mixed, blended, and cooked in a single process in the following proportion by weight:

A   3 parts; cost of A is $2 per pound
B   5 parts; cost of B is $0.025 per pound
C   2 parts; cost of C is $2 per pound

During the process, 40% of the original mixture by weight is lost. The remainder consists of 4 parts of *YIP* by weight, and 2 parts of pre-*ZIP* by weight. The pre-*ZIP* must undergo further processing by electrolysis which yields 75% pure *ZIP* by weight and 25% of an unmarketable by-product. The firm wishes to produce 80,000 pounds of *YIP* and 30,000 pounds of *ZIP*.

(*a*) Without using the procedure discussed in this section, compute the amount of each input required and compute the total cost of the material. Determine the cost per pound of YIP and ZIP due to the cost of the input material. Verify that total costs of the outputs equal the total costs of the inputs.

(*b*) Repeat (a) using the procedure discussed in this section and using the allocation rule implied by (a).

(*c*) Do your answers to (a) and (b) agree? If not, explain why.

(*d*) The firm wishes to produce x pounds of YIP and y pounds of ZIP where x and y may be any positive numbers. Develop the general solution following (a) above, then (b) above.

3. In production processes, such as those discussed in this section, there may be operating costs associated with each process. Develop a general procedure for allocating these operating costs to the final outputs.

C. THE INPUT-OUTPUT MODEL

Economists frequently find it convenient to think of a manufacturing firm as a "black box" whose input is raw materials of various kinds and whose output is finished goods. In the same way, all the firms that manufacture the same kind of goods, say, steel, automobiles, etc., can be considered as an industry or a "black box" group which takes similar kinds of inputs and transforms them into finished goods. The systematic recording of inputs used by all industries in the economy, expressed in mathematical form, is called "input-output analysis" in economics.

Suppose an economy is divided into n industries and each industry is assumed to produce exactly one kind of output. In general, industries are interconnected in the sense that, in order to operate, each one must use a certain amount of some of the others' products. Labor may be considered one of the industries and other industries must use some of its output in their manufacturing processes.

Table 14-1   Hypothetical Interindustry Commodity Flows in Millions of Dollars

Producers	User A	B	C	Final Demand	Total Output
A	100	120	100	80	400
B	200	100	200	100	600
C	50	200	400	150	800
Total inputs	350	420	700		

As an example, consider a simple hypothetical economy of three industries, A, B, and C represented in the Table 14-1. The table shows that industry A produces 400 units; 100 of these units it uses itself, 120 and 100 go to industries B and C, respectively, and 80 go to Final users.

One of the basic problems in input-output analysis is to determine the production of each of the industries if the final demand changes, assuming that the structure of the economy does not change. Under this assumption the structure can be described by the technological matrix

$$\mathbf{A} = (a_{ij})$$

where a_{ij} = the dollar value of the amount of the output of industry i that must be purchased by industry j in order that industry j may produce \$1 of its own goods.

For the economy given above, the matrix $\mathbf{A}$ is

$$\mathbf{A} = \begin{bmatrix} \frac{100}{400} & \frac{120}{600} & \frac{100}{800} \\ \frac{200}{400} & \frac{100}{600} & \frac{200}{800} \\ \frac{50}{400} & \frac{200}{600} & \frac{400}{800} \end{bmatrix} = \begin{bmatrix} 0.250 & 0.200 & 0.125 \\ 0.500 & 0.167 & 0.250 \\ 0.125 & 0.333 & 0.500 \end{bmatrix} \tag{1}$$

Let x_i denote the dollar value of the output of the ith industry, and let $\mathbf{X}$ be the column vector of outputs for the various industries. The jth industry for $j = 1, 2, \ldots, n$ needs an amount $x_j a_{ij}$ of the output of the ith industry so that the economy may operate with outputs given by the components of $\mathbf{X}$. Therefore, the ith industry must produce outputs worth

$$a_{i1}x_1 + a_{i2}x_2 + \cdots + a_{in}x_n \quad \text{for } i = 1, \ldots, n \tag{2}$$

in order to supply the needs of all the industries. The inter-industry demand vector $\mathbf{X}$ may be written in matrix notation as $\mathbf{AX}$.

An economy must usually produce some finished goods for final demand as well as for the use of other industries. Let h_i, $i = 1, \ldots, n$, denote the output of each of the n industries that goes to final demand. Then the column vector $\mathbf{H}$ is the final demand vector; it must be non-negative,

$$\mathbf{H} \geq 0 \tag{3}$$

The production of the economy must be adjusted so that the inter-industry needs, as well as the final demand, will be fulfilled. This requirement in matrix notation is:

$$\mathbf{X} = \mathbf{AX} + \mathbf{H} \tag{4}$$

and states that the output vector must equal the sum of the inter-industry demand vector plus the final demand. Rewriting (4) as

$$\mathbf{X} - \mathbf{AX} = \mathbf{IX} - \mathbf{AX} = (\mathbf{I} - \mathbf{A})\mathbf{X} = \mathbf{H} \tag{5}$$

shows that X must satisfy a set of n simultaneous equations in n unknowns, or

$$X = (I - A)^{-1}H$$

In the example

$$(I - A)^{-1} = \tfrac{1}{307}\begin{bmatrix} 640 & 272 & 296 \\ 540 & 690 & 480 \\ 520 & 528 & 1008 \end{bmatrix}; \qquad H = \begin{bmatrix} 80 \\ 100 \\ 150 \end{bmatrix}$$

and, therefore,

$$X = (I - A)^{-1}H = \begin{bmatrix} 400 \\ 600 \\ 800 \end{bmatrix}$$

If

$$H = \begin{bmatrix} 100 \\ 100 \\ 100 \end{bmatrix} \qquad \text{then} \qquad X = \tfrac{1}{307}\begin{bmatrix} 120,800 \\ 171,000 \\ 205,600 \end{bmatrix}$$

Input-output analysis presents a number of interesting mathematical problems. For example, in order for a solution X to have economic meaning for any H, each of the x_i's must be non-negative, because a negative x_i means that negative quantities of a product would be produced. This is not an economically meaningful result. It is, therefore, of interest to find necessary and sufficient conditions on the technological matrix A in order that equations (5) have a non-negative solution.

The application of input-output analysis to practical economic problems also presents many problems. For example, what industry classification should be used; how can we determine when the technological matrix changes, etc.? The mathematical and practical problems are discussed in texts and other publications listed in *Notes and References*.

EXERCISES

1. Determine the output vector for the following economy:

Producer	User			Total Output
	X	Y	Final Demand	
X	520	300	180	1000
Y	250	400	150	800

if final demand is 100 for X and 200 for Y.

2. Let h_1 and h_2 be two outside demand vectors. How will the activity levels of the various industries change if the outside demand is changed from h_1 to h_2?

3. Formulate the problem in Section A as an input-output problem.

4. Formulate the problem in Section B as an input-output problem.

Notes and References

Section A

The mathematical treatment of the parts explosion problem appears in:

Vazsonyi, A. (1955), "The use of mathematics in production and inventory control," *Management Science*, **1**, pp. 70–85.

Vazsonyi, A. (1958), *Scientific Programming in Business and Industry*, John Wiley and Sons, New York, pp. 429–439.

For the relation between this model and certain other problems, see:

Steinberg, A. W. (1963), "Some notes on the similarity of three management science models and their analysis by connectivity matrix techniques," *Management Science*, **9**, pp. 341–343.

Computational procedures for parts explosion are described in:

IBM Corporation, *Level by Level Net Requirements Planning*, Form 32-7998.

IBM Corporation, *Requirements Planning and Inventory Management*, Form E260–6014.

Section B

Mathematical models of cost allocation in joint production are discussed by:

Erdei, M. J. (1957), "Business data processing using matrix techniques," MIT Master of Science Thesis.

Smith, L. W., Jr. (1960), "An approach to costing joint production based on mathematical programming with an example from petroleum refining," Ph.D. Thesis, Graduate School of Business, Stanford University.

Section C

Input-output models are presented in:

Leontief, W. W. (1951), *Structure of the American Economy*, 1919–1939, 2nd ed., Oxford University Press, New York.

Leontief, W. W., and Hoffenberg, M. (1961), "The Economic Effects of Disarmament," *Scientific American*, **204**, pp. 47–55.

A bibliography is given by:

Riley, V., and Allen, R. L. (1955), *Interindustry Economic Studies, A Comprehensive Bibliography*, Johns Hopkins Press, Baltimore.

CHAPTER FIFTEEN

Linear Programming

The term "linear programming" refers generally to the formulation and solution of problems by the optimization of a linear function (of many variables) subject to linear inequalities. The Kuhn-Tucker conditions were applied to this problem in Chapter 11 for the case of two variables. If the number of variables is large, the exhaustive enumeration, used to solve the problem in Chapter 11, is not computationally feasible even with electronic computers. One of the most important features in linear programming is the existence of the simplex algorithm which can be used in practice to solve large problems. The simplex algorithm is described in detail in Section D. The first three sections are devoted to developing an intuitive feeling for the reasons why the simplex method works. A number of examples are given in this chapter and in the next to illustrate the range of problems to which linear programming has been, or can be, applied.

A. INTRODUCTION

Formulation of Linear Programming Problems

Firms and other economic complexes can be considered as systems which perform certain operations or activities in order to transform inputs into outputs. A business firm has a certain amount of resources available, consumes certain services, goods, and money, and, after performing various activities, provides services, goods, and products to the outside

415

world as shown in the following figure:

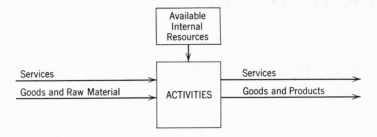

There are a number of different ways in which the problems faced by businessmen managing an economic complex can be formulated as decision-making problems. One formulation is based on the following assumptions:

1. Raw material is available in unlimited quantities at a fixed cost per unit. (The firm may be buying in a perfectly competitive market or from a monopoly with a fixed price policy.)
2. The output of each activity can be sold in unlimited quantity at a fixed price.
3. The firm engages in "activities" to transform raw materials into products. These activities require the use of "internal resources" such as machine time or plant space.

The decision variables in this formulation are the levels of each of the activities. The first step in the decision problem is to define accurately the various possible activities among which a choice should be made and to define the units in which the level of the activity will be measured. For example, the number of units produced is a fair indication of the amount of "activity" involved in a given production process and may therefore be used as a measurement of the "level of activity."

The second step is to define the objective function. Usually the objective is to maximize the "earnings" or "net revenue"; i.e., the difference between the inflows and outflows of money. In many cases it will be in dollars. Using a dollar amount is often satisfactory because earnings (or profit) is the main objective of most firms. However, other criteria are sometimes more relevant, such as the "amount of services" offered by a public company. Sometimes the revenue is fixed and maximizing earnings is equivalent to minimizing costs; in other cases, costs are fixed and maximizing earnings is equivalent to maximizing revenue.

The third step is to recognize certain restrictions on the operation of the firm. If there were no restrictions, maximum profit would be achieved by an infinite amount of "production." For example, the level of a possible activity might be restricted by plant capacity, or by availability of funds, or by lack of skilled workers, etc. These limits constitute the "constraints" of the problem, and their existence influences greatly both the solution of the problem and the technique for obtaining it.

A particular case of this general problem occurs when it can be assumed that the various relationships between the variables are linear. In all the models described in this chapter, linearity will be assumed:

(a) The objective is a linear function of the level of the activities.

(b) The amount of a resource consumed is a linear function of the level of the activities.

Linearity implies additivity; that is, the earning for the nth unit is just the same as it is for the first unit. Furthermore, the amount of each resource required is the same for the nth unit of the activity as it is for the first.

These may not be a perfect representation of the real-life problems but in many instances they are at least a sufficiently accurate approximation for practical purposes. One of the advantages of the assumption of linearity is that it allows the use of powerful mathematical tools, the effectiveness of which has already been proven in many industrial applications. These mathematical tools, which can be applied explicitly to the problem of planning certain activities of large organizations, are known as "linear programming" or LP. LP is the analysis of problems in which a linear function of a number of variables is to be maximized when those variables are subject to a number of constraints in the form of linear inequalities.

Linear programming is by far the most widely used of the programming techniques. The reason for this is that frequently linear approximations are sufficiently accurate for reaching rational decisions. Furthermore, routines for computing solutions to linear programs are generally available. There also exist some techniques by which linear programming can be used to obtain approximate solutions to nonlinear problems.

The Product-Mix Problem—Two Products and Two Machines

Formulation. The product-mix problem described in Chapters 11 and 12 is an example of a situation in which linear programming may be used. A manufacturer sells the precision screws for 10¢ for a box of wood screws and 11¢ for a box of metal screws. The material cost is 5¢ for a box of wood screws and 7¢ for a box of metal screws. There is a fixed cost of $50.00. Hence he receives net revenue or profit of 5¢ per box of wood screws and 4¢ per box of metal screws. He wishes to produce that number of each type of screw which will maximize his total earnings.

The problem can be formulated by following the procedure described in Chapter 4.

Decision Variables.   There are two possible activities for the firm—to produce wood screws and to produce metal screws; the number of screws produced is a measurement of the level of each one of these activities. Therefore, the decision variables will be:

x_1 = number of boxes of wood screws to be produced
x_2 = number of boxes of metal screws to be produced

Objective Function.   The revenue received is 10¢ per box of wood screws and 11¢ per box of metal screws; costs are 5¢ per box of wood screws and 6¢ per box of metal screws, plus a fixed cost of $50.00. The earnings (in cents) are given by

$$10x_1 + 11x_2 - 5x_1 - 7x_2 - 5,000$$

or

$$z = 5x_1 + 4x_2 - 5,000$$

The objective is to maximize the relevant earnings:

$$z = 5x_1 + 4x_2$$

The numbers 5 and 4 represent the net revenue per box. The terms "profit function" and "objective function" will be used interchangeably in this chapter for the function which will be maximized.

Uncontrollable Variables.   The possible profit is limited by the fact that the two machines which are required are available for only 4800 minutes per period, therefore

$$4x_1 + 2x_2 \leq 4,800 \quad \text{Slotting machine restriction}$$
$$2x_1 + 13x_2 \leq 4,800 \quad \text{Threading machine restriction}$$

since each box of wood screws requires 4 minutes on machine I and 2 minutes on machine II, and each box of metal screws requires 2 minutes on machine I and 13 minutes on machine II. Furthermore, the production process is a one-way process; i.e., the level of activities cannot be negative, therefore,

$$x_1 \geq 0$$
$$x_2 \geq 0$$

Allowing the x's to be negative would imply that the activity could be reversed; in other words, that machine time could be produced from screws.

Model. The linear programming model can be summarized as follows: find values for x_1 and x_2 which

maximize $z = 5x_1 + 4x_2$ (1)

and

satisfy the restrictions:

$4x_1 + 2x_2 \leq 4,800$	Slotting machine	(2)
$2x_1 + 13x_2 \leq 4,800$	Threading machine	(3)
$x_1 \geq 0$	Wood screws	(4)
$x_2 \geq 0$	Metal screws	(5)

The consistency of the dimensions in the model can be easily verified: in (1) the coefficients 5 and 4 are in cents per unit, the x_i are in units, and hence z is in cents. In (2) and (3) the coefficients are in minutes per unit and the right-hand sides are in minutes.

The model can conveniently be expressed in matrix notation; if

$$\mathbf{X} = \begin{bmatrix} x_1 \\ x_2 \end{bmatrix} \qquad \mathbf{B} = \begin{bmatrix} 4,800 \\ 4,800 \end{bmatrix} \qquad \mathbf{C}' = [5 \quad 4]$$

$$\mathbf{A} = \begin{bmatrix} 4 & 2 \\ 2 & 13 \end{bmatrix}$$

then the model is:

Find $\mathbf{X}$ which maximizes $z = \mathbf{C}'\mathbf{X}$ subject to $\mathbf{A}\mathbf{X} \leq \mathbf{B}$; $\mathbf{X} \geq 0$.

Solution. The solution will consist of values of x_1 and x_2 which satisfy restrictions (2) − (5), and result in maximum profit (1). In the next section the solution of this problem and a number of other similar problems will be obtained by graphical and enumeration methods. These methods have the advantage that they can easily be understood. In practical problems, the linear programming model tends to become large; instead of two unknowns a practical problem may have from one hundred to several thousand, and instead of two linear restrictions, a practical problem may have several hundred. The graphical and enumeration methods are completely impractical for such problems and a numerical iterative procedure known as the simplex method must be used. It will be described in Section D.

One way in which the model does not accurately represent the problem is that the model permits optimum solutions which are not integers while the problem does not. The LP solution might be $x_1 = 106.37856$ and $x_2 = 93.9932$. In many cases the solutions can be rounded to the nearest integer. Cases in which this is not satisfactory are discussed briefly in Chapter 17.

The basic objective of solving the linear programming problem is to determine the values of the decision variables which maximize the objective function. However, the model and its solution yield answers to other problems that are of vital concern to management; e.g., what is the effect on the solution and the maximum profit if:

1. a non-optimal decision is made?
2. the amounts of the resources are changed?
3. the profits per unit are changed?

The way in which the solution to a linear programming model can be used to answer these questions will be examined in Section C.

B. SOLUTION OF SIMPLE LINEAR PROGRAMMING PROBLEMS BY GRAPHICAL METHODS AND ENUMERATION OF ALTERNATIVES

In general there will be many sets of values which satisfy the restrictions (2) through (5) in A above. The basic problem in solving the linear programming model is to find, from among all of these sets, that particular one which maximizes the objective. In this section the problem formulated in the previous section and several others will be solved by graphical methods and by enumeration. The more general method of solution, known as the Simplex Method, will be described in Section D.

Two Products and Two Machines

DEFINITION 1.   *A feasible solution* (X) *is one which satisfies the restrictions* $AX \leq B, X \geq 0$.

The solutions to the inequality

$$4x_1 + 2x_2 \leq 4{,}800$$

will be all points which satisfy either

$$4x_1 + 2x_2 = 4{,}800 \tag{1}$$

or

$$4x_1 + 2x_2 < 4{,}800 \tag{2}$$

The points satisfying (1) may be illustrated graphically by drawing the line

$$4x_1 + 2x_2 = 4{,}800$$

which passes through Q and N as in Fig. 15.1. All the points which satisfy inequality (2) are those lying on one side of the straight line. Which of the two sides it is can be determined by trying one point, say,

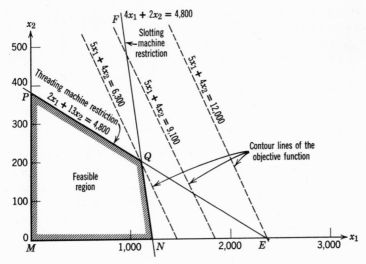

Figure 15.1 Graphical solution to the 2-product and 2-machine linear programming example.

(0, 0). In this case (0, 0) satisfies the inequality; hence, all points below the line [on the same side as (0, 0)] also satisfy the inequality. Similarly, all the points satisfying $2x_1 + 13x_2 \leq 4{,}800$ are those lying on or below the line $2x_1 + 13x_2 = 4{,}800$ (which passes through points P, Q, and E). Since x_1 and x_2 must satisfy inequalities $x_1 \geq 0$, and $x_2 \geq 0$, the values of x_1, x_2 which satisfy (A-2), (A-3), (A-4), and (A-5) are those lying in the polygon with vertices M, N, Q, P. This polygon contains all feasible solutions and will be called the *feasible polygon or feasible set*. It is important to note that the feasible polygon depends on the restrictions only and is unchanged if the profit or objective function is changed. Note also that the polygon is "convex;" that is, a straight line connecting any two points on the boundary of the polygon will not have any points outside the polygon.

DEFINITION 2.   *The optimum solution is the feasible solution which yields the maximum value of the objective (or profit) function.*

The profit function as given by (A-1) cannot be graphed in the same way as the two lines because z is not known. However, by assuming different values of z, a number of different profit lines can be shown; e.g., the lines

$$5x_1 + 4x_2 = 6{,}300$$

and

$$5x_1 + 4x_2 = 9{,}100,$$

$$5x_1 + 4x_2 = 12{,}000$$

all represent possible profit lines. From Fig. 15.1 it is clear that the profit decreases as the profit line is moved toward the origin and, conversely, increases as the profit line is moved away from the origin. Therefore the solution to the manufacturer's problem is the point Q. This point satisfies all the restrictions (i.e., it is a feasible solution) and also provides the maximum profit. The solution represented by Q is $x_1 = 1,100$, $x_2 = 200$, and therefore,

$$z_{max} = 5(1,100) + 4(200) = 6,300$$

While this example represents a very simple case of linear programming and the graphical method of solving the problem has very limited practical applicability, Fig. 15.1 illustrates several basic results in the solution of linear programming problems. An understanding of these at this point will be helpful in following procedures in the more complex situations.

The first result concerns the set of feasible solutions, which is represented by $MNQP$ in Fig. 15.1 for the example.

Result 1. *The set of all feasible solutions is a polygon.*

The second result concerns the location and number of the potential optimum solutions. The vertices of the polygon in Fig. 15.1 can be obtained by solving sets of two equations taken from:

$$4x_1 + 2x_2 = 4,800 \tag{3}$$
$$2x_1 + 13x_2 = 4,800 \tag{4}$$
$$x_1 = 0 \tag{5}$$
$$x_2 = 0 \tag{6}$$

By reference to Fig. 15.1, it can be seen that the solutions of all possible sets of equations are in the accompanying table. Not all of the possible

		Solutions		
Equation	Fig. 15.1	x_1	x_2	Profit
3, 4	Q	1,100	200	6,300
3, 5	H (Not shown)	0	2,400	Infeasible
3, 6	N	1,200	0	6,000
4, 5	P	0	$\frac{4800}{13}$	$1,446\frac{2}{13}$
4, 6	E	2,400	0	Infeasible
5, 6	M	0	0	0

sets of equations lead to vertices of the feasible set; e.g., the points H and E are not vertices of the feasible polygon. The solution to each set of two equations must be checked with all four inequalities (A-2) through (A-5) to ensure that it is a feasible solution. The point $H(x_1 = 0, x_2 = 2,400)$ is not a vertex of the polygon because it does not satisfy (A-3) $[2x_1 + 13x_2 \leq 4,800]$ since

$$2(0) + 13(2,400) \text{ is not} \leq 4,800$$

and, similarly, the point $E(x_1 = 2,400, x_2 = 0)$ is not a vertex of the polygon because it does not satisfy (A-2) $[4x_1 + 2x_2 \leq 4,800]$.

In the example, the point Q happens to be the solution which results in no idle time on either machine, but it clear that the point which results in no idle time need not always be the point which results in maximum profit. If, for example, the profit line were very steep, steeper than the line FQN, the point N would result in maximum profit. The point N would represent the solution

$$x_1 = 1,200$$

$$x_2 = 0$$

that is 1,200 boxes of wood screws would be produced and all available time on machine I would be used, but the threading machine would be idle for 2,400 minutes. If the profit line were very flat, flatter than PQE, the point P would result in maximum profit. At point P

$$x_1 = 0$$

$$x_2 = \frac{4,800}{13}$$

If this were the solution 4,800/13 boxes of metal screws would be produced and machine I (Slotting) would be idle for 11/13(4,800) minutes.

If the profit line were parallel to a side of the polygon, e.g., parallel to PQ or parallel to QN, any point on the segment would result in equal profit. Under these conditions there exist an infinite number of optimum solutions. However, within the definition of the linear programming model there is no reason for preferring any one of these solutions to any other. The second result may now be stated.

Result 2. *The optimum solution occurs at a vertex of the polygon of feasible solutions.* If there are an infinite number of optimum solutions, at least one vertex is included.

This result is of extreme importance. It guarantees that the optimum solution can be found by computing the profit for the feasible solution represented by each vertex. As will be seen later, the number of vertices in general can be very large, but fortunately a systematic procedure (the simplex method) guarantees an optimum solution without examining all vertices.

Two Products and Three Machines

In many product-mix problems to which the programming model discussed above might otherwise be applied, the number of machines will not be the same as the number of products. The case where there are more machines than products will be considered in this section.

Suppose, for example, that three machines are required to produce the screws, the third being used to plate the screws. The problem can then be formulated as follows. Let

$$x_1 = \text{number of boxes of wood screws}$$

$$x_2 = \text{number of boxes of metal screws}$$

Maximize $z = 5x_1 + 4x_2$

subject to

$$4x_1 + 2x_2 \leq 4{,}800$$

$$2x_1 + 13x_2 \leq 4{,}800$$

$$a_1x_1 + a_2x_2 \leq b_1 \qquad \text{Plating Machine Constraint (7)}$$

$$x_1 \geq 0$$

$$x_2 \geq 0$$

where a_1 is the number of minutes required to plate a box of wood screws
a_2 is the number of minutes required to plate a box of metal screws
b_1 is the number of minutes the plating machine is available

The solution to this problem will be discussed in reference to Fig. 15.2 in which the polygon $MNQP$ represents the feasible solutions before constraint (7) was introduced. Regardless of the values of a_1, a_2, and b_1, one of four conditions must exist, depending on where the line, represented by

$$a_1x_1 + a_2x_2 = b_1$$

falls in relation to $MNQP$. The four cases are represented by ①, ②, ③, or ④ in Fig. 15.2:

(a) If the line falls as represented by ① i.e., it is completely above the polygon, the set of feasible solutions is not changed and the optimum solution is the same as before. Condition (7) is redundant since it implies no new constraints on the decision variables.

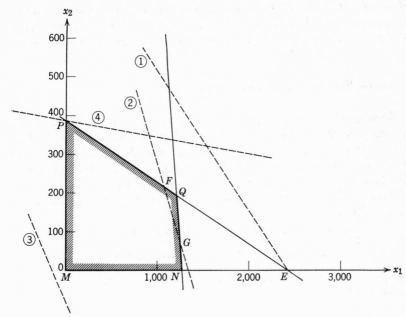

Figure 15.2 Graphical solution to the 2-product and 3-machine linear programming example.

(b) If the line falls as represented by ②, i.e., it intersects the polygon, the set of feasible solutions is reduced to the polygon $MNGFP$ and the optimum solution will be one of the vertices of this new polygon. In this case, condition (7) produces new constraints on the decision variables.

(c) If the line falls as represented by ③, i.e., it falls completely "below" the polygon $MNQP$, there will be no feasible solutions; i.e., there will be no pair of values for x_1 and x_2 which satisfy all the constraints. Since there is no feasible solution there can be no optimum solution.

(d) If the line falls as represented by ④, i.e., it intersects the feasible polygon at a vertex, the set of feasible solutions is not changed and the optimum solution is the same as before. However, this situation may create "degeneracy" problems.

The product mix problem therefore can be formulated as a linear programming problem when there are more machines than products, and an optimum solution may, or may not, exist depending on whether the constraints are, or are not, contradictory.

Result 3.   *A linear programming problem may not have a feasible solution.* If it does, it also has an optimum feasible solution, because the feasible polygon will have at least one vertex and, hence, an optimum solution.

Three Products and Two Machines

Example 1.   Another possibility is that the number of products is greater than the number of machines. Suppose, for example, that the manufacturer can produce a third product, say, aluminum screws. Each box requires 1 minute of machine I (slotting) time and 2 minutes of machine II (threading) time, and yields a net revenue of 2 cents.

This problem can be formulated as a linear programming problem as follows. Let

$$x_1 = \text{number of boxes of wood screws}$$

$$x_2 = \text{number of boxes of metal screws}$$

$$x_3 = \text{number of boxes of aluminum screws}$$

Maximize

$$z = 5x_1 + 4x_2 + 2x_3 \tag{8}$$

subject to

$$4x_1 + 2x_2 + x_3 \leq 4{,}800 \qquad \text{Slotting machine restriction} \tag{9}$$

$$2x_1 + 13x_2 + 2x_3 \leq 4{,}800 \qquad \text{Threading machine restriction} \tag{10}$$

$$x_1 \geq 0,\ x_2 \geq 0,\ x_3 \geq 0$$

Solution.   The formulation given above has three decision variables. Therefore the graph corresponding to Fig. 15.1 would require a three-dimensional graph. The equations

$$4x_1 + 2x_2 + x_3 = 4{,}800$$

$$2x_1 + 13x_2 + 2x_3 = 4{,}800$$

each represent a plane, as do the equations $x_1 = 0$, $x_2 = 0$, $x_3 = 0$. The set of *feasible solutions*, therefore, will be a *polyhedron* defined by these planes and the direction of the inequalities. The objective function will be a plane, whose location depends on the value z, and whose slope depends on the coefficients in (8).

The optimum solution will be obtained by moving the objective plane (i.e., changing the value of z) until z has the largest possible value and the plane has at least one point in the polyhedron of feasible solutions. It is again intuitively clear that the optimum point will be a vertex of the polyhedron (or a side, or edge in the case where the objective function is parallel to the side or edge).

The optimum solution can therefore be obtained without drawing the three-dimensional graph by enumerating all the feasible vertices, computing the value of the objective function at the vertex, and selecting the vertex with the largest profit.

The feasible vertices can be obtained by solving sets of three equations taken from the following:

$$4x_1 + 2x_2 + x_3 = 4{,}800 \tag{11}$$

$$2x_1 + 13x_2 + 2x_3 = 4{,}800 \tag{12}$$

$$x_1 + \qquad\qquad = 0 \tag{13}$$

$$x_2 \qquad = 0 \tag{14}$$

$$x_3 = 0 \tag{15}$$

and eliminating any solutions which do not satisfy the constraints.

Solutions

Equations	x_1	x_2	x_3	Objective	Inequality Violated
11, 12, 13	0	$-\frac{4800}{9}$	$\frac{11}{9}(4{,}800)$	Infeasible	$x_2 \geq 0$
11, 12, 14	800	0	1,600	7,200	
11, 12, 15	1,100	200	0	6,300	
11, 13, 14	0	0	4,800	Infeasible	(10)
11, 13, 15	0	2,400	0	Infeasible	(10)
11, 14, 15	1,200	0	0	6,000	
12, 13, 14	0	0	2,400	4,800	
12, 13, 15	0	$\frac{4800}{13}$	0	$\frac{4}{13}(4{,}800)$	
12, 14, 15	2,400	0	0	Infeasible	(9)
13, 14, 15	0	0	0	0	

The solution and profit for each set of three equations are given in the accompanying table. The intersections which are not vertices of the polygon of feasible solutions are so indicated and the inequality violated is shown in the last column.

The optimum solution in this example is given by:

$$x_1 = 800, \qquad x_2 = 0, \qquad x_3 = 1{,}600$$

and results in a profit of 7,200. This optimum solution states that $x_2 = 0$; i.e., no metal screws will be produced.

Basic Solutions. It might seem, intuitively, that it should be possible to increase profit by producing some metal screws. However, the following argument will show that this is not true. Note first that all the machine time is used to produce wood and aluminum screws:

$$4(800) + 1,600 = 4,800$$

$$2(800) + 2(1,600) = 4,800$$

In as much as the production of metal screws will require time on both machines, the number of boxes of either wood or aluminum screws, or both, will have to be reduced.

To determine the change in the number of wood or aluminum screws if one box of metal screws is to be produced, equations (11) and (12) may be replaced by an equivalent set. The solution to a system of linear equations is not changed if the system is replaced by an equivalent set of linear combinations (Chapter 12). Let

$$L_1: \quad 4x_1 + 2x_2 + x_3 = 4,800$$

$$L_2: \quad 2x_1 + 13x_2 + 2x_3 = 4,800$$

and consider the new set L_3 and L_4 where

$$L_3 = \tfrac{1}{3}(L_1) - \tfrac{1}{6}(L_2)$$

$$L_4 = \tfrac{2}{3}(L_2) - \tfrac{1}{3}(L_1)$$

Then

$$L_3: \quad (\tfrac{4}{3} - \tfrac{2}{6})x_1 + (\tfrac{2}{3} - \tfrac{13}{6})x_2 + (\tfrac{1}{3} - \tfrac{2}{6})x_3 = (1,600 - 800)$$

and

$$L_4: \quad (\tfrac{2}{3} \cdot 2 - \tfrac{4}{3})x_1 + (\tfrac{2}{3} \cdot 13 - \tfrac{2}{3})x_2 + (\tfrac{2}{3} \cdot 2 - \tfrac{1}{3})x_3 = (3,200 - 1,600)$$

or

$$L_3: \quad x_1 - 1.5x_2 + 0x_3 = 800 \quad \text{or} \quad x_1 = 800 + 1.5x_2$$

$$L_4: \quad 0x_1 + 8x_2 + x_3 = 1,600 \qquad\qquad x_3 = 1,600 - 8x_2$$

From these equations it may be seen immediately that

$$x_2 = 0, \quad x_1 = 800, \quad \text{and} \quad x_3 = 1,600$$

is a solution. Furthermore, if x_2 is to be increased by 1 unit, i.e., 1 unit of x_2 is to be produced, all the resources will be used if 1.5 more units of x_1 and 8 units less of x_3 are produced. The change in profit

= additional profit from x_2 and x_1 less the reduction in profit from x_3

$$= 4 + 1.5(5) - 8(2) = -4.5$$

These results may be verified by noting that

$$x_1 = 801.5, \qquad x_2 = 1, \qquad x_3 = 1,592$$

is a solution of equations (11) and (12), and that the profit is

$$5(801.5) + 4(1) + 2(1,592) = 7,195.5$$

The change in profit can also be obtained by substituting the equations L_3 and L_4 into the objective function

$$z = 5x_1 + 4x_2 + 2x_3$$
$$= 5(800 + 1.5x_2) + 4x_2 + 2(1,600 - 8x_2)$$
$$= 7200 - 4.5x_2 \tag{16}$$

This shows that z will be decreased by 4.5 cents for each metal screw produced.

Therefore, the first unit of x_2 that is produced requires the use of machine time which produces more profit if used to make x_1 and x_3. Since the constraints are linear, this statement applies to any unit of x_2 produced, and therefore profit in this case cannot be increased by producing any metal screws.

The fact that only two out of the three products have to be produced in this example to obtain maximum profit is not a coincidence. Regardless of how the numerical values are changed, the optimum solution would always call for production of two products at most. If the numbers were changed, the solution might call for production of x_1 and x_2, x_1 and x_3, x_2 and x_3, x_1 only, x_2 only, or x_3 only, but it would never call for production of all three.

This result is actually a consequence of the fact that an optimum solution will be a vertex of the polyhedron. A vertex of the polyhedron in this example must be a solution of three equations selected from (11), (12), (13), (14), and (15). Any such set is a set of three linear equations in three unknowns and hence has a single unique solution if the equations are linearly independent. However, any such set must contain at least one of (13), (14), and (15); therefore, at the vertices of the polyhedron at least one of the x's is equal to zero. If it contains two of these equations, at least two of the x's will be equal to zero.

In a linear programming problem with three decision variables and two constraints, any feasible solution in which at least one of the x's is set to zero is called a *basic* feasible solution. The variables which are not set to zero in the basic solution are called *basic variables*. If the problem has a feasible solution, it has a basic feasible solution and the optimum solution will be a basic solution. For example, in the problem discussed above, the solution

$$x_1 = 800, \qquad x_2 = 0, \qquad x_3 = 1,600$$

is a basic feasible solution, but

$$x_1 = 801.5, \qquad x_2 = 1, \qquad x_3 = 1,592$$

is not, because it requires production of three products when there are only two constraints.

These conclusions may be stated more generally:

DEFINITION 3. *In a linear programming problem with n decision variables and m($<$ n) linearly independent constraints, any feasible solution in which n − m or more of the decision variables are set to zero is called a basic feasible solution. The variables which are set to zero are the non-basic variables, the ones which are not set to zero are the basic variables.*

Result 4. *An optimum solution (if one exists) will be a basic feasible solution.*

Example 2. In the examples used so far, the optimum solution has resulted in the full use of all available resources. To further illustrate the case where not all resources are needed for the optimum solution, consider a slight modification of the previous example. Suppose, for example, that in the three-product and two-machine product-mix problem considered in Example 1, the profit function were changed to

$$z = 5x_1 + x_2 + x_3$$

while the constraints remained unchanged. The optimum solution can be obtained by computing the profit for each of the vertices of the feasible set. Since the constraints are not changed, the vertices of the feasible set are the same as those given on page 427. The profit for the feasible vertices is as follows:

Equation	x_1	x_2	x_3	Profit
(11), (12), (14)	800	0	1,600	5,600
(11), (12), (15)	1,100	200	0	5,700
(11), (14), (15)	1,200	0	0	6,000
(12), (13), (14)	0	0	2,400	1,200
(12), (13), (15)	0	$\frac{4800}{13}$	0	$\frac{2400}{13}$

The optimum solution is $x_1 = 1,200$, $x_2 = 0$, $x_3 = 0$. In this case there is only one non-zero (basic) variable, x_1.

Substituting this solution in the restrictions gives

$$4(1,200) + 2(0) + 1(0) = 4,800$$

$$2(1,200) + 13(0) + 2(0) = 2,400$$

which means that the threading machine will be idle 2,400 units of time. Rewriting equation (11) in the form

$$x_1 = 1,200 - \tfrac{1}{2}x_2 - \tfrac{1}{4}x_3$$

and substituting in the objective function (8) gives

$$\begin{aligned}
z &= 5x_1 + x_2 + x_3 \\
&= 5(1,200 - \tfrac{1}{2}x_2 - \tfrac{1}{4}x_3) + x_2 + x_3 \\
&= 6,000 - \tfrac{3}{2}x_2 - \tfrac{1}{4}x_3
\end{aligned} \qquad (17)$$

From this it follows that profit will be reduced by $\tfrac{3}{2}$ for each unit of x_2 produced, and by $\tfrac{1}{4}$ for each unit of x_3 produced.

Summary

In this section several linear programming models have been solved by graphical methods and/or enumeration. The model may be stated as:

LP Model

	Algebraic	Matrix
Find	$x_i \quad i = 1, 2, \ldots, n$	$\mathbf{X}$
which maximizes	$z = \sum\limits_{i=1}^{n} c_i x_i$	$\mathbf{Z} = \mathbf{C'X}$
subject to	$\sum\limits_{i=1}^{n} a_{ij}x_i \le b_j \quad j = 1, \ldots, m$	$\mathbf{AX} \le \mathbf{B}$
	$x_i \ge 0$	$\mathbf{X} \ge 0$

DEFINITION 1. *A feasible solution* $\mathbf{X}$ *is one which satisfies the restrictions* $\mathbf{AX} \le \mathbf{B}$ *and* $\mathbf{X} \ge 0$.

DEFINITION 2. *The optimum solution* $\mathbf{X}^*$ *is the feasible solution which maximizes the objective function* $\mathbf{C'X}$.

DEFINITION 3. *In a linear programming problem with n decision variables and* $m(< n)$ *linearly independent constraints, any feasible solution in which* $n - m$ *or more of the decision variables are set to zero is a basic feasible solution. The variables set to zero are non-basic variables and those not set to zero are basic variables.*

Result 1.   The set of all feasible solutions is a polyhedron.

Result 2.   The optimum solution occurs at a vertex of the feasible polyhedron; if there is more than one optimum solution, at least one vertex is included.

Result 3.   A linear programming model may not have a feasible solution, but if it does, then it also has an optimum feasible solution.

Result 4.   The optimum solution (if it exists) will be a basic feasible solution.

EXERCISES

1. Determine the optimum decision and maximum profit in Example 1, if the objective is to maximize
$$3x_1 + 5x_2 + 4x_3$$

2. Verify that (17) in Example 2 gives the correct optimum profit for the optimum value of x_1 if $x_2 = 150$ and $x_3 = 400$.

3. Determine the optimum decision and the maximum profit in Example 1, if $x_2 = 300$. Explain why (16) does not give the correct value for the maximum profit.

4. Use graphical or enumeration methods to find which $\mathbf{X}$ maximizes $z = \mathbf{C}'\mathbf{X}$ subject to $\mathbf{AX} \leq \mathbf{B}$, $\mathbf{X} \geq 0$ where

$$\mathbf{X} = \begin{bmatrix} x_1 \\ x_2 \end{bmatrix} \quad \mathbf{C}' = [5 \quad 4], \quad \mathbf{A} = \begin{bmatrix} 4 & 2 \\ 2 & 13 \\ 1 & 1 \end{bmatrix} \quad \mathbf{B} = \begin{bmatrix} 4800 \\ 4800 \\ 1200 \end{bmatrix}$$

5. A firm produces two products. The first has a net revenue of $5 and requires four machine-hours per unit. The second has a net revenue of $2 and requires one machine-hour per period. However, only 300,000 units of the second product can be sold during a period. How many units of each product should be produced per period if 400,000 machine hours are available?

6. The Midwestern Mink Ranch produces mink for fur and for breeding. Fur-producing mink need at least one pound of lean meat per day, while breeding mink need at least 0.4 pounds of fat per day. Assume two prepared foods are available. The first has 10% fat and 90% lean, and the second has 40% fat and 60% lean. Both types cost $1 a pound. The firm wishes to find a combination of the two types of food that can be used for both fur bearing and breeding and will fulfill the minimal diet requirements of both at the lowest possible cost.

   (a) State the problem as a linear programming model. Give an economic interpretation of each restriction and each activity. Show the direction of the inequalities and identify the criterion.

(b) Let x be the amount of the first type and y the amount of the second type purchased per day. Construct the set of points in the plane representing purchases that fulfill both minimum diet requirements.

(c) How much of each type of food is in the minimal cost diet? What is the total cost?

7. The Party Nut Company has on hand 550 pounds of peanuts, 150 pounds of cashew nuts, 90 pounds of brazil nuts, and 70 pounds of hazel nuts. It packages and sells nuts in the following varieties of standard 8-oz cans and at the indicated net wholesale price: Party Peanuts, 26c per can; Party Mix, consisting of 50% peanuts, 20% cashew nuts, 15% brazil nuts, and 15% hazel nuts, at 38c per can; Cashew Nuts (only) at 51c per can; and Luxury Mix, consisting of 40% cashew nuts, 25% brazil nuts, and 35% hazel nuts, at 54c per can. The company desires to mix these nuts in a way which will yield maximum revenue. State the problem as a linear programming model. Give an economic interpretation of each restriction and each activity. Show the direction of the inequalities and identify the criterion.

8. A publisher of paper-backed books is currently selling a line consisting of 25c short novels, 50c popular full-length novels, and $1.00 reprints of the classics. After considerable market analysis, it was proposed that the company might profitably add a fourth class of books, a series of explanations of the fundamentals of science which would sell for $1.50 each.

The company found that the profit on each of its existing items was equal to 20% of the revenue of each item. This was found to be generally true for a fairly wide range of sales of each item and was expected to hold for the con-templated $1.50 line.

The books are sold through (1) bookstores and university outlets which tend to carry a large proportion of high-level reading in their paper-backed inventory, and (2) magazine stands, drugstores, terminal, and grocery stores which tend to carry a higher proportion of less literary paper-backed books.

In order to estimate the market potential for the company's revised line of books, the market research division of the company established estimates of sales potential in terms of units which are limited as follows:

$$\text{Market 1} \quad \text{maximum sales} = 125{,}000 \text{ units}$$
$$\text{Market 2} \quad \text{maximum sales} = 140{,}000 \text{ units}$$

Each book sold consumes a portion of the market potential as shown in the accompanying Table. There is no market for $1.00 or $1.50 books in Market 2.

Book	Number of units of market potential per book	
	(1)	(2)
25c	$\frac{1}{8}$	$\frac{3}{5}$
50c	$\frac{1}{4}$	$\frac{2}{5}$
$1.00	$\frac{1}{2}$	
$1.50	$\frac{1}{8}$	

The ability to produce is limited by present manpower and equipment; both of these resources can be used to produce any number of each type of book.

Capacity is measured in terms of a "standard" book; e.g.,

Book	Capacity Required
$0.25	$\frac{1}{2}$
0.50	1
1.00	1
1.50	2

Total capacity is 1,500,000 "standard" books. Formulate this problem as a linear programming model.

9. Give the conditions on the coefficients in the objective functions under which the points P, Q, N, respectively, would be the optimum solution to LP shown in Fig. 15.1.

10. Show the feasible region for Example 1, p. 426, in a projective drawing. Give the conditions on the coefficients in the objective function (8) under which the basic variables would be, respectively, x_1; x_2; x_3; x_1 and x_2; x_1 and x_3; and x_2 and x_3.

C. MANAGEMENT PLANNING INFORMATION FROM LINEAR PROGRAMMING MODELS

Slack Variables

Solutions to LP models were obtained in the previous section. These solutions give the optimum operating decision; e.g., how much of each product to produce. These solutions of LP models can also, through the use of slack variables, yield information that is useful when changes occur in the uncontrolled variables. This is frequently termed "planning" when contrasted to the operating decision.

A slack variable takes up the "slack" in an inequality. For example, in the three-product and two-machine product-mix problem, Example 1, page 426, a new non-negative variable x_4 can be defined so that the inequality

$$4x_1 + 2x_2 + x_3 \leq 4{,}800$$

becomes the equality

$$4x_1 + 2x_2 + x_3 + x_4 = 4{,}800 \tag{1}$$

x_4 can be interpreted as the level of an activity which per unit allots 1 minute of slotting-machine time to letting the machine stand idle. The inequality

$$2x_1 + 13x_2 + 2x_3 \leq 4{,}800$$

becomes equality

$$2x_1 + 13x_2 + 2x_3 + x_5 = 4{,}800 \tag{2}$$

if x_5 is the level of an activity which per unit allots 1 minute of threading-machine time to letting the threading machine stand idle.

The economic interpretation of the inequality was that the machine time devoted to production must be less than or equal to the available machine time. Adding a slack variable to represent idle time permits the statement: the time devoted to production plus the idle time will be *equal* to the total time. Thus, when the slack variables are present, we can dispense with the inequality and state all restrictions as equalities.

The products which these two new activities produce are "idle" times; they provide no profit. Therefore, the objective function becomes:

$$z = 5x_1 + 4x_2 + 2x_3 + 0x_4 + 0x_5$$

In Example 1 (the three-product and two-machine product-mix problem), the optimum solution given in Section B above was:

$$x_1 = 800, \qquad x_2 = 0, \qquad x_3 = 1{,}600$$

The optimum solution to the problem with the two new variables is

$$x_1 = 800, \qquad x_2 = 0, \qquad x_3 = 1{,}600, \qquad x_4 = 0, \qquad \text{and} \quad x_5 = 0$$

However, in Example 2, the optimum solution was $x_1 = 1{,}200$, $x_2 = 0$, $x_3 = 0$. This solution does not satisfy the equalities; substituting in (1) and (2) gives

$$4(1{,}200) + 2(0) + 3(0) + x_4 = 4{,}800$$

$$2(1{,}200) + 4(0) + 2(0) + x_5 = 4{,}800$$

and therefore $x_4 = 0$, $x_5 = 2{,}400$. The optimum solution is:

$$x_1 = 1{,}200, \qquad x_2 = 0, \qquad x_3 = 0, \qquad x_4 = 0, \qquad x_5 = 2{,}400$$

In general, a linear programming problem with n variables and m equality constraints, where $n > m$, must have m basic variables in the optimum solution. In the three-product and two-machine product-mix problem there are two constraints and five variables. There will, therefore, be two basic variables in the optimum solution. In Example 1, the basic variables are x_1 and x_3. In Example 2, the basic variables are x_1 and x_5.

In Example 2, a slack variable appears as a basic variable. From an examination of the constraints it will be noted that in Example 1, the equality is satisfied in both constraints, e.g.,

$$4(800) + 1{,}600 = 4{,}800$$

$$2(800) + 2(1{,}600) = 4{,}800$$

In Example 2, however, one of the constraints is an inequality, e.g.,

$$4(1,200) = 4,800$$

$$2(1,200) < 4,800$$

The solution would not be changed if the resources in second constraint

$$2x_1 + 13x_2 + 2x_3 \leq 4,800$$

were reduced. This result holds in general. If a slack variable appears as a basic variable in an optimum solution, the constraint in which it appears does not actually restrict the solution and the resources may be reduced without affecting the optimum solution.

Table 15-1   Summary of 3-Product and 2-Machine Product-Mix Problem, Using Slack Variables

EXAMPLE 1	EXAMPLE 2
max $z = 5x_1 + 4x_2 + 2x_3 + 0x_4 + 0x_5$	max $z = 5x_1 + x_2 + x_3 + 0x_4 + 0x_5$
subject to:	subject to:
$4x_1 + 2x_2 + x_3 + x_4 \quad\quad = 4,800$	$4x_1 + 2x_2 + x_3 + x_4 \quad\quad = 4,800$
$2x_1 + 13x_2 + 2x_3 \quad\quad + x_5 = 4,800$	$2x_1 + 13x_2 + 2x_3 \quad\quad + x_5 = 4,800$
Basic variables in the optimal solution	Basic variables in the optimal solution
are x_1 and x_3	are x_1 and x_5
$x_1 = \quad 800 + 1.5x_2 - \frac{1}{2}x_4 + \frac{1}{6}x_5$	$x_1 = 1,200 - \frac{1}{2}x_2 - \frac{1}{4}x_3 - \frac{1}{4}x_4$
$x_3 = 1,600 - \quad 8x_2 + \frac{1}{3}x_4 - \frac{2}{3}x_5$	$x_5 = 2,400 - 12x_2 - \frac{3}{2}x_3 + \frac{1}{2}x_4$
$z = 7,200 - 4.5x_2 - x_4 - \frac{1}{2}x_5$	$z = 6,000 - \frac{3}{2}x_2 - \frac{1}{4}x_3 - \frac{5}{4}x_4$

The solutions to Examples 1 and 2 of the three-product and two-machine problem incorporating slack variables is summarized in Table 15-1. The computations can be carried out as shown, *provided it is known which variables are basic.* The fact that an optimum solution has been reached can be verified by substituting the equations for the basic variables into the profit equation, since the coefficients of the non-basic variables are the change in profit which would occur if the solution is changed by producing one unit of the non-basic variable. For example, in Example 1, Table 15-1, the profit equation is

$$z = 7,200 - 4.5x_2 - x_4 - \tfrac{1}{2}x_5$$

Since x_2, x_4, and x_5 cannot be negative, the profit z is a maximum if $x_2 = x_4 = x_5 = 0$. An optimum solution has been found in a maximization problem whenever all the coefficients of the non-basic variables in the profit function, after substituting for the basic variables, are non-positive. The reason for this was given in Section B and is repeated here because of its fundamental importance. If the coefficient is negative, the production of even one unit of a non-basic product will decrease profit. The set of equations

$$x_1 = 800 + 1.5x_2 - \tfrac{1}{3}x_4 + \tfrac{1}{6}x_5 \qquad (3)$$

$$x_3 = 1{,}600 - 8x_2 + \tfrac{1}{3}x_4 - \tfrac{2}{3}x_5 \qquad (4)$$

is equivalent to the set (1) and (2) because (3) and (4) are a linear combination of (1) and (2) and the determinant of the linear combination is not zero. One suitable linear combination is:

$$\tfrac{1}{3}(1) - \tfrac{1}{6}(2) = (3)$$

$$-\tfrac{1}{3}(1) + \tfrac{2}{3}(2) = (4)$$

The determinant is

$$\begin{vmatrix} \tfrac{1}{3} & -\tfrac{1}{6} \\ -\tfrac{1}{3} & \tfrac{2}{3} \end{vmatrix} = \tfrac{2}{9} - \tfrac{1}{18} \neq 0$$

In the optimum solution, x_2 is non-basic. If $x_2 = 1$ and $x_4 = 0$; $x_5 = 0$, the optimum solution would change to

$$x_1 = 800 + 1.5 = 801.5$$

$$x_2 = 1{,}600 - 8 = 1{,}592$$

The increase in profit

= (profit from $x_2 = 1$) + increase in profit from 1.5 more units of x_1
+ (increase due to -8 less units of x_3)
= $4 + 1.5(5) - 2(8) = -4.5$

Since this increase is negative, profit would decrease if x_2 became basic. Analogous arguments apply to x_4 and x_5, and the optimum solution is the one in which x_1 and x_3 are basic.

Linear Programming as an Aid to Management Decision-Making

The concept of slack variables may be used to provide management with further information for the operation in the system and for planning changes in the system represented by the LP model. Examples of such use are given in this section for the three-product and two-machine product-mix problem in Example 1.

What will be the effect on the optimum solution and profit if a non-optimum solution is used? Non-optimum solutions occur most frequently when a non-basic variable must be produced or when the optimum quantity of a basic variable is less than that required due to legal or other requirements.

Suppose 2 units of x_2 must be produced, say, because of a legal contract. How will the profit change?

Solution, Method A.   The capacity required to produce 2 units of x_2 can be eliminated; the inequalities become

$$4x_1' + 2x_2' + x_3' \leq 4{,}796 \tag{5}$$

$$2x_1' + 13x_2' + 2x_3' \leq 4{,}774 \tag{6}$$

Maximizing $z = 5x_1 + 4x_2 + 2x_3$ subject to (5) and (6) will lead to the solution $x_1' = 803$, $x_2' = 0$, $x_3' = 1{,}584$ or in terms of the previous variables, $x_1 = 803$, $x_2 = 2$, $x_3 = 1{,}584$, and the profit is $5(803) + 4(2) + 2(1{,}584) = 7{,}191$. Thus profit is reduced by $9 = (7{,}200 - 7{,}191)$.

Solution, Method B.   The answer to the question can be obtained more easily without resolving the LP problem by using the solution to the original problem.   From (3) and (4) it follows that if $x_2 = 2$, then

$$x_1' = 800 + 1.5(2) = 803$$

$$x_3' = 1{,}600 - 8(2) = 1{,}584$$

The profit can be obtained by substituting these solutions into the profit function as in Solution A.   However, there is an even simpler way to compute the change in profit.   Substituting (1) and (2) in the profit equation gives

$$z = 5x_1 + 4x_2 + 2x_3$$

$$= 5(800 + 1.5x_2) + 4x_2 + 2(1{,}600 - 8x_2)$$

$$= 7{,}200 - 4.5x_2$$

This equation says that if $x_2 = 0$, the profit is 7,200; and the profit will be reduced by 4.5 for each unit of x_2 produced and therefore the profit will be reduced by 9 if 2 units are produced.

It is therefore possible to determine from the answer to the original problem what the new solution and the new profit will be if a non-optimum solution is to be used.   The new solution is valid as long as non-negativity restraints on the decision variables are not violated.   In this example, if x_2 were 400, x_3 would have to be negative; it can be seen that $x_2 = 400$; $x_1 = 0$, $x_2 = 0$ violates inequality (2), and hence $x_2 = 400$, $x_1 = 0$, $x_3 = 0$ is not a feasible solution to the original problem.

A non-optimal decision will also result if non-optimal values of x_1 and x_3 are used.   Suppose, for example, that 2,000 units of x_3 must be produced. Then let

$$x_3 = 2{,}000 + x_3'$$

that is, x_3' is the excess over 2,000. The new linear programming problem becomes:

$$4x_1 + 2x_2 + x_3' \leq 2,800$$
$$2x_1 + 13x_2 + 2x_3' \leq 800$$

This problem is the same as the previous one, except that the amount of available resources is changed and hence can be solved by using the technique discussed next.

What will happen to the optimum solution and profit if the amount of available resources is changed? For example, suppose 24 more units of slotting-machine time are available.

Solution Method A. The new problem could be stated in the form: maximize

$$z = 5x_1 + 4x_2 + 2x_3$$

subject to:
$$4x_1 + 2x_2 + x_3 \leq 4,824$$
$$2x_1 + 13x_2 + 2x_3 \leq 4,800$$

and
$$x_1 \geq 0; \quad x_2 \geq 0; \quad x_3 \geq 0$$

The solution, if slack variables are used, and if x_1 and x_3 are the basic variables, is

$$x_1 + 0x_3 = 808 + 1.5x_2 - \tfrac{1}{3}x_4 + \tfrac{1}{6}x_5 \tag{7}$$

$$0x_1 + x_3 = 1,592 - 8x_2 + \tfrac{1}{3}x_4 - \tfrac{2}{3}x_5 \tag{8}$$

and

$$z = 5x_1 + 4x_2 + 2x_3$$
$$= 7,224 - 4.5x_2 - x_4 - \tfrac{1}{2}x_5 \tag{9}$$

Substituting $x_2 = 0$; $x_4 = 0$; $x_5 = 0$ gives $x_1 = 808$; $x_3 = 1,592$, and $z = 7,224$, and hence profit has been increased by 24 cents.

Solution, Method B. The new profit can be obtained by noting that the coefficients for x_4 and x_5 in (7) and (8) and in the profit equation (9) are the same as in (3) and (4). It follows that, if 24 more units are added, the new profit will be increased by 24. The optimum values of x_1 and x_3 under this condition can be obtained from

$$x_1 = 800 + 1.5x_2 - \tfrac{1}{3}x_4 + \tfrac{1}{6}x_5$$
$$x_3 = 1,600 - 8x_2 + \tfrac{1}{3}x_4 - \tfrac{2}{3}x_5$$

by setting $x_2 = 0$, $x_4 = -24$, and $x_5 = 0$; then $x_1 = 808$, $x_3 = 1,592$, and $z = 7,224$.

More generally, if the first resource (slotting-machine time) is changed by an amount ε_1 and the second (threading machine time) by an amount

ε_2, where the ε's may be either positive or negative, the LP problem becomes:

maximize $\quad 5x_1 + 4x_2 + 2x_3 + 0x_4 + 0x_5$

subject to:

$$4x_1 + 2x_2 + x_3 + x_4 = 4{,}800 + \varepsilon_1$$
$$2x_1 + 13x_2 + 2x_3 + x_5 = 4{,}800 + \varepsilon_1$$
$$x_i \geq 0 \qquad 1 = 1, 2, \ldots, 5$$

The equations may be written as:

$$4x_1 + 2x_2 + x_3 + x_4 - \varepsilon_1 = 4{,}800$$
$$2x_1 + 13x_2 + 2x_3 + x_5 - \varepsilon_2 = 4{,}800$$

The linear combinations used to obtain (3) and (4), when applied to this problem, give

$$x_1 = 800 + 1.5x_2 - \tfrac{1}{3}(x_4 - \varepsilon_1) + \tfrac{1}{6}(x_5 - \varepsilon_2) \tag{10}$$

$$x_3 = 1{,}600 - 8x_2 + \tfrac{1}{3}(x_4 - \varepsilon_1) - \tfrac{2}{3}(x_5 - \varepsilon_2) \tag{11}$$

and substituting these solutions in the objective function gives

$$z = 7{,}200 - 4.5x_2 - (x_4 - \varepsilon_1) - \tfrac{1}{2}(x_5 - \varepsilon_2) \tag{12}$$

If $\varepsilon_1 = 24$, and $\varepsilon_2 = 0$ (10), (11), and (12) reduce to (7), (8), and (9). If $\varepsilon_1 = -24$, (10), (11), and (12) become:

$$x_1 = 792 + 1.5x_2 - \tfrac{1}{3}x_4 + \tfrac{1}{6}(x_5 - \varepsilon_2)$$
$$x_3 = 1{,}608 - 8x_2 + \tfrac{1}{3}x_4 - \tfrac{2}{3}(x_5 - \varepsilon_2)$$
$$z = 7{,}176 - 4.5x_2 - x_4 - 0.5(x_5 - \varepsilon_2)$$

The General LP Model with Equality Constraints

The standard linear programming problem has been expressed as:

	Algebraic Form	Matrix Form
Find	$x_i \qquad i = 1, \ldots, n$	$\mathbf{X}$
that maximizes	$z = \displaystyle\sum_{i=1}^{n} c_i x_i$	$\mathbf{C'X}$
subject to:	$\displaystyle\sum_{i=1}^{n} a_{ij} x_i \leq b_j \qquad j = 1, \ldots, m$	$\mathbf{AX} \leq \mathbf{B}$
and	$x_i \geq 0 \qquad i = 1, \ldots, n$	$\mathbf{X} \geq 0$

Additional decision variables, called slack variables, can be added to the model without altering the optimum solution. Let x_{n+1}, x_{n+2}, ..., x_{n+m} denote the slack variables. The coefficients of the slack variables, x_{n+1}, x_{n+2}, ..., x_{n+m}, are chosen so that all the constraints become equalities. One new variable is defined for each inequality; the coefficient of x_{n+j} in the jth constraint is $+1$ and zero in the other constraints. The coefficients of the slack variables in the objective function are chosen so that these variables need not appear as basic variables in the optimum solution; in fact, they will appear in the solution only if this results in a greater value for the objective function. Normally, the coefficients of the slack variables will be zero.

The general LP model with equality constraints can be stated as:

	Algebraic Form	Matrix Form
Find	$x_i \qquad i = 1, \ldots, n + m$	$\mathbf{X}$
that maximize	$z = \sum_{i=1}^{n+m} c_i x_i$	$z = \mathbf{C'X}$
subject to:	$\sum_{i=1}^{n+m} a_{ij} x_i = b_j \qquad i = 1, \ldots, m$	$\mathbf{AX} = \mathbf{B}$
	$x_i \geq 0 \qquad i = 1, \ldots, n + m$	$\mathbf{X} \geq 0$

The previous definitions and results may be extended to the general LP model: A *feasible solution* is one which satisfies the constraints $\mathbf{AX} = \mathbf{B}$ and $\mathbf{X} \geq 0$ (Definition 1). An *optimum solution* is a feasible solution which maximizes the objective function $\mathbf{C'X}$ (Definition 2). The set of all feasible solutions is a polyhedron (Result 1). The optimum solution occurs at a vertex of the polyhedron; if there is more than one optimum solution, at least one vertex is included (Result 2). A linear programming model may not have a feasible solution; but if it does, it also has an optimum feasible solution (Result 3).

In theory, the enumeration method used in the previous section could be extended to general problems. The vertices of the feasible polyhedron are given by the solutions of the following systems of equations:

$\mathbf{AX} = \mathbf{B}$: m equations in $n + m$ unknowns: $x_1 \cdots x_n, x_{n+1} \cdots x_{n+m}$
$\mathbf{X} = \mathbf{O}$: $n + m$ equations in $n + m$ unknowns: $x_1 \cdots x_n, x_{n+1} \cdots x_{n+m}$

A vertex is a solution of $n + m$ equations selected from the $n + 2m$ equations in $n + m$ unknowns. There are

$$\frac{(n + 2m)!}{(n + 2m - n - m)!\,(n + 2m - m)!} = \frac{(n + 2m)!}{m!\,(n + m)!}$$

such sets of $n + m$ equations in $n + m$ unknowns. Each of these sets has a unique solution (if the equations are linearly independent) which may or may not be feasible (satisfy $\mathbf{AX} = \mathbf{B}$ and $\mathbf{A} \geq \mathbf{O}$). If one or more solutions are feasible, the LP model has a feasible, and hence an optimum, solution.

In any of the sets of $n + m$ equations in $n + m$ unknowns, at least n of the equations are of the form $x_i = 0$, because there are only m equations in $\mathbf{AX} = \mathbf{B}$. Therefore, in any solution which is a vertex of the feasible polyhedron, n of the x's are set equal to zero. Definition 3 may be stated as: in a linear programming problem with $n + m$ decision variables and m equality constraints, any feasible solution in which n of the variables are set to zero is a basic feasible solution. The variables set to zero are non-basic variables and those not set to zero are basic variables. The optimum solution (if it exists) is a basic feasible solution (Result 4). Note that these statements apply when n is greater than, equal to, or less than m.

In general, the enumeration of vertices is not practical, even with the fastest available or foreseeable electronic computer. For example, if $n = 50$ and $m = 25$, the number of vertices is:

$$\frac{n + 2m!}{m!\,(n + m)!} = \frac{9.3 \times 10^{157}}{(1.5 \times 10^{25})(2.5 \times 10^{109})} \sim 2.5 \times 10^{23}$$

The examination of one vertex consists of the solution of a set of m equations in m unknowns. If the computer could examine 25,000 vertices per second, the complete enumeration would require

$$\frac{2.5 \times 10^{23}}{25{,}000 \times 3{,}600} \sim 2.8 \times 10^{16} \text{ hours.}$$

Clearly, complete enumeration is out of the question for even such relatively small problems.

Verification of Optimal Solutions

The essential feature of a method of solving LP problems which is practical is that not all vertices have to be examined. One of the steps required in this method is a determination of whether a given basic set of variables results in the optimum feasible solution. The procedure for doing this has been developed in the previous sections, is summarized in Table 15-2 in both algebraic and matrix form, and illustrated below.

In the procedure, slack variables are introduced and the variables renumbered so that the (selected) basic variables appear first, and the non-basic variables last, in both the objective function and the equality

Table 15-2

Algebraic	Matrix

Maximize

$$z = c_1 x_1 + c_2 x_2 + \cdots + c_{n+m} x_{n+m}$$

$$z = CX; \quad C = \begin{bmatrix} C_1 \\ C_2 \end{bmatrix}; \quad X = \begin{bmatrix} X_1 \\ X_2 \end{bmatrix} \begin{matrix} \leftarrow \text{ basic variable} \\ \leftarrow \text{ non-basic} \\ \text{variable} \end{matrix}$$

Subject to:

$$\begin{matrix} \text{basic} & \text{non-basic} \\ A = [A_1 & A_2] \end{matrix}$$

$$B = \begin{bmatrix} b_1 \\ \cdot \\ \cdot \\ \cdot \\ b_m \end{bmatrix}$$

$$a_{11} x_1 + a_{12} x_2 + \cdots + a_{1m} x_m + a_{1,m+1} x_{m+1} + \cdots + a_{1,n+m} x_{n+m} = b_1$$

$$\cdot \qquad \cdot$$
$$\cdot \qquad \cdot$$
$$\cdot \qquad \cdot$$

$$a_{m1} x_1 + a_{m2} x_2 + \cdots + a_{mm} x_m + a_{m,m+1} x_{m+1} + \cdots + a_{m,n+m} x_{n+m} = b_m$$

$$AX = B$$
$$A_1 X_1 + A_2 X_2 = B$$

Solving the equations for the basic variables $x_1, x_2, \ldots, x_n$ gives:

$$x_1 + 0x_2 + \cdots + 0x_m = b_1' + a_{1,m+1}' x_{m+1} + \cdots + a_{1,n+m}' x_{n+m}$$

$$0x_1 + x_2 + \cdots + 0x_m = b_2' + a_{2,m+1}' x_{m+1} + \cdots + a_{2,n+m}' x_{n+m}$$

$$\cdot \qquad \cdot$$
$$\cdot \qquad \cdot$$
$$\cdot \qquad \cdot$$

$$0x_1 + 0x_2 + \cdots + x_m = b_m' + a_{m,m+1}' x_{m+1} + \cdots + a_{m,n+m}' x_{n+m}$$

$$X_1 = A_1^{-1} B - A_1^{-1} A_2 X_2$$

Substituting the solution for the basic variables in z gives

$$z = z' - c_{m+1}' x_{m+1} - c_{m+2}' x_{m+2} - \cdots - c_{n+m}' x_{n+m}$$

$$z = C_1' A_1^{-1} B - (C_1' A_1^{-1} A_2 - C_2') X_2$$

constraints. The non-basic variables are moved to the right-hand side and a solution obtained for the m equations in the m basic variables. The solution for the basic variables, if it is feasible, is then substituted in the objective function.

Example. The procedure will be illustrated, using the three-product, two-machine product-mix problem in Example 1.

Find x_i $i = 1, 3$ $X' = [x_1\ x_2\ x_3]$

that maximize $5x_1 + 4x_2 + 2x_3$ $C' = [5\ \ 4\ \ 2]$

subject to: $4x_1 + 2x_2 + x_3 \le 4{,}800$

$$A = \begin{bmatrix} 4 & 2 & 1 \\ 2 & 13 & 2 \end{bmatrix}; \ B = \begin{bmatrix} 4{,}800 \\ 4{,}800 \end{bmatrix}$$

$2x_1 + 13x_2 + 2x_3 \le 4{,}800$

$x_i \ge 0$ $i = 1, 2, 3$

Adding slack variables gives the statement of the model with equality constraints as:

Find x_i $i = 1, 2, 3, 4, 5$ $X' = [x_1\ x_2\ x_3\ x_4\ x_5]$

that maximize $5x_1 + 4x_2 + 2x_3 + 0x_4 + 0x_5$ $C' = [5\ \ 4\ \ 2\ \ 0\ \ 0]$

subject to: $4x_1 + 2x_2 + x_3 + x_4 = 4{,}800$

$$A = \begin{bmatrix} 4 & 2 & 1 & 1 & 0 \\ 2 & 13 & 2 & 0 & 1 \end{bmatrix}$$

$2x_1 + 13x_2 + 2x_3 + x_5 = 4{,}800$

$x_i \ge 0$ $i = 1, 2, 3, 4, 5$

Select x_1 and x_3 as basic, x_2, x_4, and x_5 as non-basic variables.

$$X_1 = \begin{bmatrix} x_1 \\ x_3 \end{bmatrix} \qquad X_2 = \begin{bmatrix} x_2 \\ x_4 \\ x_5 \end{bmatrix} \qquad C_1 = \begin{bmatrix} 5 \\ 2 \end{bmatrix} \qquad C_2 = \begin{bmatrix} 4 \\ 0 \\ 0 \end{bmatrix}$$

$$A_1 = \begin{bmatrix} 4 & 1 \\ 2 & 2 \end{bmatrix} \qquad A_2 = \begin{bmatrix} 2 & 1 & 0 \\ 13 & 0 & 1 \end{bmatrix}$$

$$A_1^{-1} = \begin{bmatrix} \frac{1}{3} & -\frac{1}{6} \\ -\frac{1}{3} & \frac{2}{3} \end{bmatrix}$$

$$X = A^{-1}B - A_1^{-1}A_2X_2$$

$$X_1 = \begin{bmatrix} x_1 \\ x_3 \end{bmatrix} = \begin{bmatrix} \frac{1}{3} & -\frac{1}{6} \\ -\frac{1}{3} & \frac{2}{3} \end{bmatrix}\begin{bmatrix} 4{,}800 \\ 4{,}800 \end{bmatrix} - \begin{bmatrix} \frac{1}{3} & -\frac{1}{6} \\ -\frac{1}{3} & \frac{2}{3} \end{bmatrix}\begin{bmatrix} 2 & 1 & 0 \\ 13 & 0 & 1 \end{bmatrix}\begin{bmatrix} x_2 \\ x_4 \\ x_5 \end{bmatrix}$$

$$= \begin{bmatrix} 800 \\ 1{,}600 \end{bmatrix} - \begin{bmatrix} -\frac{3}{2} & \frac{1}{3} & -\frac{1}{6} \\ 8 & -\frac{1}{3} & \frac{2}{3} \end{bmatrix}\begin{bmatrix} x_2 \\ x_4 \\ x_5 \end{bmatrix}$$

$$z = C_1'A_1^{-1}B - (C_1'A_1^{-1}A_2 - C_2')X_2$$

$$z = \begin{bmatrix} 5 & 2 \end{bmatrix} \begin{bmatrix} 800 \\ 1,600 \end{bmatrix} - \left\{ \begin{bmatrix} 5 & 2 \end{bmatrix} \begin{bmatrix} -\frac{3}{2} & \frac{1}{3} & -\frac{1}{6} \\ 8 & -\frac{1}{3} & \frac{2}{3} \end{bmatrix} - \begin{bmatrix} 4 \\ 0 \\ 0 \end{bmatrix}' \right\} \begin{bmatrix} x_2 \\ x_4 \\ x_5 \end{bmatrix}$$

$$= 7,200 - (8.5 - 4)x_2 - (1 - 0)x_4 - (\tfrac{1}{2} - 0)x_5$$

$$= 7,200 - 4.5x_2 - x_4 - \tfrac{1}{2}x_5$$

The important results may be summarized, illustrated, and interpreted as follows:

1. The solution is given by

$$x_j = b_j' \qquad j = 1, \ldots, m$$
$$x_j = 0 \qquad j = m + 1, \ldots, n + m$$

   It is feasible if all $b_j' \geq 0$. (Note that one or more of the b_j' may be zero.)

2. The matrix $A_1^{-1}A_2$ has n columns, one for each non-basic variable. The element in the ith row and jth column gives the amount by which the ith basic variable would be changed in the optimum solution if the jth non-basic variable were set to one.

3. Substituting a basic feasible solution

$$X_1 = A_1^{-1}B - A_1^{-1}A_2X_2$$

   into the objective function

$$z = C_1'X_1' + C_2'X_2$$

   gives

$$z = C_1'A^{-1}B - (C_1'A_1^{-1}A_2 - C_2')X_2$$
$$z = z' - c_{m+1}'x_{m+1} - \cdots - c_n'x_{n+m}$$

   where the $x_{n+1} \cdots x_{n+m}$ are the non-basic variables.

4. The coefficient c_j' is the jth element in

$$C_1A_1^{-1}A_2 - C_2$$

   C_1 is the vector of net revenue of the basic variables and C_2 is the vector of net revenues of the non-basic variables. $A^{-1}A_2$ gives the change in a new optimum solution for the basic variables when the non-basic variables are given unit positive values. The coefficient c_j' is:

   $c_j' = $ change in profit from the basic variable $-$ profit from x_j if $x_j = 1$

For example: $x_2 = 1$ would result in $\frac{3}{2}$ units less of x_1 and 8 units more of x_3. The change in earnings in the basic variables is

$$5(-\tfrac{3}{2}) + 8(2) = +8.5$$

The profit from 1 unit of x_2 is 4 and therefore the c coefficient for x_2 is $8.5 - 4 = 4.5$. The fact that it is positive means that increasing x_2 above zero will decrease the profit, since all the c's have a minus sign in the profit function.

5. If the solution is not feasible or any one of the $c'_{m+1}, c'_{m+2}, \ldots, c'_{n+m}$ are less than zero, the solution is not optimum.

6. If the solution is feasible and if $c'_{m+1}, c'_{m+2}, \ldots, c'_{n+m}$ are all non-negative, the optimum solution has been obtained. The maximum value of the objective function is z'. In the example, all three c's are non-negative; the optimum solution is the one in which x_1 and x_3 are basic variables.

7. If one of the original decision variables is a non-basic variable in the optimum solution, the optimum level of the corresponding activity is zero. In the example, x_2 is a non-basic variable and $x_2 = 0$ in the optimum solution. The coefficient c_j' of that original variable indicates the cost (reduction in profit) if the level of the corresponding activity is 1 unit. The coefficient 4.5 indicates the reduction in profit if $x_2 = 1$.

8. If a slack variable is a basic variable in the optimum solution, the corresponding resource for which it was defined is not completely utilized in the optimum solution. In Example 2, the slack variable x_5 is a basic variable and not all the available threading-machine time is required to maximize profit.

9. The coefficient c_j' of a slack variable which is non-basic indicates the cost of the constraint. If one additional unit of the resource is available, profit will be increased by c_j', and if one unit less is available, profit will be decreased by c_j'. In Example 2, x_4 is the slack variable for the slotting-machine constraint. The coefficient $\frac{5}{4}$ indicates the increase in profit if one more minute of slotting-machine time were available.

10. One or more of the coefficients of the non-basic variables c_j' may be zero in the optimal solution. This shows that the set of basic variables is not unique. If c_j' is zero, the non-basic variable can become a basic variable without changing the maximum value of the objective function.

The procedure described above provides a method of determining whether a selected set of variables gives a basic feasible optimum solution. Suppose it does not. One possibility is to replace one of the basic variables with a non-basic variable and try again. The non-basic variable that should become basic is clearly one which has a positive coefficient in the objective function after the solution has been substituted. However, it is not immediately apparent which basic variable should become non-basic. The simplex method (described in the next section) contains a rule for making this choice.

The examination of a set of variables for optimality requires the solution of m equations in m unknowns with n right-hand sides. If one basic variable is then replaced by a non-basic variable, the new set of equations must be solved. However, the new set differs from the old set in only one column and the amount of computation can be reduced by using this fact. Section C in Chapter 13 illustrated one possibility, using the systematic elimination method for solving linear equations. Another possibility is the use of the inverse of the matrix of basic variables (A_1 in Table 15-2). The modification of the inverse when one column is changed is given as Exercise 1 in the Chapter Exercises, Chapter 13.

LP as a Special Case of Non-linear Programming

LP is a special case of non-linear programming, and the linear programming results, obtained in this chapter by geometrical and algebraic analysis, can also be derived from the Kuhn-Tucker conditions which are given in Chapter 11 for two variables and in Chapter 18 for n variables. The application of these conditions to the standard linear programming problem is as follows:

General problem	LP
maximize $f(x_1 \cdots x_n)$	maximize $\sum_{i=1}^{n} \gamma_i x_i$
subject to:	subject to:
$g_j(x_1 \cdots x_n) \le 0; \quad j = 1, \ldots, m$	$\sum_{i=1}^{n} a_{ij} x_i \le b_j \quad j = 1, \ldots, m$
$x_i > 0 \quad i = 1, \ldots, n$	$x_i \ge 0, \quad i = 1, \ldots, n$

Lagrange statement:

$$f(x_1, \ldots, x_n) - \sum_{j=1}^{m} \lambda_j g_j(x_1, \ldots, x_n) \qquad \sum_{i=1}^{n} \gamma_i x_i - \left\{ \sum_{j=1}^{m} \lambda_j \left(\sum_{i=1}^{n} a_{ij} x_i - b_j \right) \right\}$$

Kuhn-Tucker conditions:

$$\frac{\partial f}{\partial x_i} - \sum_{j=1}^{m} \lambda_j \frac{\partial g_j}{\partial x_i} \leq 0 \qquad \gamma_i - \sum_{j=1}^{m} \lambda_j a_{ji} \leq 0 \tag{13}$$

$$\sum_{i=1}^{n} x_i \left\{ \frac{\partial f}{\partial x_i} - \sum_{j=1}^{m} \lambda_j \frac{\partial g_j}{\partial x_i} \right\} = 0 \qquad \sum_{i=1}^{n} x_i \left\{ \gamma_i - \sum_{j=1}^{m} \lambda_j a_{ij} \right\} = 0 \tag{14}$$

$$\lambda_j g_j = 0 \qquad j = 1, \ldots, m \qquad \lambda_j \left(\sum_{i=1}^{n} a_{ij} x_i - b_j \right) = 0 \tag{15}$$

$$x_i \geq 0 \qquad i = 1, \ldots, n \qquad x_i \geq 0 \qquad i = 1, \ldots, n$$

$$\lambda_j \geq 0 \qquad j = 1, \ldots, m \qquad \lambda_j \geq 0 \qquad j = 1, \ldots, m$$

The interpretation is:

1. A λ is defined for each constraint. Equations (15) state that either λ is zero or the constraint is satisfied as an *equality* in the optimum solution. A positive value of λ indicates that the constraint will be satisfied as an *equality*. The value of λ will be identical with the coefficient c' for the slack variable that makes the constraint an equality in the LP model. The slack variable will be a non-basic variable in the optimum solution.

2. The λ's give the cost of the constraints or equivalently the value of 1 unit of the resource. The a_{ij} are the amount of the jth resource required for 1 unit of x_i. The sum $\Sigma \lambda_j a_{ij}$ is the value of the resources required for 1 unit of x_i. The set of inequalities (13) states that, at the optimum solution, the profit from 1 unit of x_i cannot exceed the value of resources required for that 1 unit.

3. In the sum (14) the x_i are all non-negative and the terms in the braces are all non-positive. The only way that the sum can be zero is for each term to be zero. Either the activity is at zero level ($x_i = 0$) or the value of resources used is exactly equal to the profit $\left(\gamma_i = \sum_{j=1}^{m} \lambda_j a_{ij} \right)$.

The coefficient c' for the ith activity, if it is non-basic in the optimum LP solution, is identical to $c_i - \sum_{j=1}^{m} \lambda_j a_{ij}$.

EXERCISES

For Exercises 1–5:
  (*a*) Formulate the LP model, using slack variables.
  (*b*) Give an economic interpretation of the slack variables.
  (*c*) Find the optimum solution and verify optimality.

(*d*) Give an economic interpretation of each basic and each non-basic variable.

(*e*) Determine the extent to which each resource can be changed without requiring a different set of basic variables in the optimum solution.

1. The Problem in Exercise 1, p. 432.
2. The Problem in Exercise 4, p. 432.
3. The Problem in Exercise 5, p. 432.
4. The Problem in Exercise 6, p. 432.
5. The Problem in Exercise 8, p. 433.
6. Use the procedures described in the second part of Section E, Chapter 13, to find the optimum in the product-mix problem, Example 1, starting with x_1 and x_4 as basic variables.
7. Answer 6, using the matrix procedure from Chapter Exercise 1, p. 386.
8. Apply the Kuhn-Tucker conditions to the product-mix problem, Example 1, p. 426.

D. THE SIMPLEX METHOD FOR SOLVING LINEAR PROGRAMMING PROBLEMS

Algebraic Solution

In the previous sections a number of problems have been formulated and solved as linear programming problems. The examples have shown that by using graphical and enumeration methods it is possible to develop and solve the model when the number of activities is less than, equal to, or greater than the number of resources. In the two previous sections it has been shown that in a linear programming problem with m constraints and n variables, once we know which m variables lead to an optimum solution:

1. The optimum solution can be obtained by solving m equations in m unknowns or by inverting a $m \times m$ matrix A_1^{-1} and computing $X_1 = A_1^{-1}B$ where the subscripts relate to whether basic (1) or non-basic (2) variables are involved.

2. The optimality of the solution is verified if all the elements of $(C_1A_1^{-1}A_2 - C_2)$ are non-negative.

3. The other questions of interest can be answered by computing $A_1^{-1}A_2X_2$ and $C_1A_1^{-1}B$.

The linear programming model can be, and has been, applied to a number of decision-making problems in business, but in general the number of constraints and the number of decision variables are so large that it is not practical to use the graphical and enumeration methods.

The simplex method for solving linear programming problems is based on the fact that it is not necessary to enumerate and examine all vertices.

It is possible to compute the objective at a vertex and then at another vertex in such a way that each successive vertex examined is feasible and always results in a higher objective than the previous one. More specifically, the procedure consists of computing the profit at *a* vertex, and then examining all feasible vertices which can be reached from this one by moving along the edge of the polyhedron to determine which one results in the largest increase in the objective. The objective is computed at this new vertex and the procedure is repeated until no feasible vertex shows a higher objective. When this occurs, the optimum solution has been found.

The algebraic manipulation in the simplex method will be illustrated by using the 2-product and 2-machine product-mix example. A summary flow chart of the simplex method appears on page 462.

Example of the Simplex Method. The problem has been stated mathematically as follows: find values of the decision variables x_1 and x_2 which maximize

$$5x_1 + 4x_2$$

subject to the restrictions:

$$4x_1 + 2x_2 \leq 4,800$$
$$2x_1 + 13x_2 \leq 4,800$$
$$x_1 \geq 0; \quad x_2 \geq 0$$

The *first* step in the simplex solution is to change each inequality to an equality by defining two new decision variables, x_3 and x_4, the slack variables, such that

$$4x_1 + 2x_2 + x_3 + 0x_4 = 4,800$$

and

$$2x_1 + 13x_2 + 0x_3 + x_4 = 4,800$$

x_3 is the level of an activity which, per unit, produces 1 minute of idle time on machine 1; x_4 is the level of an activity which, per unit, produces 1 minute of idle time on machine 2.

Neither of these activities produces any product other than idle time and, therefore, the profit assigned to each of these outputs is zero.

The problem may now be stated as: find values of x_1, x_2, x_3, and x_4 which

maximize $\qquad\qquad 5x_1 + 4x_2 + 0x_3 + 0x_4$ $\qquad\qquad\qquad$ (1)

subject to the conditions:

$$4x_1 + 2x_2 + x_3 + 0x_4 = 4,800 \qquad\qquad (2)$$
$$2x_1 + 13x_2 + 0x_3 + x_4 = 4,800 \qquad\qquad (3)$$
$$x_1 \geq 0; \quad x_2 \geq 0; \quad x_3 \geq 0; \quad x_4 \geq 0$$

The *second* step is to select an initial vertex in the set of feasible solutions. There are many possible initial vertices which could be used; in general, the selection of an initial vertex is not critical because the procedure will eventually yield the optimum regardless of which initial vertex was selected. However, the choice does influence the amount of computation required to obtain the optimum. Frequently an easy way to obtain an initial solution is to use the slack variables as basic variables.

After the initial basic variables have been selected, the third step is to obtain a basic feasible solution by replacing the equations with linear combinations so that each basic variable appears with a coefficient 1 in one of the equations, and 0 in all the others; i.e., the matrix of coefficients of the basic variables must be such that by a suitable rearrangement of the columns an identity matrix can be obtained. In this particular case, Equations (2) and (3) are in the required form if the slack variables are the basic variables so no further manipulation is required. The solution is:

$$x_3 = 4{,}800 \qquad \text{(basic variable)}$$
$$x_4 = 4{,}800 \qquad \text{(basic variable)}$$
$$x_1 = 0 \qquad \text{(non-basic variable)}$$
$$x_2 = 0 \qquad \text{(non-basic variable)}$$

This initial solution states that both machines are idle all the time; this is certainly a feasible solution because it satisfies the equalities and non-negative conditions. This step, in general, provides a convenient way to compute the change in the solution if 1 unit of each of the non-basic variables were to be produced.

The equations (2) and (3) may be rewritten as

$$1x_3 + 0x_4 = 4{,}800 - 4x_1 - 2x_2 \qquad\qquad (2')$$
$$0x_3 + 1x_4 = 4{,}800 - 2x_1 - 13x_2 \qquad\qquad (3')$$

With the equations in this form, it is easy to determine the change in the solution for the basic variables (x_3, x_4) that would be necessary to produce 1 unit of any one of the non-basic variables; the ability to do this easily depends on having the coefficient of x_4 in (2) and the coefficient of x_3 in (3) equal to zero. For example, the initial solution was $x_1 = 0$, $x_2 = 0$, $x_3 = 4{,}800$, $x_4 = 4{,}800$, and from the form given above, one can immediately check by direct substitution into the original equations that

$$x_1 = 1, \quad x_2 = 0, \quad x_3 = 4{,}796, \quad x_4 = 4{,}798$$
and
$$x_2 = 1, \quad x_1 = 0, \quad x_3 = 4{,}798, \quad x_4 = 4{,}787$$

are also solutions to the two equations in four unknowns.

The *fourth* step consists of determining whether the production of any of the non-basic products would result in greater profit than the production of the equivalent combination of basic activities. An equivalent combination is one which would consume the same amount of resources. The profit is given by

$$z = 5x_1 + 4x_2 + 0x_3 + 0x_4$$

Substituting the solution from (2′) and (3′) into this equation gives

$$z = 5x_1 + 4x_2 + 0(4{,}800 - 4x_1 - 2x_2) + 0(4{,}800 - 2x_1 - 13x_2)$$
$$= 5x_1 + 4x_2 + 0 + 0 \tag{4}$$

The equation states that if x_3 and x_4 are the basic variables, the profit will be zero; and if 1 unit of x_1 is produced, the profit will be increased by 5; or if 1 unit of x_2 is produced, the profit will be increased by 4. These coefficients, 5 and 4, are called changes in profit because they indicate the change in profit if some resources are withdrawn from the basic products x_3 or x_4 to produce the non-basic products, x_1 or x_2.

The *fifth* step is to determine whether any of the "change in profit" numbers are positive. If there are no positive values, the optimum has been found. If there are positive values, as in this case, additional steps are required.

The first phase of the simplex procedure has now been completed. The initial steps may be summarized as:

Step 1: Change inequalities to equalities.   Maximize

$$5x_1 + 4x_2 + 0x_3 + 0x_4$$

subject to:

$$4x_1 + 2x_2 + x_3 + 0x_4 = 4{,}800$$
$$2x_1 + 13x_2 + 0x_4 + x_3 = 4{,}800$$

Step 2: Select basic variables.   Let x_3 and x_4 be the basic variables.

Step 3: Obtain a basic feasible solution.
$$x_3 + 0x_4 = 4{,}800 - 4x_1 - 2x_2$$
$$0x_3 + x_4 = 4{,}800 - 2x_1 - 13x_2$$

Step 4: Compute the "change in profit" by substituting the solution for the basic variables in the objective. $z = 5x_1 + 4x_2$

Step 5: Is any "change in profit" greater than zero?   Yes.

The additional iterations differ from the initial iteration in two new steps, 6 and 7, are required before steps 3, 4, and 5 are repeated.

The *sixth* step is to replace one of the basic variables with a non-basic variable if such a change results in an increase in profit. In this case there are two products, x_1 and x_2, which will result in increased profit. The *rule* is to choose the product which results in the largest change in profit. (If two coefficients have the same value, either one may be chosen.) In this case, x_1 should become a basic variable.

The *seventh* step is to determine which non-basic variable must be removed from the solution. Since the optimum solution must be a basic solution, it can have only two basic variables and, therefore, one of the basic variables x_3, x_4, will have to become a non-basic variable. The rule for determining which one should be eliminated is as follows:

1. In each equation, divide the value of the basic variable (i.e., the right-hand side) by the coefficient in the column representing the new basic variable and record the ratio, in this case

$$\frac{4,800}{4} = 1,200$$

$$\frac{4,800}{2} = 2,400$$

2. The product with the smallest ratio is the one which becomes a non-basic variable. In this case, the lowest ratio appears in the equation for x_3 and, therefore, x_3 becomes a non-basic variable.

The reason for this rule is that once it has been shown that x_1 is to become a basic variable (because each unit of x_1 results in the largest unit profit), it is obviously desirable to produce as many units of x_1 as possible. The constraints on x_1 are that it must be non-negative and satisfy the equations:

$$x_3 = 4,800 - 4x_1 - 2x_2$$

$$x_4 = 4,800 - 2x_1 - 13x_2$$

If $x_2 = 0$, the first equation limits x_1 to 1,200 or less, because if x_1 were greater than 1,200, x_3 would have to be negative. If $x_1 = 2,400$, $x_2 = 0$, then $x_3 = 4,800 - 9,600 = -4,800$. This violates the constraint that $x_3 \geq 0$. Therefore, by computing the ratios and eliminating the variable with the lowest (positive) ratio, the procedure yields the vertex which has the largest production of the new basic variable that is possible without violating the constraint that all x's must be non-negative.

Step 3 requires replacing the equations (2) and (3) with a set in which x_1 and x_4 are the basic variables. This could be done by starting with (2) and (3):

$$4x_1 + 2x_2 + x_3 + 0x_4 = 4{,}800 \tag{2}$$

$$2x_1 + 13x_2 + 0x_3 + x_4 = 4{,}800 \tag{3}$$

Since x_4 was a basic variable in the first iteration, its coefficients are 0 and 1. However, x_1 was not a basic variable and its coefficients must be changed. Multiplying (2) by $\frac{1}{4}$ gives (5), and adding -2 times (5) to (3) gives (6):

$$x_1 + 0.5x_2 + 0.25x_3 + 0x_4 = 1{,}200 \tag{5}$$

$$0x_1 + 12x_2 - 0.5x_3 + x_4 = 2{,}400 \tag{6}$$

The constants ($\frac{1}{4}$ and -2) are chosen so that x_1 has a coefficient of 1 in (5) and 0 in (6), and the coefficients of x_4 are not disturbed.

Now x_1 and x_4 are basic variables, and (5) and (6) can be written in the basic form

$$x_1 + 0x_4 = 1{,}200 - 0.5x_2 - 0.25x_3 \tag{5'}$$

$$0x_1 + x_4 = 2{,}400 - 12x_2 + 0.5x_3 \tag{6'}$$

Step 4 requires the computation of the "change in profit" if x_1 and x_4 are basic variables. Substituting (5') and (6') into (1) gives

$$z = 5x_1 + 4x_2 + 0x_3 + 0x_4 \tag{1}$$

$$= 5(1{,}200 - 0.5x_2 - 0.25x_3) + 4x_2 + 0x_3 + 0(2{,}400 - 12x_2 + 0.5x_3)$$

$$= 6{,}000 + 1.5x_2 - 1.25x_3 \tag{7}$$

Step 5. Since the coefficient of one of the non-basic variables is positive, the profit can be increased if x_2 is a basic variable. The optimum solution has not been reached.

The next iteration in summary form is:

Step 6: Select a new basic x_2
         variable.

Step 7: Remove one of the basic   From (5'): If $x_2 = 2{,}400$,
         variables.   then $x_1 = 0$
                                      From (6'): If $x_2 = 200$,
                                                 then $x_4 = 0$
                                      Therefore, x_4 becomes non-basic.

Step 3: Obtain the basic feasible   Multiply (6) by $\frac{1}{12}$ to get (9).
         solution with the new   Add $-\frac{1}{2}$ of (9) to (5) to get (8).
         basic variables.

$$x_1 + 0x_2 + \tfrac{13}{48}x_3 - \tfrac{1}{24}x_4 = 1{,}100 \tag{8}$$

$$0x_1 + x_2 - \tfrac{1}{24}x_3 + \tfrac{1}{12}x_4 = 200 \tag{9}$$

Step 4: Compute the "change in profit."

Substituting (8) and (9) into (1) gives:

$$z = 5x_1 + 4x_2 + 0x_3 + 0x_4 \tag{1}$$

$$= 5(1,100 - \tfrac{13}{48}x_3 + \tfrac{1}{24}x_4)$$

$$+ 4(200 + \tfrac{1}{24}x_3 - \tfrac{1}{12}x_4) + 0x_3 + 0x_4$$

$$= 6,300 - \tfrac{57}{48}x_3 - \tfrac{3}{24}x_4 \tag{10}$$

Note that (10) can be obtained more simply by substituting (9) into (7).

Step 5: Is there any "change in profit" greater than zero?

No. Therefore, the optimum solution is $x_1 = 1,100$; $x_2 = 200$; $x_3 = 0$; $x_4 = 0$, and $z = 6,300$.

The simplex solution has examined the feasible vertices, M, N, and Q in Fig. 15-1 in succession for optimality.

The Simplex Tableau

In large problems the algebraic form of the simplex method, as described above, becomes cumbersome and unwieldy. A system for recording the pertinent data in a tabular form, known as the simplex tableau, is shown in Tables 15-3 and 15-5. To aid in following the tableau, the example discussed above is summarized in Table 15-4. Numerical values are given in Table 15-5.

The tableau consists of a number of rows in each of which numbers and data are recorded in a number of columns:

1. In row 0 of the tableau are recorded the unit profits, and in row 1 are listed the headings for the columns.

2. The remaining rows are divided into groups by double horizontal lines. Within each set of double lines there are $m + 1$ rows containing the data for one iteration, the first m containing the equations and the last one the "change in profit" coefficients.

3. The columns are divided into three sets by two double vertical lines.

4. Column I is used to record which variables are the basic variables, and column II gives the unit profit for these variables (copied from the appropriate column in row 0).

5. The columns after the first set of vertical double lines give the coefficients of the equations and the coefficients of the vector **B**. There will be one column for each unknown and one column for the **B** vector. Therefore, in general with n unknowns there will be $n + 1$ columns; in this case there are 4 unknowns and 5 columns, III to VII.

Table 15-3 The Simplex Tableau: Example

	I	II	III	IV	V	VI	VII	VIII	IX
			c_1	c_2	c_3	c_4	$-z$		
(0)									
(1)	Basic Variables	Unit Profit	x_1	x_2	x_3	x_4	b	Check	Ratio
(2)	x_3	c_3	$a_{11\cdot0}$	$a_{12\cdot0}$	1	0	$b_{1\cdot0}$	$s_{1\cdot0}$	$b_{1\cdot0}/a_{11\cdot0}$ →
(3)	x_4	c_4	$a_{21\cdot0}$	$a_{22\cdot0}$	0	1	$b_{2\cdot0}$	$s_{2\cdot0}$	$b_{2\cdot0}/a_{21\cdot0}$
(4)	Change in Profit		$c_{1\cdot0}$ *	$c_{2\cdot0}$	0	0	$-z$	$s_{3\cdot0}$	
(5)	x_1	c_1	1	$a_{12\cdot1}$	$a_{13\cdot1}$	0	$b_{1\cdot1}$	$s_{1\cdot1}$	$b_{1\cdot1}/a_{12\cdot1}$
(6)	x_4	c_4	0	$a_{22\cdot1}$	$a_{23\cdot1}$	1	$b_{2\cdot1}$	$s_{2\cdot1}$	$b_{2\cdot1}/a_{22\cdot1}$ →
(7)	Change in Profit		0	$c_{2\cdot1}$ *	$c_{3\cdot1}$	0	$-z_{0\cdot1}$	$s_{3\cdot1}$	
(8)	x_1	c_1	1	0	$a_{13\cdot2}$	$a_{14\cdot2}$	$b_{1\cdot2}$	$s_{1\cdot2}$	
(9)	x_2	c_2	0	1	$a_{23\cdot2}$	$a_{14\cdot2}$	$b_{2\cdot2}$	$s_{2\cdot2}$	
(10)	Change in Profit		0	0	$c_{3\cdot2}$	$c_{4\cdot2}$	$-z_{0\cdot2}$	$s_{3\cdot2}$	

Table 15-4   Solution and 2-Product and 2-Machine Product-Mix Problem by the Simplex Method

	(1) Algebraic Form	(2)
(1)	$z = 5x_1 + 4x_2 + 0x_3 + 0x_4$	$z = 5x_1 + 4x_2 + 0x_3 + 0x_4$
(2)	$x_3 = 4,800 - 4x_1 - 2x_2$	$x_3 + 0x_4 = 4,800 - 4x_1 - 2x_2$
(3)	$x_4 = 4,800 - 2x_1 - 13x_2$	$0x_3 + x_4 = 4,800 - 2x_1 - 13x_2$
(4)	$z = 5x_1 + 4x_2 + 0(4,800 - 4x_1 - 2x_2) + 0(4,800 - 2x_1 - 13x_2)$ $z = 5x_1 + 4x_2$	$z - 0.0 - 0.0 = 5x_1 + 4x_2$
(5)	$x_1 = 1,200 - \frac{1}{2}x_2 - \frac{1}{4}x_3$	$x_1 + 0x_4 = 1,200 - \frac{1}{2}x_2 - \frac{1}{4}x_3$
(6)	$x_4 = 2,400 - 12x_2 + \frac{1}{2}x_3$	$0x_1 + x_4 = 2,400 - 12x_2 + \frac{1}{2}x_3$
(7)	$z = 5(1,200 - \frac{1}{2}x_2 - \frac{1}{4}x_3) + 4x_2 + 0(2,400 - 12x_2 + \frac{1}{2}x_4)$ $= 6,000 + \frac{3}{2}x_2 - \frac{5}{4}x_3$	$z - 5(1,200) - 0.0 = 1\frac{1}{2}x_2 - \frac{5}{4}x_3$
(8)	$x_1 = 1,100 - \frac{13}{48}x_3 + \frac{1}{24}x_4$	$x_1 + 0x_2 = 1,100 - \frac{13}{48}x_3 + \frac{1}{24}x_4$
(9)	$x_2 = 200 + \frac{1}{24}x_3 - \frac{1}{12}x_4$	$0x_1 + 1x_2 = 200 + \frac{1}{24}x_3 - \frac{1}{12}x_4$
(10)	$z = 5(1,100 - \frac{13}{48}x_3 + \frac{1}{24}x_4) + 4(200 + \frac{1}{24}x_3 - \frac{1}{12}x_4) + 0x_3 + 0x_4$ $= 6,300 - \frac{57}{48}x_3 - \frac{3}{24}x_4$	$z - 5(1,100) - 4(200) = -\frac{57}{48}x_3 - \frac{3}{24}x_4$

Table 15-5 The Simplex Tableau: Example

Linear Combination	(I)	(II)	(III) 5	(IV) 4	(V) 0	(VI) 0	(VII) $-z$	(VIII)	(IX)
	Basic Variables	Unit Profit	x_1	x_2	x_3	x_4	b	Check	Ratio
(2)	x_3	0	4	2	1	0	4,800	4,807	1,200→
(3)	x_4	0	2	13	0	1	4,800	4,816	2,400
(4)	Change in Profit		5*	4	0	0	0	9	
(5) = $\frac{1}{4}$(2)	x_1	5	1	$\frac{1}{2}$	$\frac{1}{4}$	0	1,200	1,201$\frac{3}{4}$	2,400
(6) = (3) − 2(5)	x_4	0	0	12	$-\frac{1}{2}$	1	2,400	2,412$\frac{1}{2}$	200→
(7) = (4) − 5(5)	Change in Profit		0	1$\frac{1}{2}$*	$-\frac{5}{4}$	0	−6,000	−5,999$\frac{3}{4}$	
(8) = (5) − $\frac{1}{2}$(9)	x_1	5	1	0	$\frac{13}{48}$	$-\frac{1}{24}$	1,100	1,101$\frac{11}{48}$	
(9) = $\frac{1}{12}$(6)	x_2	4	0	1	$-\frac{1}{24}$	$\frac{1}{12}$	200	201$\frac{1}{24}$	
(10) = (7) − $\frac{3}{2}$(9)	Change in Profit		0	0	$-\frac{57}{48}$	$-\frac{3}{24}$	−6,300	−6,301$\frac{15}{48}$	

6. There are two columns on the right of the last set of vertical lines; the first, column VIII in this case, is used to record the check sum. As each line is computed, the coefficient in column VIII in that line is computed by the same procedure. The coefficients in that line from column III to column VII are then added and a numerical error has been made if the sum does not equal the number in column VIII. Column IX is used to record the ratio that is needed to determine which basic variable is to become a non-basic variable.

The following are the general rules for the simplex method for the standard linear program model; they will be illustrated with reference to the example. The steps refer to those given above:

Step 1: The standard linear programming problem is placed in the form

maximize $\qquad\qquad$ $z = C'X$

subject to $\qquad\qquad$ $AX = B$, and $X \geq 0$

by adding slack variables so that all constraints become equalities. The simplex tableau is laid as in Table 15-3 with $n + 1$ columns between the two sets of vertical double lines. The appropriate headings are recorded in row 1 and the elements of the vector C are recorded in row 0.

Step 2: An initial set of basic variables is selected and recorded in columns I and II. In this example the slack variables form an initial set of basic variables.

Step 3: The equations are replaced by a set of linear combinations so that the coefficients of the basic variables form the identity matrix. In Table 15-3 the matrix appears in columns V and VI, and the coefficients are labeled $a_{ij \cdot 0}$. The $b_{i \cdot 0}$ must all be non-negative if the solution is to be feasible. The $s_{i \cdot 0}$ are obtained by summing the coefficients in line i; e.g.,

$$s_{1 \cdot 0} = a_{11 \cdot 0} + a_{12 \cdot 0} + 1 + 0 + b_{1 \cdot 0}$$

Step 4: The "change in profit" coefficients are computed for each non-basic variable

$$c_{j \cdot 0} = c_j - \sum_i a_{ij \cdot 0} c_i''$$

where c_i'' is the coefficient in column II in the ith row of the iteration and the summation is over all m rows. For example,

$$c_{1 \cdot 0} = 5 - [4(0) + 2(0)] = 5$$
$$c_{2 \cdot 0} = 4 - [2(0) + 13(0)] = 4$$

The total profit given in column VII is

$$-z = 0 - \sum_i b_{i \cdot 0} c_i''$$
$$= 0 - [(4,800)(0) + 4,800(0)]$$

Because of the convention used in computing the "change in profit" coefficients, the negative of total profit will appear in column VII.

Step 5: All the "change in profit" coefficients are recorded in the last row of an iteration. The coefficients for the basic variables are all zero.

Step 6: The new basic variable is usually marked with an asterisk.

Step 7: The ratio for determining which basic variable is to become non-basic is obtained by dividing the coefficient in the column of the new basic variable (column III) into the solution (column VII). The ratio is recorded in column IX if the coefficient is greater than zero. If the denominator is = 0, the ratio is irrelevant. If the denominator is negative, the equation is not restricting the variable. If there are two ratios which are equal, a convenient rule is to select the one with the largest denominator. [If all the ratios are zero (or negative) the optimum value of the objective function is $\pm \infty$.]

Step 3: The equations must be replaced by a linear combination, so that the coefficients of the basic variables form an identity matrix. In general, if there are m basic variables, $m - 1$ already satisfy the requirement, and only the coefficients of the new basic variable must be changed. This can be done by replacing each equation with a linear combination of equations from the previous iteration. The particular linear combination which is used is the same as that used in solving systems of linear equations and inverting matrices in Chapter 4. For example, in Table 15-3,

$$\text{row (5)} = \frac{1}{a_{11 \cdot 0}} \text{row (2)}$$

$$\text{row (6)} = \text{row (3)} - a_{21 \cdot 0} \text{row (5)}$$

Step 4: The change in profit, row 7, can be obtained by

$$\text{row (7)} = \text{row (4)} - c_{1 \cdot 0} \text{row (5)}$$

The effect of this is to make the coefficient of the new basic variable in row 7 equal to zero.

The computation of the profit row may be checked by using its definition, e.g.,

Column (III): Change for 1 unit in $x_1 = 5 - (5 \times 1) - (0 \times 0) = 0$

Column (IV): Change for 1 unit in $x_2 = 4 - (5 \times \frac{1}{2}) - (0 \times 12) = 1\frac{1}{2}$

Column (V): Change for 1 unit in $x_3 = 0 - (5 \times \frac{1}{4}) - (-\frac{1}{2} \times 0) = -\frac{5}{4}$

Column (VI): Change for 1 unit in $x_4 = 0 - (5 \times 0) - (0 \times 1) = 0$

Column (VII): The total profit $= -(5 \times 1,200) - (0 \times 2,400) = -6,000$

Step 5: In the example $c_{2 \cdot 1}$ is positive.

Step 6: x_2 becomes a basic variable.

Step 7: The ratios are

$$\text{row (5)} \ \frac{1,200}{\frac{1}{2}} = 2,400$$

$$\text{row (6)} \ \frac{2,400}{12} = 200$$

and therefore x_4 will be eliminated as a basic variable.

Step 3: The new feasible solution is obtained by

$$\text{row (9)} = \frac{1}{a_{22 \cdot 1}} \ \text{row (6)}$$

$$\text{row (8)} = \text{row (5)} - a_{12 \cdot 1} \ \text{row (9)}$$

Step 4: The change in profit is obtained by

$$\text{row (10)} = \text{row (7)} - c_{2 \cdot 1} \ \text{row (9)}$$

Step 5: No coefficient is greater than zero. The *optimum* basic feasible solution is

$$x_1 = 1,100$$

$$x_2 = 200$$

and the profit is, therefore,

$$(1,100)(5) + (200)(4) = 5,500 + 800 = 6,300$$

The check column (VIII) is used for checking the computations in the same way that it was used in Chapter 12. When the initial tableau is prepared, the coefficients in each row from columns (III) to (VII) are added together and recorded in column (VIII). Each row after (5) is a linear combination of some preceding lines. The linear combination is also applied to column VIII. Then the coefficients in the line from columns (III) to (VII) are added together and, if the arithmetic has been carried out correctly, this sum will be equal to the number obtained by applying linear combination to column (VIII).

The simplex algorithm as described here need not necessarily terminate. It is theoretically possible to get into a cycle in which a basic variable becomes non-basic in one iteration, and then becomes basic again in some succeeding iteration. This cycle may be repeated endlessly.

The computations in the simplex method are carried out by a computer for most practical problems. Virtually all computer programs now use a version known as the "revised simplex method" which uses less memory space and has other computational advantages. In this method the presentation of the solution consists of z_{max}, a list of the optimum values of the basic variables and the change in profit or c_j' coefficients (elements of $C_1 A_1^{-1} A_2 - C$) for the non-basic variables. Examples are given in the next chapter.

Summary flow chart of the simplex procedure for the standard LP model.

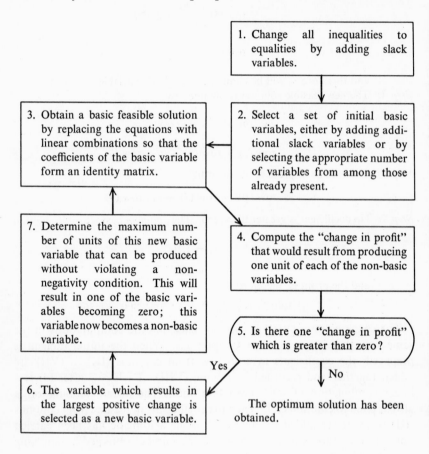

1. Change all inequalities to equalities by adding slack variables.

2. Select a set of initial basic variables, either by adding additional slack variables or by selecting the appropriate number of variables from among those already present.

3. Obtain a basic feasible solution by replacing the equations with linear combinations so that the coefficients of the basic variable form an identity matrix.

4. Compute the "change in profit" that would result from producing one unit of each of the non-basic variables.

5. Is there one "change in profit" which is greater than zero?

6. The variable which results in the largest positive change is selected as a new basic variable.

7. Determine the maximum number of units of this new basic variable that can be produced without violating a non-negativity condition. This will result in one of the basic variables becoming zero; this variable now becomes a non-basic variable.

Yes

No

The optimum solution has been obtained.

EXERCISES

Solve each of the following problems by the simplex method.

1. The two-product two-machine problem used in this section with the objective changed to $z = 1x_1 + 8x_2$.
2. The problem in Exercise 1, p. 432.
3. The problem in Exercise 4, p. 432.
4. The problem in Exercise 5, p. 432.
5. The problem in Exercise 6, p. 432.
6. The problem in Exercise 8, p. 433.
7. The Party Nut Company has on hand 550 pounds of peanuts, 150 pounds of cashew nuts, 90 pounds of brazil nuts, and 70 pounds of hazel nuts. It packages and sells nuts in the following varieties of standard 8-oz cans and at the indicated net wholesale price: Party Peanuts, 26¢ per can; Party Mix, consisting of 50% peanuts, 20% cashew nuts, 15% brazil nuts and 15% hazel nuts. at 38¢ per can; Cashew Nuts (only) at 51¢ per can; and Luzury Mix, consisting of 40% cashew nuts, 25% brazil nuts, and 35% hazel nuts, at 54¢ per can. The company desires to mix these nuts in a way which will yield maximum revenue.

E. EXAMPLES OF LINEAR PROGRAMMING MODELS

Example I. A farmer has a 100-acre farm. He can sell all the tomatoes, lettuce, or radishes he can raise. The price he can obtain is 19¢ a pound for tomatoes, 10¢ a head for lettuce, and 25¢ a pound for radishes. The average yield per acre is 2,000 pounds of tomatoes, 3,000 heads of lettuce, and 1,000 pounds of radishes. Fertilizer is available at 10¢ per pound and the amount required per acre is 100 pounds for tomatoes and lettuce, and 50 pounds for radishes. Labor required for sowing, cultivating, and harvesting per acre is 5 man-days for tomatoes and radishes and 6 man-days for lettuce. A total of 400 man-days of labor are available at $20 per man-day. Formulate this problem as an LP model and solve by the simplex method.

  (a) What action should the farmer take? (Neglect other costs such as cost of seeds, taxes, etc.)
  (b) Additional labor can be obtained at a 25% premium. Should he use this premium cost labor? If yes, how much and what for?

Solution. Let x_1 = acres of tomatoes

x_2 = acres of lettuce

x_3 = acres of radishes

Total revenue = $(19 \times 2,000)x_1 + (10 \times 3,000)x_2 + (25 \times 1,000)x_3$

$$R = 380x_1 + 300x_2 + 250x_3 \quad \text{in dollars}$$

Total cost of fertilizer (in dollars)

$$F = (0.10 \times 100)x_1 + (0.10 \times 100)x_2 + (0.10 \times 50)x_3$$
$$F = 10x_1 + 10x_2 + 5x_3$$

Total cost of labor (in dollars)

$$L = (5 \times 20)x_1 + (6 \times 20)x_2 + (5 \times 20)x_3$$
$$L = 100x_1 + 120x_2 + 100x_3$$

$\therefore$ Profit $Z = R - F - L$

$$Z = 270x_1 + 170x_2 + 145x_3$$

The constraints are:

$$x_1 + x_2 + x_3 \leq 100$$
$$5x_1 + 6x_2 + 5x_3 \leq 400$$

The objective function and the constraining equations are of the form required for a linear programming model. The simplex tableau is:

	Objective	270	170	145	0	0	0			
	Variables	x_1	x_2	x_3	x_4	x_5	b	Check Sum	Ratio
I	x_4	0	1	1	1	1	0	100	104	100
II	x_5	0	5	6	5	0	1	400	417	80 →
	ΔP	270	170	145	0	0				
III	x_4	0	0	$-\frac{1}{5}$	0	1	$-\frac{1}{5}$	20	$20\frac{3}{5}$	
IV	x_1	270	1	$\frac{6}{5}$	1	0	$\frac{1}{5}$	80	$83\frac{2}{5}$	
	ΔP	0	−154	−135	0	−54	−21,600			

From the solution above, it appears that the farmer should plant 80 acres of tomatoes and let 20 acres be idle. This solution will yield a profit of $270 per acre for the 80 acres for a total of $21,600.

The marginal value of additional man-days in the simplex solution is $54 per man-day. Cost of premium labor = 20 × 1.25 = $25 per man-day. Since relaxing the constraint in labor is worth $54 per day, he should hire premium labor.

From equation III, the number of additional man-days required to make use of the remaining 20 acres is obtained from the ratio $\dfrac{20}{\frac{1}{5}} = 100$. The reason for this may be shown explicitly by rewriting equation III

$$-\tfrac{1}{5}x_2 + x_4 - \tfrac{1}{5}x_5 = 20$$

as

$$x_4 = 20 + \tfrac{1}{5}(x_5 + \varepsilon) + \tfrac{1}{5}x_2$$

Note that x_5 and x_2 are both zero since they do not appear in the optimum solution. ε is a parameter which may be associated with changes in the variable x_5. Decreasing ε is equivalent to increasing the number of man-days since it reduces the effective slack variable $x_5 = (x_5 + \varepsilon)$ associated with the man-day constraint.

From the equation above, ε may assume a maximum negative value of 100 without violating the condition of $x_4 \geq 0$.

Checking equation IV for $\varepsilon = -100$ (and $x_2 = 0$, $x_3 = 0$) gives

$$x_1 = 80 + \tfrac{1}{5}(20)$$

which does not violate the condition of $x_1 \geq 0$.

Using 100 man-days to grow tomatoes involves the basic labor cost of $2,000 plus an additional cost for premium labor of $500. Under regular wage rates the contribution to profit from 20 acres of tomatoes is $270 \times 20 = \$5,400$. Therefore, net increase in profit brought about by using premium labor will be $4,900.

Example 2. The total production of the Western Paper Co. (Exercise 1, page 20) is to be continued at the present rate of 6,300 tons per month. Would there be any apparent advantage to shifting part of the scheduled production from one of the plants to the other? If so, which plant's production should be increased and by how much? Formulate the problem as an LP model and solve by the simplex method.

Solution. At Seattle

Capacity $\dfrac{2,700}{0.75} = 3,600$ tons

Maximum capacity using local waste paper $= \dfrac{1,440}{0.8} = 1,800$ tons

Production (present) $= 2,700$ tons
Wastepaper used (local) $(1800)(0.8) = 1,440$ tons
(brokers) $= 720$ tons
Total cost $2,700 \times 77\tfrac{1}{3} = \$208,800$
Fixed cost $= 59,400$
Wastepaper (local) $1,440 \times 18.75 = 27,000$
(broker) $720 \times 27.50 = 19,800$
Variable costs (other) $= 102,600$
$= \$38$ per ton

At Oregon

Capacity $\dfrac{3,600}{0.60} = 6,000$ tons

Maximum capacity using local wastepaper $= \dfrac{4,000}{0.8} = 5,000$ tons

Production (present)   = 3,600 tons
Wastepaper used (local)   (3,600)(0.8) = 2,880
Total cost   3,600 × 85 = 306,000
Fixed cost   = 108,000
Wastepaper (local)   2,880 × 20 = 57,600
Variable cost (other)   = 140,400
                                                                    = $39 per ton

Let x_1 = Seattle plant output using local waste
    x_2 = Seattle plant output using broker waste
    x_3 = Oregon plant output using local waste
    x_4 = Oregon plant output using broker waste

Restrictions

$x_1 + x_2 + x_3 + x_4 = 6,300$	total production requirement
$x_1 + x_2 \quad\quad\quad\leq 3,600$	capacity of Seattle plant
$x_3 + x_4 \leq 6,000$	capacity of Oregon plant
$0.8x_1 \quad\quad\quad\quad \leq 1,440$	availability of local waste at Seattle
$0.8x_3 \quad\quad \leq 4,000$	availability of local waste at Oregon

Objective Function

Total Cost = 59,400	
$+\ 18.75(0.8)x_1 + 27.50(0.8)x_2$	Seattle fixed cost
	Seattle local waste cost
$+\ 38(x_1 + x_2)$	Other Seattle variable costs
$+\ 108,000$	Oregon fixed cost
$+\ 20(0.8)x_3 + 27.50(0.8)x_4$	Oregon local waste cost
$+\ 39(x_3 + x_4)$	Other Oregon variable costs

$$= 167,400 + 53x_1 + 60x_2 + 55x_3 + 61x_4$$

Since the total cost is to be minimized, the function to be maximized is

$$-167,400 - 53x_1 - 60x_2 - 55x_3 - 61x_4$$

Production Requirement of 6,300 Tons. The tableau shows a slack variable assigned to each restriction. The one assigned to the production requirement is positive so that underproduction is permitted but at an artificially high cost of 100. The optimum solution is attained at the third iteration:

$x_1 = 1,800$: Seattle prod. using local waste; cost = 59,400 + 1,800 × 53 = 154,000
$x_2 = 4,500$: Oregon prod. using local waste; cost = 108,000 + 4,500 × 55 = 355,500
 Total cost = $\overline{510,300}$

Reduction in cost = \$(208,800 + 306,000) − 510,300 = \$4,500

Simplex Tableau

	Unit Profit	-53	-60	-55	-61	-100	0	0	0	0	167,400	
	B.V. / Profit	x_1	x_2	x_3	x_4	x_5	x_6	x_7	x_8	x_9		Ratio
1	x_5 −100	1	1	1	1	1	0	0	0	0	6,300	6,300
2	x_6 0	1	1	0	1	0	1	0	0	0	3,600	3,600
3	x_7 0	0	0	1	1	0	0	1	0	0	6,000	
4	x_8 0	0.8	0	0	0	0	0	0	1	0	1,440	1,800 →
5	x_9 0	0	0	0.8	0	0	0	0	0	1	4,000	
6	Δp	47	40	45	39	0	0	0	0	0	797,400	
11	x_5 −100	0	1	1	1	1	0	0	−1.25	0	4,500	4,500 →
12	x_6 0	0	1	0	0	0	1	0	−1.25	0	1,800	
13	x_7 0	0	0	1	1	0	0	1	0	0	6,000	6,000
14	x_1 −53	1	0	0	0	0	0	0	+1.25	0	1,800	
15	x_9 0	0	0	−0.8	0	0	0	0	0	1	4,000	5,000
16	Δp	0	40	45	39	0	0	0	−58¾	0	712,800	
21	x_3 −55	0	1	1	1	1	0	0	−1.25	0	4,500	
22	x_6 0	0	1	0	0	0	1	0	−1.25	0	1,800	
23	x_7 0	0	0	0	0	−1	0	1	−1.25	0	1,500	
24	x_1 −53	1	0	0	−0.8	0	0	0	1.25	0	1,800	
25	x_9 0	0	+0.8	0	0	−0.8	0	0	1	1	400	
26	Δp	0	−5	0	−6	−45	0	0	−2.5	0	510,300	

EXERCISES

1. Formulate the problem in Example 1 as a LP model and solve by the simplex method. Use the decision variables:

$$y_1 = \text{number of pounds of tomatoes}$$

$$y_2 = \text{number of heads of lettuce}$$

$$y_3 = \text{number of pounds of radishes}$$

2. (a) If production requirements in Example 2 were increased to 9,100 tons per month, how much should be produced at each plant? What would be the total cost per month for each plant in this case?
   (b) State the optimum production at each plant for any requirement.
   (c) How would the cost change if capacity were increased at either or both plants?

Notes and References

The literature on linear programming is large. A Bibliography is given in:
Riley, V., and Gass, S. I. (1958), *Linear Programming and Associated Techniques, A Comprehensive Bibliography*. Johns Hopkins Press, Baltimore.

Texts and reference works that discuss linear programming in detail:
Charnes, A., and Cooper, W. W. (1961), *Management Models and Industrial Applications of Linear Programming* (2 vols.), John Wiley and Sons, New York.
Dantzig, G. B. (1963), *Linear Programming and Extensions*, Princeton University Press, Princeton, N.J.
Glicksman, A. M. (1963), *An Introduction to Linear Programming and the Theory of Games*, John Wiley and Sons, New York.
Karlin, S. (1959), *Mathematical Methods and Theory in Games, Programming and Economics* (2 vols.), Addison-Wesley Publishing Co., Reading, Mass.
Vadja, S. (1961), *Mathematical Programming*, Addison-Wesley Publishing Co., Reading, Mass.

The arbitrary choices in the formulation of constrained optimization problems were discussed in Notes and References, Chapter 11. The standard formulation defined there resulted in non-negative λ's in the optimum solution. As shown in Section C the c_j's in LP are equivalent to the λ's hence, in the optimum solution, the c_j's must be non-negative. The most easily understood formulation of the LP problem for the simplex method, as presented in Section D, involves "change of profit" coefficients which are the negative values of the c_j's, The "change of profit" coefficients must, therefore, be non-positive in the optimum solution. Both the c_j's and the "change in profit" coefficients appear in the literature; once the connection between them is realized the existence of both should not cause any confusion.

CHAPTER SIXTEEN

Examples of Linear Programming

In Chapter 15 the solution of a standard linear programming model was described. A problem, when first formulated in terms of linear programming, may not fit the standard model exactly. However, some problems can be transformed into the standard format. Some of the variations and the transformations needed are illustrated in this chapter.

(i) *The objective may be to minimize.*

$$z = \sum_{j=1}^{N} c_j x_j$$

A minimization problem can be changed to a maximization problem by changing the signs of all the coefficients in the objective function; e.g.,

the minimum of $\sum_{j=1}^{N} c_j x_j$ is the maximum of $\sum_{j=1}^{N} (-c_j) x_j$

The simplex method may also be modified; the example in Section B illustrates this approach.

(ii) *One or more of the decision variables may be negative as well as positive.*

Any number can be expressed as the difference between two non-negative numbers. Let x_j be a variable which is not necessarily non-negative in the problem, and define two new variables w_j and v_j, where $w_j \geq 0$, $v_j \geq 0$
then
$$x_j = w_j - v_j$$

Substituting for x_j in the objective function and restrictions will lead to a new set in which the variables are all non-negative. The number of variables, of course, is increased. The procedure is illustrated in Section D.

(iii) The restrictions may be $\geq$ or they may be equalities.

The direction of the inequalities can be changed by multiplying by -1; the inequality $\Sigma\, a_{ij}x_j \geq b_i$ is equivalent to $-\Sigma\, a_{ij}x_j \leq -b_i$. An inequality of the form

$$\Sigma\, a_{ij}x_j \geq b_i$$

can also be changed to an equality by subtracting (rather than adding) the non-negative slack variable, x_s.

$$\Sigma\, a_{ij}x_j - x_s = b_i$$

An inequality can be left as such, or it can be treated as an inequality. A slack variable can be assigned to the constraint and the coefficient in the objective function given a value which will ensure that the equality is satisfied in the optimum solution. Another method is to replace the equality by two inequalities

$$\Sigma\, a_{ij}x_j \leq b_i \qquad \text{and} \qquad -\Sigma\, a_{ij}x_j \leq - b_i$$

The latter method is usually preferable.

The six examples in this chapter illustrate the application of LP to business problems in different functional fields and in different industries. In the first two, the optimum solution can be obtained manually by the simplex method. In the other four, computers are required; the results are presented in the form of typical computer output.

A. AN INVESTMENT PROBLEM

The investment office of an insurance company has available $1,000,000 which it wishes to invest to maximize its interest income. The opportunities are as follows:

Investment	Interest Rate
A_1	3.0
A_2	2.5
B_1	3.5
B_2	4.0
C_1	5.0
C_2	4.5

Legal restrictions state that at least 40% of the total investment must be in type A, and not more than 35% in type B, and not more than 35%

in type C. What investments should be made and what will the rate of return be?

The answer to this simple problem can readily be obtained by inspection. Since at least 40% must be in type A, and since type A has lower interest rates than either of the other two types, the best policy is to invest the minimum, namely 40%, in the type A that has the highest rate, in this case A_1. The highest rate obtainable is in C_1 and the best policy here is to invest the maximum possible, 35%. The remaining 25% is then invested in the best of the B type, or B_2, which yields 4.0.

The interest income is:

$$40(3.0) + 25(4.0) + 35(5.0) = 395$$

or $3.95 per $100 invested.

Because of its simplicity, this problem forms a good exercise in the formulation of linear programming problems and in the simplex method.

The decision variables are the amounts to be invested in each of six investment possibilities. The problem can be "normalized" by setting the total amount to be invested equal to 100%. Then x_1 is the percentage to be invested in A_1, x_2 the percentage in A_2, x_3 in B_1, x_4 in B_2, x_5 in C_1, and x_6 in C_2. Three restrictions on the x's are given:

$$\text{At least 40\% in type } A; \qquad x_1 + x_2 \geq 40 \qquad (1')$$

$$\text{Not more than 35\% in type } B; \quad x_3 + x_4 \leq 35 \qquad (2')$$

$$\text{Not more than 35\% in type } C; \quad x_5 + x_6 \leq 35 \qquad (3')$$

In addition there is the restriction that the total amount invested is 100, or

$$x_1 + x_2 + x_3 + x_4 + x_5 + x_6 = 100 \qquad (4)$$

The next step is to assign slack variables to transform the three inequalities to equalities. The first inequality becomes the equality

$$x_1 + x_2 - x_7 = 40 \qquad (1)$$

Slack variables must be non-negative; x_7 denotes the investment in type A in excess of 40%. The next inequality becomes the equality

$$x_3 + x_4 + x_8 = 35 \qquad (2)$$

Where x_8 denotes the difference between 35% and the investment in type B. Similarly, the third inequality becomes:

$$x_5 + x_6 + x_9 = 35 \qquad (3)$$

These equalities are shown in tabular form in Table 16-1.

Table 16-1   Solution to Linear Programming Problem in Investment

Eq.	Linear Combination	B.V.	A_1 x_1	A_2 x_2	B_1 x_3	B_2 x_4	C_1 x_5	C_2 x_6	x_7	x_8	x_9	Solution Amt
(1)			1	1	1	1	1	1	-1			40
(2)					1	1				1		35
(3)			1	1			1	1				35
(4)							1	1			1	100
(5)			1^{*}		1^{*}		1^{*}				$*$	
(6) = (1) $-$ (4)		z	0	0	-1	-1	-1	-1	-1	0	0	-60
(7) = (2) $+$ (6)		z	0	0	0	0	-1	-1	-1	-1	0	-25
(8) = (3) $+$ (7)		z	0	0	0	0	0	0	-1	-1	1	10
(9) = (1) $-$ (7)		z	0	0	0	0	1	1	-1	-1	0	25
(1.0)		z	3.0	2.5	3.5	4.0	5.0	4.5	0	0	0	-0
(1.1) = (1.0) $-$ 3(1)		z	0	-0.5	3.5	4.0	5.0	4.5	3.0	0	0	-120.0
(1.2) = (1.1) $-$ 3.5(2)		z	0	-0.5	0	0.5	5.0	4.5	3.0	-3.5	0	-242.5
(1.3) = (1.2) $-$ 5(9)		z	0	-0.5	0	0.5	0	-0.5	-2.0	1.5	0	-367.5
(2.1) = (1)		x_1	1	1	1	1	1	1	-1			40
(2.2) = (2)		x_3			1	1				1		35
(2.3) = (9)		x_5					1	1	-1	-1	1	25
*(2.4) = (8)		x_9							-1	-1	1	10
(2.5) = (1.3)		z	0	-0.5	0	0.5	0	-0.5	-2.0	1.5	0	-367.5
(3.1) = (2.1)		x_1	1	1	1	1			-1	0	-1	40
*(3.2) = (2.2) $-$ (2.4)		x_3			1	1			0	0	-1	25
(3.3) = (2.3) $+$ (2.4)		x_5					1	1	-1	0	-1	35
(3.4) = (2.4)		x_8							-1	1	-1	10
(3.5) = (2.5) $-$ 1.5(3.4)		z	0	-0.5	0	0.5	0	-0.5	-0.5	0	-1.5	-382.5
(4.1) = (3.1)		x_1	1	1	1	1			-1		-1	40
(4.2) = (3.2)		x_4			1	1			1		-1	25
(4.3) = (3.3)		x_5					1	1	-1			35
(4.4) = (3.4)		x_8			1				-1	1		10
(4.5) = (3.5) $-$ 0.5(4.2)		z	0	-0.5	-0.5	0	0	-0.5	-1.0	1	-1.0	-395.0

An initial feasible basic solution is first required. Since there are four equations, four basic variables are necessary. No set of four variables form an initial feasible solution with the equations as given in (1), (2), (3), and (4) in Table 16-1. One possibility is to define two new artificial variables, x_{10} with a coefficient of 1 in (1), and x_{11} with a coefficient of 1 in (4). Then x_8, x_9, x_{10}, and x_{11} would form an initial basis. (x_7 could not be used because $x_7 = -40$ would not be feasible.) Another possibility is to select, arbitrarily, four variables to be basic and solve the equations. Suppose that x_1, x_3, x_5, and x_9 have been selected as basic variables. Equations (6) to (9) in Table 16-1 are required to obtain the initial feasible solution in terms of these variables. Equation (6), for example, eliminates the 1 in equation (4) for x_1. Similarly, equation (7) clears x_3; equation 8 provides a 1 for x_9, and equation (9) clears x_5, where by "clearing" is meant eliminating all non-zero coefficients except for one 1.

The solution, with this set of basic variables, is

from (1) $x_1 = 40 - x_2 + x_7$ (2.1)

from (2) $x_3 = 35 - x_4 - x_8$ (2.2)

from (9) $x_5 = 25 - x_6 - x_7 + x_8$ (2.3)

from (8) $x_9 = 10 + x_7 - x_8$ (2.4)

This is a feasible solution since the basic variables are non-negative if the non-basic variables are set to zero.

The next step is to determine whether this basic feasible solution is the optimum solution. The objective is to maximize

$$z = 3.0x_1 + 2.5x_2 + 3.5x_3 + 4.0x_4 + 5.0x_5 + 4.5x_6 + 0x_7 + 0x_8 + 0x_9$$

$$(1.0)$$

which is recorded as equation (1.0) in Table 16-1. Substituting the solution (2.1), (2.2), (2.3), and (2.4) into (1.0) gives

$$z = 3(40) + 3.5(35) + 5(25) + x_2(2.5 - 3) + x_4(4 - 3.5) + x_6(4.5 - 5)$$

$$+ x_7(3 - 5) + x_8(-3.5 + 5.0)$$

$$z - 367.5 = -0.5x_2 + 0.5x_4 - 0.5x_6 - 2x_7 + 1.5x_8$$ (1.3)

This equation appears as (1.3). In Table 16-1 the substitution is carried out in steps: x_1 in (1.1), x_3 in (1.2) and x_5 in (1.3). Since there is at least one non-basic variable that has a positive coefficient in (1.3), the solution is not the optimum.

The initial basic feasible solution is written as (2.1), (2.2), (2.3), (2.4), and (2.5). The variable x_8 has the largest positive coefficient, and dividing elements in the column under x_8 into the elements in the solution column gives (2.4) as the smallest non-negative ratio. Therefore, the next iteration will result in the replacement of x_9 by x_8. This is illustrated in equations (3.1) to (3.5) in Table 16-1.

The objective has now been increased to 382.5, but one coefficient still remains positive. Therefore, the next iteration is obtained by replacing x_3 with x_4 and this results in an objective of 395.0. Since all the coefficients are now negative, the solution is optimum.

The solution is $x_1 = 40$, $x_4 = 25$, $x_5 = 35$, and $x_8 = 10$. The other non-basic x's—x_2, x_3, x_6, x_7, and x_9—are zero. The fact that x_8 is a basic variable implies that optimum solution does not invest as much in Type C as the restriction permits.

The profit equation is

$$z = 395 - 0.5x_2 - 0.5x_3 - 0.5x_6 - 1.0x_7 - 1.0x_9$$

The equation must be multiplied by 100 to get the profit for the $1,000,000 investment.

$$100z = 39,500 - 50x_2 - 50x_3 - 50x_6 - 100x_7 - 100x_9 \qquad (4.5)$$

From this it follows that if one unit ($10,000) is invested in x_2 or x_3 or x_6, rather than as specified in the optimum solution, the total profit will be decreased by $50. If the first condition is relaxed, i.e., if only 39% of the total investment must be in type A, the total profit will be increased by $100 since the $10,000 would be invested in B_2. If the third condition is relaxed, i.e., if 36% of the money can be invested in C, the profit would increase by $100 since the $10,000 would be invested in C_1 at 5.0% instead of B_2 at 4%. It must be emphasized that in this simple example all these conclusions are obvious from the statement of the problem; they are not quite so obvious in many problems occurring in everyday practice.

EXERCISES

1. Solve the problem by the simplex method, using two artificial variables x_{10} and x_{11} in the initial feasible basic solution.

2. Determine the optimum solution and interpret the results if the interest rates were:

Investment	Interest Rate
A_1	4.5
A_2	5.0
B_1	5.5
B_2	5.0
C_1	4.5
C_2	5.0

3. Solve the problem in the example if no more than half the money can be invested in investments with subscript 1 (A_1, B_1, C_1). Interpret the results.

4. Solve the problem in Exercise 3 if the interest rates are those given in Exercise 2.

5. Formulate as an LP model, if possible, the life insurance investment problem in Chapter 6, Section C. If the LP model is not applicable, indicate why.

B. MACHINE LOADING

A manufacturer produces three products, A, B, and C. Each product can be produced on either one of two machines, I and II. The time required to produce 1 unit of each product on a machine is:

Time to Produce 1 Unit (hours)

Product	Machine	
	I	II
A	0.5	0.6
B	0.7	0.8
C	0.9	1.05

There are 85 hours available on each machine; the operating cost is $5 per hour for machine I and $4 per hour for machine II, and the product requirements are 90 units of A, 80 units of B, and 60 units of C. The manufacturer wishes to meet the requirements at minimum cost.

This problem also can be solved by inspection as follows. The cost of producing 1 unit of each product on each machine is:

Product	Machine	
	I	II
A	2.5	2.4
B	3.5	3.2
C	4.5	4.2

Therefore, for each product, machine I is more expensive than machine II. It is advisable to load machine II with that product which has the largest difference between machine I and II. In this case, B and C have the same difference. B is chosen because it has larger requirements. To

Table 16-2 Simplex Solution of a Machine Loading Problem

		2.5	2.4	3.5	3.2	4.5	4.2	Product Slack			Machine Slack			
B.V.	Cost	x_{11}	x_{12}	x_{21}	x_{22}	x_{31}	x_{32}	10 x_{13}	10 x_{23}	10 x_{33}	0 x_{41}	0 x_{42}	b	Ratio
x_{13}	10	1	1	0	0	0	0	1	0	0	0	0	90	90 ←
x_{23}	10	0	0	1	1	0	0	0	1	0	0	0	80	∞
x_{33}	10	0	0	0	0	1	1	0	0	1	0	0	60	∞
x_{41}	0	0.5	0	0.7	0	0.9	0	0	0	0	1	0	85	∞
x_{42}	0	0	0.6	0	0.8	0	1.05	0	0	0	0	1	85	142
		−7.5	−7.6 ↑	−6.5	−6.8	−5.5	−5.8	0	0	0	0	0	−2,300	
x_{12}	2.4	1	1	0	0	0	0	1	0	0	0	0	90	∞
x_{23}	10	0	0	1	1	0	0	0	1	0	0	0	80	80
x_{33}	10	0	0	0	0	1	1	0	0	1	0	0	60	∞
x_{41}	0	0.5	0	0.7	0	0.9	0	0	0	0	1	0	85	121
x_{42}	0	−0.6	0	0	0.8	0	1.05	−0.6	0	0	0	1	31	38.75 ←
		0.1	0	−6.5	−6.8 ↑	−5.5	−5.8	7.6	0	0	0	0	−1,616	
x_{12}	2.4	1	1	0	0	0	0	1	0	0	0	0	90	∞
x_{23}	10	0.75	0	1	0	0	−1.3125	0.75	1	0	0	−1.25	41.25	41.25 ←
x_{33}	10	0	0	0	0	1	1	0	0	1	1	0	60	∞
x_{41}	0	0.5	0	0.7	0	0.9	0	0	0	0	1	0	85	$\frac{85}{0.7}$
x_{22}	3.2	−0.75	0	0	1	0	1.3125	−0.75	0	0	0	1.25	38.75	∞
		−5	0	−6.5	0	−5.5	3.125	2.5	0	0	0	8.5	−1,352.5	

Basis	c_B											b	θ
x_{12}	2.4	1	1	0	0	0	0	1	0	0	0	90	∞
x_{21}	3.5	0.75	0	1	0	-1.3125	1	0.75	1	-1.25	0	41.25	∞
x_{33}	10	0	0	0	1	1	0	0	-0.7	0	1	60	$60\leftarrow$
x_{41}	0	-0.025	0	0	0.9	0.91875	0	-0.525	0	0.875	0	56.125	$\dfrac{56.125}{0.2}$
x_{22}	3.2	-0.75	0	0	-5.5	1.3125	0	-0.75	6.5	1.25	0	38.75	∞
		$-0.125\uparrow$	0	0	$-5.5\uparrow$	-5.40625	0	7.375	6.5	0.375	0	$-1{,}084.375$	

Basis	c_B											b	θ
x_{12}	2.4	1	1	0	0	0	0	1	0	0	0	90	90
x_{21}	3.5	0.75	0	1	0	-1.3125	1	0.75	1	-1.25	0	41.25	$55\leftarrow$
x_{31}	4.5	0	0	0	1	1	0	0	-0.7	0	1	60	∞
x_{41}	0	-0.025	0	0	0	0.01875	0	-0.525	0	0.875	-0.9	2.125	-85
x_{22}	3.2	-0.75	0	0	0	1.3125	-0.75	-0.75	6.5	1.25	5.5	38.75	$-51\tfrac{2}{3}$
		-0.125	0	0	0	0.09375	7.375	7.375	6.5	0.375	5.5	-754.375	

Basis	c_B											b	θ
x_{12}	2.4	0	1	$-1\tfrac{1}{63}$	1	1.75	0	1	0	0	$1\tfrac{2}{63}$	35	$20\leftarrow$
x_{11}	2.5	1	0	$1\tfrac{1}{63}$	0	-1.75	-1	0	-1	0	$-1\tfrac{2}{63}$	55	-31.4
x_{31}	4.5	0	0	0	$\tfrac{1}{30}$	1	0	0.5	0	-0.9	0	60	60
x_{41}	0	0	0	1	0	-0.025	0	0.5	-1	0	0.733333	3.5	-140
x_{22}	3.2	0	0	0	0	$-0.125\downarrow$	0	7.5	$6\tfrac{2}{3}$	5.5	0.166667	80	∞
		0	0	0.16667	0	-0.125	0	7.5	$6\tfrac{2}{3}$	5.5	0.166667	-747.5	

Basis	c_B											b	θ
x_{32}	4.2	0	0.57142857	-0.76190474	0	1	0	0	-0.76190474	0	0.95238091	20	20
x_{11}	2.5	1	1	0.76190474	0	0	0	0	0	0	-0.95238091	90	90
x_{31}	4.5	0	-0.57142857	0.0142857	0	0	0	0	0.76190474	1	0.7571429	40	40
x_{41}	0	0	0.0142857	1	1	0	1	0	-0.685714	-0.9	0	4	4
x_{22}	3.2	0	0	0.07142857	0	0	0	0	-1	5.5	0.2857143	80	80
		0	0.07142857	0.07142857	0	0	0	0	6.571429	5.5	0.2857143	-745	

produce B requires $80 \times 0.8 = 64$ hours of time on machine II, leaving 21 hours available. Fill machine II with the next most expensive-to-move-product, i.e., product C; $20 \times 1.05 = 21$ hours which fills machine II. Balance of product C goes on machine I requiring $40 \times 0.9 = 36$ hours of machine I, leaving 49 available. Load machine I with balance of product requirements, i.e., product A; $90 \times 0.5 = 45$. This leaves 4 hours of machine I unscheduled.

The total cost can then be computed as:

Product	Units	Machine	Hours	Cost
A	90	I	45	$225
B	80	II	64	256
C	20	II	21	84
	40	I	36	180
				$745

In this example, trial and error can be used to show that this is the minimum cost; in larger problems, LP is necessary.

The linear programming formulation is developed next. Let

x_{ij} = number of units of product i produced on machine j;

$i = A, B, C \quad j = \text{I, II}$

c_{ij} = cost of producing a unit of product i on machine j

Minimize

$$\sum_{i=A}^{C} \sum_{j=I}^{II} c_{ij}x_{ij} = 2.5x_{11} + 2.4x_{12} + 3.5x_{21} + 3.2x_{22} + 4.5x_{31} + 4.2x_{32}$$

subject to:

$$x_{11} + x_{12} \leq 90$$

$$x_{21} + x_{22} \leq 80$$

$$x_{31} + x_{32} \leq 60$$

$$0.5x_{11} + 0.7x_{21} + 0.9x_{31} \leq 85$$

$$0.6x_{12} + 0.8x_{22} + 1.05x_{32} \leq 85$$

The inequalities are changed to equalities by defining artificial variables x_{13}, x_{23}, x_{33} as the number of units by which the actual production is less than the requirement for products A, B, and C, respectively. The slack variables x_{41} and x_{42} are the number of hours machines I and II, respectively, are idle. Since the requirements are to be met if at all possible, a high cost, say, 10, is assessed for each unit under requirement. There is no cost assessed for having a machine idle. The resulting formulation and simplex solution is shown in Table 16-2.

As can be seen in the final tableau, the optimum solution has x_{11}, x_{22}, x_{31}, x_{32}, and x_{41} as basic variables. The optimum values may be interpreted as:

$x_{11} = 90$ All product A requirements are produced on machine I.

$x_{22} = 80$ All product B requirements are produced on machine II.

$x_{31} = 40$ 40 units of product C are produced on machine I.

$x_{32} = 20$ 20 units of product C are produced on machine II.

$x_{41} = 4$ Machine I is idle for 4 hours.

EXERCISES

1. Formulate and solve the problem by writing the requirements as:

$$x_{11} + x_{12} \geq 90$$
$$x_{21} + x_{22} \geq 80$$
$$x_{31} + x_{32} \geq 60$$

2. Determine the value of additional machine capacity and the optimum decisions if five additional hours on each machine were available.

3. Formulate the m machine n-product analogue.

C. THE WAREHOUSING PROBLEM

The example given in this section is a simple case of what has come to be known as the warehousing problem, though it might more appropriately be called the Buy-and-Sell Problem. The particular case used here is a very simple one, designed to illustrate the basic structure of this problem. The numerical example is that used by Charnes and Cooper.

Assume a wholesaler buys and sells a single product. He knows the cost to him and the price he will receive during each period. He has an initial inventory of a units, and has a warehouse which has a maximum capacity of b units. He has an initial amount of cash of d and his cash cannot become negative. Purchases are made for cash and payment for sales are received one period later. The units are purchased at the beginning of a period and may be received any time during that period but cannot be sold until the next period. The data for this particular example is shown at top of p. 480.

Purchase and Sale Price for Five Time Periods

Period	Purchase Price $/ton	Selling Price $/ton
1	25	20
2	25	35
3	25	30
4	35	25
5	45	50

Assume that the business will terminate at the end of the five periods with the salvage value of zero for units on hand at the end of the fifth period. The decision problem of how much to buy and how much to sell each period can be developed as a linear programming model.

Decision Variables. Let

x_j be the amount to be purchased in period j

y_j be the amount to be sold in period j where $j = 1, 2, 3, 4, 5$

Then the values of x and y are the decision variables; in this example there are 10 decision variables.

The Objective. The objective is to maximize profits which are given by:

$$-c_1x_1 - c_2x_2 - c_3x_3 - c_4x_4 - c_5x_5$$
$$+ p_1y_1 + p_2y_2 + p_3y_3 + p_4y_4 + p_5y_5 \quad (1)$$

Uncontrollable Variables. The uncontrollable variables are:

a = the initial inventory

b = the fixed warehouse capacity

d = the initial cash

c_j = purchase price in period j

p_j = selling price in period j

Model. The objective is to maximize equation (1) subject to the constraints on warehouse capacity and cash. The amount purchased in the first period, x_1, is limited by the amount of warehouse space available $(b - a)$ plus any space made available by sales during the first period (y_1); therefore,

$$x_1 \leq b - a + y_1 \quad (2)$$

Similarly, x_2 must be less than $(b - a)$ plus the amount sold in period 1 plus the amount sold in period 2 minus the amount purchased in period 1 or

$$x_2 \leq b - a + y_1 + y_2 - x_1 \quad (3)$$

The inequalities for the later periods are obtained in a similar way and by rearrangement they can be written in the following form:

$$x_1 - y_1 \leq b - a$$
$$x_1 + x_2 - y_1 - y_2 \leq b - a$$
$$x_1 + x_2 + x_3 - y_1 - y_2 - y_3 \leq b - a \qquad (4)$$
$$x_1 + x_2 + x_3 + x_4 - y_1 - y_2 - y_3 - y_4 \leq b - a$$
$$x_1 + x_2 + x_3 + x_4 + x_5 - y_1 - y_2 - y_3 - y_4 - y_5 \leq b - a$$

In addition there are restrictions on the y_i, i.e., the number of units that can be sold in any period. In particular, the amount that can be sold in period 1 is limited by the amount in inventory at the beginning of period 1.

$$y_1 \leq a$$

The amount that can be sold in period 2 is the amount that was not sold in period 1 plus the amount that was purchased in period 1

$$y_2 \leq a - y_1 + x_1 \qquad (5)$$

and similarly for the later periods. These equations can be rearranged in the following form:

$$y_1 \leq a$$
$$-x_1 + y_1 + y_2 \leq a$$
$$-x_1 - x_2 + y_1 + y_2 + y_3 \leq a \qquad (6)$$
$$-x_1 - x_2 - x_3 + y_1 + y_2 + y_3 + y_4 \leq a$$
$$-x_1 - x_2 - x_3 - x_4 + y_1 + y_2 + y_3 + y_4 + y_5 \leq a$$

The amount that can be purchased in the first period also is limited by the financial restriction which is:

$$c_1 x_1 \leq d \qquad (7)$$

In the second period, the money obtained from sales in the first period can be used to purchase additional units. This leads to the restriction

$$c_1 x_1 + c_2 x_2 - p_1 y_1 \leq d \qquad (8)$$

Similarly, the inequalities for the later periods are:

$$c_1 x_1 + c_2 x_2 + c_3 x_3 - p_1 y_1 - p_2 y_2 \leq d \qquad (9)$$
$$c_1 x_1 + c_2 x_2 + c_3 x_3 + c_4 x_4 - p_1 y_1 - p_2 y_2 - p_3 y_3 \leq d \qquad (10)$$
$$c_1 x_1 + c_2 x_2 + c_3 x_3 + c_4 x_4 + c_5 x_5 - p_1 y_1 - p_2 y_2 - p_3 y_3 - p_4 y_4 \leq d \qquad (11)$$

The model can be expressed more succinctly with the definition of the following vectors and matrices. Let

$$
X = \begin{bmatrix} x_1 \\ x_2 \\ x_3 \\ x_4 \\ x_5 \\ y_1 \\ y_2 \\ y_3 \\ y_4 \\ y_5 \end{bmatrix} ; \quad
C = \begin{bmatrix} -c_1 \\ -c_2 \\ -c_3 \\ -c_4 \\ -c_5 \\ p_1 \\ p_2 \\ p_3 \\ p_4 \\ p_5 \end{bmatrix} ; \quad
B = \begin{bmatrix} b-a \\ b-a \\ b-a \\ b-a \\ b-a \\ a \\ a \\ a \\ a \\ a \\ d \\ d \\ d \\ d \\ d \end{bmatrix} ;
$$

$$
A = \begin{bmatrix}
1 & 0 & 0 & 0 & 0 & -1 & 0 & 0 & 0 & 0 \\
1 & 1 & 0 & 0 & 0 & -1 & -1 & 0 & 0 & 0 \\
1 & 1 & 1 & 0 & 0 & -1 & -1 & -1 & 0 & 0 \\
1 & 1 & 1 & 1 & 0 & -1 & -1 & -1 & -1 & 0 \\
1 & 1 & 1 & 1 & 1 & -1 & -1 & -1 & -1 & -1 \\
0 & 0 & 0 & 0 & 0 & 1 & 0 & 0 & 0 & 0 \\
-1 & 0 & 0 & 0 & 0 & 1 & 1 & 0 & 0 & 0 \\
-1 & -1 & 0 & 0 & 0 & 1 & 1 & 1 & 0 & 0 \\
-1 & -1 & -1 & 0 & 0 & 1 & 1 & 1 & 1 & 0 \\
-1 & -1 & -1 & -1 & 0 & 1 & 1 & 1 & 1 & 1 \\
c_1 & 0 & 0 & 0 & 0 & 0 & 0 & 0 & 0 & 0 \\
c_1 & c_2 & 0 & 0 & 0 & -p_1 & 0 & 0 & 0 & 0 \\
c_1 & c_2 & c_3 & 0 & 0 & -p_1 & -p_2 & 0 & 0 & 0 \\
c_1 & c_2 & c_3 & c_4 & 0 & -p_1 & -p_2 & -p_3 & 0 & 0 \\
c_1 & c_2 & c_3 & c_4 & c_5 & -p_1 & -p_2 & -p_3 & -p_4 & 0
\end{bmatrix}
$$

The problem then is to

$$\text{maximize } C'X$$

subject to

$$AX \leq B, \quad X \geq 0$$

Solution. The solution obtained by a computer program is shown in the accompanying table where z_1 is the slack variable for the first equation; z_2 is the slack variable for the second equation, etc. The values of the uncontrollable variables are $b = 200$ tons, $a = 100$ tons, $d = \$500$.

Solution to the Example of the Warehouse Problem

	Variable	Optimum Value of Basic Variables	Change in Profit for non-basic Variables
	x_1	20	
	x_2	0	
Purchases	x_3	168	
	x_4	0	
	x_5		45
	y_1		30
	y_2	120	
Sales	y_3		7.142857
	y_4		25
	y_5	168	
	z_1	80	
Warehouse	z_2	200	
space available	z_3	32	
	z_4	32	
	z_5	200	
	z_6	100	
Unsold units at	z_7		20
end of period	z_8	0	
	z_9	168	
	z_{10}		50
	z_{11}		0.8
Available	z_{12}		0
extra cash at	z_{13}		0.571429
end of period	z_{14}		0.428571
	z_{15}	0	

EXERCISES

1. Verify that the constraints are satisfied and that the solution given is optimum. Determine the total profit.

2. What is the value of:

(*a*) An additional unit of inventory?

(*b*) An additional unit of warehouse space?

(*c*) An additional dollar of initial cash?

3. Indicate how the optimum decision would be changed as a result of each of the changes in (2).

4. Determine whether the solution is unique. If not, describe the alternate solution(s).

5. The solution to the example of the Warehouse Problem with increased cash is:

Variable	Optimum Value for Basic Variable	Change in Profit for Non-Basic Variables
x_1	100	
x_2	200	
x_3	200	
x_4	0	
x_5		45
y_1		5
y_2	200	
y_3	200	
y_4		10
y_5	200	
z_1		10
z_2		5
z_3		10
z_4		15
z_5	200	
z_6	100	
z_7		10
z_8		5
z_9	200	
z_{10}		50
z_{11}	7,500	
z_{12}	2,500	
z_{13}	4,500	
z_{14}	10,500	
z_{15}	10,500	

(*a*) Verify that this solution is the optimum and determine the value of *d* used.

(*b*) Determine the maximum profit.

(*c*) Compute the increase in profit if *a* is increased.

(*d*) Compute the increase in profit if *b* is increased.

D. PRODUCTION AND EMPLOYMENT SCHEDULING

The one-period Holt, Modigliani, Muth model for production and employment scheduling was presented in Chapter 10, Section A. The following paper gives a linear programming model for the same problem.

Introduction*

The problem of production and employment scheduling may be stated as follows. Given the monthly demands for the product turned out by a factory, what should be the monthly production rates and work force levels in order to minimize the total cost of regular payroll and overtime, hiring and layoffs, inventory and shortages incurred during a given planning interval of several months? This problem has received a classical solution in two papers by Holt, Modigliani, Muth, and Simon. These authors assumed quadratic cost functions. Their treatment of the problem will be referred to as "quadratic programming." It appears, however, that in the majority of practical applications and theoretical models the cost functions are assumed to be linear. It, therefore, seems desirable to have a method of solution for the linear case as well. In the following paper it is shown that a solution can be obtained by linear programming methods. From the linear programming viewpoint, this paper is of an expository nature.

The Cost Functions

Given a planning interval of n periods, define the following quantities for period i $(i = 1, \ldots, n)$:

p_i = production rate (in a suitable unit)
R_i = demand (in the same unit)
I_i = inventory level at the end of the period (in the same unit)
w_i = work force level (in manhours which can be obtained on regular time)

In the quadratic programming approach, the costs incurred in period i

* Reprinted with permission from Hanssmann, Fred, and Sidney W. Hess, "A Linear Programming Approach to Production and Employment Scheduling," *Management Technology*, Vol. 1, No. 1, January 1960, pp. 46–51. The notation has been changed slightly.

are given by these expressions:

Regular Payroll	$c_1 w_i$	(1')
Hiring and Layoff	$c_2(w_i - w_{i-1})^2$	(2')
Overtime	$c_3(p_i - c_4 w_i)^2 + c_5 p_i - c_6 w_i$	(3')
Inventory and Shortages	$c_7(I_i - c_8 - c_9 R_i)^2$	(4')

where the C's are known positive constants. The problem of minimizing total cost for the planning interval is solved by differential calculus methods. An obvious restriction on the problem is given by

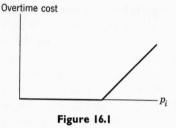

Overtime cost

Figure 16.1

$$I_i = I_{i-1} + p_i - R_i \qquad (1)$$

These cost functions have the following properties:

(a) Hiring and layoff are equally costly.

(b) The expression for the cost of overtime is a quadratic approximation to a piecewise linear function of the type pictured in Fig. 16-1.

(c) Inventory costs are a quadratic function of the inventory level.

We shall employ linear cost functions and independently choose the respective unit costs of hiring and layoffs as well as inventory and shortages. It is assumed that the amount of manhours required to turn out the production quantity p_i is

$$M_i = k p_i \qquad (2)$$

in which k is a constant of proportionality. For $m_i > w_i$ (in manhours), an amount $m_i - w_i$ of overtime is required. If now we define (for any real number a):

$$a^+ = \begin{cases} |a| & \text{for } a \geq 0 \\ 0 & \text{otherwise} \end{cases} \qquad (3a)$$

and

$$a^- = \begin{cases} 0 & \text{for } a \geq 0 \\ |a| & \text{otherwise} \end{cases} \qquad (3b)$$

then,

$$a = a^+ - a^- \qquad (3c)$$

We can now write down for the ith period the elements of our cost function in terms of the appropriate unit costs:

Regular Payroll	$c_r w_i$
Hiring	$c_h(w_i - w_{i-1})^+$
Layoffs	$c_f(w_i - w_{i-1})^-$
Overtime	$c_0(kp_i - w_i)^+$
Inventory	$c_1 I_i^+$
Shortage	$c_2 I_i^-$

Linear Programming Formulation

The problem of minimizing total costs for a period of n periods can now be formulated as one of minimizing the function

$$C(p_1, \ldots, p_n; w_1, \ldots, w_n) = \sum_{i=1}^{n} \{c_r w_i + c_h(w_i - w_{i-1})^+$$
$$+ c_f(w_i - w_{i-1})^- + c_0(kp_i - w_i)^+ + c_1 I_i^+ + c_2 I_i^- \quad (4)$$

subject to the restrictions

$$p_i \geq 0 \tag{5}$$

$$w_i \geq 0 \tag{6}$$

$$I_i = I_{i-1} + p_i - R_i \qquad (i = 1, \ldots, n) \tag{7}$$

where the R_i and the initial conditions (I_0, w_0) are given. Minimization is, of course, with respect to the "decision variables" p_i and w_i. Obviously, the cost function is only piecewise linear with respect to the decision variables. In order to arrive at a linear cost function let us introduce the following new set of variables:

$$x_i = (w_i - w_{i-1})^+$$
$$y_i = (w_i - w_{i-1})^-$$
$$s_i = (kp - w_i)^+$$
$$t_i = (kp_i - w_i)^- \tag{8}$$
$$u_i = I_i^+$$
$$v_i = I_i^- \qquad (i = 1, \ldots, n)$$

In this notation the variables p_i and w_i can be expressed as follows. From (7) and (3b) we obtain.

$$p_i = I_i - I_{i-1} + R_i$$
$$= (u_i - v_i) - (u_{i-1} - v_{i-1}) + R_i \tag{9}$$

Similarly, from (8):

$$kp_i - w_i = s_i - t_i$$

$$w_i = kp_i - (s_i - t_i) \tag{10}$$

$$= k[(u_i - v_i) - (u_{i-1} - v_{i-1}) + R_i] - (s_i - t_i)$$

Therefore, the restrictions (5) and (7) now take the form

$$(u_i - v_i) - (u_{i-1} - v_{i-1}) + R_i \geq 0 \tag{11}$$

and restriction (6) now reads:

$$(u_i - v_i) - (u_{i-1} - v_{i-1}) + R_i - \frac{1}{k}(s_i - t_i) \geq 0 \tag{12}$$

The definition of the variables x_i and y_i in (8) together with (3c) mean that

$$w_i - w_{i-1} = x_i - y_i$$

These restrictions may now be expressed in terms of the new variables. Using (10), the differences may be written in the form:

$$\frac{1}{k}(w_i - w_{i-1}) = (u_i - v_i) - 2(u_{i-1} - v_{i-1}) + (u_{i-2} - v_{i-2})$$

$$- \frac{1}{k}(s_i - t_i) + \frac{1}{k}(s_{i-1} - t_{i-1}) + (R_i - R_{i-1})$$

Thus the set of restrictions introduced by the definitions of the new variables is given by

$$(u_i - v_i) - 2(u_{i-1} - v_{i-1}) + (u_{i-2} - v_{i-2}) - \frac{1}{k}(s_i - t_i)$$

$$+ \frac{1}{k}(s_{i-1} - t_{i-1}) - (x_i - y_i) = R_{i-1} - R_i \tag{13}$$

The relations (3a) may be thought of as assumptions rather than restrictions since it is generally known that an optimum solution of a linear programming problem will automatically yield pairs of numbers (x_i, y_i) etc., with the property that either $x_i = 0$ or $y_i = 0$, etc. It may be observed, however, that these relations require that all variables be non-negative:

$$x_i, y_i \geq 0$$

$$s_i, t_i \geq 0 \tag{14}$$

$$u_i, v_i \geq 0$$

Using (8) and (10), we may write the cost function (4) in the following form:

$$C = \sum_{i=1}^{n} (c_h x_i + c_f y_i + c_0 z_i + c_1 u_i + c_2 v_i)$$
$$+ c_r k\{(u_i - v_i) - (u_{i-1} - v_{i-1}) + R_i\} - c_r\{s_i - t_i\}$$

or

$$C = \sum_{i=1}^{n} \Bigg(\quad\quad c_h x_i$$
$$+ \quad\quad c_f y_i$$
$$+ \quad (c_0 - c_r)s_j$$
$$+ \quad\quad c_r t_i \quad\quad\quad\quad (15)$$
$$+ \quad\quad c_1 u_i$$
$$+ \quad\quad c_2 v_i \Bigg)$$
$$+ c_r k \Bigg\{ (u_n - v_n) - I_0 + \sum_{1}^{n} R_i \Bigg\}$$

Our minimization problem now becomes one of linear programming. It may be stated as follows: Minimize the cost function (15) subject to the constraints (11), (12), (13) and (14) for $i = 1, \ldots, n$. Each period i of the planning interval contributes four variables and three restrictions. According to (11) and (12), the original decision variables p_i and w_i (production rate and work force level) are slack variables of the linear programming problem and can be obtained directly from the final simplex tableau turned out by the computer.

EXERCISES

Tables 16-3 and 16-4a and b give the LP solution to this model for twelve periods with the final inventory constrained to be zero, with Forecasts 1 and 2, respectively, for the following values for the parameters:

Hiring cost	$c_h = \$180$ per man
Firing cost	$c_f = 360$ per man
Overtime cost	$c_0 = 408$ per man periods
Regular wage cost	$c_r = 340$ per man periods
Inventory holding cost	$c_1 = \$$ per unit per period
Shortage cost	$c_2 = \$$ per unit per period
Production time	$k = 0.176$ man period per unit
Initial labor force	$= 65$ men
Initial inventory	$= 270$ units

The two forecasts are available:

Requirements

Period	Forecast 1	Forecast 2
1	425	450
2	400	350
3	375	300
4	425	400
5	425	500
6	425	650
7	425	500
8	425	400
9	425	300
10	425	300
11	425	400
12	425	500
	5,050	5,050

Table 16-3 LP Solution for Forecast I $c_1 = c_2 = 0.083$

Period	u: Inventory (units) (1)	(2)	v: Shortage (units) (1)	(2)	Production (units) (1)	(2)	Worker (units) (1)	(2)
1	243.33			0.166	398.33		398.33	
2	191.67			0.166	398.33		398.33	
3	190.00			0.166	398.33		398.33	
4	213.33			0.166	398.33		398.33	
5	186.67			0.166	398.33		398.33	
6	160.00			0.166	398.33		398.33	
7	133.33			0.166	398.33		398.33	
8	106.67			0.166	398.33		398.33	
9	80.00			0.166	398.33		398.33	
10	53.33			0.166	398.33		398.33	
11	26.67			0.166	398.33		398.33	
12	0.00			0.166	398.33		398.33	

Period	x: Personnel hired (men) (1)	(2)	y: Personnel fired (men) (1)	(2)	z: Production on overtime (men) (1)	(2)	w: Unused production capacity (men) (1)	(2)
1	5.11			540.000		55.594		352.406
2		12.406		527.594		55.122		352.878
3		25.284		514.716		54.651		353.349
4		38.634		501.366		54.179		353.821
5		52.455		487.545		53.707		354.293
6		66.747		473.253		53.236		354.764
7		81.511		458.489		52.764		355.236
8		96.747		443.253		52.293		355.707
9		112.455		427.545		51.821		356.179
10		128.634		411.366		51.349		356.651
11		145.284		394.716		50.878		357.122
12		162.406		377.594		0.406		357.594

(1) Optimum value of basic variables.
(2) "Change in Profit" coefficient for non-basic variables.

Table 16-4a   LP Solution for Forecast 2 $c_1 = c_2 = 3.0$

Period	u: Inventory (units)		v: Shortage (units)		Production (units)		Worker (units)	
	(1)	(2)	(1)	(2)	(1)	(2)	(1)	(2)
1	189.32			6.000	369.32		369.32	
2	208.64			6.000	369.32		369.32	
3	312.77			6.000	404.14		404.14	
4	316.91			6.000	404.14		404.14	
5	221.05			6.000	404.14		404.14	
6		6.000	24.82		404.14		404.14	
7		6.000	120.68		404.14		404.14	
8		6.000	116.55		404.14		404.14	
9		6.000	12.41		404.14		404.14	
10	91.73			6.000	404.14		404.14	
11	95.86			6.000	404.14		404.14	
12	0.00			6.000	404.14		404.14	

Period	x: Personnel hired (men)		y: Personnel fired (men)		z: Production on overtime (men)		w: Unused production capacity (men)	
	(1)	(2)	(1)	(2)	(1)	(2)	(1)	(2)
1		45.818		494.182		99.432		308.568
2		14.386		525.614		82.386		325.614
3	6.13			540.000		65.341		342.659
4		2.659		537.341		48.295		359.705
5		22.364		517.636		31.250		376.750
6		59.114		480.886		14.205		393.795
7		112.909		427.091		31.250		376.750
8		149.659		390.341		48.295		359.705
9		169.364		370.636		65.341		342.659
10		172.023		367.977		82.386		325.614
11		157.636		382.364		65.341		342.659
12		160.295		379.705		48.295		359.705

(1) Optimum value of basic variable.
(2) "Change in Profit" coefficient for non-basic variable.

Table 16-4b   LP Solution for Forecast 2 $c_1 = c_2 = 6.0$

Period	u: Inventory (units)		v: Shortage (units)		Production (units)		Worker (units)	
	(1)	(2)	(1)	(2)	(1)	(2)	(1)	(2)
1	189.32			12.000	369.32		369.32	
2	208.64			12.000	369.32		369.32	
3	277.95			12.000	369.32		369.32	
4	247.27			12.000	369.32		369.32	
5	147.27			12.000	400.00		400.00	
6		12.000	0.00		502.73		400.00	
7		12.000	100.00		400.00		400.00	
8		12.000	100.00		400.00		400.00	
9		1.355		10.645	400.00		400.00	
10	100.00			12.000	400.00		400.00	
11	100.00			12.000	400.00		400.00	
12	0.00			12.000	400.00		400.00	

Table 16-4b (continued)

Period	x: Personnel hired (men)		y: Personnel fired (men)		z: Production on overtime (men)		w: Unused production capacity (men)	
	(1)	(2)	(1)	(2)	(1)	(2)	(1)	(2)
1		205.273		334.727		170.45		237.545
2		102.818		437.182		136.34		271.636
3		34.455		505.545		102.23		305.727
4		0.182		539.818		68.12		339.818
5	5.40			540.000		34.01		373.909
6		33.909		506.091	18.08			408.000
7		101.090		438.091		34.01		373.909
8		135.818		404.182		68.12		339.818
9		135.636		404.364		102.23		305.727
10		101.364		438.636		75.89		332.121
11		93.485		446.515		41.78		366.212
12		119.697		420.303		7.67		400.303

(1) Optimum value of basic variable.
(2) "Change in Profit" coefficient for non-basic variable.

1. Formulate the LP model in terms of appropriate vectors and matrices.
2. Verify that the solution in Table 16-3 is an optimum. Interpret the variables and the solution.
3. Answer Exercise 2 for Table 16-4a.
4. Answer Exercise 2 for Table 16-4b.
5. Discuss the effects on the optimum solution of changes in the coefficients and of changes in the initial inventory and work force.

E. ALCATRAZ NATIONAL BANK

The available funds of the Alcatraz National Bank are classified into three categories and the relative proportion in each category is denoted by y_i:

Available funds	Proportion
Savings deposits	y_1
Time deposits	y_2
Surplus and retained earnings	y_3
Total	1.0

The investment, or other utilization, of these funds is classified into fourteen categories; the relative proportion in each category is denoted by x_i. The table on p. 493 shows the categories, x_i and the net annual return (interest and service charges less cost) realized.

The Board of Directors has formed an Investment Committee to determine the optimum investment. This committee, in turn, has asked the Research Department to formulate an optimization model. After a

Type	Category	Proportion	Return (%)
Term loans:	unsecured loans	x_1	4.5
	secured loans	x_2	4.25
MPL loans:	auto loans	x_3	6.0
	other monthly payment loans	x_4	5.0
Mortgages:	insured mortgages	x_5	4.0
	other mortgages	x_6	5.5
Bonds:	Government bonds, due within one year	x_7	2.0
	Government bonds, due in two to five years	x_8	3.0
	Government bonds, due in over five years	x_9	3.5
	Municipal bonds	x_{10}	6.0
	other bonds	x_{11}	4.40
Miscellaneous:	bank premises and equipment	x_{12}	0
	interest uncollected and other assets	x_{13}	0
	cash and due from banks	x_{14}	0
		1.0	

detailed analysis, the Research Department decided to develop an LP model.

The objective function is straightforward. Let r_i be the return on investment in category i; then the objective is to maximize

$$\sum_{i=1}^{14} r_i x_i$$

It is somewhat more difficult to determine the constraints on the x_i's. After an examination of past banking practices, comparison with industry data, and quantification of regulatory requirements, the constraints summarized in Table 16-5 were approved.

Each constraint is in the form of a ratio which must lie between specified limits. The first constraint states that the ratio of term loans to total loans must be between $b_{1,1}$ and $b_{1,2}$; i.e.,

$$b_{1,1} \leq \frac{\text{terms loans}}{\text{total loans}} \leq b_{1,2}$$

or

$$b_{1,1} \leq \frac{x_1 + x_2}{x_1 + x_2 + x_3 + x_4 + x_5 + x_6} \leq b_{1,2}$$

The table gives the value of $b_{1,1}$ as 0.15 and $b_{1,2}$ as 0.35.

Table 16-5 Statement of Constraints

Constraint No.	Ratio of	to	Mathematical Form	$b_{1,1}$ $b_{1,2}$	Slacks Lower	Upper
1	Secured and unsecured loans	total loans	$\dfrac{x_1 + x_2}{x_1 + x_2 + x_3 + x_4 + x_5 + x_6}$	0.15–0.35	1	2
2	Unsecured loans	secured and unsecured loans	$\dfrac{x_1}{x_1 + x_2}$	0.60–0.80	3	4
3	Monthly payment loans	total commercial loans	$\dfrac{x_3 + x_4}{x_1 + x_2 + x_3 + x_4}$	0.25–0.40	5	6
4	Auto loans	monthly payment loans	$\dfrac{x_3}{x_3 + x_4}$	0.35–0.55	7	8
5	Real estate loans	savings deposits	$\dfrac{x_5 + x_6}{y_1}$	0.50–0.60	9	10
6	Insured mortgages	total mortgages	$\dfrac{x_5}{x_5 + x_6}$	0.40–0.60	11	12
7	Governments under 5 years	total governments	$\dfrac{x_7 + x_8}{x_7 + x_8 + x_9}$	0.55–0.85	13	14
8	Governments	total bonds	$\dfrac{x_7 + x_8 + x_9}{x_7 + x_8 + x_9 + x_{10} + x_{11}}$	0.75–0.85	15	16
9	Cash and due from banks	total deposits	$\dfrac{x_{14}}{y_1 + y_2}$	0.17–0.22	17	18
10	Bank premises and equipment	surplus and retained earnings	$\dfrac{x_{12}}{y_3}$	0.12–0.15	19	20
11	Total loans	total deposits	$\dfrac{x_1 + x_2 + x_3 + x_4 + x_5 + x_6}{y_1 + y_2}$	0.55–0.65	21	22
12	(See text)		$\overline{0.80(y_1 + y_2) - (x_1 + \cdots + x_6)}$ x_7	1.00–∞	23	
13	Interest uncollected and other assets	total loans	$\dfrac{x_{13}}{x_1 + x_2 + x_3 + x_4 + x_5 + x_6}$	0.01–0.01	24	24

Constraints 2 to 11 are of the same form. Constraint 12 states that x_7 (investment in Governments due within one year) must be greater than the sum of an allowance for deposit fluctuations (15% of the total deposits) plus additional possible loan demand up to the maximum allowable (i.e., up to 65% of total deposits), or

$$x_7 \geq 0.15(y_1 + y_2) + [0.65(y_1 + y_2) - (x_1 + \cdots + x_6)]$$

$$1 \leq \frac{x_7}{0.80(y_1 + y_2) - (x_1 + \cdots + x_6)}$$

Constraint 13 is an equality.

The LP solution is given in Table 16-6. The s_i are the slack variables identified in the constraint Table 16-5. The maximum total return on $100 is $3.65. After examining this solution, the Investment Committee asked that another run be made with:

(i) the $b_{i,1}$ and $b_{i,2}$ changed to the following values:

Constraints	$b'_{i,1}$	$b'_{i,2}$
1	0.15	0.35
2	0.60	0.80
3	0.25	0.60
4	0.15	0.35
5	0.40	0.75
6	0.15	0.50
7	0.75	1.00
8	0.65	0.85
9	0.13	0.22
10	0.12	0.20
11	0.45	0.65
12	1.00	∞
13	0.01	0.01

(ii) constraint 13 changed to

$$\frac{x_{13}}{x_1 + x_2 + \cdots + x_{10} + x_{11}}$$

and (iii) the allowance for deposit fluctuations set at 13% of the total deposits.

The solution to this LP model is shown in Table 16-7. The maximum total return is 4.16 per $100. The solutions are for the case $y_1 = 0.4$, $y_2 = 0.5$, and $y_3 = 0.1$.

EXERCISES

1. Formulate the LP model and verify that the solution in Table 16-6 is the optimum.

Table 16-6 Optimum Solution to First LP Model

Variable	Optimum Values of Basic Variables	Change in Profit Coefficients for Non-Basic Variables
x_1	0.16	
x_2	0.04	
x_3	0.07	
x_4	0.06	
x_5	0.10	
x_6	0.14	
x_7	0.14	
x_8		0.5000
x_9	0.05	
x_{10}	0.06	
x_{11}		1.6000
x_{12}	0.01	
x_{13}	0.01	
x_{14}	0.15	
s_1	0.12	
s_2		8.8950
s_3	0.04	
s_4		0.2500
s_5	0.05	
s_6		9.9950
s_7	0.03	
s_8		1.0000
s_9	0.04	
s_{10}		5.3470
s_{11}		1.5000
s_{12}	0.05	
s_{13}	0.04	
s_{14}	0.02	
s_{15}		2.5000
s_{16}	0.03	
s_{17}		4.1250
s_{18}	0.04	
s_{19}		4.1250
s_{20}	0.00	
s_{21}	0.08	
s_{22}	0.01	
s_{23}		1.5000

2. Verify that the solution in Table 16-7 is the optimum.
3. Identify the constraining inequalities in each solution.
4. Give an economic interpretation of each slack variable and of the solution.

Table 16-7   Optimum Solution to Second LP Model

Variable	Optimum Values of Basic Variables	Change in Profit Coefficients for Non-Basic Variables
x_1	0.09	
x_2	0.02	
x_3	0.06	
x_4	0.11	
x_5	0.05	
x_6	0.25	
x_7		1.0000
x_8	0.14	
x_9	0.05	
x_{10}	0.10	
x_{11}		1.6000
x_{12}	0.01	
x_{13}	0.01	
x_{14}	0.12	
s_1	0.03	
s_2	0.09	
s_3	0.02	
s_4		0.2500
s_5	0.10	
s_6		0.9000
s_7	0.03	
s_8		1.0000
s_9	0.14	
s_{10}		0.2850
s_{11}		1.5000
s_{12}	0.10	
s_{13}		0.5000
s_{14}	0.05	
s_{15}		2.8750
s_{16}	0.06	
s_{17}		4.1312
s_{18}	0.08	
s_{19}		4.1312
s_{20}	0.01	
s_{21}	0.18	
s_{22}		0.8174
s_{23}	0.17	

F. THE PERSONAL TOILETRIES COMPANY

The Personal Toiletries Company manufactures toiletries in the midwestern part of the United States. Severe competition and declining profit margins have caused the chief executive to become concerned with directing sales effort and productive capacity to maintain the firm's earnings record.

The sales and manufacturing vice-presidents hold different opinions about the best course of action under existing market and operating conditions. The president's attempt to resolve the differences has not met with such success. Part of the difficulty arose because the executives looked at the problem of matching sales demands and plant capacity from different points of view. The sales executive thought of plant facilities and manpower primarily in terms of satisfying the customer with price, quality, and shipping dates equal to or better than those of competitors. He found it desirable to have flexible production schedules. Where possible, he wanted his sales force to push the products with the highest gross margin.

The manufacturing executive, on the other hand, thought of the demands placed on the facilities by sales in terms of the effect of those demands on balanced production, utilization of equipment and manpower, and other factors that contribute to an efficient operation. He believed that the desirability of satisfying varying and sometimes unexpected demands of customers should be weighed against the additional costs arising from the interruptions and changes.

The chief executive was certain that the heads of both sales and manufacturing were vitally interested in lower production costs, increased sales, and higher earnings. Because of their responsibilities, however, they appeared to be suggesting conflicting solutions. The chief executive recognized the need for some method of evaluating sales demand and plant capacity in terms of over-all benefit to the firm. He needed a sales and production program that would give earnings as great as marketing and production limitations would permit.

The Personal Toiletries Company, PTC, produces five products which will be identified by X and by a subscript; X_1 is the first product, X_2 the second, etc. Volume is measured in "units."

The selling price per unit is fixed and does not depend on the quantity produced. The gross margin is defined as the sales price less variable manufacturing costs (raw material and labor). No allocated overhead costs are included in the variable manufacturing costs. The gross margin for the five products has been calculated by the Accounting Department; the values are as follows:

Product	Gross Margin ($ per unit)
X_1	6.5
X_2	7.3
X_3	8.5
X_4	4.3
X_5	6.2

The production division consists of four departments, Y_1, Y_2, Y_3, and Y_4. The capacities of the four departments are measured in "gallons," "machine hours," "ounces," and "cases," respectively, and are:

Department	Capacity per Month
Y_1	100 gallons
Y_2	12,000 machine hours
Y_3	380,000 ounces
Y_4	3,000 cases

The Industrial Engineering Department has computed the capacity required to process 1 unit of each product in each department as:

Product	Y_1 (gal/ 1,000 unit)	Y_2 (machine hr/ 1,000 unit)	Y_3 (oz/ 1,000 unit)	Y_4 (cases/ 1000 unit)	Working Capital ($ unit)
X_1	0.134	42.6	1,600	6.94	28.7
X_2	0.340	26.2	1,200	13.88	8.5
X_3	0.267	41.0	900	6.94	23.2
X_4	0.382	30.0	800	3.47	32.5
X_5	0.300	25.0	1,200	6.94	14.8

The last column shows the working capital required for each product. A total of $7,500,000 is available.

The Marketing Research Department prepared a forecast of market potential which states the total demand in the coming year will be:

Product	Market Forecast (1,000 units)
X_1	22
X_2	73
X_3	106
X_4	85
X_5	74
Total	360

The president asked a consulting firm to study the problem. Their recommendations were:

(a) The firm should produce the following amounts of each of the products:

Product	Amount (1,000 units)
X_1	22
X_2	73
X_3	106
X_4	56.88
X_5	74

(b) The capacity of Department 1 should be increased. Earnings would be increased by $11,256.50 for each 100-gallon increase in capacity.

(c) The firm should attempt to increase demand for all products except X_4. The increase in earnings resulting from increased demand would be:

Product	Increase in Earnings (per unit increase in demand)
X_1	4.9916
X_2	3.4728
X_3	5.4945
X_5	2.8230

EXERCISES

1. Show that the solution recommended by the consultant is the optimum linear programming solution.

2. Determine the extent to which the earnings increase given in (b) and (c) hold. (*Hint:* Use the matrices given on p. 501.)

If

$A =$

0.134	0.340	0.267	0.382	0.300					
42.6	26.2	41.0	30.0	25.0		1.0			
1600	1200	900	800	1200			1.0		
6.94	13.88	6.94	3.47	6.94				1.0	
28.7	8.5	23.2	32.5	14.7					1.0
1.0									
	1.0								
		1.0							
			1.0						
				1.0					

then

$A^{-1} =$

0.57220E-07	-0.90222E-09	-0.39024E-18	0.14703E-08	0.12400E-08	-0.38528E-07	-0.94997E-08	-0.21858E-07	-0.39948E-07
-0.14644E-06	0.11641E-08	-0.72760E-11	-0.93132E-09	0.78705E-10	0.10000E 01	0.92400E-08	0.19330E-07	0.23534E-07
-0.13700E-06	-0.12171E-16	0.28659E-10	0.45133E-09	0.10906E-08	-0.33459E-08	0.99999E 00	-0.76033E-08	-0.88388E-08
0.26178E 01	-0.72264E-09	-0.26056E-10	-0.24721E-08	-0.12360E-08	-0.89005E 00	-0.69895E 00	0.44703E-07	-0.78534E 00
0.	0.	0.	0.	0.	0.	0.	0.	0.09999E 01
-0.78534E 02	0.99999E 00	-0.51489E-09	-0.11517E-07	0.16920E-08	0.50157E 00	-0.20031E 02	-0.47683E-06	-0.14398E 01
-0.20942E 04	-0.32992E-06	0.99999E 00	-0.46607E-06	0.24380E-06	-0.48796E 03	-0.34084E 03	-0.22888E-04	-0.57172E 03
-0.90838E 01	-0.54707E-08	-0.11157E-09	0.99999E 00	-0.80516E-09	-0.10791E 02	-0.45146E 01	-0.59604E-07	-0.42149E 01
-0.85079E 02	0.48114E-08	-0.16089E-09	0.19809E-07	0.10000E 00	0.20427E 02	-0.48403E 00	-0.47683E-06	0.10723E 02
-0.26178E 01	0.72264E-09	0.11504E-10	0.84233E-09	0.30475E-09	0.89005E 00	0.69895E 00	0.99999E 00	0.78534E 00

The elements are given in floating form xEy where y gives the power of 10 by which x must be multiplied, e.g.,

$$0.100E\text{-}01 = 0.010$$
$$0.100E\ 00 = 0.100$$
$$0.100E\ 01 = 1.00$$

Notes and References

Section A

The investment problem is based on:
Vajda, S. (1962), *Readings in Mathematical Programming*, 2nd ed., John Wiley and Sons, New York, p. 46.

Section B

The machine-loading problem is based on an unpublished paper by W. O. Blattner, "A machine loading problem."

Section C

The warehouse problem was initially formulated by Cahn; the example is based on the paper by Charnes and Cooper.
Cahn, A. S. (1948), "The Warehouse Problem," *Bulletin of the American Mathematical Society*, **54**, p. 1073.
Charnes, A., and Cooper, W. W. (1954), "Generalizations of the Warehousing Model," *Operations Research Quarterly*, **6**, pp. 131–171.

Section D

See also:
Hanssmann, F. (1962), *Operations Research in Production and Inventory Control*, John Wiley and Sons, New York.

Section E

The application to bank investments is based on a term paper by two Stanford Graduate School of Business MBA students: R. Gee and R. Waterman.

CHAPTER SEVENTEEN

Special Cases of Linear

Programming

The examples given in the last two chapters and those cited in the Chapter 15 Notes and References illustrate the application of linear programming to a wide variety of problems. Furthermore, the simplex method provides a general technique for the computation of numerical optimum solutions.

In some linear programming problems the coefficients in the constraints have special forms and special cases of the simplex algorithm, which require less computation, can be developed. Two classes of problems in which such algorithms exist will be described: the transportation problem in Section A and the assignment problem in Section B.

All linear programming problems can be formulated in one of two essentially equivalent ways. One formulation is called the primal and the other the dual. The relationship between the primal and the dual is discussed in Section C.

There are a number of problems which differ from the formulation of a linear programming model as described in Chapter 15 only in that the solution must be a set of integers. The simplex method does not guarantee that the optimum solution will be an integer, and hence a different algorithm must be used.

The basic reason for requiring integer solutions is that many activities or resources cannot be subdivided into less than integer amounts. For example, if the problem is one of determining how many of each kind of machine to assign to a factory, an answer such as $106\frac{7}{8}$ of machine A, $82\frac{1}{3}$ of machine B cannot be implemented. If the numbers involved are large, as they are here, rounding to the nearest integer may be acceptable, but if the numbers are small, rounding can result in non-optimal solutions.

Another case which requires an integer solution and which occurs frequently is that in which the decision is whether or not to take a certain course of action; the decision variable can take only two values, say 0 and 1. For example, the alternatives may be to build, or not to build, a new plant. If the plant is to be built, a decision variable may be defined to take the value 1; and if it is not to be built, the value zero.

The problem of obtaining the optimum integer solution to a linear programming problem, called integer programming, will not be discussed further. The status of algorithms may be obtained from current publications; some are listed in Notes and References.

A. THE TRANSPORTATION MODEL

The transportation technique is an algorithm for solving a certain sub-class of linear programming problems. It can be used in those problems in which it is necessary to fulfil certain requirements from certain resources in which both the requirements and resources are expressed in the same kind of units. The most common example of the transportation problem, and the one which will be illustrated here, concerns a business which must supply products to a number of geographically separated customers from a number of plants, and seeks to do so at the least cost.

Statement of the Problem

The XYZ Company is engaged in the manufacturing and marketing of widgets at three locations, L, M, and N. On a particular day, outstanding orders for 16 tons of widgets must be shipped to the following customers:

A Company	2 tons
B Company	2 tons
C Company	4 tons
D Company	4 tons
E Company	4 tons

Freight costs to these customers from the various plants are given in Table 17-1. A negative amount appears in Table 17-1 covering shipments from M to E to illustrate that costs may be negative. (In this case it may be interpreted as a subsidy which actually brings revenue into the company.)

Available for immediate shipment are a total of 16 tons, 5 tons each at

Table 17-1   Freight Costs from Plants to Various Customers

To From	A	B	C	D	E
L	20	10	20	30	30
M	20	20	20	10	−10
N	30	30	20	10	20

L and M, and 6 tons at N. (Note that the requirements and the availabilities are exactly equal in this example.) The problem facing this firm is to determine the most economical pattern of shipment. The computational problem is to enter numbers in Table 17-2 in such a way that the numbers have the necessary row and column totals and that the total freight costs are minimized.

First Feasible Schedule

The first step in obtaining an optimum solution to this problem is to develop a *feasible* schedule, namely, to solve the movement problem even though the costs may not be minimum. The eventual goal in using the transportation technique is to develop an *optimum* feasible schedule which satisfies the movement requirements at the smallest total cost.

The most mechanical way of developing a first feasible schedule is by what is known as the "northwest corner rule." Starting at the northwest corner of the table, the tons available at the first plant are used to fill the requirements of as many customers as possible, moving from left to right.

Table 17-2   Resources and Requirements

To From	A	B	C	D	E	Total
L						5
M						5
N						6
Total	2	2	4	4	4	16

In this case, there are 5 tons available at L. Two each are assigned to A and B companies and the remaining 1 to C. Since the resources of the first plant are now exhausted, the resources of the next plant are used to fill the requirements of as many customers as possible, moving from left to right. This procedure is repeated until all requirements are taken care of. In the example, there are 5 tons available at M. Three of these tons are assigned to C to fill its remaining requirements and the remaining 2 would go to D. Since this exhausts all of M's availability, the 6 tons at N are next assigned, 2 to complete D's needs and the remaining 4 to E. The results of this are shown as circled figures in Table 17-3.

Table 17-3   First Feasible Schedule

To From	A	B	C	D	E	Total
L	②	②	①			5
M			③	②		5
N				②	④	6
Total	2	2	4	4	4	16

That this schedule satisfies the requirements of the problem is apparent from adding the circled figures down and across, and observing that these totals equal the availabilities and requirements specified in the edges of the table.

This, then, is a feasible schedule. Sixteen tons are shipped to five customers. All available widgets are shipped and all customers' orders are filled. It is now possible to determine the total cost for this feasible schedule by multiplying the number of tons shipped from each plant to each customer by the applicable freight cost shown in Table 17-1 as follows:

$$
\begin{array}{lll}
L \text{ to } A & 2 \text{ tons at } 20 = 40 \\
L \text{ to } B & 2 \text{ tons at } 10 = 20 \\
L \text{ to } C & 1 \text{ ton at } 20 \ = 20 \\
M \text{ to } C & 3 \text{ tons at } 20 = 60 \\
M \text{ to } D & 2 \text{ tons at } 10 = 20 \\
N \text{ to } D & 2 \text{ tons at } 10 = 20 \\
N \text{ to } E & 4 \text{ tons at } 20 = 80 \\
& \text{Total cost } \overline{260}
\end{array}
$$

Evaluate the Feasible Schedule. Sixteen tons of widgets can be shipped from the three plants to fill the orders of five customers. It will cost 260 to fill these orders using this schedule. But is this schedule the best? To determine this, it is necessary that alternative possibilities be evaluated. Specifically, the costs associated with *not* using certain plant-customer combinations must be examined to determine how this first schedule could be changed to yield lower costs. The procedure, known as "evaluation," is as follows:

Table 17-4   Method of Cell Evaluation

To \ From	A	B	C	D	E	Total
L	20 ②	−10 ②	20 ① +	30	30	5
M	20	20	20 ③	−10 ② +	−10	5
N	30 10 +	+30	20	10 ②	20 ④ −	6
Total	2	2	4	4	4	16

Choose any cell in which no circled number appears (the cell covering shipment from N to A will be used as a starting point), and determine a number for this cell as follows:

1. Move along the same *row*, left or right, until a circled figure is reached which has another circled figure in the same column, above or below. In this example, proceed from N-A to N-D.

2. Now move up or down the column until a circled figure is reached which has another circled figure in the same *row*. The move from N-D to M-D satisfies this requirement.

3. Continue in this manner moving alternately first in a column and then in a row until the same column is reached which contains the cell from which this procedure was started.

4. Assign alternate plus and minus signs to each cell in the path traced, beginning with a plus sign for the starting cell.

The complete path is illustrated in Table 17-4. A value for the cell being evaluated can now be determined. To do this it is necessary to retrace the path and record the unit costs associated with the starting cell and all other cells directly included in the path, each having the same sign as its cell. The algebraic sum of these is formed. In the example, this sum is obtained as follows:

N to A	$+(30)$
N to D	$-(10)$
M to D	$+(10)$
M to C	$-(20)$
L to C	$+(20)$
L to A	$-(20)$
	Sum $+10$

This sum is now entered in the table as a non-circled number. The procedure is repeated in similar fashion until all cells have a circled or non-circled number as shown in Table 17-5:

Table 17-5   First Basic Schedule

To From	A	B	C	D	E	Total
L	20 ②	10 ②	20 ①	30 20	30 -10	5
M	20 0	20 10	20 ③	10 ②	-10 -30	5
N	30 10	30 20	20 0	10 ②	20 ④	6
Total	2	2	4	4	4	16

At this point it can be determined whether or not this solution is optimum. *If any negative numbers appear, the solution can be improved.* Since the schedule in the example contains two negative values, *M-E* and *L-E*, the best solution has not been obtained. The smallest negative value, i.e., *the negative value with the largest absolute value*, appearing in a feasible schedule indicates the plant-customer combination offering the greatest potential cost reduction. This is true by virtue of the manner in which the value is calculated. The path which is the basis of this calculation, with alternating plus-minus signs, can be interpreted as specifying the changes that must be made to utilize a previously untilized plant-customer combination at a 1-unit level. When the unit transportation costs associated with the cells in this path are added algebraically, the result is the cost equivalent of these changes; a negative cost equivalent is thus the largest potential cost reduction. Note that though all negative values denote potential cost reduction, this does not mean that all the corresponding relations will be utilized in a minimum cost schedule. If the necessary changes are made to take advantage of the largest potential cost reduction, then a new schedule and a complete re-evaluation of uncircled cells will be required, and the values in uncircled cells may change.

In Table 17-5 M-E is the smallest negative value. As mentioned in the preceding paragraph, this represents the cell offering the greatest cost reduction. Accordingly, this cell must be used to optimize the program, and then all cells without circled numbers must be re-evaluated.

Evaluation and Continuation

The schedule is not optimum since it contains negative values, and since the smallest negative value represents the spot where the greatest cost reduction is promised, it is desirable to move one of the circled values from its current position to the cell in which the smallest negative value appears. (If two equal smallest negative values appear, either one may be chosen.)

The rule for determining which circled value to move is as follows:

1. Retrace the path used to determine the value of the cell in which the smallest negative value appears.

2. Select those cells that were assigned a minus value in the alternation between plus and minus signs.

3. From the minus cells, select the one with the smallest number written in its circle. (This ensures that the new schedule will remain feasible.)

4. Move this circled value from its present position to the cell previously occupied by the smallest negative value.

5. Enter all other circles at their previous positions in the table but without any numbers inside the circles.

6. Fill in the circles with numbers according to the values in the edges. This provides a new feasible schedule.

Returning to the example, the path used to obtain the smallest negative value, -30, passed through the "minus" cells, M-D and N-E. The former had a number, 2, and the latter a number, 4. The smaller of these two numbers, i.e., the 2 in the M-D cell, is moved to the M-E cell to replace the smallest negative value. All other circles are retained in their former positions but with new amounts entered which balance the table. Table 17-6 shows the results of this procedure. The circled 2 from the M-D block now appears in place of the smallest negative value. The path used to determine the new distribution is shown by the arrows.

Table 17-6 Replacement of Smallest Negative Value

To From	A	B	C	D	E	Total
L	20 ②	10 ②	20 ①	30	30	5
M	20	20	20 ③	10 —2—→	−10 ②	5
N	30	30	20	10 ④ ←2—	20 ②	6
Total	2	2	4	4	4	16

This is the new feasible schedule. The new program is now evaluated as before, the results being shown in Table 17-7.

This is another feasible schedule which is closer to the optimum solution than was the previous one because the cost is reduced to 200. The optimum has not been achieved; this schedule shows three negative values. The procedure must be continued until no negative values appear.

Table 17-7 Second Basic Schedule

To From	A	B	C	D	E	Total
L	20 ②	10 ②	20 ①	30 50	30 40	5
M	20 0	20 10	20 ③	10 30	−10 ②	5
N	30 −20	30 −10	20 −30	10 ④	20 ②	6
Total	2	2	4	4	4	16

The third schedule and evaluation appear in Table 17-8. In this case the third solution yields the optimum because no negative values appear. All shipments are handled and costs are:

L to A	2 tons at	20 =	40
L to B	2 tons at	10 =	20
L to C	1 ton at	20 =	20
M to C	1 ton at	20 =	20
M to E	4 tons at	−10 =	−40
N to C	2 tons at	20 =	40
N to D	4 tons at	10 =	40
Total	16 tons		$140

Table 17-8 First Optimum Solution

To From	A	B	C	D	E	Total
L	20 ②	10 ②	20 ①	30 20	30 40	5
M	20 0	20 10	20 ①	10 0	−10 ④	5
N	30 10	30 20	20 ②	10 ④	20 30	6
Total	2	2	4	4	4	16

Since no negative values appear, no amount of further evaluations or experimentation will lower the costs below $140.

Shortcuts

There are some obvious shortcuts that can materially reduce the amount of computation. When a negative value appears in a cost table (as was the case here), it is obvious that a maximum amount should be shipped from the origin to the destination involved so as to take maximum benefit of the subsidy involved. Accordingly, before applying the northwest corner rule, the maximum circled figure possible should be entered in the cell corresponding to this subsidy figure.

In addition, when the lowest cost in a *row* corresponds to the lowest cost in a *column*, the cost is known as a "mutually preferred" cost. This origin can ship to this customer more cheaply than to any other customer. Also, this customer can receive goods from this plant at less expense to the company than from any other plant. Obviously, this cell should be circled and the highest possible number entered before applying the northwest corner rule. Note that this rule automatically encompasses the subsidy, but is also of greater generality. Applying this concept to the example shows that the lowest cost in the L row is in the B column, and that the lowest cost in the B column is in the L row. Since these correspond, maximum use should be made of this cell. The same is true of the M-E and N-D cells. Accordingly, the first step would be to fill out the table as shown in Table 17-9.

Now, proceeding with the northwest corner rule, the remaining cells are filled as shown in Table 17-10.

It will be noted that this schedule is the optimum (see Table 17-8). While this procedure will not yield the optimum in every instance, it will

Table 17-9   Preferred Flows

To From	A	B	C	D	E	Total
L	20	10 ②	20	30	30	5
M	20	20	20	10	−10 ④	5
N	30	30	20	10 ④	20	6
Total	2	2	4	4	4	16

Table 17-10   Optimum Solution from Preferred Flows

To From	A	B	C	D	E	Total
L	20 ②	10 ②	20 ①	30	30	5
M	20	20	20 ①	10	−10 ④	5
N	30	30	20 ②	10 ④	20	6
Total	2	2	4	4	4	16

yield a schedule closer to the optimum than might otherwise occur, and it should therefore reduce the number of necessary iterations.

Another time-saving device is to stop working immediately on a schedule when a negative value appears. Since any schedule with a negative value is discarded, it is obviously not worthwhile to continue to find values for the remaining cells. In this case, the first negative value obtained is treated as the smallest negative value in the continuation of the procedure.

Alternate Best Programs

It will be noted that zeroes appear at two places in the optimum solution (Table 17-8). These zeroes are of particular interest to the business manager since they indicate that equally good, lowest cost alternative choices of action exist. There are other schedules for shipping the products to fill the customers' needs at the same minimum price of $140.

The following method of determining alternative optimum programs applies *only after an optimum solution containing zeroes* has been reached. The method consists merely of treating zeroes in the same fashion as the smallest negative values were treated previously. For example, selecting the zero at *M-D* and retracing the path used to obtain that zero shows the minus cell numbers to be 1 at *M-C* and 4 at *N-D*. Following the procedure, the number 1 is substituted for the zero and necessary changes are made in the circled numbers to balance the table. The alternative schedule now obtained, as shown in Table 17-11, is still optimum, as it contains no negative values and results in a cost of $140.

This alternate solution is an added choice, yielding similar costs but allowing greater freedom to the decision maker. This new solution also

Table 17-11   First Alternate Optimum Solution

From \ To	A	B	C	D	E	Total
L	20 ②	10 ②	20 ①	30 20	30 40	5
M	20 0	20 10	20 0	10 ①	−10 ④	5
N	30 10	30 20	20 ③	10 ③	20 30	6
Total	2	2	4	4	4	16

reveals two zeroes, one of which is precisely at the point where the change was made in the previous solution. This zero may be ignored because changing back would only lead again to the original solution. However, both tables have a zero at *M-A* and hence another alternative is available as shown in Table 17-12. This table provides another means of supplying the demand and still costs only $140. No new zeroes have appeared; therefore, all possible optima have been discovered.

Derived Optimum Programs

Returning to the original description of the XYZ Company, assume that freight costs do not change in fractional tons of widgets and that it is more convenient for the XYZ Company to ship widgets in units of $\frac{1}{3}$ ton. It will be noted that, up to this point, all solutions have appeared as integers. As long as only integers appear in the "edges" of the table, no fractions will enter the table.

An optimum solution permitting XYZ to ship fractional parts of tons to customers can be developed if *two optimum tables* exist. Then any two fractions whose sum is one may be applied to these tables as follows. Select two fractions whose sum is one, in this case $\frac{1}{3}$ and $\frac{2}{3}$. These are

Table 17-12   Second Alternate Optimum Solution

From \ To	A	B	C	D	E	Total
L	20 ①	10 ②	20 ②	30 20	30 40	5
M	20 ①	20 10	20 0	10 0	−10 ④	5
N	30 10	30 20	20 ②	10 ④	20 50	6
Total	2	2	4	4	4	16

applied against two optimum solutions, say, Tables 17-11 and 17-12. All the circled values in Table 17-11 are multiplied by one of these two fractions and all the circled values in Table 17-12 are multiplied by the other fraction. These tables are then added together as shown in Table 17-13. The total cost of this alternative solution is the same as before,

Table 17-13   Derived Optimum Solution

From \ To	A	B	C	D	E	Total
L	20 $\frac{4}{3}$	10 2	20 $\frac{5}{3}$	30	30	5
M	20 $\frac{2}{3}$	20	20	10 $\frac{1}{3}$	−10 4	5
N	30	30	20 $\frac{7}{3}$	10 $\frac{11}{3}$	20	6
Total	2	2	4	4	4	16

namely, $140. As long as costs remain constant, an infinite number of optimum programs may be derived from these two tables by applying pairs of fractions whose sum is one ($\frac{1}{2}$, $\frac{1}{2}$; $\frac{1}{4}$, $\frac{3}{4}$; $\frac{1}{6}$, $\frac{5}{6}$; etc.).

Degenerate Solutions

An examination of the basic (not derived) solutions reveals that, in each instance, there are seven circled items. It is a property of any "normal" basic solution that the number of circled items will be one less than the number of columns plus the number of rows. This is true in the example. Moreover, the circled values should be so located in the table that evaluation of the remaining blank cells is possible by the method previously described; namely, to move along the rows and columns and end at the cell being evaluated. If these conditions do not exist at any point in the procedure, that schedule is referred to as *degenerate* and it is possible to resort to what is known as a *degeneracy procedure*. This consists of entering circles arbitrarily at the necessary point(s) in the table. A symbol *e*, representing a very small positive number, smaller than any other in the table, is entered inside this circle. It may happen that the *e* cell is one

Table 17-14 Degenerate Feasible Schedule

To From	A	B	C	D	E	Total
L	20	10 ①	20 ④	30	⬛0	5
M	20	20 ①	20	10 ④	−10	5
N	30 ②	30	20	10	20 ④	6
Total	2	2	4	4	4	16

of the minus cells used to evaluate the smallest negative value. Since *e* is the smallest number in the table, it is obviously the one moved into the smallest negative value cell as the first step in forming a new table. The remaining cells are entered as before in their previous positions and filled out by reference to the totals. In the process of determining these numbers, *e* may be ignored. It is treated as insignificant in terms of its effect on the program.

As an illustration of the degenerate solution technique, assume that a procedure other than the northwest corner rule was applied to determine the initial feasible schedule, and that in this schedule the circled values appear as shown in Table 17-14.

There are only six circles provided in this schedule although the requirements are satisfied. In attempting to perform evaluation, it soon becomes apparent that a circled value is needed to complete the table. The symbol *e* is entered at *L-E*, and the table is completed by using the regular procedures as shown in Table 17-15. The smallest negative value, −50, was calculated by affixing a negative sign to the unit transportation costs associated with the cell containing *e*. Accordingly, *e* was substituted for the −50. The entrance of the *e* item in no way alters the previous computing instructions. By repeated applications of the rules, the optimum program will be achieved. The *e* value will usually disappear en route to the optimum solution. If it does not, the optimum will be degenerate and the e value can be ignored.

Table 17-15   Degenerate Feasible Schedule after Application of Degeneracy Procedure

From \ To	A	B	C	D	E	Total
L	²⁰ −20	¹⁰ ①	²⁰ ④	³⁰ 30	³⁰ e	5
M	²⁰ 30	²⁰ ①	²⁰ −10	¹⁰ ④	⁻¹⁰ −50	5
N	³⁰ ②	³⁰ 30	²⁰ 10	¹⁰ 20	²⁰ ④	6
Total	2	2	4	4	4	16

Summary of Procedure

1. Choose an initial feasible schedule, using the northwest corner or some other rule. Inclusion of cells which are both row and column minimum cost usually reduces the steps to an optimum solution.

2. Calculate the cost of transportation entailed by this schedule.

3. Calculate the set of costs associated with introducing a unit-level utilization of each presently excluded plant-customer relation, introducing e shipments if necessary.

   (a) If none of these quantities is negative, the present schedule is optimum and the calculated costs are minimum.

   (b) If one or more of these quantities is negative, that plant-customer relation whose unit-level introduction cost is the smallest negative value will be included in an optimum solution. Substitute that relation for the presently included relation which is (1) adjacent in the same row (column); (2) itself adjacent in column (row) to a second presently included relation; and (3) utilized at the lowest level of all relations satisfying (1) and (2). Giving the introduced relation the same level of utilization as that which it replaced, balance the schedule consisting of (1) the introduced relation, and (2) all previously included relations but that replaced. Return to step 2.

4. After an optimum solution is determined, if there are any excluded relations whose unit-level introduction would entail zero costs, these may be substituted into the schedule per 2(b), with an alternative optimum solution resulting.

Linear Programming Formulation

The example given above can be stated in a linear programming model as follows:

Let y_i = number of units available at location i; $i = 1 \cdots k$
  z_j = number of units required at location j; $j = 1 \cdots m$
  x_{ij} = number of units to be shipped from location i to location j
  c_{ij} = cost of shipping one unit from location i to location j
The problem is to minimize

$$\sum_{i=1}^{k} \sum_{j=1}^{m} c_{ij} x_{ij} \tag{1}$$

subject to

$$\sum_{j=1}^{m} x_{ij} = y_i \qquad \text{for } i = 1, 2, \ldots, k \tag{2}$$

$$\sum_{i=1}^{k} x_{ij} = z_j \qquad \text{for } j = 1, 2, \ldots, m \tag{3}$$

and

$$\sum_{i=1}^{k} y_i = \sum_{j=1}^{m} z_j \tag{4}$$

Though (2) and (3) define a system of $n + m$ equations in nm unknowns, one of the equations can always be shown to be a linear combination of the others, and hence redundant. What this means for practical purposes, as mentioned above, is that any non-degenerate basic solution has exactly $k + m - 1$ unknowns greater than zero, and the rest equal to zero.

The simplex method can be used to solve the transportation problem; however, because of the special form of the program matrix a technique similar to the one outlined above is normally employed. With the large number of equations and variables usually involved in a realistic transportation problem, the transportation algorithm leads to a minimizing solution with considerably less calculating effort.

If (4) is not satisfied, then dummy locations are added and the augmented problem is solved. For example, assume $\sum_{i=1}^{k} y_i > \sum_{j=1}^{m} z_j$. Then a dummy customer with requirement

$$z_{m+1} = \sum_{i=1}^{k} y_i - \sum_{j=1}^{m} z_j$$

and unit transportation costs $c_{i,m+1} = 0$, $i = 1, 2, \ldots, k$, is added to the problem. The minimizing solution for the augmented problem is also the minimizing solution for the original problem. The dummy location and dummy customers represent unused capacity or unshipped items, respectively.

EXERCISES

1. Determine the optimum shipment schedule where

$$y_1 = 5, y_2 = 3, z_1 = 2, z_2 = 4 \quad \text{and} \quad z_3 = 2 \quad \text{and} \quad C = (c_{ij}) \text{ is}$$

$$\begin{bmatrix} 10 & 10 & 20 \\ 30 & 30 & 20 \end{bmatrix}$$

2. Determine whether the optimum solution to the transportation problem described in Table 1 is given by Table 2. If not, compute the optimum.

Table 17-16

From To	5	6	7	8	9	Total
0	73	40	9	79	20	8
1	62	93	96	8	13	7
2	96	65	80	50	65	9
3	57	58	29	12	87	3
4	56	23	87	18	12	5
Total	6	8	10	4	4	32

Table 17-17

From To	5	6	7	8	9	Total
0			8			8
1				4	3	7
2	5	4				9
3	1		2			3
4		4			1	5
Total	6	8	10	4	4	32

3. Which of the following problems can be solved by the transportation technique?

(a) Given several sources of production, each having fixed productive capacity, with total capacity in balance with market requirements, which sources should furnish which markets so as to minimize transportation costs?

(b) Given an area about which we know the market requirements, the location of sources of production and production costs as a function of volume, how should production of goods be assigned to individual plants so as to minimize transportation and manufacturing costs?

(c) Given a plant which must produce nine different types of parts and which has certain limited machine hours available, how should production be scheduled to utilize a minimum amount of machine time?

(d) Given an area about which we know market requirements and also production costs in several alternative plant locations, where should the plants be located so that the whole area can be served at minimum cost?

4. The LP solution to the problem discussed in the text is:

Variable	Optimum Value of Basic Variable	Changes in Profit Coefficients of Slack Variables
x_{11}	2	
x_{12}	2	
x_{13}	1	
x_{14}		20
x_{15}		40
x_{21}		0
x_{22}		10
x_{23}		0
x_{24}	1	
x_{25}	4	
x_{31}		10
x_{32}		20
x_{33}	3	
x_{34}	3	
x_{35}		30

Show that the c_j' coefficients of the slack variables are the values in the cells in the optimum and that the evaluation is in fact a step in the simplex method.

5. A transportation problem is given by the following tableau:

	V	W	X	Y	Z	
A	20	10	20	30	30	8
B	10	10	20	10	10	2
C	30	10	20	10	20	6
	2	4	2	4	4	

Verify that the minimum cost shipping schedule is: 2 from A to V, 4 from A to W, 2 from A to X, 2 from B to Z, 4 from C to Y, and 2 from C to Z.

6. A national car rental service has a surplus of one car in cities 1, 2, 3, 4, 5, and 6, and a need for one car in cities 7, 8, 9, 10, 11, and 12. The distances between cities with a surplus and cities with a deficit are displayed in the matrix below. How should the cars be dispatched so as to minimize the total mileage travelled?

From \ To	7	8	9	10	11	12
1	41	72	39	52	25	51
2	22	29	49	65	81	50
3	27	39	60	51	32	32
4	45	50	48	52	37	43
5	29	40	39	26	30	33
6	82	40	40	60	51	30

B. THE ASSIGNMENT PROBLEM

Consider the problem of assigning k workmen to k jobs so as to minimize the cost of completing all k jobs, when the cost associated with the ith workman doing the jth job is known. This problem is essentially the same in structure as the transportation model, with the exception that any feasible solution has exactly k non-zero and unit-valued variables. Because of this last characteristic, a special algorithm has been developed for the assignment problem which avoids the complications of degeneracy. This procedure is illustrated in the following problem.

Statement of the Problem

The Icuras Aviation Company desires to assign three salesmen, A, B, and C, to three territories, X, Y, and Z so as to maximize profit while covering all territories. The profit potential of each salesman in each territory (per period) is given below. For example, salesman B has a profit potential of $75 in territory Z.

	X	Y	Z
A	50	40	45
B	70	85	75
C	50	60	45

For purposes of consistency in treatment with the transportation problem, this problem will be converted to a minimization problem by multiplying all profit potentials by (-1). Profit potentials then become (negative) cost potentials.

	X	Y	Z
A	−50	−40	−45
B	−70	−85	−75
C	−50	−60	−45

Constructing a First Assignment

To begin the procedure, a first approximation to the optimum is constructed by assigning each salesman to his least costly territory and covering each territory with its least costly salesman. Thus, row and column component costs are chosen by taking as the row cost the smallest in each row and as the column cost the smallest remaining in each column.

In the example: first, subtract from every element of the cost matrix the smallest element in the row.

	X	Y	Z	Row Cost
A	0	10	5	−50
B	15	0	10	−85
C	10	0	15	−60

Then, subtract from every element in each column of the resulting matrix the smallest element in that column.

	X	Y	Z
A	0	10	0
B	15	0	5
C	10	0	10
Column Cost	0	0	5

The effect of this is to write the cost tableau in terms of opportunity costs; opportunity cost here has the interpretation of the profit that is lost by choosing one assignment which precludes choosing another. This tableau suggests the assignment of A to X and Z, and of B and C to Y.

Determining if the Assignment Is Feasible

If the assignment is feasible, it is the optimum. The assignment suggested by this tableau is to assign those choices with zero opportunity costs. This assignment has "minimum cost" in some sense but it is not *feasible*. There is no subset of zero cost choices such that no two occur in the same row or column. If A is assigned X, for example, there is no zero opportunity cost salesman left to cover Z.

Another way of showing that this assignment is not feasible is to select the minimum number of rows and/or columns including *all* zeros. If this is less than the number of rows, then the assignment is not feasible. The selected rows and/or columns are indicated by drawing a line through them.

	X	Y	Z
~~A~~	~~0~~	~~10~~	~~0~~
B	15	0	5
C	10	0	10

In many cases, several possible minimum sets of rows and/or columns contain all the zeros. It can be shown that any set may be chosen arbitrarily without affecting the optimum.

Revising the Assignment

If the assignment is not feasible, it is necessary to modify the non-feasible assignment by including some choice not in the selected rows and columns which include all zeros. This *may* increase the minimum number of rows and/or columns needed to include all zeros. Some entry not covered over by the lines as drawn above must be chosen. Of course, that with the least opportunity cost is chosen; in the example B to $Z = 5$. The row and column component costs must then be adjusted so that this choice has an opportunity cost of 0, while maintaining the other zeros at 0. Since the tableau has already been restated in terms of opportunity costs, changes in row and column costs are all that are required. The adjustments can be stated as: (*a*) subtract the minimum entry from all entries not covered by lines, and (*b*) add the minimum entry to all entries at the intersection of two lines. This means that zeros at the intersection of two lines are not retained; but this is appropriate, since alternate zero cost choices exist for both the row and the column. This gives the following new tableau, starting from the assumption that the row B cost = 5.

	X	Y	Z	Row Cost
A	0	15	0	0
B	10	0	0	5
C	5	0	5	5
Column Cost	0	−5	0	

The method described in (2) is used again to determine whether the assignment is feasible. The minimum set of covering lines are:

	X	Y	Z
A	0	15	0
B	10	0	0
C	5	0	5

Three lines are now needed to cover all zeros, so there is a subset of zero opportunity cost assignments which is feasible (here, A to X, B to Z, and C to Y). If the number of lines still had been less than the number of rows (or columns), we would repeat step (3) above, and so forth. This assignment results in a total profit of $50 + 75 + 60 = 185$. No assignment resulting in a larger profit can be found.

Summary of Procedure for the Assignment Problem

1. Find an initial assignment by subtracting from every element in each row of the cost matrix the smallest element in that row, and then subtracting from every element in each column of the resulting matrix the smallest element in that column.

2. Determine the smallest number of rows and/or columns which include all the zeros in the revised matrix. If this number equals the total number of rows, the problem is solved by selecting from those zeros a subset in which one and only one zero occurs in each row and column.

3. If the smallest number of rows and/or columns is less than the total number of rows in the matrix, find the smallest entry not in one of the rows and/or columns containing all zeros. Subtract this entry from all entries not in one of the rows or columns containing all zeros, and add this entry to all entries at the intersection of the rows and/or columns containing zeros. Return to step 2.

Linear Programming Formulation

The assignment problem is a special case of the transportation model described in the last subsection of Section A which has

$$y_i = 1, \qquad i = 1, 2, \ldots, k$$
$$z_j = 1, \qquad j = 1, 2, \ldots, m$$

and
$$k = m$$

The comments made previously concerning altering the problem if $m \neq k$ apply. However, feasible solutions of the assignment problem never have $m + k - 1 = 2k - 1$ variables greater than zero, and hence are always degenerate. This is true because the vector of constants is identically equal to a vector of ones, i.e., there can only be one non-zero and unit-valued variable in each row and column, or k non-zero and unit-valued variables in each row and column, or k non-zero and unit-valued variables in all. What this means is that though the general simplex and more specialized transportation algorithms are applicable, their use is complicated by the appearance of degeneracy in each iteration. This is the reason for the development of the special algorithm mentioned above.

Note the contrast between the two special algorithms. In the assignment problem the procedure first finds an assignment with optimum opportunity costs, and then modifies the assignment if it is not feasible. This is the reverse of the transportation algorithm, which first finds a feasible solution, and then evaluates alternatives in terms of opportunity costs in order to adjust the feasible solution to an optimum one. *Opportunity costs*, as used here, are the costs entailed (profits foregone) by accepting one alternative which automatically excludes others; these may be positive or negative. In the assignment problem above, the cost matrix is so modified and the procedures such that opportunity costs are always ≥ 0. In the transportation model of Section A, negative opportunity costs appear in a non-optimum solution and opportunity costs are ≥ 0 in an optimum solution.

EXERCISES

1. An assignment problem is given by the following tableau, where entries are the cost of assigning resource i to job j.

	Q	R	S	T	U
D	20	15	18	16	22
E	19	17	23	18	20
F	50	43	47	51	49
G	11	13	12	14	13
H	31	29	32	30	29

Verify that there are several minimum cost assignments, one of which is D to S, E to T, F to R, G to Q, and H to U.

2. The numbers given in the matrix below represent an index of cost of maintaining a given salesman in a given territory. How should the company assign the salesmen (one salesman per territory) so as to minimize the total cost?

		Territories				
		1	2	3	4	5
	A	24	21	9	18	27
	B	27	15	21	30	24
Salesmen	C	30	21	18	33	15
	D	36	27	12	24	30
	E	21	24	36	30	27

3. Four vacant jobs need to be filled in a large installation. An equal number of employees meet the minimum requirements of each job.

Each employee has stated his preference for each job by ranking the job 1 for his first choice and so on to 4, his last choice. Similarly, the four supervisors have stated their preferences for each employee in their job.

The ranking orders look like this:

		Jobs			
E		A	B	C	D
m					
p	a	1, 3	2, 2	3, 1	4, 3
l					
o	b	1, 4	2, 3	3, 2	4, 4
y					
e	c	3, 1	1, 4	2, 3	4, 2
e					
s	d	2, 2	3, 1	1, 4	4, 1

(The first digit indicates the employee's preference for the job; the second, the job's preference for the employee.)

The Commanding Officer has been quite concerned over the large amount of job hopping going on within his installation. He has directed you to develop a stable assignment pattern to fill these jobs with eligible employees. By stable, the CO means an assignment pattern wherein no job is filled by an employee who would prefer to be in another job, when the other job prefers that employee to its incumbent. (Taken from *Navy Management Review*, May, 1962, p. 2.)

C. THE DUAL

In general, problems can be formulated as LP models as either "primal" models or "dual" models. The relationship between the two forms is described and illustrated in this section.

A Valuation Problem

Example I. Suppose the manufacturer in the three-product two-machine product-mix problem, Chapter 15, page 426, wishes to place a value on the resources available to him. The value should be related in some way to the profit which he can derive from the resources. A set of plausible requirements on the values are:

(*a*) The value of any combination of resources should be at least as great as the profit obtained from the use of the resources.
(*b*) The value of the total resources used should be as small as possible.
(*c*) The value of a resource should not be negative.

Under these requirements the problem can be formulated in à linear programming model as follows:

Decision variables:

u_1 = value of 1 unit of time of the slotting machine

u_2 = value of 1 unit of time of the threading machine

Objective: minimize total value = y

Uncontrollable variables:

$$\mathbf{A}' = \begin{bmatrix} 4 & 2 \\ 2 & 13 \\ 1 & 2 \end{bmatrix} = (a_{ij})'$$

where a_{ij} = time on machine i required for 1 unit of jth product

$$\mathbf{B}' = [4{,}800 \quad 4{,}800] = (b_i)'$$

where b_i = total amount of each resource available

$$\mathbf{C}' = [5 \quad 4 \quad 2] = (c_i)'$$

where c_i = profit on the ith product

Model.   Minimize $y = 4{,}800u_1 + 4{,}800u_2$ subject to

$$4u_1 + 2u_2 \geq 5 \tag{1}$$

$$2u_1 + 13u_2 \geq 4 \tag{2}$$

$$u_1 + 2u_2 \geq 2 \tag{3}$$

$$u_1 \geq 0; \quad u_2 \geq 0; \tag{4}$$

Or, in matrix notation,

minimize $\qquad\qquad\qquad y = \mathbf{B'U}$

subject to $\qquad\qquad\quad \mathbf{A'U} \geq \mathbf{C}, \quad \mathbf{U} \geq 0$

where $\qquad\qquad\qquad \mathbf{U'} = [u_1 \quad u_2]$

The dimensional consistency can be verified by noting that the b_i are expressed in minutes and the u_i in cents per minute; y, the value, is therefore in cents. The a_{ij} are expressed in minutes per unit, the u_i in cents per minute and the c_i, therefore are in cents per unit.

Solution.   A graphical solution is given in Fig. 17.1. The set of feasible solutions is bounded by *RST* and the lines $u_2 = 0$, $u_1 = 0$. Since

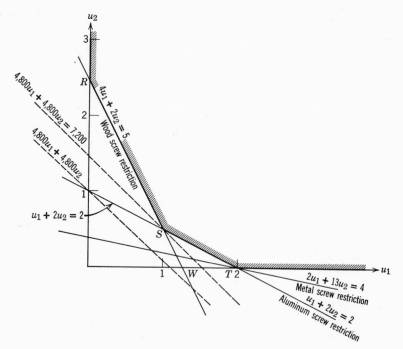

Figure 17.1   Graphical solution of the valuation problem.

the value is to be minimized, the optimum feasible solution is at the point $u_1 = 1$, $u_2 = \frac{1}{2}$. At this point the total value is

$$y = 4{,}800(1) + 4{,}800(\tfrac{1}{2}) = 7{,}200$$

The solution can also be obtained by enumeration by solving all possible sets of 2 equations taken from the set

$$4u_1 + 2u_2 = 5 \tag{5}$$

$$2u_1 + 13u_2 = 4 \tag{6}$$

$$u_1 + 2u_2 = 2 \tag{7}$$

$$u_1 \qquad\quad = 0 \tag{8}$$

$$u_2 = 0 \tag{9}$$

as given in the following table:

Equation	Solution		y	Inequality Violated
	u_1	u_2		
5, 6	$\frac{57}{48}$	$\frac{3}{24}$	Infeasible	3
5, 7	1	$\frac{1}{2}$	7,200	
5, 8	0	$\frac{5}{2}$	12,000	
5, 9	$\frac{5}{4}$	0	Infeasible	2
6, 7	2	0	9,600	
6, 8	0	$\frac{4}{13}$	Infeasible	3
6, 9	2	0	9,600	
7, 8	0	1	Infeasible	1
7, 9	2	0	9,600	
8, 9	0	0	Infeasible	2, 3

Example 2. Consider the problem which is the same as in Example 1, except that $\mathbf{C}' = [5 \quad 1 \quad 1]$; the problem becomes:

minimize $\qquad\qquad y = 4{,}800u_1 + 4{,}800u_2$

subject to $\qquad\qquad 4u_1 + 2u_2 \geq 5$

$$2u_1 + 13u_2 \geq 1$$

$$u_1 + 2u_2 \geq 1$$

$$u_1 \geq 0; \qquad u_2 \geq 0;$$

Table 17-18 Matrix Statement of the Primal and Dual Linear Programming Model for the 3-Product and 2-Machine Product-Mix Problem

Uncontrollable variables

(a_{ij}) = amount of each resource required for each product

		Product		
		1	2	3
Resource	1	4	2	1
	2	2	13	2

(b_j) = total amount of each resource available

		Amt. Avail
Resource	1	4,800
	2	4,800

(c_j) = profit per unit

		Profit
Product	1	5
	2	4
	3	2

PRIMAL

	General	Example
Decision variable	X = level of each activity	x_1 = level of Product 1 x_2 = level of Product 2 x_3 = level of Product 3
Objective	Maximize total profit	Maximize total profit
Model	$AX \le B, X \ge 0$ $z = C'X$	$4x_1 + 2x_2 + x_3 \le 4{,}800$ $2x_1 + 13x_2 + 2x_3 \le 4{,}800$ $x_1 \ge 0;\ x_2 \ge 0;\ x_3 \ge 0$ $z = 5x_1 + 4x_2 + 2x_3$
	Maximize z	Maximize z
Solution		$x_1 = 800,\ x_2 = 0,$ $x_3 = 1{,}600,\ z = 7{,}200$

DUAL

	General	Example
Decision variable	U = value of each resource	u_1 = value for resource 1 u_2 = value for resource 2
Objective	Minimize total value of resources	Minimize total value of resources
Model	$A'U \ge C,\ U \ge 0$ $y = B'U$	$4u_1 + 2u_2 \ge 5$ $2u_1 + 13u_2 \ge 4$ $u_1 + 2u_2 \ge 2$ $u_1 \ge 0;\ u_2 \ge 0;$ $y = 4{,}800u_1 + 4{,}800u_2$
	Minimize y	Minimize y
Solution		$u_1 = 1,\ u_2 = \frac{1}{2},$ $y = 7{,}200$

The solution may be obtained by reference to Fig. 17.1 with the new vector C. The *slope* of all the lines would be unchanged and in addition the *location* of the objective function and the line $4u_1 + 2u_2 = 5$ would also be unchanged. However, the line $2u_1 + 13u_2 = 1$ must now go through the point $u_1 = \frac{1}{2}$, $u_2 = 0$, and the line $u_1 + 2u_2 = 1$ must go through the point $u_1 = 1$, $u_2 = 0$. It is therefore clear that the optimum point occurs at the point W where the line $4u_1 + 2u_2 = 5$ crosses the u_1 axis; i.e., where $u_2 = 0$ and the solution is $u_1 = \frac{5}{4}$, $u_2 = 0$.

The product-mix problem described in Example 1, page 426, was to find a set of non-negative levels of production, x_1, x_2, x_3, subject to the restrictions

$$4x_1 + 2x_2 + x_3 \leq 4{,}800 \qquad \text{(Slotting machine)}$$

and

$$2x_1 + 13x_2 + 2x_3 \leq 4{,}800 \qquad \text{(Threading machine)}$$
$$x_1 \geq 0; \qquad x_2 \geq 0; \qquad x_3 \geq 0$$

which maximize the profit function z where

$$z = 5x_1 + 4x_2 + 2x_3$$

and the optimum solution was $x_1 = 800$, $x_2 = 0$, $x_3 = 1{,}600$ and $z_{max} = 7{,}200$.

The problem discussed in Example 1, page 527, was to find a set of non-negative costs, u_1 and u_2, subject to the restrictions:

$$4u_1 + 2u_2 \geq 5 \qquad \text{(Wood screws)}$$
$$2u_1 + 13u_2 \geq 4 \qquad \text{(Metal screws)}$$
$$u_1 + 2u_2 \geq 2 \qquad \text{(Aluminum screws)}$$

and

$$u_1 \geq 0; \qquad u_2 \geq 0$$

which minimizes the total value of y

$$y = 4{,}800u_1 + 4{,}800u_2$$

and the solution was

$$u_1 = 1, \ u_2 = \tfrac{1}{2}, \text{ and } y = 7{,}200.$$

Note that $y_{min} = z_{max}$.

The two problems are obviously very closely related. For any linear programming problem, called the primal problem, there exists another, called the dual. The relationship between the primal and the dual for the three-product and two-machine product-mix problem is illustrated in Tables 17-18 and 17-19.

The importance of the relationship between the primal and dual formulation lies in the fact that if one is solved, the solution to the other has also been obtained. Table 17-18 gives the solutions to the primal and dual of the three-product and two-machine product-mix problem; in the primal (maximization) problem there are two basic variables and three non-basic; in the dual there are three basic and two non-basic. The optimum basic dual variables are the coefficients of the non-basic primal variables in the objective function and vice versa. (See Table 17-19.)

Table 17-19 Summary of 3-Product and 2-Machine Product-Mix Problem Using Slack Variables

Product-Mix Problem	Valuation Problem
Case 1	
$\max z = 5x_1 + 4x_2 + 2x_3 + 0x_4 + 0x_5$ subject to:	$\min y = 4{,}800u_1 + 4{,}800u_2 + 0u_3 + 0u_4 + 0u_5$ subject to:
$4x_1 + 2x_2 + x_3 + x_4 \qquad = 4{,}800$ $2x_1 + 13x_2 + 2x_3 \qquad + x_5 = 4{,}800$	$4u_1 + 2u_2 - u_3 \qquad\qquad = 5$ $2u_1 + 13u_2 \qquad - u_4 \qquad = 4$ $u_1 + 2u_2 \qquad\qquad - u_5 = 2$
Basic variables in the optimum solution are x_1 and x_3	basic variables in the optimum solution are u_1, u_2, and u_4
$x_1 = \quad 800 + 1.5x_2 - \frac{1}{3}x_4 + \frac{1}{6}x_5$ $x_3 = 1{,}600 - \quad 8x_2 + \frac{1}{3}x_4 - \frac{2}{3}x_5$	$u_1 = 1 \ + \frac{1}{6}u_3 - \frac{1}{3}u_5$ $u_2 = \frac{1}{2} - \frac{1}{6}u_3 + \frac{2}{3}u_5$ $u_4 = 4\frac{1}{2} - \frac{3}{2}u_3 + 8u_5$
$z = 7{,}200 - 4.5x_2 - x_4 - \frac{1}{2}x_5$	$y = 7{,}200 + 800u_3 + 1{,}600u_5$
Case 2	
$\max z = 5x_1 + x_2 + x_3 + 0x_4 + 0x_5$ subject to:	$\min y = 4{,}800u_1 + 4{,}800u_2 + 0u_3 + 0u_4 + 0u_5$ subject to:
$4x_1 + 2x_2 + x_3 + x_4 \qquad = 4{,}800$ $2x_1 + 13x_2 + 2x_3 \qquad + x_5 = 4{,}800$	$4u_1 + 2u_2 - u_3 \qquad\qquad = 5$ $2u_1 + 13u_2 \qquad - u_4 \qquad = 1$ $u_1 + 2u_2 \qquad\qquad - u_5 = 1$
Basic variables in the optimum solution are x_1 and x_5	basic variables in the optimum solution are u_1, u_4, and u_5
$x_1 = 1{,}200 - \frac{1}{2}x_2 - \frac{1}{4}x_3 - \frac{1}{4}x_4$ $x_5 = 2{,}400 - 12x_2 - \frac{3}{2}x_3 + \frac{1}{2}x_4$	$u_1 = \frac{5}{4} - \frac{1}{2}u_2 + \frac{1}{4}u_3$ $u_4 = \frac{3}{2} + 12u_2 + \frac{1}{2}u_3$ $u_5 = \frac{1}{4} + \frac{3}{2}u_2 + \frac{1}{4}u_3$
$z = 6{,}000 - \frac{3}{2}x_2 - \frac{1}{4}x_3 - \frac{5}{4}x_4$	$y = 6{,}000 + 2{,}400u_2 + 1{,}200u_3$

The important consequence of the fact that all the information about the solution of the dual is in the solution of the primal and vice versa means that a problem can be formulated and solved in either form. Since the amount of computation is affected primarily by the number of equations, a problem should usually be formulated so as to minimize the number of equations. Suppose there are m-equations and n-unknowns in the primal; then, if $m < n$, it will usually be easier to solve the primal; if $m > n$, it will usually be easier to solve the dual.

The Relationship Between the Primal and the Dual Models

In matrix notation the relationship between the primal and dual is:

PRIMAL	DUAL
$\max z = C'X$	$\min y = B'U$
subject to $AX \le B$	subject to $A'U \ge C$
$X \ge 0$	$U \ge 0$

The relation between the dual and primal may also be illustrated by writing the coefficients in the form:

	x_1	x_2		x_n	$\leq$
u_1	a_{11}	a_{12}	$\cdots$	a_{1n}	b_1
u_2	a_{21}	a_{22}	$\cdots$	a_{2n}	b_2
.	.	.		.	.
.	.	.		.	.
.	.	.		.	.
u_m	a_{m1}	a_{m2}	$\cdots$	a_{mn}	b_m
$\geq$	c_1	c_2	$\cdots$	c_n	

In the primal the objective function is obtained by multiplying the top row by the bottom row ($\Sigma c_i x_i$) and the restrictions are obtained by multiplying the top row by each of the rows in the inside rectangle

$$\Sigma a_{ij} x_i \leq b_j \qquad j = 1, \ldots, m$$

In the dual the objective function is obtained by multiplying the left column by the right column

$$\Sigma u_i b_i$$

and the restrictions are obtained by multiplying the left column by each of the columns in the inside rectangle

$$\Sigma a_{ij} u_j \geq c_i \qquad i = 1, \ldots, N$$

Once the dual is formulated and slack variables are added, the existence of the optimum solution can be verified if the basic variables are known. The matrix form of the computation is shown in Table 17-20. The major results involving the primal and the dual are:

1. The optimum values of the objective function are equal, i.e., maximum z = minimum y provided both exist.

2. The solution to the primal is a set of values for the basic variables which result in maximum profit. The dual variables are defined as the values of a unit of the resources and the solution of the dual results in a minimum value of the resources. The value of a unit resource whose restricting condition is given by equation j in the primal is the increase in profit that would result from increasing the amount of the resource by one unit.

3. The value of any additional units of a resource which is not completely used in the optimum program (which is indicated by the corresponding slack variables being a basic variable) is zero.

Table 17-20 Matrix Formulation of Primal and Dual LP Models*

Primal	Dual
1. Original Problem.	
$\max z = \mathbf{C}^o \mathbf{X}^o$	$\min y = \mathbf{B}^{o\prime} \mathbf{U}^o$
subject to $\mathbf{A}^o \mathbf{X}^o \leq \mathbf{B}^o$	$\mathbf{A}^{o\prime} \mathbf{U}^o \geq \mathbf{C}^o$
$\mathbf{X}^o \geq 0$	$\mathbf{U}^o \geq 0$
Dimensions are:	
$\mathbf{C}^o$: $n \times 1$ $\mathbf{A}^o$: $m \times n$	$\mathbf{U}^o$: $m \times 1$
$\mathbf{X}^o$: $n \times 1$ $\mathbf{B}^o$: $m \times 1$	
2. Assign slack variables.	

$$\max z = [\mathbf{C}^o \quad \mathbf{C}_s^{o}]' \begin{bmatrix} \mathbf{X}^o \\ \mathbf{X}_s^{o} \end{bmatrix} \qquad\qquad \min y = [\mathbf{B}^o \quad \mathbf{B}_s^{o}]' \begin{bmatrix} \mathbf{U}^o \\ \mathbf{U}_s^{o} \end{bmatrix}$$

$$\text{subject to } [\mathbf{A}^o \quad \mathbf{A}_s^{o}] \begin{bmatrix} \mathbf{X}^o \\ \mathbf{X}_s^{o} \end{bmatrix} = \mathbf{B}^o \qquad\qquad \text{subject to } [\mathbf{A}^o \quad \mathbf{A}_{Ds}^{0}]' \begin{bmatrix} \mathbf{U}^o \\ \mathbf{U}_s^{o} \end{bmatrix} = \mathbf{C}^o$$

$$\begin{bmatrix} \mathbf{X}^o \\ \mathbf{X}_s^{o} \end{bmatrix} \geq 0 \qquad\qquad \begin{bmatrix} \mathbf{U}^o \\ \mathbf{U}_s^{o} \end{bmatrix} \geq 0$$

Primal	Dual
Dimensions are:	
$\mathbf{C}_s^{o}$: $m \times 1$ $\mathbf{A}_s^{o}$: $m \times m$	$\mathbf{U}_s^{o}$: $n \times 1$
$\mathbf{X}_s^{o}$: $m \times 1$	$\mathbf{A}_{Ds}^{0}$: $n \times m$
m basic variables, n non-basic	n basic variables, m non-basic

$$\max z = [C_B \quad C_{NB}]' \begin{bmatrix} X_B \\ X_{NB} \end{bmatrix}$$

subject to $[A_B \quad A_{NB}] \begin{bmatrix} X_B \\ X_{NB} \end{bmatrix} = B^o$

$$\begin{bmatrix} X_B \\ X_{NB} \end{bmatrix} \geq 0$$

Dimensions are:

C_B : $m \times 1$ X_B : $m \times 1$
C_{NB}: $n \times 1$ X_{NB}: $n \times 1$
A_B : $m \times m$
A_{NB}: $m \times n$

4. Equations are: $A_B X_B + A_{NB} X_{NB} = B^o$

5. Solution is: $X_B = A_B^{-1}B^o - A_B^{-1}A_{NB}X_{NB}$

$z = C_B'X_B + C_{NB}'X_{NB}$
$= C_B'A_B^{-1}B^o - (C_B'A_B^{-1}A_{NB} - C_{NB}')X_{NB}$

6. Dimensions and Equivalences:

$m \times 1$: $A_B^{-1}B^o$
$m \times n$: $A_B^{-1}A_{NB}$
$1 \times n$: $(C_B'A_B^{-1}A_{NB} - C_{NB}')$
1×1: $C_B'A_B^{-1}B^o$

$$\min y = [B_{DB} \quad B_{DNB}]' \begin{bmatrix} U_{DB} \\ U_{DNB} \end{bmatrix}$$

subject to $[A_{DB} \quad A_{DNB}] \begin{bmatrix} U_{DB} \\ U_{DNB} \end{bmatrix} = C^o$

$$\begin{bmatrix} U_{DB} \\ U_{DNB} \end{bmatrix} \geq 0$$

B_{DB} : $n \times 1$ U_{DB} : $n \times 1$
B_{DNB}: $m \times 1$ U_{DNB}: $m \times 1$
A_{DB} : $n \times n$
A_{DNB}: $n \times m$

$A_{DB}U_{DB} + A_{DNB}U_{DNB} = C^o$

$U_{DB} = A_{DB}^{-1}C^o - A_{DB}^{-1}A_{DNB}U_{DNB}$

$y = B_{DB}'U_{DB} + B_{DNB}'U_{DNB}$
$= B_{DB}'A_{DB}^{-1}C^o - (B_{DB}'A_{DB}^{-1}A_{DNB} - B_{DNB}')U_{DNB}$

$(B_{DNB}' - B_{DB}'A_{DB}^{-1}A_{DNB})'$
$(A_{DB}^{-1}A_{DNB})'$
$(A_{DB}^{-1}C^o)'$
$B_{DB}A_{DB}^{-1}C^o$

* The superscript o indicates that the variables are in their original ordering; the absence of the superscript indicates that the variables have been reordered. The subscript s denotes slack variables. The subscript D denotes dual variables.

4. The solution of the primal contains the solution to the dual; in fact, it contains all the information available from the solution of the dual. Similarly, the solution of the dual supplies all the information available from the solution of the primal.

Example 3.   The solution of the dual.   The description of the simplex method was given in Chapter 15 for the standard linear programming model: max $\mathbf{C'X}$ subject to $\mathbf{AX} \leq \mathbf{B}$; $\mathbf{X} \geq 0$. Any LP problem can be changed to this format. However, the simplex method can also be adapted to the case: minimize $\mathbf{B'U}$ subject to $\mathbf{A'U} \geq \mathbf{C}$; $\mathbf{U} \geq 0$. To illustrate the simplex method in a problem of this type, consider the dual of the example in Section D, Chapter 15:

minimize
$$4{,}800u_1 + 4{,}800u_2$$
subject to
$$4u_1 + 2u_2 \geq 5$$
$$2u_1 + 13u_2 \geq 4$$

The initial step is to eliminate the inequalities. This can be done by defining slack variables u_3 and u_4; u_3 is the amount of profit over 5 earned by producing 1 box of wood screws, and u_4 is the amount of profit over 4 earned by producing 1 box of metal screws. The equations now become:
$$4u_1 + 2u_2 - u_3 = 5$$
$$2u_1 + 13u_2 - u_4 = 4$$

Since there are two equations, a basic set of variables again consists of two variables. However, it is immediately clear that u_3 and u_4 do not lead to a basic feasible solution because, if $u_1 = 0$, $u_2 = 0$, the equations
$$u_3 = -5 + 4u_1 + 2u_2$$
$$u_4 = -4 + 2u_1 + 13u_2$$
have the solution $u_3 = -5$, $u_4 = -4$, both of which violate the non-negativity conditions. To obtain an initial basic feasible solution, two artificial variables, u_5 and u_6, are defined and the equations become:
$$4u_1 + 2u_2 - u_3 + u_5 = 5$$
$$2u_1 + 13u_2 - u_4 + u_6 = 4$$

The objective function will have to be of the form
$$y = 4{,}800u_1 + 4{,}800u_2 + 0u_3 + 0u_4 + ku_5 + ku_6$$
when k is a large positive number, so that the optimum solution will not

have u_5 or u_6 as basic variables. The cost assigned to u_3 and u_4 are zero since they may appear as basic variables.

An initial basic feasible solution can be obtained by using u_5 and u_6 as basic variables. The equations are:

$$u_5 = 5 - 4u_1 - 2u_2 + u_3$$
$$u_6 = 4 - 2u_1 - 13u_2 + u_4$$

and substituting these into the objective function gives:

$$y = 4{,}800u_1 + 4{,}800u_2 + 0u_3 + 0u_4 + k(5 - 4u_1 - 2u_2 + u_3)$$
$$+ k(4 - 2u_1 - 13u_2 + u_4)$$
$$= u_1(4{,}800 - 4k - 2k) + u_2(4{,}800 - 2k - 13k) + ku_3 + ku_4 + 9k$$

Regardless of the value of k (assuming it is $> 4{,}800$), it is clear that the cost function can be reduced most by making u_2 a basic variable. With u_2 and u_5 as the basic variables, the equations become:

$$u_5 = \tfrac{57}{13} - \tfrac{48}{13}u_1 + u_3 - \tfrac{2}{13}u_4 + \tfrac{2}{13}u_6$$
$$u_2 = \tfrac{4}{13} - \tfrac{2}{13}u_1 + \tfrac{1}{13}u_4 - \tfrac{1}{13}u_6$$

and substituting these into the objective function gives:

$$y = 4{,}800u_1 + 4{,}800(\tfrac{4}{13} - \tfrac{2}{13}u_1 + \tfrac{1}{13}u_4 - \tfrac{1}{13}u_6) + 0u_3 + 0u_4$$
$$+ k(\tfrac{57}{13} - \tfrac{48}{13}u_1 + u_3 - \tfrac{2}{13}u_4 + \tfrac{2}{13}u_6) + ku_6$$
$$= 4{,}800(\tfrac{4}{13}) + \tfrac{57}{13}k + u_1[4{,}800 - \tfrac{2}{13}(4{,}800) - \tfrac{48}{13}k] + ku_3$$
$$+ u_4[\tfrac{4800}{13} - \tfrac{2}{13}k] + u_6[-\tfrac{4800}{13} + \tfrac{2}{13}k + k]$$

Again, regardless of the value of k ($> 4{,}800$), the cost can be reduced most by removing u_5 as a basic variable and replacing it with u_1. The equations become:

$$u_1 = \tfrac{57}{48} + \tfrac{13}{48}u_3 - \tfrac{1}{24}u_4 - \tfrac{13}{48}u_5 + \tfrac{1}{24}u_6$$
$$u_2 = \tfrac{1}{8} - \tfrac{1}{24}u_3 + \tfrac{1}{12}u_4 + \tfrac{1}{24}u_5 - \tfrac{1}{12}u_6$$

and substituting these into the cost function gives:

$$y = 4{,}800[\tfrac{57}{48} + \tfrac{13}{48}u_3 - \tfrac{1}{24}u_4 - \tfrac{13}{48}u_5 + \tfrac{1}{24}u_6]$$
$$+ 4{,}800[\tfrac{3}{24} + \tfrac{1}{24}u_3 + \tfrac{1}{12}u_4 + \tfrac{1}{24}u_5 - \tfrac{1}{12}u_6]$$
$$+ 0u_3 + 0u_4 + ku_5 + ku_6$$
$$= 4{,}800[\tfrac{57}{48} + \tfrac{3}{24}] + u_3[\tfrac{13}{48}(4{,}800) - \tfrac{1}{24}(4{,}800)]$$
$$+ u_4[-\tfrac{4800}{24} + \tfrac{4800}{12}] + u_5[-\tfrac{13}{48}(4{,}800) + \tfrac{1}{24}(4{,}800) + k]$$
$$+ u_6[\tfrac{4800}{24} - \tfrac{4800}{12} + k]$$
$$= 6{,}300 + u_3(1{,}100) + u_4(200) + u_5(-1{,}100 + k) + u_6(-200 + k)$$

Table 17-21 Simplex Solution of the Dual Formulation of the 2-Product and 2-Machine Product-Mix Problem

	I	II	III	IV	V	VI	VII	VIII	IX	X	XI
			4,800	4,800	0	0	k	k			
(1)	Basic Variable	Unit Cost	u_1	u_2	u_3	u_4	u_5	u_6	b	Check	Ratio
(2)	u_5	k	4	2	-1	0	1	0	5	11	$\frac{5}{2}$
(3)	u_6	k	2	13	0	-1	0	1	4	19	$\frac{4}{13}$ →
(4)	Change in cost		$4,800 - 6k$ *	$4,800 - 15k$ *	k	k	0	0	$-9k$	$9,600 - 28k$	
(5)	u_5	k	$\frac{48}{13}$	0	-1	$\frac{2}{13}$	1	$-\frac{2}{13}$	$\frac{57}{13}$	$\frac{105}{13}$	$\frac{57}{48}$ →
(6)	u_2	4,800	$\frac{2}{13}$	1	0	$-\frac{1}{13}$	0	$\frac{1}{13}$	$\frac{4}{13}$	$\frac{19}{13}$	2
(7)	Change in cost		$\frac{11}{13}(4,800) - \frac{48}{13}k$ *		k	$\frac{4800}{13} - \frac{2}{13}k$	0	$-\frac{1}{13}(4,800) - 15k$	$-\frac{4}{13}(4,800) - \frac{57}{13}k$	$\frac{11}{13}(4,800) - \frac{79}{13}k$	
(8)	u_1	4,800	1	0	$-\frac{13}{48}$	$\frac{1}{24}$	$\frac{13}{48}$	$-\frac{1}{24}$	$\frac{57}{48}$	$\frac{57}{48}$	
(9)	u_2	4,800	0	1	$\frac{1}{24}$	$-\frac{1}{12}$	$-\frac{1}{24}$	$\frac{1}{12}$	$\frac{1}{8}$	$\frac{1}{8}$	
(10)	Change in cost		0	0	1,100	200	$-1,100 + k$	$-200 + k$	$-6,300$		

Since all coefficients are positive, the optimum solution has been obtained. The solution in the simplex tableau is given in Table 17-21.

EXERCISES

1. Formulate and solve the following problem as a primal and as a dual model. Interpret the results.

Maximize $5x_1 + 4x_2$

subject to $x_1 + x_2 = 1,200$

$4x_1 + 2x_2 \leq 4,800$

$2x_1 + 13x_2 \geq 4,800$

$x_1 \geq 0; \quad x_2 \geq 0$

2. A person wishes to select a diet consisting of bread, butter, and/or milk, which has a minimum cost, but yields an adequate amount of vitamins A and B. The minimum vitamin requirements are 11 units of A and 10 units of B. The diet should not contain more than 13 units of A, because more may be harmful. Furthermore, he likes milk, and requires that the diet include at least 3 units of milk, but is indifferent to the amounts of butter or bread. A dietitian has measured the vitamin contents and found, per unit of product, 1 unit of A and 3 of B in bread, 4 units of A and 1 of B in butter, 2 units of A and 2 of B in milk. The market price of one unit of bread, butter, and milk is 2¢, 9¢, and 1¢, respectively. Determine the minimum cost diet.

(a) Formulate this problem in both the primal and dual form.

(b) Show that the optimum diet is $5\frac{1}{2}$ units of milk.

(c) How is the cost of the diet affected by relaxing each one of the vitamin requirements?

3. Apply the Kuhn-Tucker conditions to the dual LP model. Discuss the relationship between the primal, the dual, and the Kuhn-Tucker conditions.

4. Formulate the dual for each of the models in chapter XV, Section E. State and verify the optimum solution. Interpret the results.

Notes and References

Section A and B

The following publications contain material on one or both of the transportation and assignment problems.

Churchman, C. W., Ackoff, R. L., and Arnoff, E. L. (1957), *Introduction to Operations Research*, John Wiley and Sons, New York.

Cooper, W. W., and Charnes, A. (1953), "Transportation Scheduling by Linear Programming," *Proceedings of the Conference on Operations Research in Marketing*, Case Institute of Technology, 1953, pp. 62–71.

Charnes, A., and Cooper, W. W. (1954), "The stepping stone method for explaining Linear Programming Calculations in Transportation Problems," *Management Science*, **1**, pp. 49–69.

Ford, L. R., Jr., and Fulkerson, D. R. (1956), "Solving the Transportation Problem," *Management Science*, **3**, pp. 24–32.

Hitchcock, F. L. (1941), "The Distribution of a product from Several Sources to Numerous Localities," *Journal of Mathematics and Physics*, **20**, pp. 224–230.

Houthakker, H. S. (1955), "On the Numerical Solution of the Transportation Problem," *Operations Research*, **3**, pp. 210–214.

Koopmans, T. C. (1949), "Optimum Utilization of the Transportation System," *Econometrica*, 17 supplement, pp. 136–146.

Manne, A. S. (1961), *Economic Analysis for Business Decisions*, McGraw-Hill Book Co., New York.

Orden, A. (1956), "The Transshipment Problem," *Management Science*, **2**, pp. 276–285.

Vidale, M. L. (1956), "A Graphical Solution to the Transportation Problem," *Operations Research*, **4**, pp. 193–203.

For a discussion of integer programming see:

Gomory, R. E. (1958), "Outline of an Algorithm for Integer Solutions to Linear Programs," *Bulletin American Mathematical Society*, **64**, pp. 275–278.

Dorn, W. S. (1963), "Non-Linear Programming—A Survey," *Management Science*, **9**, pp. 171–208.

Exercises 2 and 6 in Section A appear in Sasieni, M., Yaspan, A., and Friedman, L. (1959), *Operations Research*, John Wiley and Sons, New York.

Part Five

MULTIVARIATE

OPTIMIZATION MODELS

CHAPTER EIGHTEEN

Optimization Models
with Many Variables

General techniques for optimizing functions of two variables subject to equality or inequality constraints were developed in Chapter 11. Numerical solution to a particular problem requires solving of a set of equations. Both the statement of the conditions and the numerical computation became unwieldy without additional notation. The intervening six chapters, 12 to 17, have been devoted to developing the notation of matrices and to developing specific algorithms for numerical solutions in particular cases. The simplex algorithm, in particular, guarantees a numerical solution to the optimization of linear objective functions subject to linear inequality constraints including non-negativity of the decision variables. It is now possible to state the techniques and solution in general for any number of variables.

In Section A the general problem of determining the optimum of a function of many variables is discussed as a generalization of the problem of optimizing functions of two variables. In Section B the Lagrange multiplier is extended to any number of variables and any number of equality constraints (less than the number of variables). In Section C general techniques for optimizing under inequality constraints are discussed. As before, the existence of the appropriate partial derivatives is assumed.

This chapter describes the techniques and states general conditions for optima. Some proofs are given in Chapter 20. Examples of the use of the techniques are contained in the next chapter for four models in which the objective function is a polynomial of degree 2. A special optimization procedure known as dynamic programming is described and illustrated in Chapter 21.

A. OPTIMIZATION OF FUNCTIONS OF MANY VARIABLES

Calculus of Functions of Many Variables

Differentiation.   The definition of functions of many variables is an extension of the definition of functions of two variables given in Chapter 9. A variable f is said to be a function of the variables $x_1, x_2, \ldots, x_n$ if a value of f can be determined for each set of values of the n variables. Linear functions

$$f(x_1, x_2, \ldots, x_n) = a_0 + a_1 x_1 + a_2 x_2 + \cdots + a_n x_n$$

have already been used extensively in Chapters 12 to 17. Polynomials, rationals, and other classes of functions are generalizations of the forms presented in Chapter 9.

The concepts of limit, continuity, and differentiation are also direct generalizations from the two-variable case. The partial derivative of f with respect to x_k is denoted by

$$\frac{\partial f(x_1, \ldots, x_n)}{\partial x_k}$$

and is obtained by treating all x_i except x_k as constants and differentiating as if f were a function of one variable, x_k. Higher order and mixed partial derivatives are obtained similarly. If the partial derivatives are continuous in a region, the order of differentiation is immaterial; e.g.,

$$\frac{\partial^2 f}{\partial x_i \, \partial x_j} = \frac{\partial^2 f}{\partial x_j \, \partial x_i}$$

and similarly for other mixed derivatives.

To simplify the notation the symbol $\mathbf{X}$ will be used to represent the vector

$$\mathbf{X} = \begin{bmatrix} x_1 \\ \cdot \\ \cdot \\ \cdot \\ x_n \end{bmatrix}$$

and the function f will be denoted by

$$f(\mathbf{X}) = f(x_1, x_2, \ldots, x_n)$$

The vector of partial derivatives will be denoted by

$$\frac{\partial f(\mathbf{X})}{\partial \mathbf{X}} = \begin{bmatrix} \dfrac{\partial f}{\partial x_1} \\ \dfrac{\partial f}{\partial x_2} \\ \cdot \\ \cdot \\ \cdot \\ \dfrac{\partial f}{\partial x_n} \end{bmatrix}$$

Example I. If

$$u(x_1, x_2, x_3) = -x_1{}^2 - x_2{}^2 + x_2 x_3 - x_3{}^2 + x_1 + 2x_3$$

then

$$\frac{\partial u}{\partial x_1} = -2x_1 + 1$$

$$\frac{\partial u}{\partial x_2} = -2x_2 + x_3$$

$$\frac{\partial u}{\partial x_3} = x_2 - 2x_3 + 2$$

$$\frac{\partial^2 u}{\partial x_1{}^2} = -2 \qquad \frac{\partial^2 u}{\partial x_1 \partial x_2} = \frac{\partial^2 u}{\partial x_2 \partial x_1} = 0$$

$$\frac{\partial^2 u}{\partial x_2{}^2} = -2 \qquad \frac{\partial^2 u}{\partial x_2 \partial x_3} = \frac{\partial^2 u}{\partial x_3 \partial x_2} = 1$$

$$\frac{\partial^2 u}{\partial x_3{}^2} = -2 \qquad \frac{\partial^2 u}{\partial x_3 \partial x_1} = \frac{\partial^2 u}{\partial x_1 \partial x_3} = 0$$

All higher-order derivatives are zero.

The general statement of the chain rule is as follows:

If $f(v_1, v_2, \ldots, v_m)$, is a differentiable function of m variables, each of which is a differentiable function of n variables $x_1, x_2, \ldots, x_n$, then the partial derivatives of

$$f[v_1(x_1, \ldots, x_n), v_2(x_1, \ldots, x_n), \ldots, v_m(x_1, \ldots, x_n)] = f(x_1, \ldots, x_n)$$

are given by

$$\frac{\partial f}{\partial x_1} = \frac{\partial f}{\partial v_1}\frac{\partial v_1}{\partial x_1} + \frac{\partial f}{\partial v_2}\frac{\partial v_2}{\partial x_1} + \cdots + \frac{\partial f}{\partial v_m}\frac{\partial v_m}{\partial x_1}$$

$$\frac{\partial f}{\partial x_2} = \frac{\partial f}{\partial v_1}\frac{\partial v_1}{\partial x_2} + \frac{\partial f}{\partial v_2}\frac{\partial v_2}{\partial x_2} + \cdots + \frac{\partial f}{\partial v_m}\frac{\partial v_m}{\partial x_2}$$

$$\cdots \qquad\qquad \cdots \qquad\qquad \cdots$$

$$\frac{\partial f}{\partial x_n} = \frac{\partial f}{\partial v_1}\frac{\partial v_1}{\partial x_n} + \frac{\partial f}{\partial v_2}\frac{\partial v_2}{\partial x_n} + \cdots + \frac{\partial f}{\partial v_m}\frac{\partial v_m}{\partial x_n}$$

Example 2.   A firm produces during each period as much of a product as it can sell. Let

$$x = \text{number of units produced and sold}$$
$$y = \text{price (\$ per unit)}$$
$$z = \text{marketing expenditure (\$)}$$
$$q = \text{quality index}$$

Assume that:
1. Number of units sold is a function, x, of price, marketing expenditure, and quality:

$$x = x(y, z, q)$$

2. Cost, C, is a function of number of units sold, marketing expenditure, and quality index:

$$C = C(x, z, q)$$

The Earnings function is:

$$\text{Earnings} = \text{Revenue} - \text{Cost}$$
$$= (\text{Price})(\text{Number of units sold}) - \text{Cost}$$

or

$$E(y, z, q) = yx(y, z, q) - C(x, z, q)$$

The partial derivatives of E may be obtained by using the chain rule:

$$\frac{\partial E}{\partial y} = x + y\frac{\partial x}{\partial y} - \frac{\partial C}{\partial x}\frac{\partial x}{\partial y}$$

$$\frac{\partial E}{\partial z} = y\frac{\partial x}{\partial z} - \frac{\partial C}{\partial x}\frac{\partial x}{\partial z} - \frac{\partial C}{\partial z}$$

$$\frac{\partial E}{\partial q} = y\frac{\partial x}{\partial q} - \frac{\partial C}{\partial x}\frac{\partial x}{\partial q} - \frac{\partial C}{\partial q}$$

Extreme Values

In Chapter 9 the sufficient conditions for a stationary point (x^*, y^*) to be local extrema of a function of two variables $f(x, y)$ were stated as follows: Let

$$\Delta_1 = \Delta_1(x^*, y^*) = \frac{\partial^2 f}{\partial x^2}(x^*, y^*)$$

$$\Delta_2 = \Delta_2(x^*, y^*)$$

$$= \left[\frac{\partial^2 f}{\partial x^2}(x^*, y^*)\right]\left[\frac{\partial^2 f}{\partial y^2}(x^*, y^*)\right] - \left[\frac{\partial^2 f}{\partial x\, \partial y}(x^*, y^*)\right]^2$$

then (x^*, y^*) is:

a local maximum if $\Delta_1 < 0$ and $\Delta_2 > 0$
a local minimum if $\Delta_1 > 0$ and $\Delta_2 > 0$
not a local extreme point if $\Delta_2 < 0$
may or may not be a local extreme point if $\Delta_2 = 0$

If Δ_2 is now expressed as a determinant:

$$\Delta_2 = \begin{vmatrix} \dfrac{\partial^2 f}{\partial x^2} & \dfrac{\partial^2 f}{\partial x\, \partial y} \\[2mm] \dfrac{\partial^2 f}{\partial x\, \partial y} & \dfrac{\partial^2 f}{\partial y^2} \end{vmatrix}$$

Δ_1 and Δ_2 are nothing more than the principal minors of Δ_2. In this form results can be generalized to functions of n variables.

A function of n variables cannot have a local extremum at an interior point where the first derivatives do not all vanish; a stationary point is one where all partial derivatives are zero:

$$\frac{\partial f}{\partial x_1} = 0; \qquad \frac{\partial f}{\partial x_2} = 0; \qquad \cdots; \qquad \frac{\partial f}{\partial x_n} = 0.$$

As in the case of one or two variables, a function does not necessarily have an extremum at a stationary point. The sufficient condition for a local maximum or minimum is stated in terms of the determinant Δ_n of partial derivatives:

$$\Delta_n = \begin{vmatrix} \dfrac{\partial^2 f}{\partial x_1^2} & \dfrac{\partial^2 f}{\partial x_1\, \partial x_2} & \cdots & \dfrac{\partial^2 f}{\partial x_1\, \partial x_n} \\[2mm] & \cdots & \cdots & \cdots \\[2mm] \dfrac{\partial^2 f}{\partial x_n\, \partial x_1} & \dfrac{\partial^2 f}{\partial x_n\, \partial x_2} & \cdots & \dfrac{\partial^2 f}{\partial x_n^2} \end{vmatrix}$$

The principal minors of Δ_n are:

$$\Delta_1 = \frac{\partial^2 f}{\partial x_1}, \Delta_2 = \begin{vmatrix} \dfrac{\partial^2 f}{\partial x_1^2} & \dfrac{\partial^2 f}{\partial x_1 \partial x_2} \\ \dfrac{\partial^2 f}{\partial x_2 \partial x_1} & \dfrac{\partial^2 f}{\partial x_2^2} \end{vmatrix}; \ \Delta_3 = \begin{vmatrix} \dfrac{\partial^2 f}{\partial x_1^2} & \dfrac{\partial^2 f}{\partial x_1 \partial x_2} & \dfrac{\partial^2 f}{\partial x_1 \partial x_3} \\ \dfrac{\partial^2 f}{\partial x_2 \partial x_1} & \dfrac{\partial^2 f}{\partial x_2^2} & \dfrac{\partial^2 f}{\partial x_2 \partial x_3} \\ \dfrac{\partial^2 f}{\partial x_3 \partial x_1} & \dfrac{\partial^2 f}{\partial x_3 \partial x_2} & \dfrac{\partial^2 f}{\partial x_3^2} \end{vmatrix}, \ldots, \Delta_n$$

A stationary point, $(x_1, x_2, \ldots, x_n)$, is a

local maximum if $\Delta_1 < 0, \quad \Delta_2 > 0, \quad \Delta_3 < 0, \ldots$

local minimum if $\Delta_1 > 0, \quad \Delta_2 > 0, \quad \Delta_3 > 0, \ldots$

If neither of these conditions holds, further investigation is necessary. The proof of these conditions will be given in Chapter 20, Section C.

As in the case of functions of one or two variables, a most useful concept in the discussion of extreme values is that of convexity and concavity. A function $f(x_1, x_2, \ldots, x_n)$ is convex in a region if for any two points $(\tilde{x}_1, \tilde{x}_2, \ldots, \tilde{x}_n)$ and $(\bar{x}_1, \bar{x}_2, \ldots, \bar{x}_n)$

$$f[(1 - t)\tilde{x}_1 + t\bar{x}_1, \ldots, (1 - t)\tilde{x}_n + t\bar{x}_n]$$
$$\leq (1 - t)f(\tilde{x}_1, \tilde{x}_2, \ldots, \tilde{x}_n) + tf(\bar{x}_1, \bar{x}_2, \ldots, \bar{x}_n)$$

The function is strictly convex if $\leq$ can be replaced everywhere by $<$, and strictly concave if the sign is $\geq(>)$. A function that is convex in a region and has one stationary point has a global minimum value at that point. Similarly, a function that has one stationary point and is concave in a region has a global maximum value at that point.

Example 3. The derivatives of the second-degree polynomial in three variables

$$u(x_1, x_2, x_3) = -x_1^2 - x_2^2 + x_2 x_3 - x_3^2 + x_1 + 2x_3$$

were evaluated in Example 1. The stationary points are the solutions of the three linear equations:

$$-2x_1 + 1 = 0$$
$$-2x_2 + x_3 = 0$$
$$x_2 - 2x_3 + 2 = 0$$

These three equations have one unique solution $x_1 = \frac{1}{2}$; $x_2 = \frac{2}{3}$, and $x_3 = \frac{4}{3}$ and, consequently, there is only one stationary point $(\frac{1}{2}, \frac{2}{3}, \frac{4}{3})$.

The second partial derivatives give Δ_3 at the stationary point as:

$$\Delta_3 = \begin{vmatrix} -2 & 0 & 0 \\ 0 & -2 & 1 \\ 0 & 1 & -2 \end{vmatrix}$$

and the principal minors are

$$\Delta_1 = -2, \qquad \Delta_2 = \begin{vmatrix} -2 & 0 \\ 0 & -2 \end{vmatrix} = 4, \qquad \Delta_3 = \begin{vmatrix} -2 & 0 & 0 \\ 0 & -2 & 1 \\ 0 & 1 & -2 \end{vmatrix} = -6$$

which are <0, >0, and <0. Hence the value $u(\tfrac{1}{2}, \tfrac{2}{3}, \tfrac{4}{3}) = \tfrac{19}{12}$ is a maximum.

In this case the function has a single stationary point; hence it is a global maximum in the whole three-dimensional space. It can be shown that u is, in fact, everywhere concave.

EXERCISES

For each of the following functions:
(a) Compute the first and second order partial derivatives.
(b) Determine the stationary points.
(c) Determine the local extreme points.
(d) State the region in which the function is concave or convex.

1. $f(x_1, x_2, x_3) = x_1^2 + x_2^2 + x_3^2 + 4x_1 + 2x_2 - 40$
2. $f(x, y, z) = e^{x^2 + y^2 + z^2 - 2x + 3yz}$
3. $f(x, y, z) = \ln(x^2 + y^2 + z^2 - xy)$

Exercises 4, 5, 6, and 7 refer to Example 2.
4. Determine the necessary conditions for a stationary point.
5. State the conditions for x and C necessary to satisfy the sufficient conditions for a maximum at a stationary point.
6. Show that

$$\frac{y}{\eta} = \frac{C}{x\eta_c} = \frac{C}{x\eta_z}$$

at a stationary point where

$$\eta = -\frac{y}{x}\frac{dx}{dy} \qquad \eta_c = \frac{C}{x}\frac{\partial x/\partial q}{\partial C/\partial q} \qquad \eta_z = \frac{C}{x}\frac{\partial x/\partial z}{\partial C/\partial z}$$

Show further that

$$y = \frac{C}{x\eta_c} + MC \qquad \text{where } MC = \text{marginal cost} = \frac{\partial C}{\partial x}$$

Give the economic interpretation of these results.

7. Solve 4, 5, and 6 for the case where x is a general polynomial of degree 2 in y, z, and q, and C is a general polynomial of degree 2 in x, z, and q.

8. An industry contains n firms, each producing the same product.

i = firm number $1 = 1, \ldots, n$
y_i = price charged by ith firm (\$ per unit)
z_i = advertising expenditure of the ith firm (\$ per period)
s_i = sales of the ith firm (units per period)
c = variable manufacturing cost (\$ per unit)

Assume that:
A. Production costs are directly proportional to production volume and fixed costs are zero.
B. Sales for the ith firm are given by

$$s_i = \frac{1}{n}(\alpha - \beta y_i)(1 + \gamma\sqrt{n\bar{z}})\left[(1 - \delta)\frac{z_i}{n\bar{z}} + \delta\right]$$

where $\bar{y} = \frac{1}{n}\sum_{i=1}^{n} y_i$ and $\bar{z} = \frac{1}{n}\sum_{i=1}^{n} z_i$

α, β, γ, and δ are parameters

$\alpha > 0;\ \beta \geq 0;\ \gamma \geq 0;\ 0 \leq \delta \leq 1$

Sales depend on three factors:

$\alpha - \beta y_i$:   sales of the ith firm decrease as its price increases.

$1 + \gamma\sqrt{n\bar{z}}$:   sales of the ith firm increase as the total advertising expenditures of the industry increase. The influence of this factor depends on the parameter γ; the larger γ is, the more important is total advertising.

$(1 - \delta)\frac{z_i}{n\bar{z}} + \delta$:   sales of the ith firm increase as its share of total advertising expenditures increases. The influence of this factor depends on the parameter δ. $1 - \delta$ is the proportion of the market "affected" by the firm's advertising.

C. Each firm produces during each period only as much as it can sell.
D. The manufacturing cost per unit is the same for all firms.
   (a) Determine the optimum values of y_i and z_i to maximize total earnings for the industry.
   (b) Interpret the results of (a).
   (c) Solve (a) if the variable manufacturing cost varies from firm to firm.
   (d) What modification must be made in the formulation and solution if the amount produced by the ith firm, say, x_i, is a decision variable?
   (e) What modifications are necessary to extend the analysis of (d) to maximization of earnings over many periods?

9. A firm produces during each period as much of a product as it can sell. The demand for the product during any period depends on the price charged during the period and on the quantity produced in each of the previous periods. The production cost for a period is an increasing concave function of the quantity produced. Future earnings are discounted. Under what conditions will the firm maximize the present value of future earnings if it determines the production level of any period by setting marginal revenue during that period equal to marginal cost during that period?

B. OPTIMIZATION SUBJECT TO EQUALITY CONSTRAINTS

Substitution Method

The optimization technique described in the previous section can be used to determine the optimum values of $f(X)$ if the feasible region is restricted by the requirement that X must satisfy an equation of the form

$$g(X) = 0 \tag{1}$$

If (1) can be solved for one of the x_i, say, x_n,

$$x_n = h(x_1, x_2, \ldots, x_{n-1})$$

This is substituted in $f(X)$ to give

$$f_1(x_1, x_2, \ldots, x_{n-1}) \tag{2}$$

in which the x's are now independent.

Example I. Among all three-dimensional rectangular parallelepipeds with constant volume, find the one with minimum surface. The problem is to:

minimize $S(x, y, z) = 2xz + 2yz + 2yx$ (3)

subject to $xyz = c$ (4)

and $x \geq 0; \quad y \geq 0; \quad z \geq 0$ (5)

Solving (4) for z gives

$$z = \frac{c}{xy} \tag{6}$$

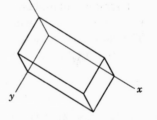

Figure 18.1

and substituting in (3) gives

$$S_1(x, y) = \frac{2xc}{xy} + \frac{2yc}{xy} + 2yx$$

$$= \frac{2c}{y} + \frac{2c}{x} + 2yx$$

$$\frac{\partial S_1}{\partial x} = 0; \quad -\frac{2c}{x^2} + 2y = 0$$

$$\frac{\partial S_1}{\partial y} = 0; \quad -\frac{2c}{y^2} + 2x = 0$$

Solving these equations gives a single unique solution

$$x = c^{1/3}, \qquad y = c^{1/3} \qquad \text{and, from (4),} \quad z = c^{1/3}$$

As we would expect, the solution is a cube. To verify that the solution is a minimum:

$$\frac{\partial^2 S_1}{\partial x^2} = +\frac{4c}{x^3} \qquad \frac{\partial^2 S_1}{\partial x\, \partial y} = 2$$

$$\frac{\partial^2 S_1}{\partial y^2} = \frac{4c}{y^3}$$

Evaluating these at the point $x = y = c^{1/3}$

gives

$$\Delta_1 = 4 \qquad \Delta_2 = \begin{vmatrix} 4 & 2 \\ 2 & 4 \end{vmatrix} = 16 - 4 = 12$$

$\therefore \Delta_1 > 0$ and $\Delta_2 > 0$. The stationary point is an interior point of the feasible region defined by (5), and hence the function (3) has a global minimum at the stationary point.

Lagrange Multipliers

Lagrange multipliers were presented in Chapter 11 as a method of solving problems in which the decision variables must satisfy an equality. The necessary conditions for point x^*, y^* to be an extreme point of $f(x, y)$ subject to $g(x, y) = 0$ were:

$$\frac{\partial h}{\partial x} = 0, \qquad \frac{\partial h}{\partial y} = 0, \qquad \frac{\partial h}{\partial \lambda} = 0$$

where $h(x, y, \lambda) = f(x, y) - \lambda g(x, y)$.

Thus sufficient conditions for a maximum (minimum) were that Δ_3 be positive (negative) where

$$\Delta_3 = \{-g_x^2[f_{yy} - \lambda g_{yy}] - g_y^2[f_{xx} - \lambda g_{xx}] + 2g_x g_y[f_{xy} - \lambda g_{xy}]\}$$

$$\lambda = \frac{f_x}{g_x} = \frac{f_y}{g_y}$$

As with Δ_2 in the case where there are no equality constraints, Δ_3 can be conveniently expressed in the form of a determinant:

$$\Delta_3 = \begin{vmatrix} 0 & g_x & g_y \\ g_x & f_{xx} - \lambda g_{xx} & f_{xy} - \lambda g_{xy} \\ g_y & f_{xy} - \lambda g_{xy} & f_{yy} - \lambda g_{yy} \end{vmatrix}$$

The method of Lagrange multipliers can now be generalized to the case of a function f of n variables, $\mathbf{X}$, subject to one inequality constraint $g(\mathbf{X}) = 0$. The necessary condition is that X^* satisfy the $n + 1$ equations

$$\frac{\partial f(\mathbf{X})}{\partial \mathbf{X}} - \lambda \frac{\partial g(\mathbf{X})}{\partial \mathbf{X}} = 0 \tag{7}$$

$$g(\mathbf{X}) = 0$$

which are obtained by setting the derivatives of

$$h(\mathbf{X}, \lambda) = f(\mathbf{X}) - \lambda g(\mathbf{X})$$

with respect to $\mathbf{X}$ and λ, equal to zero. At least one of the partial derivatives $\partial g / \partial x_i$ must be different from zero at this point.

From (7) it follows that at a stationary point

$$\lambda = \frac{f_{x_i}}{g_{x_i}}; \qquad i = 1, \ldots, n \tag{8}$$

To determine whether the stationary points are local maxima or local minima requires the evaluation of the $n - 1$ principal minors of Δ_{n+1}:

$$\Delta_3, \Delta_4, \ldots, \Delta_{n+1}$$

$$\Delta_{n+1} = \begin{vmatrix} 0 & g_{x_1} & g_{x_2} & \cdots & g_{x_n} \\ g_{x_1} & f_{x_1 x_1} - \lambda g_{x_1 x_1} & f_{x_1 x_2} - \lambda g_{x_1 x_2} & \cdots & f_{x_1 x_n} - \lambda g_{x_1 x_n} \\ g_{x_2} & f_{x_2 x_1} - \lambda g_{x_2 x_1} & f_{x_2 x_2} - \lambda g_{x_2 x_2} & \cdots & f_{x_2 x_n} - \lambda g_{x_2 x_n} \\ \cdots & \cdots & \cdots & \cdots & \cdots \\ g_{x_n} & f_{x_n x_1} - \lambda g_{x_n x_1} & f_{x_n x_2} - \lambda g_{x_2 x_2} & \cdots & f_{x_n x_n} - \lambda g_{x_n x_n} \end{vmatrix}$$

Δ_i consists of the first i rows and i columns of Δ_{n+1}. All the derivatives are evaluated at the stationary point and λ is given by (8). The function f has a local extremum at a stationary point, subject to $g(\mathbf{X}) = 0$ which is a

      local minimum if $\Delta_3 < 0$; $\Delta_4 < 0, \ldots, \Delta_{n+1} < 0$

or

      local maximum if $\Delta_3 > 0$; $\Delta_4 < 0, \Delta_5 > 0 \cdots$

If neither of these conditions holds, further investigation is necessary. The proof will be given in Chapter 20, Section C.

Example 2. To use Lagrange multipliers in the problem described in Example 1, let

$$F(x, y, z, \lambda) = 2xz + 2yz + 2yx - \lambda(xyz - c)$$

The stationary points are given by

$$\frac{\partial F}{\partial x} = 0; \qquad 2z + 2y - \lambda yz = 0$$

$$\frac{\partial F}{\partial y} = 0; \qquad 2z + 2x - \lambda xz = 0$$

$$\frac{\partial F}{\partial z} = 0; \qquad 2x + 2y - \lambda xy = 0$$

$$xyz - c = 0$$

Solving these equations gives, as before, $x = y = z = c^{\frac{1}{3}}$ and also $\lambda = 4c^{-\frac{1}{3}}$.

The partial derivatives give

$$
\begin{array}{ccc}
f_{xx} = 0 & f_{yy} = 0 & f_{zz} = 0 \\
f_{xy} = 2 & f_{xz} = 2 & f_{yz} = 2 \\
g_x = yz & g_y = xz & g_z = xy \\
g_{xx} = 0 & g_{yy} = 0 & g_{zz} = 0 \\
g_{xy} = z & g_{xz} = y & g_{yz} = x
\end{array}
$$

Evaluating these at the stationary point gives

$$\Delta_4 = \begin{vmatrix} 0 & c^{\frac{2}{3}} & c^{\frac{2}{3}} & c^{\frac{2}{3}} \\ c^{\frac{2}{3}} & 0 & 2 - \lambda c^{\frac{1}{3}} & 2 - \lambda c^{\frac{1}{3}} \\ c^{\frac{2}{3}} & 2 - \lambda c^{\frac{1}{3}} & 0 & 2 - \lambda c^{\frac{1}{3}} \\ c^{\frac{2}{3}} & 2 - \lambda c^{\frac{1}{3}} & 2 - \lambda c^{\frac{1}{3}} & 0 \end{vmatrix}$$

$$= -c^{\frac{2}{3}}(4c^{\frac{2}{3}}) + c^{\frac{2}{3}}(-4c^{\frac{2}{3}}) - c^{\frac{2}{3}}(4c^{\frac{2}{3}}) = -12c^{\frac{4}{3}} < 0$$

and

$$\Delta_3 = \begin{vmatrix} 0 & c^{\frac{2}{3}} & c^{\frac{2}{3}} \\ c^{\frac{2}{3}} & 0 & 2 - \lambda c^{\frac{1}{3}} \\ c^{\frac{2}{3}} & 2 - \lambda c^{\frac{1}{3}} & 0 \end{vmatrix} = 2c^{\frac{2}{3}}(2 - \lambda c^{\frac{1}{3}}) = -4c^{\frac{2}{3}} < 0$$

This verifies that the function subject to the constraint $xyz = c$ has a minimum at the stationary point.

Example 3. The usual expression for the economic order quantity of an inventory item takes into account the costs of placing an order, the cost of holding the item in inventory, and the expected sales rate. Often there are several items in inventory, and economic order quantities must be developed for each item subject to some over-all constraints. Limits on total dollars invested in inventory or on warehouse space are examples of such constraints.

Develop the formula for the economic order quantity for each item when there is an equality constraint on the *average* value of inventory. Assume that holding costs are a constant percentage of value, the same for all items. Verify by use of second order conditions. What is the physical significance of the various terms in the resulting expression for minimum total inventory cost?

Solution.   *Decision variables:*

$$x_i = \text{order size} \qquad i = 1, 2, \ldots, n$$

Objective: To minimize the total variable cost T subject to constant total average value of inventory.
Uncontrollable variables:

R_i = Sales rate
I = Carrying cost as percent of value of the item
U_i = Cost of item
C_0 = Cost of placing an order
K = Average value of inventory

Objective: Minimize T = order cost + holding cost

$$T = \sum_i \left[C_0 \frac{R_i}{x_i} + \frac{x_i}{2} IU_i \right]$$

Let

$$\phi = \sum_i \frac{x_i U_i}{2} - K$$

At a stationary point

$$\frac{\partial T}{\partial x_i} - \lambda \frac{\partial \phi}{\partial x_i} = 0 \qquad i = 1, \ldots, n$$

Substituting for the partial derivatives gives

$$\frac{IU_i}{2} - \frac{C_0 R_i}{x_i^2} - \lambda \frac{U_i}{2} = 0$$

$$\frac{U_i}{2}(I - \lambda) = \frac{C_0 R_i}{x_i^2}$$

and

$$x_i = \left(\frac{2C_0 R_i}{U_i(I - \lambda)} \right)^{1/2}$$

Here

$$\frac{IU_i}{2} \qquad \text{is the marginal holding cost}$$

$$-\frac{C_0 R_i}{x_i^2} \quad \text{is the marginal order cost,}$$

and

$$-\frac{\lambda U_i}{2} \qquad \text{represents an addition to the marginal cost by the average value of inventory constraint}$$

The second-order condition for $n = 2$ is that Δ_3 must be negative.

$$\Delta_3 = \begin{vmatrix} 0 & \dfrac{U_1}{2} & \dfrac{U_2}{2} \\ \dfrac{U_1}{2} & \dfrac{2C_0 R_1}{x_1^3} & 0 \\ \dfrac{U_2}{2} & 0 & \dfrac{2C_0 R_2}{x_2^3} \end{vmatrix} = -\frac{U_1^2}{2}\frac{C_0 R_2}{x_2^3} - \frac{U_2^2}{2}\frac{C_0 R_1}{x_1^3} < 0$$

for all $x > 0$. An analogous result will also hold for any n.

This verifies that the solution does give minimum cost; however the solution is expressed in terms of λ. An explicit solution not involving λ can be obtained by using the fact that $\phi = 0$.

This constraint requires that

$$\sum_i \frac{x_i U_i}{2} = K \qquad \text{or}$$

$$K = \sum \frac{U_i}{2}\sqrt{\frac{2C_0 R_i}{U_i(I - \lambda)}} = \frac{1}{\sqrt{I - \lambda}}\sum_i \sqrt{\frac{U_i C_0 R_i}{2}}$$

but

$$x_i = \sqrt{\frac{2C_0 R_i}{U_i(I - \lambda)}}$$

or

$$x_i = \left(\frac{2C_0 R_i}{U_i}\right)^{1/2} \cdot \frac{1}{\sqrt{I - \lambda}}$$

$$\frac{1}{\sqrt{I - \lambda}} = x_i\left(\frac{U_i}{2C_0 R_i}\right)^{1/2}$$

$$K = x_i\left(\frac{U_i}{2C_0 R_i}\right)^{1/2}\sum_i \left(\frac{U_i C_0 R_i}{2}\right)^{1/2}$$

hence

$$x_i = \frac{K(2C_0 R_i/U_i)^{\frac{1}{2}}}{\sum_i (U_i C_0 R_i/2)^{\frac{1}{2}}}$$

This expression gives x_i in terms of known quantities; the value of λ can be obtained by substitution.

Example 4.   An advertiser, by examining historical data, has found that response produced by a short intense advertising compaign is

$$R = a \ln A + b; \qquad R \geq 0$$

where R is the response to A, the dollar amount of advertising. The constant a is positive while the constant b is negative; this may be interpreted as implying that there is a "threshold" amount of advertising; say A_T, below which no response is obtained.

Determine the optimum allocation of an advertising budget of $\$B$ if there are n geographical areas in which compaigns can be conducted. Assume that the constants a and b are the same in each area and that the time period over which B can be spent is sufficiently long so that several campaigns can be conducted in one area without interfering with each other. Verify that this allocation is optimal and determine the additional response obtainable for another dollar of advertising budget.

Solution.   The "threshold" amount of advertising can be determined by solving

$$R = a \ln A + b$$

for A when $R = 0$.

$$0 = a \ln A_T + b$$

$$A_T = e^{-b/a}$$

Since the constants are equal in all periods and R is a monotonic concave function of A, the optimum policy is to spend equal amounts on all campaigns. This can be shown by supposing that unequal amounts are

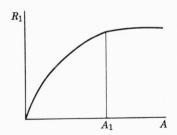
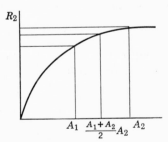

Figure 18.2

to be spent. The above figure 18.2, shows the responses R_1 and R_2 for two campaigns with amounts A_1 and A_2, respectively. Since

$$R_2(A_2) - R_2\left(\frac{A_1 + A_2}{2}\right) < R_2\left(\frac{A_1 + A_2}{2}\right) - R_2(A_1)$$

additional response will be obtained by transferring funds from campaign 2 to campaign 1 as long as $A_2 > A_1$.

Let x be the number of campaigns. The amount A for each campaign will be B/x; the total response TR is

$$TR = x\left[a \ln \frac{B}{x} + b\right] = -ax \ln x + x[a \ln B + b]$$

and

$$\frac{dTR}{dx} = -a - a \ln x + a \ln B + b$$

The stationary point is given by

$$\frac{dTR}{dx} = 0 = -a + a \ln \frac{B}{x} + b; \qquad \ln \frac{B}{x} = \frac{a - b}{a}$$

$$x^* = \frac{B}{e^{\frac{(a-b)}{a}}} = \frac{B}{eA_T}$$

Since

$$\frac{d^2TR}{dx^2} = -\frac{a}{x} < 0 \text{ as } x^* \geq 0 \qquad TR \text{ has a maximum at } x^*$$

For fractional values of x, the optimum policy is determined as follows: let x_1 and x_2 be the whole number values of either side of x^*.

Compare the changes by going to x_1 or x_2:

$$R_1 = x_1\left[a \ln \frac{B}{x_1} + b\right] \qquad R_2 = x_2\left[a \ln \frac{B}{x_2} + b\right]$$

remembering that $R(x) \geq 0$

if $R_1 > R_2$, use x_1 campaigns; if $R_2 > R_1$, use x_2 campaigns

The change in response when \$1 is added to B is the partial derivative of TR with respect to B

$$TR = \frac{B}{eA_T}[a \ln eA_T + b]$$

$$\frac{\partial TR}{\partial B} = \frac{1}{eA_T}[a \ln eA_T + b]$$

More than One Equality Constraint

If the variables $x_1, \ldots, x_n$ are constrained by m equations

$$g_j(x_1, \ldots, x_n) = 0 \qquad j = 1, \ldots m \qquad (9)$$

m multipliers $\lambda_1, \lambda_2, \ldots, \lambda_m$ are used to define the function

$$F(x_1, \ldots, x_n, \lambda, \ldots, \lambda_m) = f(x_1, \ldots, x_n) - \lambda_1 g_1 - \lambda_2 g_2 - \cdots - \lambda_m g_m$$

A stationary point is one which satisfies the $n + m$ equations

$$\frac{\partial F}{\partial x_i} = 0 \qquad i = 1, \ldots, n$$

$$\frac{\partial F}{\partial \lambda_j} = g_j = 0 \qquad j = 1, \ldots, m$$

The function f can have an extreme value in the feasible region defined by (9) only at points satisfying the $n + m$ equations.

In the case of one constraint it was necessary to require that

$$\frac{\partial g}{\partial x_i} \neq 0$$

for at least one i. The analogous conditions in this case are that at least one of the determinants

$$\begin{vmatrix} \dfrac{\partial g_1}{\partial x_1} & \cdots & \dfrac{\partial g_1}{\partial x_m} \\ \cdot & & \cdot \\ \cdot & & \cdot \\ \cdot & & \cdot \\ \dfrac{\partial g_m}{\partial x_1} & \cdots & \dfrac{\partial g_m}{\partial x_m} \end{vmatrix} \neq 0$$

for some m of the variables. A statement of the second-order conditions for this case is given in Chapter 20, page 608.

EXERCISES

1. A firm produces n different products from a basic raw material. The selling price per unit, y, of each product is the same. The amount of the raw material required for 1 unit of the ith product is a_i. The variable cost (excluding raw material cost) of producing a quantity x_i of the ith product per period is x_i^2.

If the total amount of raw material available is K, determine the optimal amount of each product.

2. (a) Answer (1) if the cost of producing a quantity x_i of the ith product in a period is given by $x_i{}^k$.

(b) State the conditions under which equal amounts of the products would be produced.

3. Among all three-dimensional parallelepipeds with constant surface, determine the one with maximum volume. Comment on the difference between this problem and Example 2.

4. Find the rectangular block of maximum volume which can be cut from a sphere of radius a.

5. (a) Determine the maximum earnings in Example 2, p. 546, if the marketing expenditure is a fixed proportion of the total revenue.

(b) Answer (a) if marketing expenditure is a fixed proportion of earnings.

6. The earnings of the ith department (in \$100,000) in a store are given by

$$E_i(x_i, y_i): \quad E_i(x_i, y_i) = 4x_i + 5y_i + x_iy_i - x_i{}^2 - y_i{}^2 + 5$$

where x_i = investment in inventory in the ith department (\$1,000,000)

y_i = floor space used for display in the ith department (10,000 sq ft)
In particular if $i = 2$:

$$E_2(x_2, y_2) = 4x_2 + 2y_2 + 2x_2y_2 - 2x_2{}^2 - y_2{}^2 - 5$$

The store wishes to use \$8,000,000 for investment in inventory and 70,000 sq ft of floor space.

(a) Determine the optimum allocation.

(b) Verify that the solution is a maximum.

(c) How much money and floor space would be required if each department operated at its own optimum level?

7. Answer (6) if one clerk is required for each \$25,000 invested in inventory and for each 10,000 sq ft of floor space, and if 60 clerks are to be used.

8. Answer (6) in the general case. There are n departments, the earnings function in each department is a second-degree polynomial, the money to be invested in inventory is \$$K$,000,000 and the amount of floor space is V0,000 sq ft.

9. In Exercise 6, let $i = 2$ and let $E_i(x_i, y_i)$ have the following properties:

(i) $\dfrac{\partial E_i}{\partial x_i}$ and $\dfrac{\partial E_i}{\partial y_i}$ increase for low values of (x_i, y_i)

(ii) They decrease for large values of (x_i, y_i) and

(iii) $\dfrac{\partial^2 E_i}{\partial x_i{}^2}$ and $\dfrac{\partial^2 E_i}{\partial y_i{}^2}$ are negative for values of (x_i, y_i) for which (ii) holds.

(a) Show that

$$E_i(x_i, y_i) = a_i + b_ix_i + c_iy_i - e_ix_iy_i$$

satisfies the requirements.

(b) Determine the conditions under which the store is maximizing its total earnings when each of the departments is maximizing its earnings. Assume the total investment in inventory is \$$K$,000,000 and the amount of floor space is V0,000 sq ft.

C. OPTIMIZATION SUBJECT TO INEQUALITY CONSTRAINTS

The General Optimization Problem

The Lagrange multiplier technique described above can be used to give practical (numerical) results if the following conditions hold.

1. The derivatives

$$\frac{\partial F(\mathbf{X})}{\partial \mathbf{X}} = 0$$

must exist.

2. It is possible to determine *all* solutions to these equations, which are in or on the boundary of the feasible region, either analytically or numerically.
3. The second partial derivatives must be computable in order to determine where the stationary points are maxima, minima or neither.

The techniques for locating local extreme points for differentiable functions of many variables are summarized in Table 18-1. The appropriateness of the various techniques depends on whether the objective function is linear or non-linear, whether there are any constraints and, if so, whether they are equalities and whether they are linear or non-linear.

The simplest case is that in which there are no constraints. If $f(\mathbf{X})$ is

Table 18-1 Summary of Applicability of Optimization Techniques

Constraints Defining Feasible Region		Objective Function: $f(X)$	
Type	Form	*Linear*	*Non-linear*
None		$x_i = \pm\infty$	Solve $\dfrac{\partial f(\mathbf{X})}{\partial \mathbf{X}} = 0$
Equality	All linear	Substitution or linear programming	Substitution or Lagrange multipliers
	Some non-linear	Non-linear programming	
Inequality	All linear	Linear Programming	
	Some non-linear	Non-linear programming	

linear, the problem is trivial. If $f(\mathbf{X})$ is non-linear and satisfies the necessary conditions, the technique given in Section A, page 547, can be used.

If the constraints are all equalities and the objective function is non-linear, the problem can be solved as described in the previous section, by substitution or by the use of Lagrange multipliers.

The use of the partial derivatives is valid only if they exist. Any points or regions in which the function or its first derivatives are discontinuous must, as in the case of one variable, be examined separately.

In many problems it is necessary to resort to numerical methods. Methods for solving systems of equations are described in texts on numerical analysis: see, for example, Householder [1953] or Hamming [1962]. These texts also describe classical optimization techniques such as the method of steepest ascent, gradient methods, etc.

Linear programming, described in Chapter 15, is the appropriate technique for the case in which the objective function is linear and the constraints, either equalities or inequalities, are all linear.

If the objective function is linear and there are some non-linear equality or inequality constraints, or if the objective function is non-linear and the constraints are inequalities, the methods described above cannot, in general, be used to determine the extreme values.

In linear programming the optimum occurs at the vertex of the feasible polyhedron. If the constraints are non-linear, the set of feasible solutions will not be a polyhedron and the optimum may occur in the interior of the feasible set, or it may occur on the boundary. If it occurs in the interior, the constraints may be ignored. Hence, the first step in solving such a problem is to determine the stationary points without regard to the constraints. If no constraints are violated, the problem has been solved.

If one or more constraints are violated, a more advanced technique must be used. These techniques are commonly referred to as non-linear programming or mathematical programming. These terms include many procedures designed for various special cases. There are, for example, special procedures for the quadratic programming case, i.e., where the objective function is quadratic. Sometimes problems can be solved by special methods, such as marginal analysis, by reasoning to an intuitive solution and then verifying it (see Example 2, page 565). General methods are based on the Kuhn-Tucker conditions given on the next page.

One of the most difficult problems in the optimization of functions of many variables is proving that a local optimum is a global optimum. A widely used practice is that of assuming away the problem by restricting consideration to functions which have at most one stationary point in the feasible region, e.g., functions which are either convex everywhere or concave everywhere.

General Statement of the Kuhn-Tucker Conditions

The Kuhn-Tucker conditions for the general case are:

A point $(x_1, x_2, \ldots, x_n)$ maximizes a function $f(x_1, \ldots, x_n)$ subject to $g_j(x_1, \ldots, x_n) \leq 0, j = 1, \ldots, m$ if there exists a set of non-negative values $\lambda_1, \ldots, \lambda_m$ such that

$$h_i = \frac{\partial f}{\partial x_i} - \sum_{j=1}^{m} \lambda_j \frac{\partial g_j}{\partial x_i} = 0$$

$$\lambda_j g_j = 0$$

$$g_j \leq 0$$

These conditions are sufficient for a global maximum if f and g_j are all concave (and differentiable) functions.

The necessary conditions if the x's are to be non-negative are:

$$h_i \leq 0$$
$$\Sigma \, h_i x_i = 0$$
$$g_j \lambda_j = 0$$
$$g_j \leq 0$$
$$x_i \geq 0$$

These conditions are expressed in various forms in the literature. A summary is given in Table 18-2.

Example I. A firm produces the same item in each of three successive periods. The requirements for the item are 5 units at the end of the first period, 10 at the end of the second, and 15 at the end of the third. The cost of producing x items in any period is

$$c(x) = x^2$$

Items may be produced in one period and carried over to a subsequent period. A holding cost of 2 per unit is charged for any items carried over from one period to the next. Assuming no initial inventory, how many units should be produced each period?

Let x_1, x_2, x_3 represent production in periods one, two, and three, respectively.

The total cost = production cost + holding cost

$$C(x_1, x_2, x_3) = x_1^2 + x_2^2 + x_3^2 + 2(x_1 - 5) + 2(x_1 + x_2 - 15)$$

The feasible region is determined by

$$x_1 \geq 5$$
$$x_1 + x_2 \geq 15 \qquad \text{and} \qquad x_2 \geq 0$$
$$x_1 + x_2 + x_3 = 30 \qquad \text{and} \qquad x_3 \geq 0.$$

Table 18-2

{Optimize} $f(x_1, x_2, \ldots, x_n)$ subject to $g_j(x_1, x_2, \ldots, x_n)$

	{Max} {Min}	{Max} {Min}	{Min} {Max}	Min	Min	Min	Max	Max
Constraints variables	none	$g_j = 0; \; m < n$	$g_j \geq 0$	$g_j = 0$ $x_i \geq 0$	$g_j \leq 0$ $x_i \geq 0$	$g_j \geq 0$ $x_i \geq 0$	$g_j \leq 0$ $x_i \geq 0$	$g_j \geq 0$ $x_i \geq 0$
Necessary conditions for local extremum	$\dfrac{\partial f}{\partial x_i} = 0$	$h_i^+ = \dfrac{\partial f}{\partial x_i} + \sum_{j=1}^{m} \lambda_j \dfrac{\partial g_i}{\partial x_i}$ $h_i^+ = 0$	$h_i^- = \dfrac{\partial f}{\partial x_i} - \sum_j^m \lambda_j \dfrac{\partial g_j}{\partial x_i}$ $h_i^- = 0$ $\lambda_j h_j = 0$	$h_i \geq 0$	$h_i^+ \geq 0$ $\sum_i x_i h_i^+ = 0$ $\sum_j \lambda_j g_j = 0$	$h_i^+ \geq 0$ $x_i h_i^- = 0$ $\lambda_j g_j = 0$	$h_i^- \leq 0$ $\sum_i x_i h_i^- = 0$ $\lambda_j g_j = 0$	$h_i^+ \leq 0$ $\sum x_i h_i^+ = 0$ $\lambda_j g_j = 0$
Sufficient condition for local extremum	Principal minors of Δ are {alternately negative and positive} {positive} where $\Delta_{ij} = \dfrac{\partial^2 f}{\partial x_i \partial x_j}$	Last $n - m$ principal minors of $\begin{bmatrix} 0 & B \\ B' & A \end{bmatrix}$ {alternate in sign, the first one being of sign $(-1)^{m+1}$, etc.} {be of sign $(-1)^m$} where $b_{ij} = \dfrac{\partial^2 g_j}{\partial x_i \partial x_j}$ $a_{ij} = \Delta_{ij} + \sum_k \lambda_k \dfrac{\partial^2 g_k}{\partial x_i \partial x_j}$	$\lambda_j \geq 0$; $\{\lambda_j > 0\}$		$\lambda_j \geq 0$	$\lambda_j \geq 0$	$\lambda_j \geq 0$	$\lambda_j \geq 0$
Sufficient condition for global extremum	f {concave} {convex}		If f is convex and g_j concave, then conditions are sufficient for global minimum.	f is convex	If f and g_i are all convex and differentiable functions	If f and the g_i are differentiable, and if $\lambda_j > 0$ for $j = 1$ P and $h_j > 0$ for $j = P + 1, \ldots, n$		f and g_j are differentiable and concave.
Reference		Samuelson, p. 377	Dorn, p. 171	Vajda, p. 236	Vajda, p. 233	Wilde, p. 769	Dorfman, p. 199	Kuhn, Tucker, p. 482 Charnes, Cooper, I, p. 405

This is a problem in non-linear programming, since the objective function is non-linear and the constraints are inequalities.

An initial attempt at a solution can be made by disregarding the inequality constraints and using one Lagrange multiplier. The function to be minimized is

$$F(x_1, x_2, x_3) = x_1{}^2 + x_2{}^2 + x_3{}^2 + 2(x_1 - 5) + 2(x_1 + x_2 - 15)$$
$$- \lambda(x_1 + x_2 + x_3 - 30)$$

$$\frac{\partial F}{\partial x_1} = 0; \qquad 2x_1 + 2 + 2 - \lambda = 0 \qquad\qquad 2x_1 = -4 + \lambda$$

$$\frac{\partial F}{\partial x_2} = 0; \qquad 2x_2 + 2 - \lambda = 0 \qquad\qquad 2x_2 = -2 + \lambda$$

$$\frac{\partial F}{\partial x_3} = 0; \qquad 2x_3 - \lambda = 0 \qquad\qquad 2x_3 = +\lambda$$

$$\frac{\partial F}{\partial \lambda} = 0; \qquad x_1 + x_2 + x_3 = 30$$

$$-4 + \lambda - 2 + \lambda + \lambda = 60; \qquad \lambda = \tfrac{66}{3} = 22$$

$$x_1 = 9; \qquad x_2 = 10; \qquad x_3 = 11$$

Because these values satisfy all the inequalities, the optimum occurs at an interior point.

The second-order conditions are verified by computing Δ_4 and Δ_3 as follows:

$$\Delta_4 = \begin{vmatrix} 0 & 1 & 1 & 1 \\ 1 & 2 & 0 & 0 \\ 1 & 0 & 2 & 0 \\ 1 & 0 & 0 & 2 \end{vmatrix} = -1(4) + 2(-4) = -12$$

$$\Delta_3 = \begin{vmatrix} 0 & 1 & 1 \\ 1 & 2 & 0 \\ 1 & 0 & 2 \end{vmatrix} = -2 - 2 = -4$$

Production of 9 units in the first period, 10 in the second, and 11 in the third will lead to minimum cost over the periods.

Example 2. In Example 1 the inequality constraints were satisfied at the local minimum obtained without consideration of the constraints. However, this will not always be true. Let the requirement be 5 units at the end of the first period, 5 units at the end of the second period and 5 at the end of the third period. Substituting for x_3,

$$x_3 = 15 - x_1 - x_2$$

gives

$$C_1(x_1, x_2) = x_1{}^2 + x_2{}^2 + (15 - x_1 - x_2)^2 + 2(x_1 - 5) + 2(x_1 + x_2 - 10)$$

Differentiating and setting the derivatives equal to zero gives:

$$\frac{\partial C_1}{\partial x_1} = 0; \qquad 4x_1 + 2x_2 = 26$$

$$\frac{\partial C_1}{\partial x_2} = 0; \qquad 2x_1 + 4x_2 = 28$$

and the stationary point is $x_1 = 4$, $x_2 = 5$, and $x_3 = 6$. This solution does not meet the inequalities:

$$x_1 \geq 5; \qquad x_1 + x_2 \geq 10$$

This indicates that at least one of the two inequalities will be satisfied as an equality and that the problem will have to be solved by non-linear programming, as illustrated in Example 3 below. Sometimes it is possible to solve problems by marginal analysis. In period 1, at least 5 units must be produced. How will total cost be changed if n units more than the minimum requirement are produced in period 1? The cost in period 1 will be

$$(5 + n)^2$$

The cost in period 2 is $2n + (5 - n)^2$ if the extra units are used to satisfy requirements in period 2, for a total of

$$(5 + n)^2 + (5 - n)^2 + 2n$$

This must be compared with the cost of producing 5 units in each period

$$5^2 + 5^2$$

Hence, n should be > 0 if

$$(5 + n)^2 + (5 - n)^2 + 2n - 5^2 - 5^2 < 0$$

or

$$10n + n^2 - 10n + n^2 + 2n < 0$$

but

$$2n^2 + 2n > 0$$

Therefore, costs cannot be decreased by producing over immediate requirements in the first period. The same argument applies to extra production in the second period and carrying units from the first and/or second periods to the third. Hence total costs will be minimized if 5 units are produced in each period.

Example 3. This example illustrates the use of the Kuhn-Tucker condition for the solution of the inventory problem in Example 2. The problem may be stated as minimizing

$$C = x_1^2 + x_2^2 + x_3^2 + 2(x_1 - 5) + 2(x_1 + x_2 - 10)$$

subject to:

$$x_1 \geq 5$$
$$x_1 + x_2 \geq 10$$
$$x_1 + x_2 + x_3 \geq 15$$
$$x_i \geq 0 \qquad i = 1, 2, 3$$

For the application of the Kuhn-Tucker conditions, let

$$h = -C - \lambda_1 g_1 - \lambda_2 g_2 - \lambda_3 g_3$$

where $g_1 = 5 - x_1$

$$g_2 = 10 - x_1 - x_2$$
$$g_3 = 15 - x_1 - x_2 - x_3$$

The necessary conditions for a maximum are:

(a) $\dfrac{\partial h}{\partial x_i} = h_i \leq 0$: $\quad h_1 = -2x_1 - 2 - 2 + \lambda_1 + \lambda_2 + \lambda_3$

$$h_2 = -2x_2 - 2 + \lambda_2 + \lambda_3$$
$$h_3 = -2x_3 + \lambda_3$$

(b) $\Sigma\, h_i x_i = 0$

(c) $\lambda_i g_i = 0$

(d) $\lambda_i \geq 0$

Each of the three λ's may be zero or different from zero. A total of eight cases must be examined. Here one of these (all λ's $\neq 0$) will be selected as the case for illustration. If all λ's are not zero, the g's must be zero. These can be solved immediately:

$$x_1 = 5, \qquad x_2 = 5, \qquad x_3 = 5$$

Since the x's are all non-zero, all the h_i must be equal to zero to satisfy (b). The quations (a) are now three equations in three unknowns with solution:

$$\lambda_1 = 2, \qquad \lambda_2 = 2, \qquad \lambda_3 = 10$$

Since these are non-negative, all the necessary conditions for a maximum are satisfied. All the functions (the g's and $-C$) are concave and therefore the solution is the global maximum of $-C$ and the global minimum of C.

This example is a particular case of quadratic programming. Another example is given in Chapter 19, Section D. For most problems the trial and error method used here is not practical. A number of algorithms are described in the recent literature and computer programs are available for a number of the larger computers.

EXERCISES

Answer exercises 1–5 if the constraints are considered as inequalities.
1. Exercise 6, p. 560.
2. Exercise 7, p. 560.
3. Exercise 8, p. 560.
4. Exercise 9, p. 560.
5. Exercise 5, p. 560.
6. Develop the "Kuhn–Tucker" conditions for the case where some constraints are equalities and others are inequalities.

Notes and References

Charnes, A., and Cooper, W. W. (1961), *Management Models and Industrial Applications of Linear Programming*, John Wiley and Sons, New York.

Debreu, G. (1952), "Definite and Semidefinite Quadratic Forms," *Econometrica*, **20**, pp. 295–300.

Dorfman, R., Samuelson, P. A. and Solow, R. M. (1958), *Linear Programming and Economic Analysis*, McGraw-Hill Book Co., New York.

Dorn, W. S. (1963), "Non-linear Programming—A Survey," *Management Science*, **9**, pp. 171–208.

Hancock, H. (1917), *Theory of Maxima and Minima*, 1960 ed. Dover Publications, New York.

Hicks, J. R. (1939), *Value and Capital*, Clarendon Press, Oxford, England.

Kuhn, H. W., and Tucker, A. W. (1951), "Nonlinear Programming" *Proceedings of the Second Berkeley Symposium on Mathematical Statistics and Probability*, J. Neyman, Ed., University of California Press, Berkeley, Calif. pp. 481–492.

Samuelson, P. A. (1955), *Foundations of Economic Analysis*, Harvard University Press, Cambridge, Mass.

Vajda, S. (1961), *Mathematical Programming*, Addison-Wesley, Reading, Mass.

Wilde, D. J. (1962), "Differential Calculus in Nonlinear Programming," *Operations Research*, **10**, pp. 764–773.

Exercise 8 is based on

Shubik, M. (1961), "Construction of a Business Game for Teaching and Research Purposes." Cowles Foundation Research Papers No. 115, Part 2A.

CHAPTER NINETEEN

Examples of Optimization Models with Many Variables

The objective function in all the models discussed in this chapter are polynomials of degree 2. Section A is devoted to the representation and optimization of this particular function in matrix form. Section B gives the generalization of the Holt, Modigliani, Muth model to an arbitrary number of time periods. The optimization by substitution and by Lagrange multipliers is illustrated. Section C also contains a generalization of a two-variable model discussed in Chapter 10. In this section, "least squares" curve-fitting theory is developed for n independent variables. This technique is applied in Section D to the Portfolio Selection problem, which is presented as an example of non-linear programming.

A. POLYNOMIALS OF DEGREE TWO

The discussion in Chapter 18 was valid for a general function of n variables. Analysis of some functions of n variables can be quite complex but many applications can be adequately discussed in terms of more elementary functions, such as second-degree polynomials. This section will deal with such functions, and particularly with their representation in matrix form.

Representation in Matrix Form

A general quadratic function of two variables was written in Chapter 9 as:

$$g(x, y) = ax^2 + bxy + cy^2 + dx + ey + f \qquad (1)$$

569

This notation would become cumbersome if it were extended to the case of many variables and it is therefore desirable to introduce a new notation using subscripts and matrices. Let the variables be denoted by x_1 and x_2; then (1) can be written as:

$$g(x_1, x_2) = ax_1^2 + bx_1x_2 + cx_2^2 + dx_1 + ex_2 + f \qquad (2)$$

Further, if the coefficients are relabeled as:

$$a_{11} = a$$
$$a_{12} = a_{21} = \tfrac{1}{2}b$$
$$a_{22} = c \qquad (3)$$
$$b_1 = d$$
$$b_2 = e$$

(2) may be written as

$$g(x_1, x_2) = a_{11}x_1^2 + a_{12}x_1x_2 + a_{21}x_2x_1 + a_{22}x_2^2 + b_1x_1 + b_2x_2 + f \qquad (4)$$

or using the summation notation, as

$$g(x_1, x_2) = \sum_{i=1}^{2} \sum_{j=1}^{2} a_{ij}x_ix_j + \sum_{i=1}^{2} b_ix_i + f \qquad (5)$$

The expression becomes even more compact if matrix notation is used. Let

$$\mathbf{A} = \begin{bmatrix} a_{11} & a_{12} \\ a_{21} & a_{22} \end{bmatrix}; \qquad \mathbf{B} = \begin{bmatrix} b_1 \\ b_2 \end{bmatrix}; \qquad \mathbf{X} = \begin{bmatrix} x_1 \\ x_2 \end{bmatrix} \qquad (6)$$

Then (5) may be written as

$$g(\mathbf{X}) = \mathbf{X}'\mathbf{AX} + \mathbf{B}'\mathbf{X} + f \qquad (7)$$

It should be noted that $\mathbf{A}$ is a symmetric matrix, since by definition

$$a_{12} = a_{21}$$

The obvious advantage of using the notation in (5) or (7) is that the expressions do not change for quadratic functions in 3, 4, or n variables. Only the upper limit of the summation sign changes with n in (5), and only the size of the matrices changes with n in (7). The general polynomial of degree 2 in n variables has the prime form

$$g(x_1, x_2, \ldots, x_n) = \alpha_1'x_1^2 + \cdots + \alpha_n'x_n^2 + \alpha_{12}'x_1x_2 + \cdots$$
$$+ \alpha_{n-1,n}'x_{n-1}x_n + b_1x_1 + \cdots + b_nx_n + f \qquad (8)$$

and can be written

$$= \sum_{i=1}^{n} \sum_{j=1}^{n} a_{ij} x_i x_j + \sum_{i=1}^{n} b_i x_i + f \tag{9}$$

or

$$= X'AX + B'X + f \tag{10}$$

where $a_{ij} = \alpha_i{}'$, $i = j$

$$a_{ij} = \tfrac{1}{2}(\alpha'_{ij} + \alpha'_{ji}) \quad i \neq j \tag{11}$$

Here $\mathbf{A}$ is a symmetric $n \times n$ matrix, $\mathbf{B}$ and $\mathbf{X}$ are column vectors with n elements, and f is a scalar.

Differentiation

The partial derivatives of (4), are

$$\frac{\partial g}{\partial x_1} = 2a_{11}x_1 + a_{12}x_2 + a_{21}x_2 + b_1$$

$$= a_{11}x_1 + a_{12}x_2 + a_{11}x_1 + a_{21}x_2 + b_1 \tag{12}$$

$$\frac{\partial g}{\partial x_2} = a_{12}x_1 + a_{21}x_1 + 2a_{22}x_2 + b_2$$

$$= a_{21}x_1 + a_{22}x_2 + a_{12}x_1 + a_{22}x_2 + b_2$$

The symbol $\dfrac{\partial g(\mathbf{X})}{\partial \mathbf{X}}$ denotes the vector $\begin{bmatrix} \dfrac{\partial g}{\partial x_1} \\ \dfrac{\partial g}{\partial x_2} \end{bmatrix}$; from (12) it can be written in this case as

$$\frac{\partial g(\mathbf{X})}{\partial \mathbf{X}} = AX + A'X + B \tag{13}$$

where $\mathbf{A}$, $\mathbf{X}$, and $\mathbf{B}$ are defined by (6).

Since $\mathbf{A}$ is a symmetric matrix, $\mathbf{A}' = \mathbf{A}$, and (13) reduces to

$$\frac{\partial g(\mathbf{X})}{\partial \mathbf{X}} = 2AX + B \tag{14}$$

These results, (13) and (14), hold for any value of n.

From (9)

$$\frac{\partial g(x_1 \cdots x_n)}{\partial x_k} = \sum_{i \neq k} a_{ik} x_i + \sum_{j \neq k} a_{kj} x_j + 2a_{kk} x_k + b_k \tag{15}$$

The symbol $\partial g(\mathbf{X})/\partial \mathbf{X}$ now denotes the column vector with n elements whose kth element is

$$\frac{\partial g(x_1, \ldots, x_n)}{\partial x_k}$$

then

$$\frac{\partial g(\mathbf{X})}{\partial \mathbf{X}} = \mathbf{AX} + \mathbf{A'X} + \mathbf{B'} \qquad \text{in general} \qquad (16)$$

$$= 2\mathbf{AX} + \mathbf{B} \qquad \text{if } \mathbf{A} \text{ is symmetric} \qquad (17)$$

Optimization

The necessary conditions for a stationary point of the general polynomial of degree two, are that

$$\frac{\partial g(\mathbf{X})}{\partial \mathbf{X}} = 0$$

or from (17)

$$2\mathbf{AX} + \mathbf{B} = 0$$

Hence the stationary point is given by

$$\mathbf{X} = -\tfrac{1}{2}\mathbf{A}^{-1}\mathbf{B} \qquad (18)$$

The second-order conditions depend on Δ. Here

$$\frac{\partial^2 g}{\partial x_k^{\,2}} = 2a_{kk} \qquad \text{and} \qquad \frac{\partial^2 g}{\partial x_k \, \partial x_{k'}} = a_{kk'} \qquad k \neq k'$$

Since

$$a_{kk'} = a_{k'k} \qquad \Delta = 2\mathbf{A}$$

The matrix Δ is identically the matrix $2\mathbf{A}$ and the polynomial has a minimum at the stationary point if all the principal minors of $|\mathbf{A}|$ are positive; and a maximum at the stationary point if the determinant of the principal minors of $|\mathbf{A}|$ are alternately negative and positive.

The existence of a stationary point depends on the existence of $\mathbf{A}^{-1}$ which guarantees that Δ_n will be different from zero.

Example I. In Chapter 9, page 269, it was shown that the polynomial

$$g(x_1, x_2) = x_1^{\,2} - x_1 x_2 + x_2^{\,2} + 2x_1 + 2x_2 - 4$$

has a stationary point at $x_1 = -2$; $x_2 = -2$; and that g has a maximum at this point.

To use the techniques of this section let

$$\mathbf{A} = \begin{bmatrix} 1 & -\frac{1}{2} \\ -\frac{1}{2} & 1 \end{bmatrix}; \quad \mathbf{B} = \begin{bmatrix} 2 \\ 2 \end{bmatrix}; \quad \mathbf{X} = \begin{bmatrix} x_1 \\ x_2 \end{bmatrix}$$

Then, as may be verified by carrying out the matrix operations,

$$g(x_1, x_2) = g(\mathbf{X}) = \mathbf{X'AX} + \mathbf{B'X} - 4$$

and the stationary point is given by

$$\mathbf{X} = -\tfrac{1}{2}\mathbf{A}^{-1}\mathbf{B}$$

$$= -\tfrac{1}{2}\begin{bmatrix} \frac{4}{3} & \frac{2}{3} \\ \frac{2}{3} & \frac{4}{3} \end{bmatrix}\begin{bmatrix} 2 \\ 2 \end{bmatrix} = \begin{bmatrix} -2 \\ -2 \end{bmatrix}$$

Example 2. For the case $n = 2$, the $\mathbf{A}$ and $\mathbf{B}$ matrices are given by (6). The necessary conditions for a stationary point are given by

$$\mathbf{X} = -\tfrac{1}{2}\mathbf{A}^{-1}\mathbf{B}$$

Substituting from (6) gives

$$= -\frac{1}{2(a_{11}a_{22} - a_{12}a_{21})} \begin{bmatrix} a_{22} & -a_{12} \\ -a_{21} & a_{11} \end{bmatrix}\begin{bmatrix} b_1 \\ b_2 \end{bmatrix}$$

$$= -\frac{1}{2(a_{11}a_{22} - a_{12}a_{21})} \begin{bmatrix} a_{22}b_1 - a_{12}b_2 \\ -a_{21}b_1 + a_{11}b_2 \end{bmatrix}$$

Changing back to the original form of the coefficients as defined by (3) gives

$$= -\frac{1}{2[ac - (b^2/4)]} \begin{bmatrix} cd - \dfrac{b}{2}e \\ -\dfrac{1}{2}bd + ae \end{bmatrix}$$

$$= \begin{bmatrix} \dfrac{2cd - be}{b^2 - 4ac} \\ \dfrac{2ae - bd}{b^2 - 4ac} \end{bmatrix}$$

This is the result that was obtained in Example 5, page 272.

Example 3. In Example 1, page 548, it was shown that the polynomial in three variables

$$u(x_1, x_2, x_3) = -x_1{}^2 - x_2{}^2 + x_2x_3 - x_3{}^2 + x_1 + 2x_3$$

has a global maximum at $(\tfrac{1}{2}, \tfrac{2}{3}, \tfrac{4}{3})$

It can be verified that if

$$A = \begin{bmatrix} -1 & 0 & 0 \\ 0 & -1 & \frac{1}{2} \\ 0 & \frac{1}{2} & -1 \end{bmatrix}; \quad B = \begin{bmatrix} 1 \\ 0 \\ 2 \end{bmatrix}; \quad X = \begin{bmatrix} x_1 \\ x_2 \\ x_3 \end{bmatrix}$$

then

$$u(x_1, x_2, x_3) = X'AX + B'X$$

The stationary point is given by

$$X = -\tfrac{1}{2}A^{-1}B = -\tfrac{1}{2}\begin{bmatrix} -1 & 0 & 0 \\ 0 & -\frac{4}{3} & -\frac{2}{3} \\ 0 & -\frac{2}{3} & -\frac{4}{3} \end{bmatrix}\begin{bmatrix} 1 \\ 0 \\ 2 \end{bmatrix} = \begin{bmatrix} \frac{1}{2} \\ \frac{2}{3} \\ \frac{4}{3} \end{bmatrix}$$

as before.

EXERCISES

1. Solve Exercise 1, p. 549, using matrices.
2. Solve Example 1, p. 563, using matrices.

B. HOLT, MODIGLIANI, MUTH MODEL

Matrix Formulation

In Chapter 10, Section A, the Holt, Modigliani, Muth Model was used as an example of a model in which the objective function was a polynomial of second degree in two variables. The variables were the work force w_1 and, the production level, p_1 in a period. The objective was to minimize the total cost for the period. In practice, it is more reasonable to want to minimize the cost for a number of periods, say n. Under these conditions the objective function becomes a quadratic function of $2n$ variables. The optimization of this function can be simplified if matrix notation, as outlined in Section A, is used.

Let $C_i(w_i, p_i)$ denote the cost during the ith period. The objective, then, is to minimize

$$C_n(w_1, w_2, \ldots, w_n, p_1, p_2, \ldots, p_n) = \sum_{i=1}^{n} C_i(w_i, p_i) \tag{1}$$

where

$$C_i(w_i, p_i) = (c_1 - c_6)w_i + c_2(w_i - w_{i-1})^2 + c_3(p_i - c_4w_i)^2$$
$$+ c_5p_i + c_7(z_i - c_8)^2 \tag{2}$$
$$z_i = z_{i-1} + p_i - v_i, \quad i = 1, 2, \ldots, n \tag{3}$$

and where $w_0, z_0, v_1, v_2, \ldots, v_n$ are given. (Note that this notation differs slightly from that used in Chapter 9. Here z_i replaces I_i as the net inventory at the end of period i and v_i replaces R_i as the requirement during period i.)

Expanding (2) gives

$$C_i(w_i, p_i) = (c_1 - c_6)w_i + c_2 w_i^2 - 2c_2 w_i w_{i-1} + c_2 w_{i-1}^2 + c_3 p_i^2 - 2c_3 c_4 p_i w_i$$

$$+ c_3 c_4^2 w_i^2 + c_5 p_i + c_7 z_i^2 - 2c_7 c_8 z_i + c_7 c_8^2$$

Rearranging the terms gives

$$= (c_2 + c_3 c_4^2)w_i^2 - 2c_3 c_4 p_i w_i + c_3 p_i^2 + c_2 w_{i-1}^2 - 2c_2 w_i w_{i-1}$$

$$+ (c_1 - c_6)w_i + c_5 p_i + c_7 z_i^2 - 2c_7 c_8 z_i + c_7 c_8^2 \qquad (4)$$

Substituting C_i into (1) gives an expression for C_n. Using matrix notation, C_n may be written in the form

$$C_n = \sum_{i=1}^{n} C_i(w_i, p_i) = \mathbf{X'AX} + \mathbf{E'X} + \mathbf{Z'BZ} + \mathbf{G'Z} + f \qquad (5)$$

The matrices are defined as follows. Let $\mathbf{A} =$

$$
\begin{bmatrix}
2c_2 + c_3 c_4^2 & -c_3 c_4 & -c_2 & 0 & \cdots & 0 & 0 \\
-c_3 c_4 & c_3 & 0 & 0 & \cdots & 0 & 0 \\
-c_2 & 0 & 2c_2 + c_3 c_4^2 & -c_3 c_4 & \cdots & 0 & 0 \\
0 & 0 & -c_3 c_4 & c_3 & \cdots & 0 & 0 \\
\cdot & \cdot & \cdot & \cdot & & \cdot & \cdot \\
\cdot & \cdot & \cdot & \cdot & \cdots & \cdot & \cdot \\
\cdot & \cdot & \cdot & \cdot & & \cdot & \cdot \\
0 & 0 & 0 & 0 & \cdots & c_2 + c_3 c_4^2 & -c_3 c_4 \\
0 & 0 & 0 & 0 & \cdots & -c_3 c_4 & c_3
\end{bmatrix}
$$

The elements of $\mathbf{A}$ on the diagonal of the even rows and columns are c_3; on the diagonal of the odd rows and columns are $(2c_2 + c_3 c_4^2)$, except for the last one which is $(c_2 + c_3 c_4^2)$. All other elements are zero, except the following: those that stand on the left of or above c_3 which have the value $-c_3 c_4$; the elements on the right of or immediately below the $(-c_3 c_4)$ term which have the value $-c_2$.

$$
X = \begin{bmatrix} w_1 \\ p_1 \\ w_2 \\ p_2 \\ \cdot \\ \cdot \\ \cdot \\ w_n \\ p_n \end{bmatrix} ; \quad
E = \begin{bmatrix} c_1 - c_6 - 2c_2w_0 \\ c_5 \\ c_1 - c_6 \\ c_5 \\ \cdot \\ \cdot \\ \cdot \\ c_1 - c_6 \\ c_5 \end{bmatrix} ; \quad
G = -2c_7c_8 \begin{bmatrix} 1 \\ 1 \\ \cdot \\ \cdot \\ 1 \end{bmatrix} ;
$$

$$
B = c_7[I]; \quad Z = \begin{bmatrix} z_1 \\ \cdot \\ \cdot \\ \cdot \\ \cdot \\ z_n \end{bmatrix}
$$

Here X is $2n \times 1$, E is $2n \times 1$, G is $n \times 1$, B is $n \times n$, Z is $n \times 1$, and A is $2n \times 2n$ and symmetric.

The set of equation (3) can be solved successively by substitution to give

$$
z_1 = p_1 - v_1 + z_0
$$
$$
z_2 = p_2 - v_2 + z_1 = p_1 + p_2 - v_1 - v_2 + z_0
$$
$$
z_3 = p_1 + p_2 + p_3 - v_1 - v_2 - v_3 + z_0 \tag{7}
$$
$$
\cdot
$$
$$
\cdot
$$
$$
\cdot
$$
$$
z_n = \sum_{i=1}^{n} p_i - \sum_{i=1}^{n} v_i + z_0
$$

Let

$$
R = \begin{bmatrix}
0 & 1 & 0 & 0 & \cdots & 0 \\
0 & 1 & 0 & 1 & \cdots & 0 \\
0 & 1 & 0 & 1 & \cdots & 0 \\
\cdot & \cdot & \cdot & \cdot & \cdots & \cdot \\
\cdot & \cdot & \cdot & \cdot & \cdots & \cdot \\
\cdot & \cdot & \cdot & \cdot & \cdots & \cdot \\
0 & 1 & 0 & 1 & \cdots & 1
\end{bmatrix}
$$

and
$$S = -\begin{bmatrix} v_1 - z_0 \\ v_1 + v_2 - z_0 \\ \cdot \\ \cdot \\ \cdot \\ \Sigma\, v_i - z_0 \end{bmatrix} \tag{8}$$

where R is $n \times 2n$ and S is $n \times 1$. Then (7) can be written as

$$Z = RX + S \tag{9}$$

Optimization

The uncontrollable variable Z may be eliminated by substituting (9) into (5) to give

$$C_n = X'AX + E'X + (RX + S)'B(RX + S) + G'(RX + S) + f$$

$$= X'AX + E'X + X'R'BRX + X'R'BS + S'BRX$$
$$+ S'BS + G'RX + G'S + f$$

$$= X'(A + R'BR)X + (E' + 2S'BR + G'R)X + S'BS + G'S + f \tag{10}$$

since

$(RX + S)' = X'R' + S'$ and $X'R'BS = S'B'RX$ because B is symmetric.

$$\frac{\partial C_n}{\partial X} = 2(A + R'BR)X + E + 2R'BS + R'G$$

$$= KX + M \quad \text{since } A + R'BR \text{ is symmetric} \tag{11}$$

where
$$K = 2(A + R'BR) \tag{12}$$

$$M = E + 2R'BS + R'G \tag{13}$$

the stationary point is
$$X^* = -K^{-1}M \tag{14}$$

Example. For the case $n = 1$:

$$C_1(w_1, p_1) = c_1 w_1 + c_2(w_1^2 - 2w_1 w_0 + w_0^2) + c_3(p_1^2 - 2c_4 w_1 p_1 + c_4^2 w_1^2)$$
$$+ c_5 p_1 - c_6 w_1 + c_7(z_1^2 - 2c_8 z_1 + c_8^2)$$

$$= w_1^2(c_2 + c_3 c_4^2) - 2c_3 c_4 w_1 p_1 + p_1^2 c_3 + w_1(c_1 - c_6) + c_5 p_1$$
$$- 2c_2 w_1 w_0 + c_2 w_0^2 + c_7 z_1^2 - 2c_7 c_8 z_1 + c_7 c_8^2 \tag{15}$$

The matrices are:

$$\mathbf{X} = \begin{bmatrix} w_1 \\ p_1 \end{bmatrix} \quad \mathbf{Z} = [z_1] \quad \mathbf{R} = [0 \quad 1] \quad \mathbf{S} = -[v_1 - z_0]$$

$$\mathbf{Z} = \mathbf{RX} + \mathbf{S} = [0 \quad 1]\begin{bmatrix} w_1 \\ p_1 \end{bmatrix} + \{-[v_1 - z_0]\}$$

$$= p_1 - (v_1 - z_0)$$

$$\mathbf{A} = \begin{bmatrix} c_2 + c_3c_4{}^2 & -c_3c_4 \\ -c_3c_4 & +c_3 \end{bmatrix}$$

$$\mathbf{X'AX} = [w_1 \quad p_1]\begin{bmatrix} c_2 + c_3c_4{}^2 & -c_3c_4 \\ -c_3c_4 & +c_3 \end{bmatrix}\begin{bmatrix} w_1 \\ p_1 \end{bmatrix}$$

$$= [w_1(c_2 + c_3c_4{}^2) - p_1c_3c_4 - w_1c_3c_4 + c_3p_1]\begin{bmatrix} w_1 \\ p_1 \end{bmatrix}$$

$$= w_1{}^2(c_2 + c_3c_4{}^2) - w_1p_1c_3c_4 - w_1p_1c_3c_4 + c_3p_1{}^2$$

$$\mathbf{E} = \begin{bmatrix} c_1 - c_6 - 2c_2w_0 \\ c_5 \end{bmatrix}$$

$$\mathbf{E'X} = [c_1 - c_6 - 2c_2w_0 \quad c_5]\begin{bmatrix} w_1 \\ p_1 \end{bmatrix}$$

$$= w_1c_1 - w_1c_6 - 2c_2w_0w_1 + c_5p_1$$

$$\mathbf{G} = [-2c_7c_8] \quad \mathbf{B} = +c_7$$

$$\mathbf{Z'BZ} = z_1(c_7)z_1 = +c_7z_1{}^2$$

$$\mathbf{G'Z} = -2c_7c_8z_1, \quad f = c_2w_0{}^2 + c_7c_8{}^2$$

Hence

$$\mathbf{X'AX} + \mathbf{E'X} + \mathbf{Z'BZ} + \mathbf{G'Z} + f$$

is equivalent to (15).

The stationary point by (14) is given by

$$\mathbf{X^*} = -\mathbf{K}^{-1}\mathbf{M}$$

where

$$\mathbf{K} = 2(\mathbf{A} + \mathbf{R'BR})$$

For this case

$$R'BR = \begin{bmatrix} 0 \\ 1 \end{bmatrix} [c_7][0 \quad 1] = \begin{bmatrix} 0 & 0 \\ 0 & c_7 \end{bmatrix}$$

$$K = 2 \begin{bmatrix} c_2 + c_3 c_4{}^2 & -c_3 c_4 \\ -c_3 c_4 & c_3 + c_7 \end{bmatrix}$$

and

$$M = E + 2R'BS + R'G$$

$$= \begin{bmatrix} c_1 - c_6 - 2c_2 w_0 \\ c_5 \end{bmatrix} + 2 \begin{bmatrix} 0 \\ 1 \end{bmatrix} [c_7][-(v_1 - z_0)] + \begin{bmatrix} 0 \\ 1 \end{bmatrix} [-2c_7 c_8]$$

$$= \begin{bmatrix} c_1 - c_6 - 2c_2 w_0 \\ c_5 - 2c_7(v_1 - z_0) - 2c_7 c_8 \end{bmatrix}$$

Computing $-K^{-1}M$ using numerical values will yield the values given as (7), page 284.

Optimization Using Lagrange Multipliers

The function to be minimized is

$$C_n(X, Z) = X'AX + E'X + Z'BZ + G'Z$$

subject to

$$Z = RX + S$$

Differentiating

$$C_n(X, Z) - \lambda'(Z - RX - S) \tag{16}$$

with respect to X, Z, and λ, where λ is an $n \times 1$ vector of undetermined multipliers, gives the matrix equations

$$E + 2AX + R'\lambda = 0$$

$$G + 2BZ - \lambda = 0 \tag{17}$$

$$S + RX - Z = 0$$

The size of the various matrices may be verified by noting that E is $2n \times 1$, A is $2n \times 2n$, X is $2n \times 1$, R is $n \times 2n$, λ is $n \times 1$, G is $n \times 1$, B is $n \times n$, Z is $n \times 1$, and S is $n \times 1$.

In matrix form the equations (17) may be written as

$$
\begin{bmatrix} 2A & 0 & R' \\ 0 & 2B & -I \\ R & -I & 0 \end{bmatrix} \begin{bmatrix} X \\ Z \\ \lambda \end{bmatrix} = - \begin{bmatrix} E \\ G \\ S \end{bmatrix} \tag{18}
$$

The solution is

$$
\begin{bmatrix} X \\ Z \\ \lambda \end{bmatrix} = - \begin{bmatrix} 2A & 0 & R' \\ 0 & 2B & -I \\ R & -I & 0 \end{bmatrix}^{-1} \begin{bmatrix} E \\ G \\ S \end{bmatrix} \tag{19}
$$

By partitioning the inverse in (19) in the same manner as the matrix in (18), multiplying, equating to the identity matrix also suitably partitioned, and solving gives the inverse in the form

$$
\begin{bmatrix} \frac{1}{2}(A + R'BR)^{-1} & \frac{1}{2}(A + R'BR)^{-1}R' & (A + R'BR)^{-1}R'B \\ R(A + R'BR)^{-1} & \frac{1}{2}R(A + R'BR)^{-1}R' & R(A + R'BR)^{-1}R'B - I \\ BR(A + R'BR)^{-1} & BR(A + R'BR)^{-1}R' - I & 2[BR(A + R'BR)^{-1}R'B - B] \end{bmatrix} \tag{20}
$$

EXERCISES

1. For the model (1) with $n = 2$, compute the matrices K and M (12) and (13), p. 577 by:
   (a) Direct optimization of (1), p. 574.
   (b) Using the definition of A, R, B, E, S, and G.

2. Using (16), (17), (18), (19), and (20), p. 579:
   (a) Verify that the expression for the optimum values of X is identical to that obtained in 1
   (b) Develop an expression for the value of λ in the optimum solution and very briefly state its interpretation.

3. Give the expression for verifying that the minimum values have been obtained in 1 and 2.

C. CURVE FITTING BY LEAST SQUARES

The general theory of curve fitting by least squares can be developed and stated most conveniently in matrix notation. To begin with a simple illustration, consider the example given in Chapter 10, Section B.

A relationship of the form

$$y = a + bx$$

is assumed to hold between the independent variable x and the dependent variable y. Three values have been selected: x_1, x_2, x_3, and the corresponding values of y observed: y_1, y_2, y_3. The values of the unknown parameters that "best" fit the data are those that minimize the squared distance

$$s = \sum_{i=1}^{3} (y_i - a - bx_i)^2$$

To make the notation more symmetrical, let

$$x_{0i} \equiv 1$$

$$x_{1i} = x_i$$

Suppose there are n observations instead of just three, so that $i = 1$, $2, \ldots, n$. Let

$$a = b_0 \quad \text{and} \quad b = b_1$$

and

$$y = b_0 x_0 + b_1 x_1$$

$$s = \sum_{i=1}^{n} (y_i - b_0 x_{0i} - b_1 x_{1i})^2 \tag{1}$$

$$\frac{\partial s}{\partial b_0} = (-2) \sum_{i=1}^{n} x_{0i}(y_i - b_0 x_{0i} - b_1 x_{1i}) \tag{2}$$

$$\frac{\partial s}{\partial b_1} = (-2) \sum_{i=1}^{n} x_{1i}(y_i - b_0 x_{0i} - b_1 x_{1i}) \tag{3}$$

Setting the derivatives equal to zero and rearranging terms gives

$$b_0 \sum x_{0i}^2 + b_1 \sum x_{0i}x_{1i} = \sum x_{0i}y_i \tag{4}$$

$$b_0 \sum x_{0i}x_{1i} + b_1 \sum x_{1i}^2 = \sum x_{1i}y_i \tag{5}$$

These two linear equations in two unknowns b_0 and b_1 can be solved and the solutions are

$$\hat{b}_0 = \frac{1}{n} [\sum y_i - \hat{b}_1 \sum x_{1i}]$$

$$\hat{b}_1 = \frac{n \sum x_{1i}y_i - (\sum x_{1i})(\sum y_i)}{n \sum x_{1i}^2 - (\sum x_{1i})^2} \tag{6}$$

To express these results in matrix notation, let $\mathbf{X}$ denote the matrix of values of the independent variables in which the observations on one variable are given in successive columns in one row and there is one row for each variable. Then for the case considered in the example,

$$\mathbf{X} = \begin{bmatrix} x_{01} & x_{02} & \cdots & x_{0n} \\ x_{11} & x_{12} & & x_{1n} \end{bmatrix} = \begin{bmatrix} 1 & 1 & \cdots & 1 \\ x_{11} & x_{12} & & x_{1n} \end{bmatrix}$$

$\mathbf{X}$ is a $2 \times n$ matrix. Similarly, let

$$\mathbf{Y} = \begin{bmatrix} y_1 \\ \cdot \\ \cdot \\ \cdot \\ y_n \end{bmatrix} \quad \text{and} \quad \mathbf{B} = \begin{bmatrix} b_0 \\ b_1 \end{bmatrix}$$

Then

$$(y_i - b_0 x_{0i} + b_1 x_{1i}) \qquad i = 1, \ldots, n$$

may be written as

$$\mathbf{Y} - \mathbf{X'B}$$

which is an $n \times 1$ matrix
and then

$$s = (\mathbf{Y} - \mathbf{X'B})'(\mathbf{Y} - \mathbf{X'B}) \qquad (7)$$

Note that s is a polynomial of degree 2 in two variables b_0 and b_1; the values of all x_{0i}, x_{1i}, and y_i are known.

Expanding gives

$$s = (\mathbf{Y} - \mathbf{X'B})'(\mathbf{Y} - \mathbf{X'B})$$
$$= (\mathbf{Y'} - \mathbf{B'X})(\mathbf{Y} - \mathbf{X'B})$$
$$= \mathbf{Y'Y} - \mathbf{Y'X'B} - \mathbf{B'XY} + \mathbf{B'XX'B}$$
$$= \mathbf{B'XX'B} - 2\mathbf{Y'X'B} + \mathbf{Y'Y} \qquad (8)$$

Here $\mathbf{X'X}$ is a symmetric matrix, and from (14, Section A)

$$\frac{\partial s}{\partial \mathbf{B}} = 2\mathbf{XX'B} - 2\mathbf{XY}$$

$$0 = \mathbf{XX'\hat{B}} - \mathbf{XY}$$

Therefore,

$$\hat{\mathbf{B}} = (\mathbf{XX'})^{-1}\mathbf{XY} \qquad (9)$$

where $\hat{\mathbf{B}}$ denotes the value of $\mathbf{B}$ which minimizes s.

Substituting (9) into (8), the minimum value of s is given by

$$s = \hat{\mathbf{B}}'\mathbf{XX'\hat{B}} - 2\mathbf{Y'X'\hat{B}} + \mathbf{Y'Y}$$
$$= \hat{\mathbf{B}}'(\mathbf{XX'})(\mathbf{XX'})^{-1}\mathbf{XY} - 2\mathbf{Y'X'\hat{B}} + \mathbf{Y'Y}$$
$$= \mathbf{Y'Y} - \mathbf{Y'X'\hat{B}} \qquad (10)$$

The fact that a minimum has been obtained is verified by computing the second derivatives

$$\frac{\partial^2 s}{\partial b_0{}^2} = +2 \Sigma\, x_{0i}^2; \quad \frac{\partial^2 s}{\partial b_0 \partial b_1} = \Sigma\, x_{0i} x_{1i}; \quad \frac{\partial^2 s}{\partial b_1{}^2} = 2 \Sigma\, x_{1i}^2$$

and noting that

$$2\Sigma\, x_{0i}^2 > 0 \quad \text{and} \quad \begin{vmatrix} 2\Sigma\, x_{0i}^2 & \Sigma\, x_{0i} x_{1i} \\ \Sigma\, x_{0i} x_{1i} & 2\Sigma\, x_{1i}^2 \end{vmatrix} > 0$$

The results given above for the case of one independent variable can be generalized immediately to the case of m independent variables. The number of observations is still denoted by n. In this case:

$\mathbf{X}$ is an $m + 1 \times n$ matrix

$\mathbf{Y}$ is an $n \times 1$ matrix

$\mathbf{B}$ is an $m + 1 \times 1$ matrix

$\mathbf{XX}'$ is a symmetric $m + 1 \times m + 1$ matrix

$\mathbf{XY}$ is an $m + 1 \times 1$ matrix

and again

$$s = (\mathbf{Y} - \mathbf{X}'\mathbf{B})'(\mathbf{Y} - \mathbf{X}'\mathbf{B}) \tag{11}$$

$$\frac{1}{2}\frac{\partial s}{d\mathbf{B}} = \mathbf{X}'\mathbf{XB} - \mathbf{XY}$$

$$\hat{\mathbf{B}} = [\mathbf{XX}']^{-1}\mathbf{XY} \tag{12}$$

and the conditions for a minimum are satisfied.

EXERCISES

1. Verify that, for the example considered above,

$$\mathbf{XX}' = \begin{bmatrix} n & \Sigma\, x_{1i} \\ \Sigma\, x_{1i} & \Sigma\, x_{1i}^2 \end{bmatrix}$$

$$[\mathbf{XX}']^{-1} = \begin{bmatrix} \dfrac{\Sigma x_{1i}^2}{n \Sigma x_{1i}^2 - (\Sigma x_{1i})^2} & -\dfrac{\Sigma x_{1i}}{n \Sigma x_{1i}^2 - (\Sigma x_{1i})^2} \\ -\dfrac{\Sigma x_{1i}}{n \Sigma x_{1i}^2 - (\Sigma x_{1i})^2} & \dfrac{n}{n \Sigma x_{1i}^2 - (\Sigma x_{1i})^2} \end{bmatrix}$$

$$\mathbf{XY} = \begin{bmatrix} \Sigma y_i \\ \Sigma x_{1i} y_i \end{bmatrix}$$

and hence verify Equation (6).

2. Develop the formula of $\hat{\mathbf{B}}$ for the case where

$$\sum_{j=1}^{m} b_j = 1$$

3. Verify the example p. 286, using (9) and (10).

D. PORTFOLIO SELECTION

An investor has an amount which he wishes to invest. There are available n activities in which he may invest any amount. The returns (interest, dividend, etc.) from the activities differ; some consistently pay a reasonable return, other fluctuate widely. Data are available for the past m periods. Let a_{ij} denote the return per dollar invested in the jth activity in the ith period $(i = 1, \ldots m; \; j = 1, \ldots n)$. The investor wishes to invest his money in the various activities in such amounts as to achieve at least a certain rate of return, r, and he wishes to minimize the deviation of his actual return from r. This problem can be formulated as an optimization problem, if there are no constraints other than that all money must be invested, if the total amount invested in certain sets of activities must be equal to predetermined constants, or if these conditions are stated as inequalities.

Assume that conditions do not change; that is, on the average the pattern of returns that existed in the past can be expected to continue.

Solution. Let z_j denote the proportion to be invested in the jth activity $(j = 1, \ldots n)$. Then

$$\sum_{j=1}^{n} z_j = 1 \tag{1}$$

The average yield of the jth activity is

$$\bar{a}_j = \frac{1}{m} \sum_{i=1}^{m} a_{ij} \tag{2}$$

and the yield for any values $z_1, z_2, \ldots z_n$ for year i is given by

$$x_i = \sum_{j=1}^{n} a_{ij} z_j$$

and the average or expected yield is

$$x = \frac{1}{m} \sum_{i=1}^{m} x_i = \sum_{i=1}^{m} \frac{1}{m} \sum_{j=1}^{n} a_{ij} z_j = \sum_{j=1}^{n} (\bar{a}_j)(z_j) \tag{3}$$

The expected yield must equal or exceed the desired rate of return. This may be expressed as:

$$x \geq r \quad \text{or} \quad \bar{\mathbf{A}}'\mathbf{Z} \geq r$$

where

$$\bar{\mathbf{A}} = \begin{bmatrix} \bar{a}_1 \\ \bar{a}_2 \\ \cdot \\ \cdot \\ \cdot \\ \bar{a}_n \end{bmatrix} \quad \text{and} \quad \mathbf{Z} = \begin{bmatrix} z_1 \\ z_2 \\ \cdot \\ \cdot \\ \cdot \\ z_n \end{bmatrix}$$

The deviation is usually defined as the least squares deviation over the m years divided by $m - 1$:

$$v = \frac{1}{m-1} \sum_{i=1}^{m} (x_i - x)^2 \tag{4}$$

Substituting

$$x_i = \sum_{j=1}^{n} a_{ij} z_j, \quad x = \sum_{j=1}^{n} \bar{a}_j z_j$$

$$v = \frac{1}{m-1} \sum_{i=1}^{m} \left(\sum_{j=1}^{n} (a_{ij} - \bar{a}_j) z_j \right)^2$$

Let $a_{ij} - \bar{a}_j = b_{ij}$, then

$$v = \frac{1}{m-1} \sum_{i=1}^{m} \left(\sum_{j=1}^{n} b_{ij} z_j \right)^2$$

expanding

$$v = \frac{1}{m-1} \sum_{i=1}^{m} (b_{i1} z_1 + b_{i2} z_2 + \cdots + b_{in} z_n)^2$$

and

$$v = \frac{1}{m-1} \sum_{i=1}^{m} (b_{i1} b_{i1} z_1^2 + 2 b_{i1} b_{i2} z_1 z_2 + \cdots + 2 b_{i1} b_{in} z_1 z_n + \cdots + b_{in} b_{in} z_n^2)$$

but since the terms z_j do not depend on i,

$$v = \frac{1}{m-1} \left[z_1^2 \sum_{i=1}^{m} b_{i1} b_{i1} + 2 z_1 z_2 \sum_{i=1}^{m} b_{i1} b_{i2} + \cdots + z_n^2 \sum_{i=1}^{m} b_{in} b_{in} \right]$$

let

$$\frac{1}{m-1} \sum_{k=1}^{m} b_{ki} b_{kj} = c_{ij}$$

Then

$$v = c_{11} z_1^2 + 2 c_{12} z_1 z_2 + \cdots + c_{nn} z_n^2$$

which is just $\mathbf{Z'CZ}$ where

$$C = \begin{bmatrix} c_{11} & \cdots & c_{1n} \\ \cdot & & \cdot \\ \cdot & & \cdot \\ \cdot & & \cdot \\ c_{n1} & \cdots & c_{nn} \end{bmatrix}$$

Let $\mathbf{1'} = [1, 1 \cdots 1]$. If all the money must be invested and the desired rate of return is temporarily disregarded, the problem may be stated as:

$$\text{minimize } \mathbf{Z'CZ} \qquad \text{subject to } \mathbf{1'Z} = 1$$

Let λ be a Lagrange multiplier; the problem then is to minimize

$$\mathbf{Z'CZ} + \lambda(\mathbf{1'Z} - 1)$$

The feasible region is defined by $\mathbf{Z} \geq 0$, i.e., all elements of Z must be non-negative.

The general solution is

$$\mathbf{Z^*} = -\tfrac{1}{2}\lambda\mathbf{C^{-1}1}$$

If $\mathbf{Z^*} \geq 0$ and $\mathbf{\bar{A}Z^*} \geq r$, the optimum solution has been obtained. If not, the problem must be solved as a non-linear programming problem in which the objective function is quadratic and the constraints are linear. The statement of the general problem is:

minimize $\mathbf{Z'CZ}$

subject to $\mathbf{1\,Z} \leq 1$

                      $\mathbf{\bar{A}'Z} \geq r$

                      $\mathbf{Z} \geq 0$

The use of the Kuhn-Tucker conditions to solve a simple problem is illustrated in the following example.

Example I.   An investor has \$100 which he wishes to invest. He has narrowed the alternatives to three: a savings account, preferred stock in the Stable State Utility Company, and listed common stock in the National Motors Company. The current dividend yields are 3.3%, 4.0%, and 4.8% for Stable Company, National Company, and savings account, respectively. Both stocks have appreciated in the past and are expected to do so in the future. From an extrapolation of average prices in past years, the investor expects 10% return in dividends and capital appreciation from State stock and 24.7% from National stock.

If all the money is invested in a savings account, the yield will be 4.8%; if all money is invested in National stock, the expected yield will be 24.7%;

and if portions of the money are invested in two or all three alternatives, the expected yield will be somewhere between 4.8% and 24.7%. Stock prices fluctuate and any investment in stock carries some risk. The investor is naturally interested in minimizing his risk. The minimum risk occurs when all the money is invested in the savings bank and the maximum risk occurs when all the money is invested in National Stock. In general, the higher the return, the higher the risk. A given return, say, 10%, however, can be obtained by different investments. Investing all the money in State stock will yield 10%, and so will investing approximately 75% in a savings account and the remainder in National stock. Which alternative has the minimum risk?

Let j denote the alternative investments:

$$j = 1 \text{ for State stock}$$

$$j = 2 \text{ for National stock}$$

$$j = 3 \text{ for savings account}$$

$$z_j = \text{proportion of funds invested in security } j$$

and let a_j denote the expected return from the jth investment per dollar of investment. The total return per dollar of investment is

$$x = a_1 z_1 + a_2 z_2 + a_3 z_3$$

Let r = desired yield and let the risk be defined as the expected value of the square of the difference between desired yield and actual yield:

$$\text{Risk} = \text{Expected value of } \{(x - r)^2\}$$

The risk will be estimated by extrapolating from the past. Let

a_{ij} = return that would have been obtained per dollar
of investment for year i from investment j.

The return for the past six years are given in the accompanying table.

Year	i	$j =$	Investment State Co. 1	National Co. 2	Savings Account 3
1957	1		6.4	14.5	4.8
1958	2		6.0	21.8	4.8
1959	3		12.2	17.1	4.8
1960	4		12.6	29.1	4.8
1961	5		10.7	32.2	4.8
1962	6		12.0	33.3	4.8
average			10.0	24.7	4.8

For any set of values of z_1, z_2, z_3 the return from (2) in year i would have been:

$$x_i = a_{i1}z_1 + a_{i2}z_2 + a_{i3}z_3 = \sum_{j=1}^{3} a_{ij}z_j$$

and the average return from (3) would have been:

$$x = \frac{1}{6}\sum_{i=1}^{6} x_i = \frac{1}{6}\sum_{i=1}^{6}\sum_{j=1}^{3} a_{ij}z_j = \sum_{j=1}^{3}\left(\frac{1}{6}\sum_{i=1}^{6} a_{ij}\right)z_j = \sum_{j=1}^{3} \bar{a}_j z_j$$

$\bar{a}_j$ is the average return from investment j; let $b_{ij} = a_{ij} - \bar{a}_j$.
From (4) the risk is

$$\text{Risk} = v = \frac{1}{5}\sum_{i=1}^{6}(x_i - x)^2$$

$$= \frac{1}{5}\sum_{i=1}^{6}\left\{\sum_{j=1}^{3} a_{ij}z_j - \sum_{j=1}^{3}\bar{a}_j z_j\right\}^2 = \frac{1}{5}\sum_{i=1}^{6}\left\{\sum_{j=1}^{3} b_{ij}z_j\right\}^2$$

$$= \frac{1}{5}\sum_{i=1}^{6}(b_{i1}z_1 + b_{i2}z_2 + b_{i3}z_3)^2$$

$$= \frac{1}{5}\sum_{i=1}^{6}\{b_{i1}^2 z_1^2 + 2b_{i1}b_{i2}z_1 z_2 + 2b_{i1}b_{i3}z_1 z_3 + b_{i2}^2 z_2^2$$

$$+ 2b_{i2}b_{i3}z_2 z_3 + b_{i3}^2 z_3^2\}$$

$$= \sum_{k=1}^{3}\sum_{j=1}^{3} z_k z_j c_{kj} \quad \text{where} \quad c_{kj} = \frac{1}{5}\sum_{r=1}^{6} b_{kr}b_{rj}$$

The computation of the c_{kj} is given in the following table.

		b_{ij}			b_{ii}^2			b_{12}
j		1	2	3	1	2	3	
i	$\bar{a}_j$	10.0	24.7	4.8				
1		−3.6	−10.2	0	12.96	104.04	0	36.72
2		−4.0	−2.9	0	16.00	8.41	0	11.60
3		+2.2	−7.6	0	4.84	57.76	0	−16.72
4		+2.6	+4.4	0	6.76	19.36	0	11.44
5		+0.7	+7.5	0	0.49	56.25	0	5.25
6		+2.0	+8.6	0	4.00	73.96	0	17.20
					45.05	319.78	0	65.49

$$c_{11} = \frac{45}{5} = 9; \quad c_{22} = \frac{320}{5} = 64; \quad c_{12} = \frac{65.5}{5} = 13.1$$

The problem can be stated as:

minimize $\quad v = \sum_{k=1}^{3} \sum_{j=1}^{3} z_k z_j c_{kj} = 9z_1{}^2 + 26.2z_1z_2 + 64z_2{}^2$

subject to $\quad\quad\quad\quad \sum_{j=1}^{3} \bar{a}_j z_j \geq r$

and $\quad\quad\quad\quad\quad\quad \sum_{j=1}^{3} z_j \leq 1.00$

$$z_i \geq 0$$

The first restriction states that the expected return is to be at least r, the second states that no more than 100% of the money is to be invested, and the third states that the proportions invested cannot be negative.

Suppose the investor wishes to keep at least 10% of his money in the savings account, but at the same time he wants an average return of 10% with minimum risk. Then the problem is:

minimize $\quad\quad\quad v = 9z_1{}^2 + 26.2z_1z_2 + 64z_2{}^2$

subject to $\quad\quad\quad\quad\quad z_1 + z_2 + z_3 \leq 1$

$$z_3 \geq 0.1$$

$$10z_1 + 24.7z_2 + 4.8z_3 \geq 10$$

$$z_i \geq 0$$

The mathematical programming formulation is:

maximize $\quad\quad\quad h = -v - \lambda_1 g_1 - \lambda_2 g_2 - \lambda_3 g_3$

where $\quad\quad\quad\quad\quad g_1 = z_1 + z_2 + z_3 - 1$

$$g_2 = 0.1 - z_3$$

$$g_3 = 10 - 10z_1 - 24.7z_2 - 4.8z_3$$

The necessary conditions are:

(a) $\quad \dfrac{\partial h}{\partial z_i} = h_i \leq 0 \quad\quad h_1 = -18z_1 - 26.2z_2 - \lambda_1 + 10\lambda_3$

$$h_2 = -26.2z_1 - 128z_2 - \lambda_1 + 24.7\lambda_3$$

$$h_3 = \quad\quad\quad\quad\quad\quad - \lambda_1 + \lambda_2 + 4.8\lambda_3$$

(b) $\quad\quad\quad\quad\quad\quad \Sigma h_i z_i = 0$

(c) $\quad\quad\quad\quad\quad\quad \lambda_i g_i = 0$

(d) $\quad\quad\quad\quad\quad\quad \lambda_i \geq 0$

There are initially eight cases that must be examined, since each of the λ's may be equal to or different from zero. Suppose, for example,

$$\lambda_1 \neq 0; \qquad \lambda_2 = 0; \qquad \lambda_3 \neq 0$$

Then
$$g_1 = 0 \qquad z_1 + \quad z_2 + \quad z_3 = 1$$
$$g_3 = 0 \qquad 10z_1 + 24.7z_2 + 4.8z_3 = 10$$

This is a set of two linear equations in three unknowns and does not have a unique solution.

From (b), either $h_i = 0$ or $z_i = 0$. Since z_3 must be greater than 0.1, h_3 must be zero and since $\lambda_2 = 0$ for the case being considered,

$$\lambda_1 = 4.8\lambda_3$$

Substituting for λ_1 in h_1 and h_2 gives

$$H_1 = -18z_1 - 26.2z_2 + 5.2\lambda_3$$

$$H_2 = -26.2z_1 - 128z_2 + 19.5\lambda_3$$

If it is now assumed further that $z_1 \neq 0$ and $z_2 \neq 0$, then $h_1 = 0$ and $h_2 = 0$. This is a set of four equations in four unknowns: $g_1 = 0$; $g_3 = 0$; $H_1 = 0$; $H_2 = 0$. The solution to this set is $z_1 = 0.145$, $z_2 = 0.222$, $z_3 = 0.633$, $\lambda_3 = 1.62$. This solution is feasible and satisfies all the necessary conditions. The functions $-v$ and g_i are concave; hence the solution is a global maximum.

Complete enumeration in this example would require examination of 64 cases (each of the λ's may be zero or not zero and each of the h's may be zero or not zero). Since the h_i are linear, it is possible to develop an algorithm suitable for computation.. (See Markowitz, 1959.)

EXERCISES

Determine the optimum in Example 1 for the following cases:
1. Minimum v subject to a yield ≥ 0.10 and $\Sigma z_i \leq 1$
2. Minimum v subject to a yield ≥ 0.20 and $\Sigma z_i \leq 1$
3. Minimum v subject to a yield $\geq r$ $(0.048 < r < 0.247)$ and $\Sigma z_i \leq 1$

Notes and References

Section B

See Notes and References, Chapter 10 and Chapter 16, Section D, for references to the Holt, Modigliani, Muth model. The development in this section is based on:
van de Panne, C., and Averink, G. J. A. (1961), "Imperfect management decisions and predictions and their financial implications in dynamic quadratic cost minimization," *Statsitica Neerlandica*, **15**, pp. 293–318.

Section D

For a complete discussion of the Portfolio Selection Model see:

Markowitz, H. (1952), "Portfolio Selection," *Journal of Finance*. **VII**, 77–91.

Markowitz, H. (1956), "The Optimization of a Quadratic Function Subject to Linear Constraints," Naval Research Logistics Quarterly, **III**, 111–133.

Markowitz, H. (1959), *Portfolio Selection: Efficient Diversification of Investment*, John Wiley and Sons, New York.

For an empirical analysis, see:

Farrar, D. E. (1962), *The Investment Decision Under Uncertainty*, Prentice-Hall, Englewood Cliffs, N.J.

CHAPTER TWENTY

Quadratic Forms

The proof of the sufficient conditions for local maxima and minima given in Chapter 18 rests on certain properties of polynomials of degree two. Furthermore, the examples in Chapter 19 have illustrated the practical importance of this class of functions in business models. It is therefore worthwhile to investigate them in more detail.

The first section in this chapter shows how linear transformations can be used to reduce a polynomial of degree two, first into *quadratic forms* and then into a *sum of squares*. The second section is devoted to the conditions under which a quadratic form will be positive (or negative) for all values of the arguments except **0**. In Section C these conditions are then applied to proving the sufficient conditions for local extrema.

A. TRANSFORMATIONS OF POLYNOMIALS OF DEGREE TWO

Linear Transformations

The techniques described in Chapter 18 provide a convenient method for determining the extreme values of a second degree polynomial. However, it is frequently helpful to determine the geometric form of the function or to compute contour lines in two dimensions. This problem is considered in analytic geometry for polynomials of second degree in two variables. The equation obtained setting a general second degree polynomial in two variables to zero

$$ax_1^2 + bx_1x_2 + cx_2^2 + dx_1 + ex_2 + f = 0 \qquad (1)$$

is reduced to a standard form

$$a''z_1{}^2 + c''z_2{}^2 + f'' = 0 \tag{2}$$

or to a degenerate version of this form in which one or both variables appears to the first power. The reduction is performed in two steps:

(a) The coefficient of the x_1x_2 term in (1) is made zero by a change to a new set of variables, y_1, y_2 given by the equations

$$x_1 = y_1 \cos \theta - y_2 \sin \theta$$
$$\tag{3}$$
$$x_2 = y_1 \sin \theta + y_2 \cos \theta$$

where θ is determined by the formula $\tan 2\theta = b/(a - c)$. After substituting (3) into (1), and collecting terms, (1) becomes

$$a'y_1{}^2 + c'y_2{}^2 + d'y_1 + e'y_2 + f' = 0 \tag{4}$$

(b) The coefficients of the linear terms are then made zero by a change to a new set of variables z_1, z_2 given by the equations

$$y_1 = z_1 - \frac{d'}{2a'}$$
$$\tag{5}$$
$$y_2 = z_2 - \frac{e'}{2c'}$$

The equation (2) or a degenerate case is obtained by substituting (5) in (4).

The values of a'', c'', and f'' are used to determine whether the contour lines are ellipses, hyperbolas, parabolas or imaginary.

Each of the two steps involves a *transformation*: a change from one set of variables to another. The transformations used above are special cases of linear transformations; each of the original variables is a linear function of the new variables. A linear transformation of variables $x_1, x_2, \ldots, x_n$ to another set of variables $y_1, y_2, \ldots, y_n$ is given by

$$x_1 = p_{11}y_1 + p_{12}y_2 + \cdots + p_{1n}y_n$$
$$\vdots$$
$$\tag{6}$$
$$x_n = p_{n1}y_1 + p_{n2}y_n + \cdots + p_{nn}y_n$$

This transformation can be represented as a matrix equation; if

$$\mathbf{X} = \begin{bmatrix} x_1 \\ \cdot \\ \cdot \\ \cdot \\ x_n \end{bmatrix} \qquad \mathbf{Y} = \begin{bmatrix} y_1 \\ \cdot \\ \cdot \\ \cdot \\ y_n \end{bmatrix} \qquad \text{and} \qquad \mathbf{P} = \begin{bmatrix} p_{11} & \cdots & p_{1n} \\ \cdot & & \cdot \\ \cdot & & \cdot \\ \cdot & & \cdot \\ p_{n1} & & p_{nn} \end{bmatrix}$$

then (6) can be written as

$$\mathbf{X} = \mathbf{PY} \tag{7}$$

Further, if $|\mathbf{P}| \neq 0$, then

$$\mathbf{Y} = \mathbf{P^{-1}X} \tag{8}$$

and, therefore, there is a unique inverse transformation which expresses the new variables, $\mathbf{Y}$, as linear functions of the original variables, $\mathbf{X}$. Transformations for which this is not true, i.e., which are not reversible, are of limited practical importance and this section will be limited to transformations in which $|\mathbf{P}| \neq 0$. From (7) and (8) it follows that any linear transformation of one set of n variables into another set of n variables is completely determined by its non-singular n by n matrix $\mathbf{P}$, and conversely, each such matrix, represents a linear transformation.

The direction of the transformation ($\mathbf{Y}$ to $\mathbf{X}$ or $\mathbf{X}$ to $\mathbf{Y}$) which is most convenient depends on the intended use. For reducing the polynomial, it is most convenient to have the old variables, x_1, x_2, expressed as functions of the new variables, y_1 and y_2, as in (6). These functions can be substituted directly into the polynomial to obtain a reduced form. However, if a value of the new variable which corresponds to a particular set of values of the old variables is required, then the form given by (8) is more convenient.

The second transformation used above in (5) is also a linear transformation. This form can also be represented by a matrix equation; let

$$\mathbf{K_1} = \begin{bmatrix} k_1 \\ \cdot \\ \cdot \\ \cdot \\ k_n \end{bmatrix} \tag{9}$$

Then

$$\mathbf{Y} = \mathbf{Z} + \mathbf{K_1} \tag{10}$$

is a *translation* from the variables $y_1, \ldots, y_n$ to $z_1, \ldots, z_n$.

The value of $\mathbf{Y}$ from (10) can be substituted into (7) to give

$$\mathbf{X} = \mathbf{P(Z + K_1)} = \mathbf{PZ + PK_1} = \mathbf{PZ + K}$$

where $\mathbf{K} = \mathbf{PK_1}$.

A general linear transformation which combines (7) and (10) is:

$$X = PZ + K \tag{11}$$

The general quadratic form in n variables can be expressed in the form

$$g(X) = X'AX + B'X + f \tag{12}$$

in which A is a symmetric matrix. If the variables are transformed by (11).

$$g_1(Z) = (PZ + K)'A(PZ + K) + B'(PZ + K) + f$$
$$= (Z'P' + K')(APZ + AK) + B'PZ + B'K + f$$
$$= Z'P'APZ + Z'P'AK + K'APZ + K'AK + B'PZ + B'K + f$$

$Z'P'AK$ is a scalar because Z and K are both column vectors, and the transpose of a scalar is the scalar itself. Hence

$$Z'P'AK = K'A'PZ = K'APZ$$

since A is symmetric and

$$g_1(Z) = Z'P'APZ + (2K'AP + B'P)Z + K'AK + B'K + f \tag{13}$$

$g_1(Z)$ is a polynomial of degree 2 with the matrix $P'AP$ replacing the A matrix, $2K'AP + B'P$ replacing the B' vector and $K'AK + B'K + f$ replacing f. Before reducing $g_1(Z)$ the method will be illustrated by an example.

Example I. The polynomial

$$f(x_1, x_2) = 3x_1{}^2 + \sqrt{3}\,x_1x_2 + 2x_2{}^2 + x_1 - x_2 + 6$$

can be reduced to

$$f_2(z_1, z_2) = \frac{7}{2}z_1{}^2 + \frac{3}{2}z_2{}^2 + \left(6 - \frac{5 + \sqrt{3}}{21}\right)$$

by the transformations

$$x_1 = \frac{\sqrt{3}}{2}\,y_1 - \frac{1}{2}\,y_2 \qquad x_2 = \frac{1}{2}\,y_1 + \frac{\sqrt{3}}{2}\,y_2 \tag{14}$$

and

$$y_1 = z_1 + \frac{1 - \sqrt{3}}{14} \qquad y_2 = z_2 + \frac{1 + \sqrt{3}}{6} \tag{15}$$

If

$$A = \begin{bmatrix} 3 & \dfrac{\sqrt{3}}{2} \\ \dfrac{\sqrt{3}}{2} & 2 \end{bmatrix}; \qquad B = \begin{bmatrix} 1 \\ -1 \end{bmatrix}; \qquad X = \begin{bmatrix} x_1 \\ x_2 \end{bmatrix}$$

then f may be written as

$$f(\mathbf{X}) = \mathbf{X}'\mathbf{AX} + \mathbf{B}'\mathbf{X} + 6$$

Here

$$\mathbf{P} = \begin{bmatrix} \dfrac{\sqrt{3}}{2} & -\dfrac{1}{2} \\ \dfrac{1}{2} & \dfrac{\sqrt{3}}{2} \end{bmatrix} \text{ from (14) and } \mathbf{K}_1 = \begin{bmatrix} \dfrac{1-\sqrt{3}}{14} \\ \dfrac{1+\sqrt{3}}{6} \end{bmatrix} \text{ from (15)}$$

$$\mathbf{K} = \mathbf{PK}_1 = \begin{bmatrix} \dfrac{\sqrt{3}}{2} & -\dfrac{1}{2} \\ \dfrac{1}{2} & \dfrac{\sqrt{3}}{2} \end{bmatrix} \begin{bmatrix} \dfrac{1-\sqrt{3}}{14} \\ \dfrac{1+\sqrt{3}}{6} \end{bmatrix} = \begin{bmatrix} -\dfrac{4+\sqrt{3}}{21} \\ \dfrac{6+\sqrt{3}}{21} \end{bmatrix}$$

$$\mathbf{P}'\mathbf{AP} = \begin{bmatrix} \dfrac{\sqrt{3}}{2} & \dfrac{1}{2} \\ -\dfrac{1}{2} & \dfrac{\sqrt{3}}{2} \end{bmatrix} \begin{bmatrix} 3 & \dfrac{\sqrt{3}}{2} \\ \dfrac{\sqrt{3}}{2} & 2 \end{bmatrix} \begin{bmatrix} \dfrac{\sqrt{3}}{2} & -\dfrac{1}{2} \\ \dfrac{1}{2} & \dfrac{\sqrt{3}}{2} \end{bmatrix} = \begin{bmatrix} \dfrac{7}{2} & 0 \\ 0 & \dfrac{3}{2} \end{bmatrix} \qquad (16)$$

$$2\mathbf{K}'\mathbf{AP} + \mathbf{B}'\mathbf{P} = 2\begin{bmatrix} -\dfrac{4+\sqrt{3}}{21} & \dfrac{6+\sqrt{3}}{21} \end{bmatrix} \begin{bmatrix} 3 & \dfrac{\sqrt{3}}{2} \\ \dfrac{\sqrt{3}}{2} & 2 \end{bmatrix} \begin{bmatrix} \dfrac{\sqrt{3}}{2} & -\dfrac{1}{2} \\ \dfrac{1}{2} & \dfrac{\sqrt{3}}{2} \end{bmatrix}$$

$$+ \begin{bmatrix} 1 & -1 \end{bmatrix} \begin{bmatrix} \dfrac{\sqrt{3}}{2} & -\dfrac{1}{2} \\ \dfrac{1}{2} & \dfrac{\sqrt{3}}{2} \end{bmatrix} = \begin{bmatrix} 0 & 0 \end{bmatrix} \qquad (17)$$

$$\mathbf{K}'\mathbf{AK} + \mathbf{B}'\mathbf{K} + 6 = \left[\begin{bmatrix} \dfrac{-4-\sqrt{3}}{21} & \dfrac{6+\sqrt{3}}{21} \end{bmatrix} \begin{bmatrix} 3 & \dfrac{\sqrt{3}}{2} \\ \dfrac{\sqrt{3}}{2} & 2 \end{bmatrix} + \begin{bmatrix} 1 & -1 \end{bmatrix} \right]$$

$$\times \begin{bmatrix} \dfrac{-4-\sqrt{3}}{21} \\ \dfrac{6+\sqrt{3}}{21} \end{bmatrix} + 6 = 6 - \dfrac{5+\sqrt{3}}{21}$$

and hence

$$f_2(z_1, z_2) = \frac{7}{2} z_1^2 + \frac{3}{2} z_2^2 + 6 - \frac{5 + \sqrt{3}}{21}$$

In the above example the polynomial was reduced to a sum of squares by the transformation

$$\mathbf{Z} = \mathbf{PX} + \mathbf{K}$$

The coefficients of all linear terms in the z's are zeros because, from (17), $\mathbf{P}$ and $\mathbf{K}'$ were such that

$$2\mathbf{K}'\mathbf{AP} + \mathbf{B}'\mathbf{P} = 0$$

Furthermore, the coefficients of the cross product terms $z_i z_j$ with $i \neq j$ are zero because from (16)

$$\mathbf{Q} = \mathbf{P}'\mathbf{AP}$$

is a diagonal matrix.

For the particular polynomial in the example it was possible to find $\mathbf{P}$ and $\mathbf{K}$ which reduced the polynomial of degree 2 to a sum of squares. The next step is to determine whether the necessary matrices $\mathbf{P}$ and $\mathbf{K}$ can be found for the general second-degree polynomial of n variables.

From (13) the condition that the linear terms be zero is that

$$2\mathbf{K}'\mathbf{AP} + \mathbf{B}'\mathbf{P} = 0 \tag{18}$$

The condition can be satisfied, since by assumption $\mathbf{P}^{-1}$ exists, if $\mathbf{A}^{-1}$ exists. From (18),

$$\mathbf{K}'\mathbf{AP} = -\tfrac{1}{2}\mathbf{B}'\mathbf{P}$$

$$\mathbf{K}'\mathbf{APP}^{-1} = -\tfrac{1}{2}\mathbf{B}'\mathbf{PP}^{-1}$$

$$\mathbf{K}' = -\tfrac{1}{2}\mathbf{B}'\mathbf{A}^{-1}$$

$$\mathbf{K} = -\tfrac{1}{2}\mathbf{A}^{-1}\mathbf{B} \tag{19}$$

since $\mathbf{A}$ is symmetric.

Therefore, if $\mathbf{A}$ is non-singular, the linear terms can be eliminated and the polynomial has the form

$$g_1(\mathbf{Z}) = \mathbf{Z}'\mathbf{QZ} + \text{constant}$$

It may be noted that the formula for the $\mathbf{K}$ required to eliminate the linear terms, given by (19), is exactly the same as the value for $\mathbf{X}$ to be a stationary point of g as given by (18), page 572. The transformation implied by (19) has translated the origin of coordinate system to the stationary point; $g_1(\mathbf{Z})$ has a stationary point at $\mathbf{Z}^* = 0$.

Reduction to Sums of Squares

A function of the form

$$h(\mathbf{X}) = \mathbf{X}'\mathbf{A}\mathbf{X}$$

is called a *quadratic form*. It differs from the general polynomial of degree 2 in that only second-degree terms x_i^2 and $x_i x_j$ appear; the polynomial contains first-degree terms, in x_i, as well as second-degree terms. The theory of quadratic forms plays a key role in the optimization of functions of many variables. The central problem is the reduction to a sum of squares.

The reduction of a second-degree polynomial to a sum of squares requires, first, the elimination of the linear terms, and then the diagonalization of the matrix $\mathbf{A}$. As was seen above, the linear terms can be eliminated if $\mathbf{A}$ is non-singular. The reduction of the matrix $\mathbf{A}$ to diagonal form is somewhat more difficult and is more easily understood by examination of the cases $n = 1, 2, 3, \ldots$.

The quadratic form $g_1(\mathbf{Z}) = \mathbf{Z}'\mathbf{Q}\mathbf{Z}$ will be a sum of squares if

$$\mathbf{Q} = \mathbf{P}'\mathbf{A}\mathbf{P}$$

is a diagonal matrix.

For the case $n = 1$, the general quadratic form is

$$h(x_1) = a_{11}x_1^2$$

which is already a sum of squares. h will be positive for all x, other than $x = 0$, if $a_{11} > 0$, and negative if a_{11} is negative.

For the case $n = 2$, the general quadratic form is

$$h(x_1, x_2) = a_{11}x_1^2 + 2a_{12}x_1x_2 + a_{22}x_2^2$$

It may be rewritten as

$$h(x_1, x_2) = a_{11}\left[x_1^2 + \frac{2a_{12}}{a_{11}} x_1 x_2 + \frac{a_{12}^2 x_2^2}{a_{11}^2} \right] - \frac{a_{12}^2 x_2^2}{a_{11}} + a_{22}x_2^2$$

$$= a_{11}\left[x_1 + \frac{a_{12}}{a_{11}} x_2 \right]^2 + \left[\frac{a_{11}a_{22} - a_{12}^2}{a_{11}} \right][x_2]^2 \qquad (20)$$

and hence the transformation

$$y_1 = x_1 + \frac{a_{12}}{a_{11}} x_2$$

$$y_2 = x_2$$

will result in a sum of squares provided $a_{11} \neq 0$ and $a_{11}a_{22} - a_{12}^2 \neq 0$.

(If $a_{11} \neq 0$, but $a_{11}a_{22} - a_{12}^2 = 0$, the quadratic form is in fact a function of only one variable, and is one of the degenerate forms.)

The quadratic form has in effect been reduced to a sum of squares by a transformation in which the matrix $\mathbf{A}$ is changed to a diagonal matrix $\mathbf{Q}$. The transformation $\mathbf{X} = \mathbf{PY}$ or $(\mathbf{Y} = \mathbf{P}^{-1}\mathbf{X})$ reduces

$$h(\mathbf{X}) = \mathbf{X}'\mathbf{A}\mathbf{X}$$

to

$$h(\mathbf{Y}) = \mathbf{Y}'\mathbf{P}'\mathbf{A}\mathbf{P}\mathbf{Y}$$

Here

$$\mathbf{P}^{-1} = \begin{bmatrix} 1 & \dfrac{a_{12}}{a_{11}} \\ 0 & 1 \end{bmatrix} \quad \text{and} \quad \mathbf{P} = \begin{bmatrix} 1 & -\dfrac{a_{12}}{a_{11}} \\ 0 & 1 \end{bmatrix}$$

Hence

$$\mathbf{P}'\mathbf{A}\mathbf{P} = \begin{bmatrix} 1 & 0 \\ -\dfrac{a_{12}}{a_{11}} & 1 \end{bmatrix} \begin{bmatrix} a_{11} & a_{12} \\ a_{12} & a_{22} \end{bmatrix} \begin{bmatrix} 1 & -\dfrac{a_{12}}{a_{11}} \\ 0 & 1 \end{bmatrix} = \begin{bmatrix} a_{11} & 0 \\ 0 & \dfrac{a_{11}a_{22} - a_{12}^2}{a_{11}} \end{bmatrix} = \mathbf{Q}$$

For the case $n = 3$:

$$h(x_1, x_2, x_3)$$

$$= a_{11}x_1{}^2 + 2a_{12}x_1x_2 + a_{22}x_2{}^2 + 2a_{13}x_1x_3 + 2a_{23}x_2x_3 + a_{33}x_3{}^2$$

$$= a_{11}\left(x_1 + \frac{a_{12}}{a_{11}}x_2 + \frac{a_{13}}{a_{11}}x_3\right)^2 + \frac{a_{11}a_{22} - a_{12}^2}{a_{11}}\left(x_2 + \frac{a_{11}a_{23} - a_{12}a_{13}}{a_{11}a_{22} - a_{12}^2}x_3\right)^2$$

$$+ \frac{a_{11}a_{22}a_{33} + 2a_{23}a_{13}a_{12} - a_{11}a_{23}^2 - a_{22}a_{13}^2 - a_{33}a_{12}^2}{a_{11}a_{22} - a_{12}^2}(x_3)^2 \qquad (21)$$

and the transformation

$$y_1 = x_1 + \frac{a_{12}}{a_{11}}x_2 + \frac{a_{13}}{a_{11}}x_3$$

$$y_2 = x_2 + \frac{a_{11}a_{23} - a_{12}a_{13}}{(a_{11}a_{22} - a_{12})^2}x_3$$

$$y_3 = x_3$$

will reduce the quadratic form to a sum of square if $a_{11} \neq 0$; $a_{11}a_{22} - a_{12}^2 \neq 0$ and

$$a_{11}a_{22}a_{33} + 2a_{23}a_{13}a_{12} - a_{11}a_{23}^2 - a_{22}a_{13}^2 - a_{33}a_{12}^2 \neq 0$$

Here

$$
\mathbf{P} = \begin{bmatrix} 1 & -\dfrac{a_{12}}{a_{11}} & \dfrac{a_{12}}{a_{11}}\left(\dfrac{a_{11}a_{23} - a_{12}a_{13}}{a_{11}a_{22} - a_{12}^2}\right) - \dfrac{a_{13}}{a_{11}} \\ 0 & 1 & -\left(\dfrac{a_{11}a_{23} - a_{12}a_{13}}{a_{11}a_{22} - a_{12}^2}\right) \\ 0 & 0 & 1 \end{bmatrix} = \begin{bmatrix} 1 & b_{12} & b_{13} \\ 0 & 1 & b_{23} \\ 0 & 0 & 1 \end{bmatrix}
$$

where

$$
\mathbf{P}^{-1} = \begin{bmatrix} 1 & \dfrac{a_{12}}{a_{11}} & -\dfrac{a_{13}}{a_{11}} \\ 0 & 1 & \dfrac{a_{11}a_{23} - a_{12}a_{13}}{(a_{11}a_{22} - a_{12})^2} \\ 0 & 0 & 1 \end{bmatrix}
$$

Then

$$
\mathbf{P'AP} = \mathbf{Q} = \begin{bmatrix} 1 & 0 & 0 \\ b_{12} & 1 & 0 \\ b_{13} & b_{23} & 1 \end{bmatrix} \begin{bmatrix} a_{11} & a_{12} & a_{13} \\ a_{12} & a_{22} & a_{23} \\ a_{13} & a_{23} & a_{33} \end{bmatrix} \begin{bmatrix} 1 & b_{12} & b_{13} \\ 0 & 1 & b_{23} \\ 0 & 0 & 1 \end{bmatrix}
$$

$$
= \begin{bmatrix} q_{11} & q_{12} & q_{13} \\ q_{12} & q_{22} & q_{23} \\ q_{13} & q_{23} & q_{33} \end{bmatrix} = \begin{bmatrix} q_{11} & 0 & 0 \\ 0 & q_{22} & 0 \\ 0 & 0 & q_{33} \end{bmatrix}
$$

It may be verified that

$$
q_{11} = a_{11}
$$

$$
q_{22} = \frac{|\mathbf{A}_2|}{a_{11}}
$$

$$
q_{33} = \frac{|\mathbf{A}_3|}{|\mathbf{A}_2|}
$$

where

$$
\mathbf{A}_2 = \begin{bmatrix} a_{11} & a_{12} \\ a_{12} & a_{22} \end{bmatrix} \quad \text{and} \quad \mathbf{A}_3 = \begin{bmatrix} a_{11} & a_{12} & a_{13} \\ a_{12} & a_{22} & a_{23} \\ a_{13} & a_{23} & a_{33} \end{bmatrix}
$$

These results can be generalized to the case of n variables. A quadratic form

$$
h(\mathbf{X}) = \mathbf{X'AX}
$$

can be reduced to a sum of squares

$$h(\mathbf{Y}) = \mathbf{Y}'\mathbf{Q}\mathbf{Y}$$

where

$$q_{ii} = \frac{|\mathbf{A}_i|}{|\mathbf{A}_{i-1}|}$$

provided

$$|\mathbf{A}_i| \neq 0 \qquad i = 1, 2 \cdots n.$$

EXERCISES

Reduce the following polynomials to a sum of squares.

1. $P(x, y) = -60x^2 + 100xy - 60y^2 + 1760x + 1320y - 5000$
2. $u(x_1, x_2, x_3,) = -x_1{}^2 - x_2{}^2 + x_2 x_3 - x_3{}^2 + x_1 + 2x_3$
3. $f(x_1, x_2, x_3) = x_1{}^2 + x_2{}^2 + x_3{}^2 + 4x_1 + x_2 x_3 - x_1 x_2 + 2x_2 - 40$

B. CONDITIONS FOR POSITIVE DEFINITENESS

Unconstrained Variables

A general quadratic form:

$$h(\mathbf{X}) = \mathbf{X}'\mathbf{A}\mathbf{X}$$

is said to be positive definite if

$$h(\mathbf{X}) > 0 \text{ for any } \mathbf{X} \neq 0 \text{ and}$$

$$h(\mathbf{X}) = 0 \text{ if } \mathbf{X} = 0$$

and positive or positive semi-definite if

$$h(\mathbf{X}) \geq 0 \text{ for all } \mathbf{X}, \text{ and}$$

$$h(\mathbf{X}) = 0 \text{ for some } \mathbf{X} \neq 0.$$

The quadratic form $h(\mathbf{X})$ is negative definite if $-h(\mathbf{X})$ is positive definite.

In (20) the variables appear only in terms which are squared; hence, the quadratic form in 2 variables is positive definite if, and only if, the coefficients in (20) are all positive, i.e., if

$$a_{11} > 0 \text{ and } a_{22}a_{11} - a_{12}^2 = \begin{vmatrix} a_{11} & a_{12} \\ a_{12} & a_{22} \end{vmatrix} > 0$$

For the case of three variables the quadratic form (21) is positive definite if and only if the coefficients in (21) are all positive, i.e., if

$$a_{11} > 0; \quad |\mathbf{A}_2| = \begin{vmatrix} a_{11} & a_{12} \\ a_{12} & a_{22} \end{vmatrix} > 0 \quad \text{and} \quad |\mathbf{A}_3| = \begin{vmatrix} a_{11} & a_{12} & a_{13} \\ a_{12} & a_{22} & a_{23} \\ a_{13} & a_{23} & a_{33} \end{vmatrix} > 0 \quad (1)$$

or negative definite if

$$|\mathbf{A}_1| < 0, \quad |\mathbf{A}_2| > 0, \quad \text{and} \quad |\mathbf{A}_3| < 0$$

since the values of all three squared terms would be negative only if this were true; i.e., if the coefficients of the squared terms,

$$a_{11}, \frac{|\mathbf{A}_2|}{|\mathbf{A}_1|} \text{ and } \frac{|\mathbf{A}_3|}{|\mathbf{A}_2|} \text{ are all negative.}$$

The above results can be generalized to any number of variables. The general quadratic form

$$h(\mathbf{X}) = \mathbf{X}'\mathbf{A}\mathbf{X}$$

$$= a_{11}x_1^2 + a_{22}x_2^2 + \cdots + a_{nn}x_n^2 + 2a_{12}x_1x_2 + 2a_{13}x_1x_3 + \cdots$$

will be > 0 for all values of $\mathbf{X} \neq 0$ if the determinants

$$a_{11}, \begin{vmatrix} a_{11} & a_{12} \\ a_{21} & a_{22} \end{vmatrix}, \begin{vmatrix} a_{11} & a_{12} & a_{13} \\ a_{12} & a_{22} & a_{23} \\ a_{13} & a_{23} & a_{33} \end{vmatrix}, \ldots, \begin{vmatrix} a_{11} & a_{12} & \cdots & a_{1n} \\ a_{12} & a_{22} & \cdots & a_{2n} \\ \cdots\cdots\cdots\cdots \\ a_{1n} & a_{2n} & & a_{nn} \end{vmatrix}$$

are positive, and will be < 0 for all values of $\mathbf{X} \neq 0$ if they are alternately negative and positive.

Positive Definiteness Under One Linear Constraint

Suppose the n variables $x_1, x_2 \cdots x_n$ are subject to a linear restriction of the form

$$b_1x_1 + b_2x_2 + \cdots + b_nx_n = 0 \qquad (2)$$

Let

$$\mathbf{B} = \begin{bmatrix} b_1 \\ \\ \mathbf{B}_1 \end{bmatrix} \quad \text{where} \quad \mathbf{B}_1 = \begin{bmatrix} b_2 \\ \cdot \\ \cdot \\ \cdot \\ b_n \end{bmatrix} \quad \text{and} \quad \mathbf{X} = \begin{bmatrix} x_1 \\ \\ \mathbf{X}_1 \end{bmatrix} \quad \text{where} \quad \mathbf{X}_1 = \begin{bmatrix} x_2 \\ \cdot \\ \cdot \\ \cdot \\ x_n \end{bmatrix}$$

The equation (2) may be written as

$$\mathbf{B'X} = 0 \quad \text{or} \quad [b_1 \quad \mathbf{B_1'}]\begin{bmatrix} x_1 \\ \mathbf{X_1} \end{bmatrix} = [b_1 x_1 + \mathbf{B_1'X_1}] = 0$$

and solved for x_1

$$x_1 = -\frac{1}{b_1}\mathbf{B_1'X_1} \tag{3}$$

The variable x_1 may be eliminated from the quadratic form

$$h(\mathbf{X}) = \mathbf{X'AX}$$

by writing

$$\mathbf{A} = \begin{bmatrix} a_{11} & \mathbf{A_1} \\ \mathbf{A_2} & \mathbf{A_3} \end{bmatrix}$$

where $\mathbf{A_1}$ is 1 by $n - 1$, $\mathbf{A_2}$ is $n - 1$ by 1, and $\mathbf{A_3}$ is $n - 1$ by $n - 1$. Then

$$\mathbf{X'AX} = [x_1' \quad \mathbf{X_1'}]\begin{bmatrix} a_{11} & \mathbf{A_1} \\ \mathbf{A_2} & \mathbf{A_3} \end{bmatrix}\begin{bmatrix} x_1 \\ \mathbf{X_1} \end{bmatrix}$$

$$[x_1'a_{11} + \mathbf{X_1'A_2} \quad x_1'\mathbf{A_1} + \mathbf{X_1'A_3}]\begin{bmatrix} x_1 \\ \mathbf{X_1} \end{bmatrix}$$

$$= x_1'a_{11}x_1 + \mathbf{X_1'A_2}x_1 + x_1'\mathbf{A_1X_1} + \mathbf{X_1'A_3X_1}$$

$$= \left(-\frac{1}{b}\mathbf{X_1'B_1}\right)a_{11}\left(-\frac{1}{b}\mathbf{B_1'X_1}\right) + \mathbf{X_1'A_2}\left(-\frac{1}{b}\mathbf{B_1'X_1}\right)$$

$$+ \left(-\frac{1}{b}\mathbf{X_1'B_1}\right)\mathbf{A_1X_1} + \mathbf{X_1'A_3X_1}$$

$$= \frac{1}{b^2}(\mathbf{X_1'B_1}a_{11}\mathbf{B_1'X_1}) - \frac{1}{b}(\mathbf{X_1'A_2B_1'X_1} + \mathbf{X_1'B_1A_1X_1}) + \mathbf{X_1'A_3X_1}$$

$$= \mathbf{X_1'}\left[\frac{1}{b^2}\mathbf{B_1}a_{11}\mathbf{B_1'} - \frac{1}{b}(\mathbf{A_2B_1'} + \mathbf{B_1A_1}) + \mathbf{A_3}\right]\mathbf{X_1}$$

$$= \mathbf{X_1'CX_1}$$

where

$$c_{ij} = \frac{1}{b_1^2}b_ib_ja_{11} - \frac{1}{b_1}(a_{1i}b_j + a_{1j}b_i) + a_{ij} \quad \begin{matrix} i = 2, \ldots, n \\ j = 2, \ldots, n \end{matrix} \tag{4}$$

The quadratic form $\mathbf{X_1'CX_1}$ is a function of $n - 1$ independent variables;

hence the conditions for positive definiteness are

$$c_{22}, |\mathbf{C}_3| = \begin{vmatrix} c_{22} & c_{23} \\ c_{23} & c_{33} \end{vmatrix}, \ldots |\mathbf{C}_n| \text{ are all positive.} \qquad (5)$$

These conditions can be expressed more symmetrically in a way that shows that they do not depend on which of the x_i is eliminated in (3). If all of the determinants in (5) are multiplied by $-b_1{}^2$, they become

$$\begin{vmatrix} 0 & b_1 & b_2 \\ b_1 & a_{11} & a_{12} \\ b_2 & a_{12} & a_{22} \end{vmatrix}; \quad \begin{vmatrix} 0 & b_1 & b_2 & b_3 \\ b_1 & a_{11} & a_{12} & a_{13} \\ b_2 & a_{12} & a_{22} & a_{23} \\ b_3 & a_{13} & a_{23} & a_{33} \end{vmatrix}, \ldots, \quad \begin{vmatrix} 0 & b_1 & b_2 & \cdots & b_n \\ b_1 & a_{11} & a_{12} & & a_{1n} \\ b_2 & a_{12} & a_{22} & & a_{2n} \\ \cdot & \cdot & \cdot & \cdot & \cdot \\ b_n & a_{1n} & & & a_{nn} \end{vmatrix}$$

For example, multiplying c_{22} from (4) by $-b_1{}^2$ gives

$$-b_1{}^2 c_{22} = -b_2 b_2 a_{11} + b_1 b_2 a_{12} + b_1 b_2 a_{12} - b_1{}^2 a_{22}$$

$$= -b_1(b_1 a_{22} - b_2 a_{12}) + b_2(b_1 a_{12} - b_2 a_{11})$$

$$= -b_1 \begin{vmatrix} b_1 & a_{12} \\ b_2 & a_{22} \end{vmatrix} + b_2 \begin{vmatrix} b_1 & a_{11} \\ b_2 & a_{12} \end{vmatrix} = \begin{vmatrix} 0 & b_1 & b_2 \\ b_1 & a_{11} & a_{12} \\ b_2 & a_{12} & a_{22} \end{vmatrix}$$

Similarly

$$-b_1{}^2 \begin{vmatrix} c_{22} & c_{23} \\ c_{23} & c_{33} \end{vmatrix} = \begin{vmatrix} 0 & b_1 & 0 & 0 \\ b_1 & a_{11} & 0 & 0 \\ b_2 & a_{12} & c_{22} & c_{23} \\ b_3 & a_{13} & c_{23} & c_{33} \end{vmatrix} = \begin{vmatrix} 0 & b_1 & b_2 & b_3 \\ b_1 & a_{11} & a_{12} & a_{13} \\ b_2 & a_{12} & a_{22} & a_{23} \\ b_3 & a_{13} & a_{23} & a_{33} \end{vmatrix}$$

Hence the conditions for a quadratic form to be positive (negative) definite subject to a linear condition on the variables are that all the determinants be negative (alternately positive and negative).

Positive Definiteness under More than One Linear Constraint

The development used above can be generalized to the case of more than one linear constraint; however, the algebra becomes tedious. Since the result is a straightforward extension of (5) it will suffice to state it substantially in the form proved by Samuelson (1955), pp. 376–379.

The necessary and sufficient conditions that the quadratic form

$$h(\mathbf{X}) = \mathbf{X'AX}$$

be *positive definite* for values of x_i, satisfying the equation

$$\mathbf{BX} = 0$$

(where $\mathbf{B}$ is an $m \times n$ matrix ($m < n$) with at least one $m \times m$ determinant different from zero), are that the last $n - m$ principal minors of

$$\begin{vmatrix} 0 & \mathbf{B} \\ \mathbf{B'} & \mathbf{A} \end{vmatrix}$$

be of the sign $(-1)^m$.

The necessary and sufficient conditions for the quadratic form to be *negative definite* is that the principal minors alternate in sign with the first one being of the sign of $(-1)^{m+1}$.

C. SUFFICIENT CONDITIONS FOR LOCAL EXTREMA

Interior Points

It has been shown in Section B that the matrix of the coefficients of a quadratic form can be used to determine what the form is, or is not, positive (negative) definite. It will be shown in this section that a matrix of second derivatives in respect to the different variables can be used to determine if a stationary point is a local maximum or minimum for a general function which has a convergent Taylor expansion:

$$f(x_1, x_2, \ldots, x_n) = \underbrace{f(x_1{}^*, x_2{}^*, \ldots, x_n{}^*)}_{1}$$

$$+ \underbrace{\sum_{k=1}^{n} h_k \frac{\partial f(x_1 \cdots x_n)}{\partial x_k}}_{2} + \underbrace{\sum_{j=1}^{n} \sum_{k=1}^{n} h_j h_k \frac{\partial^2 f(x_1 \cdots x_n)}{\partial x_k \partial x_j}}_{3} + \cdots \quad (1)$$

where

$$x_i = x_i{}^* + h_i$$

At a stationary point:

Term 1 will be a constant.

Term 2 will equal zero.

Term 3 will be the dominant term in the expansion because the h's are very small and appear in higher powers in succeeding terms.

The third term is a quadratic form and can be expressed as:

$$\mathbf{H'\Delta H}$$

in which the $\mathbf{\Delta}$ is the matrix of second partial derivatives:

$$
\begin{bmatrix}
\dfrac{\partial^2 f}{\partial x_1{}^2} & \cdots & \dfrac{\partial^2 f}{\partial x_1\,\partial x_n} \\[2ex]
\cdot & & \cdot \\
\cdot & & \cdot \\
\cdot & & \cdot \\[1ex]
\dfrac{\partial^2 f}{\partial x_1\,\partial x_n} & \cdots & \dfrac{\partial^2 f}{\partial x_n{}^2}
\end{bmatrix}
\tag{2}
$$

where the derivatives are evaluated at the point $x_1{}^*$, $x_2{}^*$, ..., $x_n{}^*$. If this quadratic form is positive definite for any value of $\mathbf{H}$ when $\mathbf{\Delta}$ is evaluated at a stationary point, then clearly f has a minimum at this point. The sufficient condition for a stationary point to be maximum (minimum) can therefore be determined from the sufficient condition for a matrix to be negative (positive) definite.

If f is a function of one variable ($n = 1$), $\mathbf{\Delta}$ consists of one element

$$\frac{d^2 f}{dx^2}$$

and hence f has a maximum (minimum) at a stationary point if the second derivative is negative (positive).

If $f = f(x, y)$ is a function of two variables ($n = 2$) the matrix $\mathbf{\Delta}$ becomes

$$
\begin{bmatrix}
f_{xx} & f_{xy} \\
f_{xy} & f_{yy}
\end{bmatrix}
\tag{3}
$$

A stationary point is a local minimum if

$$f_{xx} > 0 \tag{4}$$

and

$$f_{xx}f_{yy} - (f_{xy})^2 > 0$$

and a local maximum if

$$f_{xx} < 0 \quad \text{and} \quad f_{xx}f_{yy} - (f_{xy})^2 > 0$$

These are the conditions that were given in Chapter 9.

If $f = f(x, y, z)$ is a function of three variables the matrix Δ is

$$
\begin{bmatrix}
f_{xx} & f_{xy} & f_{xz} \\
f_{xy} & f_{yy} & f_{yz} \\
f_{xz} & f_{yz} & f_{zz}
\end{bmatrix} \tag{5}
$$

and a stationary point is a local minimum if

$$
f_{xx} > 0; \quad
\begin{vmatrix}
f_{xx} & f_{xy} \\
f_{xy} & f_{yy}
\end{vmatrix} > 0 \quad \text{and} \quad
\begin{vmatrix}
f_{xx} & f_{xy} & f_{xz} \\
f_{xy} & f_{yy} & f_{yz} \\
f_{xz} & f_{yz} & f_{zz}
\end{vmatrix} > 0 \tag{6}
$$

and a local maximum if the signs are alternately negative and positive.

If the quadratic form is semi-definite (determinant of Δ equals zero) the behavior of the function in the neighborhood of the stationary point must be examined, either directly or by examining higher derivatives.

Sufficient Conditions for Extrema Under One Constraint

The results given above may be applied to the case where the variables are subject to constraints if the function f is everywhere replaced by the appropriate constrainted function; in general by

$$
f(x_1, x_2, \ldots, x_n) - \lambda g(x_1, x_2, \ldots, x_n) \tag{7}
$$

and the constraints are taken into account.

The elements in the matrix Δ defined by (2) now take the form

$$
\Delta_{ij} = \frac{\partial^2 f}{\partial x_i\, \partial x_j} - \lambda \frac{\partial^2 g}{\partial x_i\, \partial x_j}
$$

However since the x's are constrained by

$$
g(x_1, x_2, \ldots, x_n)
$$

The h's in the quadratic form $\mathbf{H'\Delta H}$ are constrained by

$$
\frac{\partial g}{\partial x_1} h_1 + \frac{\partial g}{\partial x_2} h_2 + \cdots + \frac{\partial g}{\partial x_n} h_n = 0
$$

The results of Section B, page 602, may now applied directly to give the criterion stated on page 553.

A function $f(x_1 \cdots x_n)$ has a local maximum (minimum) subject to

$$g(x_1, x_2, \ldots, x_n) = 0$$

at a point satisfying the equations

$$\frac{\partial f}{\partial x_k} - \lambda \frac{\partial g}{\partial x_k} = 0 \qquad k = 1, \ldots, n$$

$$g(x_1 \cdots x_n) = 0$$

if the principal minors

$\Delta_3, \Delta_4, \ldots, \Delta_{n+1}$ are alternately positive and negative (negative).

Sufficient Conditions for Extrema under More than One Constraint

The previous statement may be generalized to the case of m constraints. Let

$$E(\mathbf{X}, \boldsymbol{\Gamma}) = f(\mathbf{X}) - \sum_{j=1}^{m} \lambda_j g_j(\mathbf{X})$$

The necessary conditions for E to have a local extremum is that

$$\frac{\partial E}{\partial x_i} = 0 \qquad\qquad i = 1, \ldots, n$$

$$\frac{\partial E}{\partial \lambda_j} = g_j(\mathbf{X}) = 0 \qquad j = 1, \ldots, m$$

The sufficient conditions are that

$$\mathbf{H'\Delta H}$$

be positive definite when the h's are constrained by

$$\mathbf{BH} = 0$$

where

$$b_{ij} = \frac{\partial g_j}{\partial x_i}$$

The necessary and sufficient conditions for this are given in Section B and hence the general statement is the following:

The necessary and sufficient conditions for a point $\mathbf{X}^\circ$ to be a local minimum of a function of n variables with continuous second partial derivatives, $f(\mathbf{X})$, subject to

$$g_j(\mathbf{X}) = 0 \qquad j = 1, \ldots, m \qquad (m < n)$$

where the g_j have continuous second partial derivatives, and where at least one of the determinants of order m of the matrix $\mathbf{B}$ is not zero, are:

(a) $\dfrac{\partial f}{\partial x_i} - \displaystyle\sum_{j=1}^{m} \lambda_j \dfrac{\partial g_j}{\partial x_i} = 0 \qquad i = 1, \ldots, n$

(b) $g_j = 0 \qquad\qquad\qquad j = 1, \ldots, m$

(c) the last $n - m$ principal minors of

$$\Delta = \begin{vmatrix} \mathbf{O} & \mathbf{B} \\ \mathbf{B'} & \mathbf{A} \end{vmatrix} \tag{8}$$

be of sign $(-1)^m$ where

$$a_{ij} = \frac{\partial^2 f}{\partial x_i\, \partial x_j} - \sum_k \frac{\partial^2 g_k}{\partial x_i\, \partial x_j} \lambda_k$$

$$b_{ij} = \frac{\partial g_j}{\partial x_i}$$

All partial derivatives are evaluated at the point X°.

The necessary and sufficient conditions that X° be a *local maximum* are (a) and (b) and that the last $n - m$ principal minors alternate in sign with the first one being of the sign of $(-1)^{m+1}$.

SUMMARY

Sufficient Conditions for Definiteness and Extreme Values

Matrix	Size	No. of Minors	Positive Definite	Negative Definite
For all $X \neq 0$ Principal minors	n	n	$X'AX > 0$ $\|A_i\| > 0$	$X'AX < 0$ $\|A_i\|(-1)^i > 0$
Function extremum $i = 1, \ldots, n$	n	n	Local minimum f has a *minimum* if Δ is positive definite $\Delta_i > 0$	Local maximum f has a *maximum* if Δ is negative definite $(\Delta_i)(-1)^i > 0$
One equality constraint Last $n - 1$ principal minors of Δ_{n+1} are $i = 3, 4, \ldots, n+1$	$n+1$	$n-1$	$- - - - - - -$ $(\Delta_i)(-1) > 0$	$+ - + -$ $(\Delta_i)(-1)^{i+1} > 0$
m equality constraints Last $n - m$ principal minors of Δ_{m+n} are if m is odd if m is even $i = m+2, \ldots, n+m$	$n+m$	$n-m$	$- - - - \cdots -$ $+ + + + \cdots +$ $(\Delta_i)(-1)^m > 0$	$+ - + - \cdots$ $- + - + \cdots$ $(\Delta_i)(-1)^{i+1} > 0$

CHAPTER TWENTY-ONE

Dynamic Programming

Dynamic programming is an optimization technique which permits a function of n variables to be optimized in a sequence of steps, each of which may involve only the optimization of a function of one variable. The basic concepts are illustrated by examples in Sections A and B, and the general theory is described in Section C.

A. THE BACKWARD ALGORITHM

Analytic Solution

Example I. Consider again the inventory problem discussed in Chapter 18 as Example 1 (page 563). The requirements are for 5 units during the first period, 10 during the second, and 15 during the third. A holding cost of 2 per unit is charged for any items brought into a period and the production cost per period is x^2 where x is the number produced in the period. The problem is to determine the number to be produced in each period so as to minimize the sum of holding and production costs subject to meeting the requirements.

As before, let x_i denote the number to be produced in each period; the objective function, which is to be minimized, is:

$$C(x_1, x_2, x_3) = x_1^2 + x_2^2 + x_3^2 + 2(x_1 - 5) + 2(x_1 + x_2 - 15) \quad (1)$$

In the example it was shown that solving the three equations

$$\frac{\partial C}{\partial x_1} = 0; \quad \frac{\partial C}{\partial x_2} = 0; \quad \frac{\partial C}{\partial x_3} = 0 \quad (2)$$

lead to the optimum solution

$$x_1{}^* = 9, \quad x_2{}^* = 10, \quad \text{and} \quad x_3{}^* = 11. \tag{3}$$

The decision as to how many to produce in the third period does not actually have to be made until the beginning of the third period. Let z_3 denote the number of units on hand at the beginning of the third period. Since 15 units are required in this period the optimum decision $x_3{}^*$ in the third period is to produce the remainder, i.e.,

$$x_3{}^* = 15 - z_3 \tag{4}$$

The cost incurred in the third period, denoted by $f_3(z_3, x_3)$, is the sum of the holding cost plus the production cost

$$f_3(z_3, x_3) = 2z_3 + x_3{}^2$$

The cost, if the optimum decision is made in period three, is denoted by $f_3(z_3; x_3{}^*)$ and is

$$f_3(z_3; x_3{}^*) = 2z_3 + (15 - z_3)^2 \quad x_3{}^*, z_3 \geq 0 \tag{5}$$

Note that $f_3(z_3; x_3{}^*)$ is clearly a function of z_3 and only of z_3; this is indicated by using the semicolon after z_3 and an asterisk on x_3 to show that the optimum decision has been made with the given value of z_3.

Now consider the situation at the beginning of the second period. Let z_2 denote the inventory at the beginning of the period. For any given decision x_2 the cost during the second period $f_2(z_2, x_2)$ is the sum of holding costs plus the production costs, or

$$f_2(z_2, x_2) = 2z_2 + x_2{}^2 \tag{6}$$

The decision x_2 will affect the inventory at the beginning of the third period, in fact

$$z_3 = z_2 + x_2 - 10 \quad z_2 \geq 0 \tag{7}$$

The inventory at the beginning of the third period (z_3) is the inventory at the beginning of the second period (z_2) plus the production during the second period less the requirement during the second period.

The decision made in period 2 will, therefore, affect the cost in period 3 and the optimum value of x_2 is the one which will minimize the sum of the costs in period 2 and period 3. Let $F_2(z_2, x_2; x_3{}^*)$ denote the cost in period 2 plus the cost in period 3 if the inventory is z_2 at the beginning of the second period, the decision x_2 is made in period 2 and the optimum decision is then made in period 3 using (4):

$$F_2(z_2, x_2; x_3{}^*) = f_2(z_2, x_2) + F_3(z_3; x_3{}^*) \tag{8}$$
$$= f_2(z_2, x_2) + F_3(z_2 + x_2 - 10; x_3{}^*) \quad \text{from (7)}$$
$$= 2z_2 + x_2{}^2 + 2z_3 + (15 - z_3)^2$$
$$= 2z_2 + x_2{}^2 + 2(z_2 + x_2 - 10) + (25 - z_2 - x_2)^2 \tag{9}$$
$$\text{from (4), (5), (6), and (7)}$$

Here $F_3(z_3; x_3{}^*) = f_3(z_3; x_3{}^*)$ since the third period is the last period.

The first two terms of (9) are the holding and production costs, respectively, in period 2; while the last two are the holding and production costs, respectively, in period 3. The number of units carried from period 2 to period 3 is $z_2 + x_2 - 10$ if initial inventory is z_2, and x_2 are produced in period 2. The last two terms are obtained by substituting (7) into (5). The optimum value of x_2 is the solution of $dF_2/dx_2 = 0$; z_2 being treated as a (given) constant

$$\frac{dF_2}{dx_2} = 0; \qquad 2x_2 + 2 - 2(25 - z_2 - x_2) = 0$$

or

$$x_2{}^* = 12 - \frac{z_2}{2} \tag{10}$$

Then the minimum value of F_2, given z_2, for the optimum decisions, in periods 2 and 3 is

$$F_2(z_2; x_2{}^*, x_3{}^*) = 2z_2 + \left(12 - \frac{z_2}{2}\right)^2 + 2\left(z_2 + 12 - \frac{z_2}{2} - 10\right)$$
$$+ \left(25 - z_2 - 12 + \frac{z_2}{2}\right)^2$$
$$= 3z_2 + 4 + \left(12 - \frac{z_2}{2}\right)^2 + \left(13 - \frac{z_2}{2}\right)^2 \tag{11}$$

The same sequence of steps can now be carried out for the first period. Let z_1 denote the inventory at the beginning of the first period. Then, assuming the holding cost applies to this period,

$$f_1(z_1, x_1) = 2z_1 + x_1{}^2 \tag{12}$$

and if z_1 is given and x_1 units are produced in period 1, the inventory at the beginning of the second period is:

$$z_2 = z_1 + x_1 - 5 \qquad z_1 \geq 0; \quad x_1 \geq 0 \tag{13}$$

If z_1 is given and x_1 units are produced in period 1, and the optimum decisions are made in periods 2 and 3, the total cost in periods 1, 2, and 3 is:

$$F_1(z_1, x_1; x_2{}^*, x_3{}^*)$$

$$= f_1(z_1, x_1) + F_2(z_2; x_2{}^*, x_3{}^*)$$

$$= 2z_1 + x_1{}^2 + 3z_2 + 4 + \left(12 - \frac{z_2}{2}\right)^2 + \left(13 - \frac{z_2}{2}\right)^2 \quad (14)$$

Differentiating with respect to x_1, assuming z_1 given and z_2 given by (13), and setting the derivative equal to zero, gives:

$$2x_1 + 3 - \left(12 - \frac{z_1 + x_1 - 5}{2}\right) - \left(13 - \frac{z_1 + x_1 - 5}{2}\right) = 0$$

$$x_1{}^* = 9 - \frac{z_1}{3} \quad (15)$$

and the minimum total cost for all these periods, starting with an initial inventory of z_1 and making the optimum decision in each period, is:

$$F_1(z_1; x_1{}^*, x_2{}^*, x_3{}^*) = 4z_1 + 16 + \left(9 - \frac{z_1}{3}\right)^2$$

$$+ \left(10 - \frac{z_1}{3}\right)^2 + \left(11 - \frac{z_1}{3}\right)^2 \quad (16)$$

If the initial inventory is zero, i.e., $z_1 = 0$ then $x_1{}^* = 9$ from (15), $z_2 = 4$ from (13), $x_2{}^* = 10$ from (10), $z_3 = 4$ from (7), and $x_3{}^* = 11$ from (4).

This is the same solution as obtained previously, but it has been obtained here by optimizing three functions of one variable rather than one function of three variables. In this example, the optimum of each of these functions was obtained by setting the derivative equal to zero and resulting optimum satisfied all the restrictions. The same formulas (15), (13), (10), (7), and (4) may be used to determine the optimum production for any initial inventory. This solution will be feasible provided the resulting z's and x's are integral and satisfy the restrictions. The dynamic programming technique can also be adapted to the case when the optimum occurs on the boundary of the feasible region as is illustrated in the following example.

Example 2. Suppose the requirements in the previous example are 5 each in the three periods. This problem was considered in Chapter 18 as Example 2 (page 565), and it was shown that the techniques available there were not in general adequate to solve the problem. However, the optimum solution can be obtained by dynamic programming.

The first approach will be to use the analytic method illustrated in the previous example. The notation used here is identical to that used above.

The optimum value of x_3 will again be the difference between the requirement and the inventory at the beginning of the period, since the optimum inventory at the beginning of the fourth period is clearly zero:

$$x_3{}^* = 5 - z_3$$

The total cost in the third period is given by:

$$F_3(z_3; x_3{}^*) = f_3(z_3, x_3{}^*) = 2z_3 + (5 - z_3)^2$$

For the second period

$$z_3 = z_2 + x_2 - 5$$

$$F_2(z_2, x_2; x_3{}^*) = f_2(z_2, x_2) + F_3(z_3; x_3{}^*)$$
$$= 2z_2 + x_2{}^2 + 2(z_2 + x_2 - 5) + (10 - z_2 - x_2)^2$$

$$\frac{dF_2}{dx_2} = 0; \qquad 2x_2 + 2 - 2(10 - z_2 - x_2) = 0$$

or

$$x_2{}^* = \frac{9}{2} - \frac{z_2}{2}$$

$$F_2(z_2; x_2{}^*, x_3{}^*) = 3z_2 + \tfrac{1}{4}(9 - z_2)^2 - 1 + \left(\frac{11}{2} - \frac{z_2}{2}\right)^2$$

For the first period:

$$z_2 = z_1 + x_1 - 5 \qquad z_1 \geq 0; \quad x_1 \geq 0$$

$$f_1(z_1, x_1) = 2z_1 + x_1{}^2$$

$$F_1(z_1, x_1; x_2{}^*, x_3{}^*) = f_1(z_1, x_1) + F_2(z_1 + x_1 - 5; x_2{}^*, x_3{}^*)$$
$$= 2z_1 + x_1{}^2 + 3z_2 + \tfrac{1}{4}(9 - z_2)^2 - 1 + \left(\frac{11}{2} - \frac{z_2}{2}\right)^2$$
$$= 2z_1 + x_1{}^2 + 3(z_1 + x_1 - 5) + \tfrac{1}{4}(14 - z_1 - x_1)^2 - 1$$
$$+ \left(8 - \frac{z_1}{2} - \frac{x_1}{2}\right)^2$$

$$\frac{dF_1}{dx_1} = 0; \qquad 2x_1 + 3 - \tfrac{1}{2}[14 - z_1 - x_1] - \left(8 - \frac{z_1}{2} - \frac{x_1}{2}\right) = 0$$

$$x_1{}^* = 4 - \frac{z_1}{3}$$

$$F_1(z_1; x_1{}^*, x_2{}^*, x_3{}^*) = 2z_1 + \left(4 - \frac{z_1}{3}\right)^2 + 3\left(z_1 + 4 - \frac{z_1}{3} - 5\right)$$
$$+ \frac{1}{4}\left(14 - z_1 - 4 + \frac{z_1}{3}\right)^2 - 1$$
$$+ \left(8 - \frac{z_1}{2} - 2 + \frac{z_1}{6}\right)^2$$
$$= 4(z_1 - 1) + \left(4 - \frac{z_1}{3}\right)^2 + \frac{1}{4}\left(10 - \frac{2z_1}{3}\right)^2 + \left(6 - \frac{z_1}{3}\right)^2$$

The optimum solution as given by this analytic method (if $z_1 = 0$) is $x_1^* = 4$, $z_2 = -1$. Since by definition z_2 cannot be negative, the solution is not feasible. The tabular method described next will illustrate how the dynamic programming technique can be modified so that only feasible alternatives are considered.

The Tabular Method

The analytic method, applied in a direct manner, does not provide a feasible optimum if the unconstrained optimum is not feasible. The solution obtained in the previous example is not necessarily an integer and not necessarily non-negative. There is, however, a way in which dynamic programming can be used. The method, which consists of enumerating certain feasible alternatives, will be illustrated by using the same example; i.e., the requirement is 5 units in each of the three periods.

Example 3. The first step consists of listing all feasible alternatives in the last period as a function of that period's initial inventory;

$$x_3^* = 5 - z_3 \tag{17}$$

and computing the cost during the period

$$f_3(z_3, x_3^*) = 2z_3 + (5 - z_3)^2 \tag{18}$$

as shown in Table 21-1.

Table 21-1

z_3	x_3^*	$F_3(z_3; x_3^*)$
0	5	$0 + 25 = 25$
1	4	$2 + 16 = 18$
2	3	$4 + 9 = 13$
3	2	$6 + 4 = 10$
4	1	$8 + 1 = 9$
5	0	$10 + 0 = 10$

The next step is the evaluation of the cost in period 2 which, as before, is given by

$$F_2(z_2, x_2; x_3^*) = 2z_2 + x_2^2 + F_3(z_3; x_3^*) \tag{19}$$

For each initial inventory z_2 there is a set of feasible values of x_2, and for each such feasible pair (z_2, x_2) the initial inventory for period three z_3, is determined by

$$z_3 = z_2 + x_2 - 5 \tag{20}$$

Table 21-2 shows z_3 for the feasible pairs. The pairs (z_2, x_2) represented by the lower right hand part are feasible but are clearly not optimum since the inventory at the beginning of period four would be greater than zero.

Table 21-2

$$z_3(z_2, x_2, 5) = z_2 + x_2 - 5$$

z_2 \\ x_2	0	1	2	3	4	5	6	7	8	9	10
0	Not	feasible				0	1	2	3	4	5
1					0	1	2	3	4	5	
2				0	1	2	3	4	5		
3			0	1	2	3	4	5			
4		0	1	2	3	4	5				
5	0	1	2	3	4	5					
6	1	2	3	4	5			$z_4 > 0$			
7	2	3	4	5				Not optimal			
8	3	4	5								
9	4	5									
10	5										

The computation of (19) and the determination of the optimum value of x_2 for possible values of z_2 is illustrated in Table 21-3. The first part of the table (A) shows the costs. The production cost depends only on x_2 and is shown underneath x_2; the carrying cost depends only on z_2 and is shown beside z_2. The cost in the body of the table is the cost in period three if the initial inventory in period 2 is z_2 and x_2 are produced. This cost is obtained by selecting the correct z_3 for (z_2, x_2) from Table 21-2 and then "looking up" F_3 for that argument in Table 21-1. For example, if

$$z_2 = 4; \qquad x_2 = 3$$

then

$$z_3 = 2; \qquad F(2; x_3{}^*) = 13$$

The three costs are added in the second part of the table, (B), to give $F_2(z_2, x_2; x_3{}^*)$. E.g., if

$$z_2 = 4 \qquad \text{carrying cost} = 8$$

$$x_2 = 3 \qquad \text{production cost} = 9$$

$$z_3 = 2 \quad x_2{}^* = 2 \qquad \text{and} \qquad F_3(2; x_3{}^*) = 13$$

Then

$$F_2(4, 3; x_3{}^*) = 8 + 9 + 13 = 30$$

Table 21-3

(A) $2z_2$; x_2^2; $F_1(z_2 + x_2 - 5;\ x_3^*)$

z_2	$2z_2$	$x_2 = 0$	1	2	3	4	5	6	7	8	9	10
		$x_2^2 = 0$	1	4	9	16	25	36	49	64	81	100
0	0						25	18	13	10	9	10
1	2	Not feasible				25	18	13	10	9	10	
2	4				25	18	13	10	9	10	Not optimal	
3	6			25	18	13	10	9	10			
4	8		25	18	13	10	9	10				
5	10	25	18	13	10	9	10					
6	12	18	13	10	9	10						
7	14	13	10	9	10							
8	16	10	9	10								
9	18	9	10									
10	20	10										

(B) $F_2(z_3, x_2;\ x_3^*)$

z_2	$x_2 = 0$	1	2	3	4	5	6	7	8	9	10
0						50	54	62	74	90	110
1					43	45	51	61	75	93	
2				38	38	42	50	62	78		
3			35	33	35	41	51	65			
4		34	30	30	34	42	54				
5	35	29	27	29	35	45					
6	30	26	26	30	38						
7	27	25	27	33							
8	26	26	30								
9	27	29									
10	30										

(C)

z_2	x_2^*	$F_2(z_2;\ x_2^*, x_3^*)$
0	5	50
1	4	43
2	4,3	38
3	3	33
4	3,2	30
5	2	27
6	2,1	26
7	1	25
8	1,0	26
9	0	27
10	0	30

The optimum value of x_2 for any z_2 can now be selected by merely examining all the values in a row of Table 21-3(B) and choosing the smallest. The corresponding x_2 is shown in the third part of the table (C) as x_2^*. The minimum cost is shown under $F_2(z_2; x_2^*, x_3^*)$.

Analogous steps can now be carried out for period 1 using only Table 21-3(C). Theoretically x_1 could take values to 15 but since these are not optimum, the calculations have been carried only to $x_1 = 8$.

Table 21-4

$$z_2(z_1, x_1, 5) = z_1 + x_1 - 5$$

z_1 \ x_1	0	1	2	3	4	5	6	7	8	9
0	Not					0	1	2	3	4
1	feasible				0	1	2	3	4	5
2				0	1	2	3	4	5	6
3			0	1	2	3	4	5	6	7
4		0	1	2	3	4	5	6	7	8
5	0	1	2	3	4	5	6	7	8	9

From Table 21-5(C) it follows that if $z_1 = 0$, then $x_1^* = 5$; this would result in $z_2 = 0$ and from Table 21-3(C) the optimum value of x_2 is 5; again $z_3 = 0$ and from Table 21-1, $x_3^* = 5$. The optimum solution to this problem, if $z_1 = 0$, is

$$x_1^* = x_2^* = x_3^* = 5$$

The example illustrates that the dynamic programming technique may be used to obtain an optimum solution in problems in which there are a finite number of discrete feasible alternatives.

It should be noted that the method does not depend on carrying costs or production costs being the same from period to period. The amount of computation and the algorithm would have been the same even if they had varied. The "tabular" method illustrated in the example could not have been used if numerical values for the parameters and the demand had not been given explicitly. However, the analytic method can be used without numerical values being specified. This will be illustrated in the next section.

Example 4. The previous examples have all dealt with situations where the decisions would be made in a sequence by the very nature of the problem. However, dynamic programming can also be applied to cases

Table 21-5

(A) $2z_1,\ x_1^2,\ F_1(z_1 + x_1 - 5;\ x_2^*, x_3^*)$

z_1 \ x_1	$2z_1$ \ x_1^2	0	2	4	9	16	25	36	49	64	81
	(x_1 →)	(0)	(1)	(2)	(3)	(4)	(5)	(6)	(7)	(8)	(9)
0	0						50	43	38	33	30
1	2		Not			50	43	38	33	30	27
2	4		feasible		50	43	38	33	30	27	26
3	6			50	43	38	33	30	27	26	25
4	8		50	43	38	33	30	27	26	25	26
5	10	50	43	38	33	30	27	26	25	26	27
6	12	43	38	33	30	27	26	25	26	27	
7	14	38	33	30	27	26	25	26	27	Not	
8	16	33	30	27	26	25	26	27		optimal	

(B) $F_1(z_1, x_1;\ x_2^*, x_3^*)$

z_1 \ x_1	0	1	2	3	4	5	6	7	8	9
0						75	79	87	97	111
1					68	70	76	84	96	110
2				63	63	67	73	83	95	111
3			60	58	60	64	72	82	96	112
4		60	55	55	57	63	71	83	97	115
5	60	55	52	52	56	62	72	84	100	118
6	55	52	49	51	55	63	73	87		
7	52	49	48	50	56	64	76			
8	49	48	47	51	57	67	79			

(C)

z_1	x_1^*	$F_1(z_1;\ x_1^*, x_2^*, x_3^*)$
0	5	75
1	4	68
2	3, 4	63
3	3	58
4	2, 3	55
5	2, 3	52
6	2	49
7	2	48
8	2	47

where there is no natural ordering of the decision variables by time or any other criterion.

Suppose the objective is to minimize a function $S(x_1, x_2, x_3)$ over x_1, x_2, x_3 in a set R. The minimum can be expressed as

$$
\begin{aligned}
\min_{(x_1,x_2,x_3)\in R} [S(x_1, x_2, x_3)] &= \min_{x_1\in R_1} \left[\min_{x_2\in R_2} [\min_{x_3\in R_3} S(x_1, x_2, x_3)] \right] \\
&= \min_{x_1\in R_1} \left[\min_{x_2\in R_2} [S_2(x_1, x_2; x_3{}^*)] \right] \\
&= \min_{x_1\in R_1} S_1(x_1; x_2{}^*, x_3{}^*) \\
&= S_0
\end{aligned}
$$

The nested brackets indicate that the minimum of S for all permissible values is to be obtained first. The minimum of the resulting function of x_1 and x_2 is obtained next. Finally the minimum of this function of x_1 is obtained last. In general, the permissible domains R_2 would depend on x_1 and the permissible domain R_3 would depend on x_1 and x_2.

Consider the problem of finding the three-dimensional rectangular parallelepiped, with minimum surface from among all those with constant volumes (Chapter 18, Example 1, page 551. Here

$$ S(x_1, x_2, x_3) = 2(x_1x_2 + x_2x_3 + x_1x_3) $$

and R is given by $x_1x_2x_3 = C$.

Let

$$ S_2(x_1, x_2; x_3{}^*) = \min_{x_3= \frac{C}{x_1x_2}} [2(x_1x_2 + x_2x_3 + x_1x_3)] = 2\left(x_1x_2 + \frac{C}{x_1} + \frac{C}{x_2}\right) $$

Here $x_3{}^* = \dfrac{C}{x_1x_2}$ since this is the only possible value.

Next let

$$ S_1(x_1; x_2{}^*, x_3{}^*) = \min_{0<x_2<\infty} [S_2(x_1, x_2; x_3{}^*)] = \min_{0<x_2<\infty} \left[2\left(x_1x_2 + \frac{C}{x_1} + \frac{C}{x_2}\right) \right] $$

At this point any positive value of x_2 is permissible.

The minimum is obtained by setting the derivative of S_2 with respect to x_2 equal to zero and solving for x_2:

$$ 2\left(x_1 - \frac{C}{x_2{}^2}\right) = 0; \quad x_2{}^* = \frac{\sqrt{C}}{\sqrt{x_1}}; \quad S_1(x_1; x_2{}^*, x_3{}^*) = 2\left(2\sqrt{C}\sqrt{x_1} + \frac{C}{x_1}\right) $$

Finally, let

$$ S_0 = \min_{0<x_1<\infty} [S_1(x_1; x_2{}^*, x_3{}^*)] = \min_{0<x_1<\infty} 2\left(2\sqrt{Cx_1} + \frac{C}{x_1}\right) = 6C^{2/3} $$

since

$$ \frac{dS_1}{dx_1} \quad 2\left(\frac{\sqrt{C}}{\sqrt{x_1}} - \frac{C}{x_1{}^2}\right) = 0 \quad \text{gives} \quad x_1{}^* = C^{1/3} $$

Again any positive value is permissible.

The optimum solution is given by

$$x_1{}^* = C^{1/3}; \qquad x_2{}^* = \left(\frac{C}{x_1{}^*}\right)^{1/2} = C^{1/3}$$

and

$$x_3{}^* = \frac{C}{x_1{}^* x_2{}^*} = C^{1/3}$$

This example illustrates the symmetry of the variables in the method. Theoretically we can use the variables in any order. In practice, the value of the dynamic programming approach in problems such as this depends on the ease with which the regions R_3, R_2, and R_1 and the functions S_2, S_1, and S_0 can be obtained. In problems which can be solved by other methods, the dynamic programming approach is usually less attractive from a computational point of view. However, in some situations the regions and the necessary functions appear naturally, and then dynamic programming can be more efficient than other methods.

EXERCISES

1. Verify, by using second-order condititions that the stationary points in the analytic solution in Example 1 are actually minima.
2. Answer 1 for Example 4.
3. Determine the optimum solution in Example 1 if the production cost is $a + bx^2$ and the carrying cost is c per unit.

B. THE FORWARD ALGORITHM

Dynamic programming can also be applied in a forward manner—beginning with period 1 and working forward to the last period.

Analytic Solution

Consider again the inventory situation described in Examples 1 and 2 in the previous section. Let the requirement be y_1, y_2, y_3 in periods 1, 2 and 3, respectively. In contrast to the definition in the previous section, the variable z_i here represents the ending inventory in period i; z_0 is the ending inventory at the end of period zero and, hence, the initial inventory in period one. The inventory carrying cost in this example is assessed for the inventory on hand at the end of the period. The total cost in period one, given z_0 and making the optimum decision in period one which leads to z_1, is:

$$F_1(z_1; x_1^*) \equiv f_1(z_1; x_1^*) = x_1^{*\,2} + 2z_1$$

and
$$= (y_1 + z_1 - z_0)^2 + 2z_1 \qquad x_1^* z_1 \geq 0$$

$$x_1^* = y_1 + z_1 - z_0$$

(Since z_1 and y_1 are given, there is actually only one possible value of x_1.)

In period two, x_2^* is to be chosen, for any z_2, so as to minimize the sum of the costs in periods 1 and 2, for a given value of z_1. The relation between z_1 and z_2 is

$$z_1 = z_2 - x_2 + y_2$$

$$F_2(z_2, x_2; x_1^*) = f_2(z_2, x_2) + F_1(z_1; x_1^*)$$

$$= f_2(z_2, x_2) + F_1(z_2 - x_2 + y_2; x_1^*)$$

$$= x_2^2 + 2z_2 + (y_1 + y_2 + z_2 - x_2 - z_0)^2 + 2(z_2 - x_2 + y_2)$$

$$\frac{dF_2}{dx_2} = 0; \qquad 2x_2 - 2(y_1 + y_2 + z_2 - x_2 - z_0) - 2 = 0$$

$$x_2^* = \tfrac{1}{2}[y_1 + y_2 + z_2 - z_0 + 1]$$

$$= \tfrac{1}{2}[Y_2 + z_2 - z_0 + 1]$$

where

$$Y_2 = y_1 + y_2$$

$$F_2(z_2; x_2^*, x_1^*) = \tfrac{1}{4}[(Y_2 + z_2 - z_0 + 1)^2 + (Y_2 + z_2 - z_0 - 1)^2]$$
$$+ 3z_2 + (y_2 - y_1 + z_0 - 1)$$

In period 3 the objective is to select x_3^* so as to minimize the sum of the costs in period 1, 2, and 3. The relation between z_2 and z_3 is:

$$z_2 = z_3 - x_3 + y_3$$

$$F_3(z_3, x_3; x_2^*, x_1^*) = f_3(z_3, x_3) + F_2(z_2; x_2^*, x_1^*)$$

$$= x_3^2 + 2z_3 + F_2(z_3 - x_3 + y_3; x_2^*, x_1^*)$$

$$= x_3^2 + 2z_3 + \tfrac{1}{4}(Y_3 + 1 + z_3 - x_3 - z_0)^2$$
$$+ 3(z_3 - x_3 + y_3) + \tfrac{1}{4}(Y_3 - 1 + z_3 - x_3 - z_0)^2$$
$$+ (y_2 - y_1 + z_0 - 1)$$

where

$$Y_3 = y_1 + y_2 + y_3$$

$$\frac{dF_3}{dx_3} = 0; \quad 2x_3 - \tfrac{1}{2}(Y_3 + 1 + z_3 - x_3 - z_0) - 3 - \tfrac{1}{2}(Y_3 - 1 + z_3 - x_3 - z_0)$$

$$x_3^* = \tfrac{1}{3}[Y_3 + z_3 + 3 - z_0]$$

The minimum value of F_3 is given by

$$F_3(z_3; x_3{}^*, x_2{}^*, x_1{}^*)$$

$$= x_3{}^{*2} + \left[x_2{}^* + \frac{z_3 - z_0}{2} \right]^2 + \left[x_1{}^* + \frac{z_3}{2} \right]^2 + 5z_3 + 2(y_3 - y_1) + z_0 - 4$$

If z_3 is to be zero and $z_0 = 0$ by assumption; then

$$x_3{}^* = \frac{Y_3}{3} + 1 = \frac{1}{3}(y_1 + y_2 + y_3) + 1$$

$$z_2 = y_3 - \frac{Y_3}{3} - 1 = \frac{1}{3}(2y_3 - y_1 - y_2) - 1$$

$$x_2{}^* = \frac{1}{2}(y_1 + y_2 + 1) + \frac{1}{6}(2y_3 - y_1 - y_2) - \frac{1}{2}$$

$$= \frac{1}{3}(y_1 + y_2 + y_3)$$

$$z_1 = \frac{1}{3}(2y_3 - y_1 - y_2) - 1 - \frac{1}{3}(y_1 + y_2 + y_3) + y_2$$

$$= \frac{1}{3}[-2y_1 + y_2 + y_3] - 1$$

$$x_1{}^* = y_1 + \frac{1}{3}[-2y_1 + y_2 + y_3] - 1$$

$$= \frac{1}{3}(y_1 + y_2 + y_3) - 1$$

In particular, if $y_1 = 5$, $y_2 = 10$, $y_3 = 15$, then

$$x_3 = 11; \qquad z_2 = 4$$
$$x_2 = 10; \qquad z_1 = 4$$
$$x_1 = 9$$

Tabular Method

The tabular method based on the forward algorithm will be illustrated by the inventory example with the requirements equal to 5 in each of three periods. Again z_i will denote the inventory at the end of the period and the inventory carrying cost will be assessed at the end of the period.

The initial inventory at the beginning of the problem, z_0, is assumed to be known. Then

$$z_1 = z_0 + x_1 - 5$$

The forward technique is based on answering the following question: if the system is in state z_1 at the end of period 1, what is the optimum

Table 21-6A

$$z_0 = z_1 - x_1 + 5$$

z_1 \ x_1	0	1	2	3	4	5	6	7	8	9	10
0	5	4	3	2	1	0		Not			
1	6	5	4	3	2	1	0	feasible			
2	7	6	5	4	3	2	1	0			
3	8	7	6	5	4	3	2	1	0		
4	9	8	7	6	5	4	3	2	1	0	
5	10	9	8	7	6	5	4	3	2	1	0
6	11	10	9	8	7	6	5	4	3	2	1
7	12	11	10	9	8	7	6	5	4	3	2
8	13	12	11	10	9	8	7	6	5	4	3
9	14	13	12	11	10	9	8	7	6	5	4

decision in period 1 assuming optimum decisions have been made in previous periods? Table 21-6A gives the state z_0 for various pairs (z_1, x_1).

At this point it must be assumed that z_0 and the cost associated with z_0 is given; here $z_0 = 0$ and $F_0(z_0) = 0$. Then the optimum x_1 for any z_1 is determined by

$$x_1^* = z_1 + 5$$

and

$$f_1(z_1; x_1^*) = 2z_1 + (z_1 + 5)^2$$

and

$$F_1(z_1; x_1^*) = f_1(z_1; x_1)$$

e.g.,

$$f_1(5, 10) = 10 + 100 = 110 \qquad F_1(5, 10) = 110.$$

The values are shown in Tables 21-6B and 21-6C.

Table 21-6B

$$f_1(z_1, x_1) = 2z_1 + x_1^2 + F_0(z_0)$$

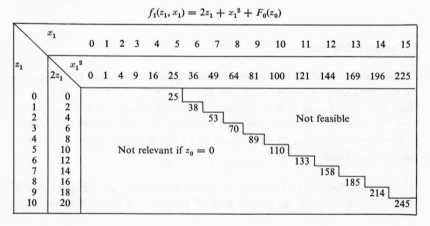

Table 21-6C

z_1	$x_1{}^*$	$F_1(z_1; x_1{}^*)$
0	5	25
1	6	38
2	7	53
3	8	70
4	9	89
5	10	110
6	11	133
7	12	158
8	13	185
9	14	214
10	15	245

If z_0 had been some value other than zero,

$$x_1{}^* = z_1 - z_0 + 5$$

and other entries in Table 21-6B would have been relevant.

The procedure can now be repeated for period 2. The optimum x_2 for any z_2 is that x_2 which minimizes the cost of ending with inventory z_2 in period 2 assuming the optimum decision in period 1.

$$z_1 = z_2 - x_2 + 5$$

and

$$F_2(z_2, x_2; x_1{}^*) = f_2(z_2, x_2) + F_1(z_1; x_1{}^*)$$
$$= 2z_2 + x_2{}^2 + F_1(z_2 - x_2 + 5; x_1{}^*)$$

For example,

$$F_2(4, 6; x_1{}^*) = 2(4) + 6^2 + 70 = 114 \quad \text{since} \quad F_1(3; x_1{}^*) = 70$$

The values of $F_2(z_2, x_2; x_1{}^*)$ are given in Table 21-7A and the values of $x_2{}^*$ and $F_2(z_2; x_2{}^*, x_1{}^*)$ are given in Table 21-7B.

In period 3

$$z_2 = z_3 - x_3 + 5$$

and

$$F_3(z_3, x_3; x_2{}^*, x_1{}^*) = f_3(z_3, x_3) + F_2(z_2; x_2{}^*, x_1{}^*)$$
$$= 2z_3 + x_3{}^2 + F_2(z_3 - x_3 + 5)$$

For example,

$$F(3, 5; x_2{}^*, x_1{}^*) = 6 + 25 + 93 = 124$$

Table 21-7A

$$F_2(z_2, x_2; x_1{}^*) = f_2(z_2, x_2) + F(z_1; x_1{}^*)$$

z_2	$\dfrac{x_2^{\,2}}{2z_2}$	x_2 → 0	1	2	3	4	5	6	7	8	9	10
		0	1	4	9	16	25	36	49	64	81	110
0	0	110	90	74	62	54	50			Not		
1	2	135	113	95	81	71	65	63		feasible		
2	4	162	138	118	102	90	82	78	78			
3	6	191	165	143	125	111	101	95	93	95		
4	8	222	194	170	150	134	122	114	110	110	114	
5	10	255	225	199	177	159	145	135	129	127	129	135
6	12											

Table 21-7B

z_2	$x_2{}^*$	$F_2(z_2; x_2{}^*, x_1{}^*)$
0	5	50
1	6	63
2	6, 7	78
3	7	93
4	7, 8	110
5	8	127

Table 21-8A

$$F_3(z_3, x_2; x_2{}^*, x_1{}^*) = f_3(z_3, x_3) + F_2(z_2; x_2{}^*, x_1{}^*)$$

z_3	$\dfrac{x_1^{\,2}}{2z_2}$	x_2 → 0	1	2	3	4	5	6	7	8	9	10
		0	1	4	9	16	25	36	49	64	81	100
0	0	127	111	97	87	79	75			Not		
1	2		130	116	104	96	90	88		feasible		
2	4			135	123	113	107	103	103			
3	6	Not			142	132	124	120	118	120		
4	8	optimal				151	143	137	135	135	139	
5	10						162	156	152	152	154	160

Table 21-8B

z_3	$x_3{}^*$	$F_3(z_3; x_3{}^*, x_2{}^*, x_1{}^*)$
0	5	75
1	6	88
2	6, 7	103
3	7	118
4	7, 8	135
5	7, 8	152

The values are given in Table 21-8A and values of $x_3{}^*$ and $F_3(z_3; x_3{}^*, x_2{}^*, x_1{}^*)$ are given in Table 21-8B.

From Tables 21-6C, -7B, and -8B the optimum policy for any ending inventory and the associated costs can be determined, assuming $z_0 = 0$. E.g., if $z_3 = 0$, $x_3{}^* = 5$, then $z_2 = 0$, $x_2{}^* = 5$, and $z_1 = 0$, $x_1{}^* = 5$, and the minimum total cost is 75.

EXERCISES

1. Verify, by using second-order conditions, that the stationary points in the analytic solution are actually minima.
2. Use the analytic method and the forward algorithm to solve the inventory problem for the case where demand is y_1, y_2, and y_3 in each of the three periods, respectively; the production cost is $a + bx^2$ and the carrying cost is c per unit.
3. Solve 2 by using the tabular method; assume $y_1 = 5$, $y_2 = 6$, $y_3 = 7$, $a = 5$, $b = 2$, and $c = 3$. Assume that production cost is zero if $x = 0$.

C. GENERAL STATEMENT

The previous examples have illustrated how the backward and forward dynamic programming algorithms can be applied to problems formulated as a sequence of events. In this section a more general statement will be given. Further examples are also included. The elements in a "discrete" problem are the following:

Stages or Periods. The system under consideration will exist in a number of finite states or periods. These stages will be numbered successively, 1, 2, 3, . . . , n.

State of the System. In each period or stage the system is described by a single number called the "state." The state of the system in period i will be denoted by z_i; z_i can be any one of a set of possible states, $[z_i]$, in which the system can exist during the period. The problem is discrete because z_i can assume only discrete values.

Uncontrollable Variable. The state of the system may be changed at the end of a period as the result of an uncontrollable variable. The value of the variable at the end of period i will be denoted by y_i.

Decision Variable. The decision maker has control over a variable, x; the value chosen by the decision maker in the ith period is denoted by x_i. This choice affects the state in the next period.

Change of State. The system changes from one state to another at the beginning of each period. The new state is a function of the state of the system in the previous period, the uncontrollable variable during the ith period and the decision variable for the ith period, e.g.,

$$z_{i+1} = z_{i+1}(x_i, y_i, z_i)$$

This formulation permits the function determining the new state to change from period to period.

Period	1	2	3		n
State	z_1	z_2	z_3		z_n
Uncontrollable variable	y_1	y_2	y_3	$\cdots$	y_n
Decision variable	x_1	x_2	x_3	$\cdots$	x_n

In a particular problem it is sometimes desirable to define z_i, x_i, and y_i as occurring at points in the period other than those given above. This is permissible. However, the sequence in which x_i and y_i occur must be stated explicitly.

Objective. Costs (benefits) are associated with the system being in a particular state in a particular period and with a given value of the decision. The general cost function is a function of all the variables:

$$x_1, x_2, \ldots, x_n; \quad z_0, z_1, \ldots, z_n; \quad y_1, \ldots, y_n$$

The cost function is expressed as a series of functions; let

$f_i(z_i, x_i)$ = cost incurred if the system is in state z_i at the beginning of period i and decision x_i is made in period i

Actually, f_i is also a function of the uncontrollable, but known, variable; the symbol y_i is usually understood and included only if necessary.

$F_i(z_i, x_i; X_{i+1}^*)$ = total cost incurred during periods i, $i +$ $1, \ldots, n$, if the system is in state z_i at the beginning of period i, decision x_i is made in period i and optimal decisions are made in periods $i + 1, i + 2, \ldots, n$.

The backward algorithm is based on the Principle of Optimality, stated by Bellman [1957] as: "An optimal policy has the property that whatever the initial state and the initial decisions are, the remaining decisions must constitute an optimal policy with regard to the state resulting from the first decision." This leads to the optimization of the sequence of functions

$$F_i(z_i; X_i^*) = \operatorname*{opt}_{x_i} [F_i(z_i, x_i; X_{i+1}^*)] = \operatorname*{opt}_{x_i} [f_i(z_i, x_i) + F_{i+1}(z_{i+1}; X_{i+1}^*)]$$

for $i = n, n - 1, n - 2, \ldots, 1$.

The optimization must be over all feasible values of x_i and the method used may be either the analytic or the tabular, as appropriate.

The forward algorithm is based on the Dual of the Principal of Optimality stated by Bhavnani and Chen [1962] as: "An optimal policy has the property that whatever the ensuing state and decisions are, the preceding decisions must constitute an optimal policy with regard to the state ensuing from the last decision." This leads to the optimization of the sequence:

$$F_i(z_i; X_i^*) = \operatorname*{opt}_{x_i} [F_i(z_i, x_i; X_{i-1}^*)] = \operatorname*{opt}_{x_i} [f_i(z_i, x_i) + F_{i-1}(z_{i-1}; X_{i-1}^*)]$$

where $z_{i-1} = z_{i-1}(x_i, y_i, z_i)$ for $i = 1, 2, \ldots, n$. Here X_i^* denotes the optimal decisions made in periods $1, 2, \ldots, i$, and F_i denotes the total cost for periods $1, 2, \ldots, i$.

Example I. A firm operates a rubber plantation of A units in size in a country which has just passed a law expropriating all foreign owned land in n years from the present with no compensation. In the meantime the government will purchase any land offered for a total price $g(y)$ where y is the number of units offered. The function is concave because the government does not want all the land offered immediately. The return is a per unit in normal use.

Let z_i = land remaining at the beginning of the ith year, and let x_i denote the amount of land sold at the beginning of the ith period. Then $z_i - x_i$ = amount of land used as plantation during the ith period. The return in the ith period is return from sale and return from normal use:

$$f_i(z_i; x_i) = g(x_i) + (z_i - x_i)a$$

and

$$z_i = z_{i-1} - x_{i-1}$$

Consider a specific case in which $A = 4$; $a = 1, n = 3$ and the purchase price is given by $g(y) = \frac{1}{2}[9y - y^2]$. Furthermore, suppose only complete units can be sold.

$$F_3(z_3, x_3) = g(x_3) + (z_3 - x_3) = \frac{1}{2}[9x_3 - x_3^2] + (z_3 - x_3)$$

The values of $f_3(z_3, x_3)$, and x_3^*, $F_3(z_3, x_3^*)$ are given in Tables 21-9A and 21-9B, respectively. For example $f_3(3, 1) = g(1) + (3 - 1) = \frac{1}{2}[9(1) - (1)^2] + 2 = 6$.

$$F_3(z_3; x_3^*) = \max_{x_3} f_3(z_3, x_3)$$

$$= \max_{x_3} [\tfrac{1}{2}(9x_3 - x_3^2) + (z_3 - x_3)]$$

For example,

$$F_3(3; x_3^*) = \max_{x_3} [f_3(z_3; x_3)] = \max_{0,1,2,3} [3, 6, 8, 9] = 9; \ x_3^* = 3$$

Table 21-9A

$$f_3(z_3, x_3)$$

z_3 \ x_3	0	1	2	3	4
0	0		Not feasible		
1	1	4			
2	2	5	7		
3	3	6	8	9	
4	4	7	9	10	10

Table 21-9B

z_3	x_3^*	$F_3(z_3, x_3^*)$
0	0	0
1	1	4
2	2	7
3	3	9
4	3, 4	10

The total return for years 2 and 3 is given by

$$F_2(z_2, x_2; x_3^*) = f_2(z_2, x_2) + F_3(z_3; x_3^*)$$

$$= f_2(z_2, x_2) + F_3(z_2 - x_2; x_3^*)$$

$$= g(x_2) + (z_2 - x_3) + F_3(z_2 - x_2; x_3^*)$$

For example,

$$F_2(3, 2; x_3^*) = f_2(3, 2) + F_3(z_2 - x_2; x_3^*)$$

$$= \tfrac{1}{2}[18 - 4] + 3 - 2 + 4 = 7 + 1 + 4 = 12.$$

The values of $F_2(z_2, x_2; x_3^*)$, x_2^* and $F_2(z_2; x_2^*, x_3^*)$ are given in Tables 21-10A and 21-10B, respectively.

where $F_2(z_2; x_2^*, x_3^*) = \max_{x_2} \{f_2(z_2, x_2) + F_3(z_3; x_3^*)\}$

$$= \max_{x_2} \{f_2(z_2, x_2) + F_3(z_2 - x_2; x_3^*)\}$$

Table 21-10A

$$F_2(z_2, x_2; x_3{}^*)$$

z_2 \ x_2	0	1	2	3	4
0	0		Not feasible		
1	5	4			
2	9	9	7		
3	12	13	12	9	
4	14	16	16	14	10

Table 21-10B

z_2	$x_2{}^*$	$F_2(z_2; x_2{}^*, x_3{}^*)$
0	0	0
1	0	5
2	0, 1	9
3	1	13
4	1, 2	16

The total return for years 1, 2, and 3 is given by

$$F_1(z_1, x_1; x_2{}^*, x_3{}^*) = f_1(z_1, x_1) + F_2(z_2; x_2{}^*, x_3{}^*)$$

The values of $F_1(z_1, x_1; x_2{}^*, x_3{}^*)$, $x_1{}^*$ and $F_1(z_1; x_1{}^*, x_2{}^*, x_3{}^*)$ are given in Tables 21-11A and 21-11B, respectively.

Table 21-11A

z_1 \ x_1	0	1	2	3	4
0	0				
1	6	4	Not feasible		
2	11	10	7		
3	16	15	13	9	
4	20	20	18	15	10

Table 21-11B

z_1	$x_1{}^*$	$F(z_1; x_1{}^*, x_2{}^*, x_3{}^*)$
0	0	0
1	0	6
2	0	11
3	0	16
4	0, 1	20

Since $z_1 = 4$ the sequence of initial states and decisions are

$$z_1 = 4; x_1{}^* = \begin{cases} 0; z_2 = 4; x_2{}^* = \begin{cases} 1; z_3 = 3; x_3{}^* = 3; \\ 2; z_3 = 2; x_3{}^* = 2; \end{cases} \\ 1; z_2 = 3; x_2{}^* = 1; \end{cases} \bigg\} z_4 = 0$$

Example 2. The same example can also be solved by the forward algorithm. Let z_i denote the land remaining at the end of the ith year and x_i denote the land sold at the beginning of the ith period. Then

$$z_i = z_{i-1} - x_i \quad \text{or} \quad x_i = -z_i + z_{i-1}$$

This relationship is shown in Table 21-12A.

The return in year one, using the fact that $z_0 = 4$, is

$$F_1(z_1, x_1) = g(x_1) + z_1 + F(z_0)$$

$$= \tfrac{1}{2}[9x_1 - x_1^2] + 3$$

For example,

$$F_1(3, 1) = \tfrac{1}{2}[9 - 1] + 3 = 7$$

Values of $F_1(z_1, x_1)$ are given in Table 21-12B. The optimum value of x_1 for any z_1 is that value of x_1 which maximizes the return, given that $z_0 = 4$. The maximum return is the maximum in the row, hence $F_1(z_1; x_1{}^*)$ is the maximum value in each row and $x_1{}^*$ is the value of x heading the column in which $F_1(z_1; x_1{}^*)$ appears. These appear in Table 21-12C.

Table 21-12

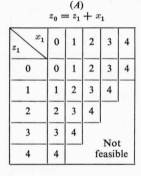

(A) $z_0 = z_1 + x_1$

z_1 \ x_1	0	1	2	3	4
0	0	1	2	3	4
1	1	2	3	4	
2	2	3	4		
3	3	4			
4	4		Not feasible		

(B) $F_1(z_1, x_1)$

z_1 \ x_1	0	1	2	3	4
0	0	4	7	9	10
1	1	5	8	10	
2	2	6	9		
3	3	7			
4	4				

(C)

z_1	$x_1{}^*$	$F_1(z_1; x_1{}^*)$
0	4	10
3	3	10
2	2	9
3	1	7
4	0	4

In period two,

$$z_2 = z_1 - x_2$$

and

$$F_2(z_2, x_2; x_1{}^*) = g(x_2) + z_2 + F_1(z_1; x_1{}^*)$$

$$= \tfrac{1}{2}[9x_2 - x_2^2] + z_2 + F_1(z_2 + x_2; x_1{}^*)$$

For example,

$$F(2, 2) = \tfrac{1}{2}[18 - 4] + 2 + 4 = 13$$

These values are shown in Table 21-13A and the optima in Table 21-13B.

Table 21-13

(A)

$$F_2(z_2, x_2; x_1{}^*)$$

z_2 \\ x_2	0	1	2	3	4
0	10	14	16	16	14
1	11	14	15	14	
2	11	13	13		
3	10	11	Not feasible		
4	8				

(B)

z_2	$x_2{}^*$	$F_2(z_2; x_2{}^*, x_1{}^*)$
0	2, 3	16
1	2	15
2	1, 2	13
3	1	11
4	0	8

In period 3

$$z_3 = z_2 - x_3$$

and

$$F_3(z_3, x_3; x_2{}^*, x_1{}^*) = g(x_3) + z_3 + F_2(z_2; x_2{}^*, x_1{}^*)$$

$$= \tfrac{1}{2}[9x_3 - x_3{}^2] + z_3 + F_2(z_3 + x_3; x_2{}^*, x_1{}^*)$$

For example,

$$F_3(1, 3; x_2{}^*, x_1{}^*) = \tfrac{1}{2}[27 - 9] + 1 + 8 = 18$$

The values and the optima are shown in Table 21-14A and 21-14B.

Table 21-14

(A)

$$F_3(z_3, x_3; x_2{}^*, x_1{}^*)$$

z_3 \\ x_3	0	1	2	3	4
0	16	19	20	20	18
1	16	18	19	18	
2	15	17	17		
3	14	15			
4	12		Not feasible		

(B)

z_3	$x_3{}^*$	$F_3(z_3; x_3{}^*, x_2{}^*, x_1{}^*)$
0	2, 3	20
1	2	19
2	1, 2	17
3	1	15
4	0	12

The optimum policy is:

Table 21-14B	Table 21-13B	Table 21-12C
$z_2 = z_3 + x_3{}^*$	$z_1 = z_2 + x_2{}^*$	$z_0 = z_1 + x_1{}^2$

$$z_3 = 0;\, x_3{}^* = \begin{array}{c} 2;\, z_2 = 2;\, x_2{}^* = \begin{array}{c} 1;\, z_1 = 3;\, x_1{}^* = 1; \\ \\ 2;\, z_1 = 4 \end{array} \\ \\ 3;\, z_2 = 3;\, x_2{}^* = 1;\, z_1 = 4 \end{array} \left.\begin{array}{c} \\ \\ \end{array}\right\} x_1{}^* = 0;$$

$$z_0 = 4$$

This sequence of optimum decisions is the same as that obtained in Example 1.

EXERCISES

1. Solve Exercise 3, p. 154, by dynamic programming.
2. A mining firm has unlimited ore reserves of two minerals, X and Y. The refining of both ores requires the use of a plant which has an initial capacity of C_0 units per period. Refining either mineral deteriorates the plant so that the capacity for the next period is reduced. In particular, if x units of X and y units of Y are refined in one period, the capacity at the end of the first period C_1 is given by

$$C_1 = \alpha x + \beta y$$
$$= \alpha x + \beta(C_0 - x)$$

if the plant is fully utilized.

The return per unit of x refined is given by $h(x)$ and by $g(y)$ for each unit of y. The total return in one period, if the plant is fully utilized, is

$$h(x) + g(C_0 - x)$$

(a) Formulate this as a dynamic programming problem. Assume the interest rate is i and h and g are unchanged over time.
(b) Compute the optimum decisions for the case where

$$C_0 = 1,000; \quad i = 0$$

$$h(x) = 0.02x^2 - 2,000 \quad \text{if} \quad 0.02x^2 - 2,000 \geq 0$$
$$= 0 \text{ otherwise}$$

$$g(y) = 0.03y^2 - 5,000 \quad \text{if} \quad 0.03y^2 - 5,000 \geq 0$$
$$= 0 \text{ otherwise}$$

$$\alpha = 0.9 \,\, \beta = 0.8$$

Assume that refining will be carried out for three periods and that the capacity remaining at the end of the third period has no value.

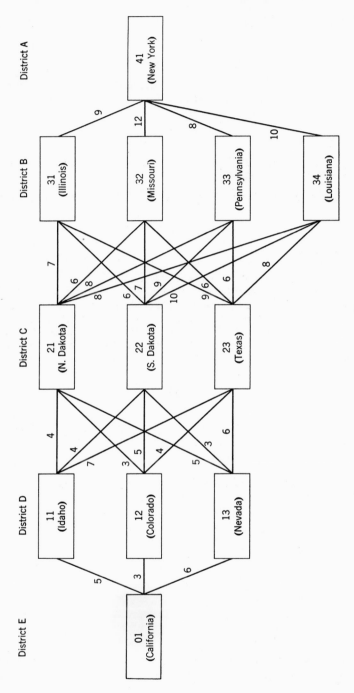

Figure 21.1   Travel costs.

(c) Show that if h and g are both convex functions and $h(0) = g(0) = 0$; then at each stage x takes either the upper or lower limit.

3. Use dynamic programming to determine the optimum path to go from New York to California by plane when business commitments require that at least one state in each of the company's business districts be visited, and when the objective is to minimize travel costs. Rates between cities are shown in the various line segments in Fig. 21.1.

Notes and References

Bellman, R. (1957), *Dynamic Programming*, Princeton University Press, Princeton, N. J.
Bhavnani, K. H., and Chen, K. (1962), "Dual of the Optimality Principle in Dynamic Programming," Scientific Paper 62–163–292–P1, Westinghouse Electric Corporation.

Appendices

A. Miscellaneous Formulas   638

1. Greek alphabet,   638
2. Permutations and Combinations,   638

B. Interest Tables   640

1. Value of 1 n Periods Hence with Interest Rate i per Period

$$F(i, n) = (1 + i)^n, \quad 642$$

2. Present Value, P, of 1 to be Received n Periods Hence with Interest Rate i per Period $P(i, n) = (1 + i)^{-n}$,   648

3. Value of 1 per Period, n Periods Hence, at Interest Rate i per Period

$$F(i, n) = \frac{(1 + i)^n - 1}{i}, \quad 654$$

4. Present Value of 1 per Period at Interest Rate i per Period

$$P(i, n) = \frac{1 - (1 + i)^{-n}}{i}, \quad 660$$

5. Value of 1 n Periods Hence with Continuous Compounding at Rate δ

$$F(\delta, n) = e^{\delta n}, \quad 666$$

6. Present Value, P, of 1 to be Received n Periods Hence with Continuous Compounding at Rate δ $P(\delta, n) = e^{-\delta n}$ 672

7. Value of 1 Received Uniformly per Period, n Periods Hence, with Continuous Compounding at Effective Rate i per Period

$$\delta = \ln(1 + i) \qquad F(\delta, n) = \frac{e^{\delta n} - 1}{\delta}, \quad 678$$

8. Present Value of 1 Received Uniformly with Continuous Compounding at Effective Rate i per Period $\delta = \ln(1 + i) \qquad P(\delta, n) = \dfrac{1 - e^{-\delta n}}{\delta}$,

684

C. Contour Lines of Polynomials of Degree 2 in Two Variables   690

1. Summary of procedures for reducing second-degree polynomial functions in two independent variables to standard form,   690
2. Summary of standard forms,   692

APPENDIX A

Miscellaneous Formulas

Greek Alphabet

Letters	Names	Letters	Names	Letters	Names
A α	Alpha	I ι	Iota	P ρ	Rho
B β	Beta	K κ	Kappa	Σ σ	Sigma
Γ γ	Gamma	Λ λ	Lambda	T τ	Tau
Δ δ	Delta	M μ	Mu	Υ υ	Upsilon
E ε	Epsilon	N ν	Nu	Φ ϕ	Phi
Z ζ	Zeta	Ξ ξ	Xi	X χ	Chi
H η	Eta	O o	Omicron	Ψ ψ	Psi
Θ θ	Theta	Π π	Pi	Ω ω	Omega

Permutations and Combinations

Each different arrangement (ordering) of all or a part of n different objects is called a *permutation*. The number of permutations, of n different things taken r at a time, is

$$P_r^n = n(n-1)(n-2)\cdots(n-r+1) = \frac{n!}{(n-r)!} \tag{1}$$

The number of *combinations* of n different things taken without regard to the arrangement, r at a time, is

$$C_r^n = \binom{n}{r} = \frac{P_r^n}{r!} = \frac{n(n-1)\cdots(n-r+1)}{r(r-1)\cdots(1)} = \frac{n!}{r!\,(n-r)!} \tag{2}$$

By definition, $0! = 1$; hence $C_0^n = C_n^n = 1$.

638

The number N of distinguishable permutations of n things taken n at a time, of which p are alike, q others alike, $\ldots$, z others alike, where $p + q + \cdots + z = n$, is:

$$N = n!/p!\,q!\cdots z!$$

The Binomial expansion is:

$$(q + p)^n = q^n + C_1{}^n pq^{n-1} + \cdots + C_r{}^n p^r q^{n-r} + \cdots + p^n \qquad (3)$$

where the *binomial coefficients* $C_r{}^n$ are given by (2).

APPENDIX B

Interest Tables

The tables in this appendix are designed to facilitate computation in financial problems for both discrete and continuous compounding for ranges of parameters commonly encountered. References to more extensive tables are given on page 84. The tables give present and future values for single payments and periodic payments under discrete and continuous discounting and compounding for 1 to 50 periods for selected compounding rates. The particular rates chosen for *discrete discounting and compounding* for both single payments and periodic payments are those occurring frequently in practical problems. The rates chosen for *continuous discounting and compounding for the* single payment case are different from those for the periodic payment case. For the periodic payments (Tables 7 and 8) the rates δ are the same as the effective rate per period i under the discrete case (Tables 3 and 4). This permits the present and future value under discrete compounding to be compared directly with the value under continuous compounding for the same effective rate per period. The values selected for continuous compounding of a single payment are values of δ that are the same as values of i in the discrete case. Tables for uniform payments for these values of δ can be computed from Tables 5 and 6 by using the formulas:

$$F(\delta, n) = \frac{e^{\delta n} - 1}{\delta} \tag{1}$$

$$P(\delta, n) = \frac{1 - e^{-\delta n}}{\delta} \tag{2}$$

The different cases are illustrated in the accompanying table.

Compounding and Discounting Rates Used in Interest Tables

	Discrete Compounding	Continuous Compounding	Continuous Compounding
Single Payment	Tables 1, 2 $i =$ [1]	Tables 5, 6 $\delta =$ [1]	$i =$ [1] Same as Tables 1 and 2
Periodic Payment	Tables 3, 4 $i =$ [1]	Tables 7, 8 $i =$ [1] $\delta = \ln (1 + i)$	$\delta =$ [1] Use Tables 5, 6 and formulas (1) and (2)

[1] 0.01, 0.015, 0.02, 0.03, 0.04, 0.05, 0.06, 0.08, 0.10, 0.12, 0.15, 0.20, 0.25, 0.30, 0.35, 0.40, 0.45, 0.50.

All entries in the tables are given with five significant digits. Each number is in the form xEy where x is a five-digit number not less than 0.1 and not greater than 0.99999 and y gives the power of 10 by which x must be multiplied, e.g.,

$$0.101000E\ \ 02 = 10.1000$$
$$0.101000E\ \ 01 = 1.01000$$
$$0.101000E\ \ 00 = 0.101000$$
$$0.101000E{-}01 = 0.0101000$$
$$0.101000E{-}02 = 0.00101000$$

Table I.   Value of I n Periods Hence with Interest Rate i per Period

$$F(i, n) = (1 + i)^n$$

n	.01	.015	.02
1	0.101000E 01	0.101500E 01	0.102000E 01
2	0.102010E 01	0.103023E 01	0.104040E 01
3	0.103030E 01	0.104568E 01	0.106121E 01
4	0.104060E 01	0.106136E 01	0.108243E 01
5	0.105101E 01	0.107728E 01	0.110408E 01
6	0.106152E 01	0.109344E 01	0.112616E 01
7	0.107214E 01	0.110984E 01	0.114869E 01
8	0.108286E 01	0.112649E 01	0.117166E 01
9	0.109369E 01	0.114339E 01	0.119509E 01
10	0.110462E 01	0.116054E 01	0.121899E 01
11	0.111567E 01	0.117795E 01	0.124337E 01
12	0.112683E 01	0.119562E 01	0.126824E 01
13	0.113809E 01	0.121355E 01	0.129361E 01
14	0.114947E 01	0.123176E 01	0.131948E 01
15	0.116097E 01	0.125023E 01	0.134587E 01
16	0.117258E 01	0.126899E 01	0.137279E 01
17	0.118430E 01	0.128802E 01	0.140024E 01
18	0.119615E 01	0.130734E 01	0.142825E 01
19	0.120811E 01	0.132695E 01	0.145681E 01
20	0.122019E 01	0.134686E 01	0.148595E 01
21	0.123239E 01	0.136706E 01	0.151567E 01
22	0.124472E 01	0.138756E 01	0.154598E 01
23	0.125716E 01	0.140838E 01	0.157690E 01
24	0.126973E 01	0.142950E 01	0.160844E 01
25	0.128243E 01	0.145095E 01	0.164061E 01
26	0.129526E 01	0.147271E 01	0.167342E 01
27	0.130821E 01	0.149480E 01	0.170689E 01
28	0.132129E 01	0.151722E 01	0.174102E 01
29	0.133450E 01	0.153998E 01	0.177584E 01
30	0.134785E 01	0.156308E 01	0.181136E 01
31	0.136133E 01	0.158653E 01	0.184759E 01
32	0.137494E 01	0.161032E 01	0.188454E 01
33	0.138869E 01	0.163448E 01	0.192223E 01
34	0.140258E 01	0.165900E 01	0.196068E 01
35	0.141660E 01	0.168388E 01	0.199989E 01
36	0.143077E 01	0.170914E 01	0.203989E 01
37	0.144508E 01	0.173478E 01	0.208069E 01
38	0.145953E 01	0.176080E 01	0.212230E 01
39	0.147412E 01	0.178721E 01	0.216474E 01
40	0.148886E 01	0.181402E 01	0.220804E 01
41	0.150375E 01	0.184123E 01	0.225220E 01
42	0.151879E 01	0.186885E 01	0.229724E 01
43	0.153398E 01	0.189688E 01	0.234319E 01
44	0.154932E 01	0.192533E 01	0.239005E 01
45	0.156481E 01	0.195421E 01	0.243785E 01
46	0.158046E 01	0.198353E 01	0.248661E 01
47	0.159626E 01	0.201328E 01	0.253634E 01
48	0.161223E 01	0.204348E 01	0.258707E 01
49	0.162835E 01	0.207413E 01	0.263881E 01
50	0.164463E 01	0.210524E 01	0.269159E 01

Table I (Continued).   **Value of I** n **Periods Hence with Interest Rate**
i **per Period**

$$F(i, n) = (1 + i)^n$$

.03	.04	.05
0.103000E 01	0.104000E 01	0.105000E 01
0.106090E 01	0.108160E 01	0.110250E 01
0.109273E 01	0.112486E 01	0.115763E 01
0.112551E 01	0.116986E 01	0.121551E 01
0.115927E 01	0.121665E 01	0.127628E 01
0.119405E 01	0.126532E 01	0.134010E 01
0.122987E 01	0.131593E 01	0.140710E 01
0.126677E 01	0.136857E 01	0.147746E 01
0.130477E 01	0.142331E 01	0.155133E 01
0.134392E 01	0.148024E 01	0.162889E 01
0.138423E 01	0.153945E 01	0.171034E 01
0.142576E 01	0.160103E 01	0.179586E 01
0.146853E 01	0.166507E 01	0.188565E 01
0.151259E 01	0.173168E 01	0.197993E 01
0.155797E 01	0.180094E 01	0.207893E 01
0.160471E 01	0.187298E 01	0.218287E 01
0.165285E 01	0.194790E 01	0.229202E 01
0.170243E 01	0.202582E 01	0.240662E 01
0.175351E 01	0.210685E 01	0.252695E 01
0.180611E 01	0.219112E 01	0.265330E 01
0.186029E 01	0.227877E 01	0.278596E 01
0.191610E 01	0.236992E 01	0.292526E 01
0.197359E 01	0.246472E 01	0.307152E 01
0.203279E 01	0.256330E 01	0.322510E 01
0.209378E 01	0.266584E 01	0.338635E 01
0.215659E 01	0.277247E 01	0.355567E 01
0.222129E 01	0.288337E 01	0.373346E 01
0.228793E 01	0.299870E 01	0.392013E 01
0.235657E 01	0.311865E 01	0.411614E 01
0.242726E 01	0.324340E 01	0.432194E 01
0.250008E 01	0.337313E 01	0.453804E 01
0.257508E 01	0.350806E 01	0.476494E 01
0.265234E 01	0.364838E 01	0.500319E 01
0.273191E 01	0.379432E 01	0.525335E 01
0.281386E 01	0.394609E 01	0.551602E 01
0.289828E 01	0.410393E 01	0.579182E 01
0.298523E 01	0.426809E 01	0.608141E 01
0.307478E 01	0.443881E 01	0.638548E 01
0.316703E 01	0.461637E 01	0.670475E 01
0.326204E 01	0.480102E 01	0.703999E 01
0.335990E 01	0.499306E 01	0.739199E 01
0.346070E 01	0.519278E 01	0.776159E 01
0.356452E 01	0.540050E 01	0.814967E 01
0.367145E 01	0.561652E 01	0.855715E 01
0.378160E 01	0.584118E 01	0.898501E 01
0.389504E 01	0.607482E 01	0.943426E 01
0.401190E 01	0.631782E 01	0.990597E 01
0.413225E 01	0.657053E 01	0.104013E 02
0.425622E 01	0.683335E 01	0.109213E 02
0.438391E 01	0.710668E 01	0.114674E 02

Table I (Continued).   Value of I n Periods Hence with Interest Rate
i per Period

$$F(i, n) = (1 + i)^n$$

.06	.08	.10
0.106000E 01	0.108000E 01	0.110000E 01
0.112360E 01	0.116640E 01	0.121000E 01
0.119102E 01	0.125971E 01	0.133100E 01
0.126248E 01	0.136049E 01	0.146410E 01
0.133823E 01	0.146933E 01	0.161051E 01
0.141852E 01	0.158687E 01	0.177156E 01
0.150363E 01	0.171382E 01	0.194872E 01
0.159385E 01	0.185093E 01	0.214359E 01
0.168948E 01	0.199900E 01	0.235795E 01
0.179085E 01	0.215892E 01	0.259374E 01
0.189830E 01	0.233164E 01	0.285312E 01
0.201220E 01	0.251817E 01	0.313843E 01
0.213293E 01	0.271962E 01	0.345227E 01
0.226090E 01	0.293719E 01	0.379750E 01
0.239656E 01	0.317217E 01	0.417725E 01
0.254035E 01	0.342594E 01	0.459497E 01
0.269277E 01	0.370002E 01	0.505447E 01
0.285434E 01	0.399602E 01	0.555992E 01
0.302560E 01	0.431570E 01	0.611591E 01
0.320714E 01	0.466096E 01	0.672750E 01
0.339956E 01	0.503383E 01	0.740025E 01
0.360354E 01	0.543654E 01	0.814027E 01
0.381975E 01	0.587146E 01	0.895430E 01
0.404893E 01	0.634118E 01	0.984973E 01
0.429187E 01	0.684848E 01	0.108347E 02
0.454938E 01	0.739635E 01	0.119182E 02
0.482235E 01	0.798806E 01	0.131100E 02
0.511169E 01	0.862711E 01	0.144210E 02
0.541839E 01	0.931727E 01	0.158631E 02
0.574349E 01	0.100627E 02	0.174494E 02
0.608810E 01	0.108677E 02	0.191943E 02
0.645339E 01	0.117371E 02	0.211138E 02
0.684059E 01	0.126760E 02	0.232252E 02
0.725103E 01	0.136901E 02	0.255477E 02
0.768609E 01	0.147853E 02	0.281024E 02
0.814725E 01	0.159682E 02	0.309127E 02
0.863609E 01	0.172456E 02	0.340039E 02
0.915425E 01	0.186253E 02	0.374043E 02
0.970351E 01	0.201153E 02	0.411448E 02
0.102857E 02	0.217245E 02	0.452593E 02
0.109029E 02	0.234625E 02	0.497852E 02
0.115570E 02	0.253395E 02	0.547637E 02
0.122505E 02	0.273666E 02	0.602401E 02
0.129855E 02	0.295560E 02	0.662641E 02
0.137646E 02	0.319204E 02	0.728905E 02
0.145905E 02	0.344741E 02	0.801795E 02
0.154659E 02	0.372320E 02	0.881975E 02
0.163939E 02	0.402106E 02	0.970172E 02
0.173775E 02	0.434274E 02	0.106719E 03
0.184202E 02	0.469016E 02	0.117391E 03

Table I (*Continued*).   **Value of I n Periods Hence with Interest Rate**
i per Period

$$F(i, n) = (1 + i)^n$$

n	.12		.15		.20	
1	0.112000E	01	0.115000E	01	0.120000E	01
2	0.125440E	01	0.132250E	01	0.144000E	01
3	0.140493E	01	0.152088E	01	0.172800E	01
4	0.157352E	01	0.174901E	01	0.207360E	01
5	0.176234E	01	0.201136E	01	0.248832E	01
6	0.197382E	01	0.231306E	01	0.298598E	01
7	0.221068E	01	0.266002E	01	0.358318E	01
8	0.247596E	01	0.305902E	01	0.429982E	01
9	0.277308E	01	0.351788E	01	0.515978E	01
10	0.310585E	01	0.404556E	01	0.619174E	01
11	0.347855E	01	0.465239E	01	0.743008E	01
12	0.389598E	01	0.535025E	01	0.891610E	01
13	0.436349E	01	0.615279E	01	0.106993E	02
14	0.488711E	01	0.707571E	01	0.128392E	02
15	0.547357E	01	0.813706E	01	0.154070E	02
16	0.613039E	01	0.935762E	01	0.184884E	02
17	0.686604E	01	0.107613E	02	0.221861E	02
18	0.768997E	01	0.123755E	02	0.266233E	02
19	0.861276E	01	0.142318E	02	0.319480E	02
20	0.964629E	01	0.163665E	02	0.383376E	02
21	0.108038E	02	0.188215E	02	0.460051E	02
22	0.121003E	02	0.216447E	02	0.552061E	02
23	0.135523E	02	0.248915E	02	0.662474E	02
24	0.151786E	02	0.286252E	02	0.794968E	02
25	0.170001E	02	0.329190E	02	0.953962E	02
26	0.190401E	02	0.378568E	02	0.114475E	03
27	0.213249E	02	0.435353E	02	0.137371E	03
28	0.238839E	02	0.500656E	02	0.164845E	03
29	0.267499E	02	0.575755E	02	0.197814E	03
30	0.299599E	02	0.662118E	02	0.237376E	03
31	0.335551E	02	0.761435E	02	0.284852E	03
32	0.375817E	02	0.875565E	02	0.341822E	03
33	0.420915E	02	0.100700E	03	0.410186E	03
34	0.471425E	02	0.115805E	03	0.492224E	03
35	0.527996E	02	0.133176E	03	0.590668E	03
36	0.591356E	02	0.153152E	03	0.708802E	03
37	0.662318E	02	0.176125E	03	0.850562E	03
38	0.741797E	02	0.202543E	03	0.102067E	04
39	0.830812E	02	0.232925E	03	0.122481E	04
40	0.930510E	02	0.267864E	03	0.146977E	04
41	0.104217E	03	0.308043E	03	0.176373E	04
42	0.116723E	03	0.354250E	03	0.211647E	04
43	0.130730E	03	0.407387E	03	0.253977E	04
44	0.146418E	03	0.468495E	03	0.304772E	04
45	0.163988E	03	0.538769E	03	0.365726E	04
46	0.183666E	03	0.619585E	03	0.438871E	04
47	0.205706E	03	0.712522E	03	0.526646E	04
48	0.230391E	03	0.819401E	03	0.631975E	04
49	0.258038E	03	0.942311E	03	0.758370E	04
50	0.289002E	03	0.108366E	04	0.910044E	04

Table I (Continued).   *Value of I n Periods Hence with Interest Rate i per Period*

$$F(i, n) = (1 + i)^n$$

.25	.30	.35
0.125000E 01	0.130000E 01	0.135000E 01
0.156250E 01	0.169000E 01	0.182250E 01
0.195313E 01	0.219700E 01	0.246038E 01
0.244141E 01	0.285610E 01	0.332151E 01
0.305176E 01	0.371293E 01	0.448403E 01
0.381470E 01	0.482681E 01	0.605345E 01
0.476837E 01	0.627485E 01	0.817215E 01
0.596046E 01	0.815731E 01	0.110324E 02
0.745058E 01	0.106045E 02	0.148937E 02
0.931323E 01	0.137858E 02	0.201066E 02
0.116415E 02	0.179216E 02	0.271439E 02
0.145519E 02	0.232981E 02	0.366442E 02
0.181899E 02	0.302875E 02	0.494697E 02
0.227374E 02	0.393738E 02	0.667841E 02
0.284217E 02	0.511859E 02	0.901585E 02
0.355271E 02	0.665417E 02	0.121714E 03
0.444089E 02	0.865042E 02	0.164314E 03
0.555112E 02	0.112455E 03	0.221824E 03
0.693889E 02	0.146192E 03	0.299462E 03
0.867362E 02	0.190050E 03	0.404274E 03
0.108420E 03	0.247065E 03	0.545769E 03
0.135525E 03	0.321184E 03	0.736789E 03
0.169407E 03	0.417539E 03	0.994665E 03
0.211758E 03	0.542801E 03	0.134280E 04
0.264698E 03	0.705641E 03	0.181278E 04
0.330872E 03	0.917333E 03	0.244725E 04
0.413590E 03	0.119253E 04	0.330378E 04
0.516988E 03	0.155029E 04	0.446011E 04
0.646235E 03	0.201538E 04	0.602115E 04
0.807794E 03	0.262000E 04	0.812855E 04
0.100974E 04	0.340599E 04	0.109735E 05
0.126218E 04	0.442779E 04	0.148143E 05
0.157772E 04	0.575613E 04	0.199993E 05
0.197215E 04	0.748297E 04	0.269990E 05
0.246519E 04	0.972786E 04	0.364487E 05
0.308149E 04	0.126462E 05	0.492057E 05
0.385186E 04	0.164401E 05	0.664277E 05
0.481482E 04	0.213721E 05	0.896774E 05
0.601853E 04	0.277837E 05	0.121065E 06
0.752316E 04	0.361189E 05	0.163437E 06
0.940395E 04	0.469545E 05	0.220640E 06
0.117549E 05	0.610409E 05	0.297864E 06
0.146937E 05	0.793531E 05	0.402117E 06
0.183671E 05	0.103159E 06	0.542857E 06
0.229589E 05	0.134107E 06	0.732858E 06
0.286986E 05	0.174339E 06	0.989358E 06
0.358732E 05	0.226641E 06	0.133563E 07
0.448416E 05	0.294633E 06	0.180310E 07
0.560519E 05	0.383022E 06	0.243419E 07
0.700649E 05	0.497929E 06	0.328616E 07

Table I (*Continued*). *Value of I n Periods Hence with Interest Rate i per Period*

$$F(i, n) = (1 + i)^n$$

.40	.45	.50
0.140000E 01	0.145000E 01	0.150000E 01
0.196000E 01	0.210250E 01	0.225000E 01
0.274400E 01	0.304863E 01	0.337500E 01
0.384160E 01	0.442051E 01	0.506250E 01
0.537824E 01	0.640973E 01	0.759375E 01
0.752954E 01	0.929411E 01	0.113906E 02
0.105414E 02	0.134765E 02	0.170859E 02
0.147579E 02	0.195409E 02	0.256289E 02
0.206610E 02	0.283343E 02	0.384434E 02
0.289255E 02	0.410847E 02	0.576650E 02
0.404957E 02	0.595728E 02	0.864976E 02
0.566939E 02	0.863806E 02	0.129746E 03
0.793715E 02	0.125252E 03	0.194620E 03
0.111120E 03	0.181615E 03	0.291929E 03
0.155568E 03	0.263342E 03	0.437894E 03
0.217795E 03	0.381846E 03	0.656841E 03
0.304913E 03	0.553676E 03	0.985261E 03
0.426879E 03	0.802831E 03	0.147789E 04
0.597630E 03	0.116410E 04	0.221684E 04
0.836683E 03	0.168795E 04	0.332526E 04
0.117136E 04	0.244753E 04	0.498789E 04
0.163990E 04	0.354892E 04	0.748183E 04
0.229586E 04	0.514593E 04	0.112227E 05
0.321420E 04	0.746160E 04	0.168341E 05
0.449988E 04	0.108193E 05	0.252512E 05
0.629983E 04	0.156880E 05	0.378768E 05
0.881976E 04	0.227476E 05	0.568151E 05
0.123477E 05	0.329841E 05	0.852227E 05
0.172867E 05	0.478269E 05	0.127834E 06
0.242014E 05	0.693490E 05	0.191751E 06
0.338820E 05	0.100556E 06	0.287627E 06
0.474348E 05	0.145806E 06	0.431440E 06
0.664087E 05	0.211419E 06	0.647160E 06
0.929722E 05	0.306558E 06	0.970740E 06
0.130161E 06	0.444509E 06	0.145611E 07
0.182226E 06	0.644537E 06	0.218416E 07
0.255116E 06	0.934579E 06	0.327625E 07
0.357162E 06	0.135514E 07	0.491437E 07
0.500027E 06	0.196495E 07	0.737155E 07
0.700038E 06	0.284918E 07	0.110573E 08
0.980053E 06	0.413131E 07	0.165860E 08
0.137207E 07	0.599040E 07	0.248790E 08
0.192090E 07	0.868609E 07	0.373185E 08
0.268926E 07	0.125948E 08	0.559777E 08
0.376497E 07	0.182625E 08	0.839666E 08
0.527096E 07	0.264806E 08	0.125950E 09
0.737934E 07	0.383969E 08	0.188925E 09
0.103311E 08	0.556755E 08	0.283387E 09
0.144635E 08	0.807295E 08	0.425081E 09
0.202489E 08	0.117058E 09	0.637622E 09

Table 2. Present Value, *P*, of *I* to be Received *n* Periods Hence with Interest Rate *i* per Period

$$P(i, n) = (1 + i)^{-n}$$

n	.01		.015		.02	
1	0.990099E	00	0.985222E	00	0.980392E	00
2	0.980296E	00	0.970662E	00	0.961169E	00
3	0.970590E	00	0.956317E	00	0.942322E	00
4	0.960980E	00	0.942184E	00	0.923845E	00
5	0.951466E	00	0.928260E	00	0.905731E	00
6	0.942045E	00	0.914542E	00	0.887971E	00
7	0.932718E	00	0.901027E	00	0.870560E	00
8	0.923483E	00	0.887711E	00	0.853490E	00
9	0.914340E	00	0.874592E	00	0.836755E	00
10	0.905287E	00	0.861667E	00	0.820348E	00
11	0.896324E	00	0.848933E	00	0.804263E	00
12	0.887449E	00	0.836387E	00	0.788493E	00
13	0.878663E	00	0.824027E	00	0.773033E	00
14	0.869963E	00	0.811849E	00	0.757875E	00
15	0.861349E	00	0.799852E	00	0.743015E	00
16	0.852821E	00	0.788031E	00	0.728446E	00
17	0.844377E	00	0.776385E	00	0.714163E	00
18	0.836017E	00	0.764912E	00	0.700159E	00
19	0.827740E	00	0.753607E	00	0.686431E	00
20	0.819544E	00	0.742470E	00	0.672971E	00
21	0.811430E	00	0.731498E	00	0.659776E	00
22	0.803396E	00	0.720688E	00	0.646839E	00
23	0.795442E	00	0.710037E	00	0.634156E	00
24	0.787566E	00	0.699544E	00	0.621721E	00
25	0.779768E	00	0.689206E	00	0.609531E	00
26	0.772048E	00	0.679021E	00	0.597579E	00
27	0.764404E	00	0.668986E	00	0.585862E	00
28	0.756836E	00	0.659099E	00	0.574375E	00
29	0.749342E	00	0.649359E	00	0.563112E	00
30	0.741923E	00	0.639762E	00	0.552071E	00
31	0.734577E	00	0.630308E	00	0.541246E	00
32	0.727304E	00	0.620993E	00	0.530633E	00
33	0.720103E	00	0.611816E	00	0.520229E	00
34	0.712973E	00	0.602774E	00	0.510028E	00
35	0.705914E	00	0.593866E	00	0.500028E	00
36	0.698925E	00	0.585090E	00	0.490223E	00
37	0.692005E	00	0.576443E	00	0.480611E	00
38	0.685153E	00	0.567924E	00	0.471187E	00
39	0.678370E	00	0.559531E	00	0.461948E	00
40	0.671653E	00	0.551262E	00	0.452890E	00
41	0.665003E	00	0.543116E	00	0.444010E	00
42	0.658419E	00	0.535089E	00	0.435304E	00
43	0.651900E	00	0.527182E	00	0.426769E	00
44	0.645445E	00	0.519391E	00	0.418401E	00
45	0.639055E	00	0.511715E	00	0.410197E	00
46	0.632728E	00	0.504153E	00	0.402154E	00
47	0.626463E	00	0.496702E	00	0.394268E	00
48	0.620260E	00	0.489362E	00	0.386538E	00
49	0.614119E	00	0.482130E	00	0.378958E	00
50	0.608039E	00	0.475005E	00	0.371528E	00

$$P(i, n) = (1 + i)^{-n}$$

.03	.04	.05
0.970874E 00	0.961538E 00	0.952381E 00
0.942596E 00	0.924556E 00	0.907029E 00
0.915142E 00	0.888996E 00	0.863838E 00
0.888487E 00	0.854804E 00	0.822702E 00
0.862609E 00	0.821927E 00	0.783526E 00
0.837484E 00	0.790315E 00	0.746215E 00
0.813092E 00	0.759918E 00	0.710681E 00
0.789409E 00	0.730690E 00	0.676839E 00
0.766417E 00	0.702587E 00	0.644609E 00
0.744094E 00	0.675564E 00	0.613913E 00
0.722421E 00	0.649581E 00	0.584679E 00
0.701380E 00	0.624597E 00	0.556837E 00
0.680951E 00	0.600574E 00	0.530321E 00
0.661118E 00	0.577475E 00	0.505068E 00
0.641862E 00	0.555265E 00	0.481017E 00
0.623167E 00	0.533908E 00	0.458112E 00
0.605016E 00	0.513373E 00	0.436297E 00
0.587395E 00	0.493628E 00	0.415521E 00
0.570286E 00	0.474642E 00	0.395734E 00
0.553676E 00	0.456387E 00	0.376889E 00
0.537549E 00	0.438834E 00	0.358942E 00
0.521893E 00	0.421955E 00	0.341850E 00
0.506692E 00	0.405726E 00	0.325571E 00
0.491934E 00	0.390121E 00	0.310068E 00
0.477606E 00	0.375117E 00	0.295303E 00
0.463695E 00	0.360689E 00	0.281241E 00
0.450189E 00	0.346817E 00	0.267848E 00
0.437077E 00	0.333477E 00	0.255094E 00
0.424346E 00	0.320651E 00	0.242946E 00
0.411987E 00	0.308319E 00	0.231377E 00
0.399987E 00	0.296460E 00	0.220359E 00
0.388337E 00	0.285058E 00	0.209866E 00
0.377026E 00	0.274094E 00	0.199873E 00
0.366045E 00	0.263552E 00	0.190355E 00
0.355383E 00	0.253415E 00	0.181290E 00
0.345032E 00	0.243669E 00	0.172657E 00
0.334983E 00	0.234297E 00	0.164436E 00
0.325226E 00	0.225285E 00	0.156605E 00
0.315754E 00	0.216621E 00	0.149148E 00
0.306557E 00	0.208289E 00	0.142046E 00
0.297628E 00	0.200278E 00	0.135282E 00
0.288959E 00	0.192575E 00	0.128840E 00
0.280543E 00	0.185168E 00	0.122704E 00
0.272372E 00	0.178046E 00	0.116861E 00
0.264439E 00	0.171198E 00	0.111297E 00
0.256737E 00	0.164614E 00	0.105997E 00
0.249259E 00	0.158283E 00	0.100949E 00
0.241999E 00	0.152195E 00	0.961421E-01
0.234950E 00	0.146341E 00	0.915639E-01
0.228107E 00	0.140713E 00	0.872037E-01

Table 2 (Continued).   Present value, P, of 1 to be Received n Periods Hence with Interest Rate i per Period

$$P(i, n) = (1 + i)^{-n}$$

.06	.08	.10
0.943396E 00	0.925926E 00	0.909091E 00
0.889996E 00	0.857339E 00	0.826446E 00
0.839619E 00	0.793832E 00	0.751315E 00
0.792094E 00	0.735030E 00	0.683013E 00
0.747258E 00	0.680583E 00	0.620921E 00
0.704961E 00	0.630170E 00	0.564474E 00
0.665057E 00	0.583490E 00	0.513158E 00
0.627412E 00	0.540269E 00	0.466507E 00
0.591898E 00	0.500249E 00	0.424098E 00
0.558395E 00	0.463193E 00	0.385543E 00
0.526788E 00	0.428883E 00	0.350494E 00
0.496969E 00	0.397114E 00	0.318631E 00
0.468839E 00	0.367698E 00	0.289664E 00
0.442301E 00	0.340461E 00	0.263331E 00
0.417265E 00	0.315242E 00	0.239392E 00
0.393646E 00	0.291890E 00	0.217629E 00
0.371364E 00	0.270269E 00	0.197845E 00
0.350344E 00	0.250249E 00	0.179859E 00
0.330513E 00	0.231712E 00	0.163508E 00
0.311805E 00	0.214548E 00	0.148644E 00
0.294155E 00	0.198656E 00	0.135131E 00
0.277505E 00	0.183941E 00	0.122846E 00
0.261797E 00	0.170315E 00	0.111678E 00
0.246979E 00	0.157699E 00	0.101526E 00
0.232999E 00	0.146018E 00	0.922960E-01
0.219810E 00	0.135202E 00	0.839055E-01
0.207368E 00	0.125187E 00	0.762777E-01
0.195630E 00	0.115914E 00	0.693433E-01
0.184557E 00	0.107328E 00	0.630394E-01
0.174110E 00	0.993773E-01	0.573086E-01
0.164255E 00	0.920160E-01	0.520987E-01
0.154957E 00	0.852000E-01	0.473624E-01
0.146186E 00	0.788889E-01	0.430568E-01
0.137912E 00	0.730453E-01	0.391425E-01
0.130105E 00	0.676345E-01	0.355841E-01
0.122741E 00	0.626246E-01	0.323492E-01
0.115793E 00	0.579857E-01	0.294083E-01
0.109239E 00	0.536905E-01	0.267349E-01
0.103056E 00	0.497134E-01	0.243044E-01
0.972222E-01	0.460309E-01	0.220949E-01
0.917190E-01	0.426212E-01	0.200863E-01
0.865274E-01	0.394641E-01	0.182603E-01
0.816296E-01	0.365408E-01	0.166002E-01
0.770091E-01	0.338341E-01	0.150911E-01
0.726501E-01	0.313279E-01	0.137192E-01
0.685378E-01	0.290073E-01	0.124720E-01
0.646583E-01	0.268586E-01	0.113382E-01
0.609984E-01	0.248691E-01	0.103074E-01
0.575457E-01	0.230269E-01	0.937041E-02
0.542884E-01	0.213212E-01	0.851855E-02

Table 2 (Continued).   *Present value, P, of I to be Received n Periods Hence with Interest Rate i per Period*

$$P(i, n) = (1 + i)^{-n}$$

n	.12	.15	.20
1	0.892857E 00	0.869565E 00	0.833333E 00
2	0.797194E 00	0.756144E 00	0.694444E 00
3	0.711780E 00	0.657516E 00	0.578704E 00
4	0.635518E 00	0.571753E 00	0.482253E 00
5	0.567427E 00	0.497177E 00	0.401878E 00
6	0.506631E 00	0.432328E 00	0.334898E 00
7	0.452349E 00	0.375937E 00	0.279082E 00
8	0.403883E 00	0.326902E 00	0.232568E 00
9	0.360610E 00	0.284262E 00	0.193807E 00
10	0.321973E 00	0.247185E 00	0.161506E 00
11	0.287476E 00	0.214943E 00	0.134588E 00
12	0.256675E 00	0.186907E 00	0.112157E 00
13	0.229174E 00	0.162528E 00	0.934639E-01
14	0.204620E 00	0.141329E 00	0.778866E-01
15	0.182696E 00	0.122894E 00	0.649055E-01
16	0.163122E 00	0.106865E 00	0.540879E-01
17	0.145644E 00	0.929259E-01	0.450732E-01
18	0.130040E 00	0.808051E-01	0.375610E-01
19	0.116107E 00	0.702653E-01	0.313009E-01
20	0.103667E 00	0.611003E-01	0.260841E-01
21	0.925596E-01	0.531307E-01	0.217367E-01
22	0.826425E-01	0.462006E-01	0.181139E-01
23	0.737880E-01	0.401744E-01	0.150949E-01
24	0.658821E-01	0.349343E-01	0.125791E-01
25	0.588233E-01	0.303776E-01	0.104826E-01
26	0.525208E-01	0.264153E-01	0.873550E-02
27	0.468936E-01	0.229699E-01	0.727958E-02
28	0.418693E-01	0.199738E-01	0.606632E-02
29	0.373833E-01	0.173685E-01	0.505526E-02
30	0.333779E-01	0.151031E-01	0.421272E-02
31	0.298017E-01	0.131331E-01	0.351060E-02
32	0.266087E-01	0.114201E-01	0.292550E-02
33	0.237577E-01	0.993050E-02	0.243792E-02
34	0.212123E-01	0.863522E-02	0.203160E-02
35	0.189395E-01	0.750889E-02	0.169300E-02
36	0.169103E-01	0.652947E-02	0.141083E-02
37	0.150985E-01	0.567780E-02	0.117569E-02
38	0.134808E-01	0.493722E-02	0.979744E-03
39	0.120364E-01	0.429323E-02	0.816453E-03
40	0.107468E-01	0.373324E-02	0.680378E-03
41	0.959536E-02	0.324630E-02	0.566982E-03
42	0.856728E-02	0.282287E-02	0.472485E-03
43	0.764936E-02	0.245467E-02	0.393737E-03
44	0.682978E-02	0.213449E-02	0.328114E-03
45	0.609802E-02	0.185608E-02	0.273429E-03
46	0.544466E-02	0.161398E-02	0.227857E-03
47	0.486131E-02	0.140346E-02	0.189881E-03
48	0.434045E-02	0.122040E-02	0.158234E-03
49	0.387540E-02	0.106122E-02	0.131862E-03
50	0.346018E-02	0.922801E-03	0.109885E-03

Table 2 (Continued).   *Present value, P, of 1 to be Received n Periods Hence with Interest Rate i per Period*

$$P(i, n) = (1 + i)^{-n}$$

.25	.30	.35
0.800000E 00	0.769231E 00	0.740741E 00
0.640000E 00	0.591716E 00	0.548697E 00
0.512000E 00	0.455166E 00	0.406442E 00
0.409600E 00	0.350128E 00	0.301068E 00
0.327680E 00	0.269329E 00	0.223014E 00
0.262144E 00	0.207176E 00	0.165195E 00
0.209715E 00	0.159366E 00	0.122367E 00
0.167772E 00	0.122589E 00	0.906421E-01
0.134218E 00	0.942996E-01	0.671423E-01
0.107374E 00	0.725382E-01	0.497350E-01
0.858993E-01	0.557986E-01	0.368408E-01
0.687195E-01	0.429220E-01	0.272894E-01
0.549756E-01	0.330169E-01	0.202144E-01
0.439805E-01	0.253976E-01	0.149736E-01
0.351844E-01	0.195366E-01	0.110916E-01
0.281475E-01	0.150282E-01	0.821599E-02
0.225180E-01	0.115601E-01	0.608592E-02
0.180144E-01	0.889241E-02	0.450809E-02
0.144115E-01	0.684032E-02	0.333932E-02
0.115292E-01	0.526178E-02	0.247357E-02
0.922337E-02	0.404753E-02	0.183228E-02
0.737870E-02	0.311348E-02	0.135724E-02
0.590296E-02	0.239499E-02	0.100536E-02
0.472237E-02	0.184230E-02	0.744714E-03
0.377789E-02	0.141715E-02	0.551640E-03
0.302231E-02	0.109012E-02	0.408622E-03
0.241785E-02	0.838551E-03	0.302683E-03
0.193428E-02	0.645039E-03	0.224210E-03
0.154743E-02	0.496184E-03	0.166081E-03
0.123794E-02	0.381680E-03	0.123023E-03
0.990352E-03	0.293600E-03	0.911283E-04
0.792282E-03	0.225846E-03	0.675024E-04
0.633825E-03	0.173728E-03	0.500018E-04
0.507060E-03	0.133637E-03	0.370384E-04
0.405648E-03	0.102798E-03	0.274358E-04
0.324519E-03	0.790750E-04	0.203228E-04
0.259615E-03	0.608269E-04	0.150540E-04
0.207692E-03	0.467900E-04	0.111511E-04
0.166153E-03	0.359923E-04	0.826006E-05
0.132923E-03	0.276864E-04	0.611856E-05
0.106338E-03	0.212972E-04	0.453227E-05
0.850706E-04	0.163825E-04	0.335723E-05
0.680565E-04	0.126019E-04	0.248684E-05
0.544452E-04	0.969377E-05	0.184210E-05
0.435561E-04	0.745674E-05	0.136452E-05
0.348449E-04	0.573596E-05	0.101076E-05
0.278759E-04	0.441227E-05	0.748709E-06
0.223007E-04	0.339406E-05	0.554599E-06
0.178406E-04	0.261081E-05	0.410814E-06
0.142725E-04	0.200832E-05	0.304307E-06

Table 2 (Continued).   **Present value, P, of I to be Received** n **Periods Hence with Interest Rate** i **per Period**

$$P(i, n) = (1 + i)^{-n}$$

.40	.45	.50
0.714286E 00	0.689655E 00	0.666667E 00
0.510204E 00	0.475624E 00	0.444444E 00
0.364431E 00	0.328017E 00	0.296296E 00
0.260308E 00	0.226218E 00	0.197531E 00
0.185934E 00	0.156013E 00	0.131687E 00
0.132810E 00	0.107595E 00	0.877915E-01
0.948645E-01	0.742034E-01	0.585277E-01
0.677604E-01	0.511748E-01	0.390184E-01
0.484003E-01	0.352930E-01	0.260123E-01
0.345716E-01	0.243400E-01	0.173415E-01
0.246940E-01	0.167862E-01	0.115610E-01
0.176386E-01	0.115767E-01	0.770735E-02
0.125990E-01	0.798392E-02	0.513823E-02
0.899927E-02	0.550615E-02	0.342549E-02
0.642805E-02	0.379734E-02	0.228366E-02
0.459147E-02	0.261886E-02	0.152244E-02
0.327962E-02	0.180611E-02	0.101496E-02
0.234258E-02	0.124559E-02	0.676639E-03
0.167327E-02	0.859029E-03	0.451093E-03
0.119520E-02	0.592434E-03	0.300729E-03
0.853712E-03	0.408575E-03	0.200486E-03
0.609794E-03	0.281776E-03	0.133657E-03
0.435567E-03	0.194328E-03	0.891048E-04
0.311119E-03	0.134019E-03	0.594032E-04
0.222228E-03	0.924272E-04	0.396021E-04
0.158734E-03	0.637429E-04	0.264014E-04
0.113382E-03	0.439606E-04	0.176009E-04
0.809869E-04	0.303177E-04	0.117340E-04
0.578478E-04	0.209087E-04	0.782264E-05
0.413199E-04	0.144198E-04	0.521510E-05
0.295142E-04	0.994471E-05	0.347673E-05
0.210816E-04	0.685842E-05	0.231782E-05
0.150583E-04	0.472994E-05	0.154521E-05
0.107559E-04	0.326203E-05	0.103014E-05
0.768279E-05	0.224968E-05	0.686761E-06
0.548770E-05	0.155150E-05	0.457841E-06
0.391979E-05	0.107000E-05	0.305227E-06
0.279985E-05	0.737931E-06	0.203485E-06
0.199989E-05	0.508918E-06	0.135657E-06
0.142849E-05	0.350978E-06	0.904377E-07
0.102035E-05	0.242054E-06	0.602918E-07
0.728824E-06	0.166934E-06	0.401945E-07
0.520588E-06	0.115127E-06	0.267964E-07
0.371849E-06	0.793977E-07	0.178642E-07
0.265606E-06	0.547570E-07	0.119095E-07
0.189719E-06	0.377635E-07	0.793966E-08
0.135513E-06	0.260438E-07	0.529311E-08
0.967953E-07	0.179612E-07	0.352874E-08
0.691395E-07	0.123870E-07	0.235249E-08
0.493854E-07	0.854279E-08	0.156833E-08

Table 3.   Value of I per Period, n Periods Hence
at Interest Rate i per Period

$$F(i, n) = \frac{(1 + i)^n - 1}{i}$$

n	.01		.015		.02	
1	1.000000E	00	1.000000E	00	1.000000E	00
2	0.201000E	01	0.201500E	01	0.202000E	01
3	0.303010E	01	0.304522E	01	0.306040E	01
4	0.406040E	01	0.409090E	01	0.412161E	01
5	0.510101E	01	0.515227E	01	0.520404E	01
6	0.615202E	01	0.622955E	01	0.630812E	01
7	0.721354E	01	0.732299E	01	0.743428E	01
8	0.828567E	01	0.843284E	01	0.858297E	01
9	0.936853E	01	0.955933E	01	0.975463E	01
10	0.104622E	02	0.107027E	02	0.109497E	02
11	0.115668E	02	0.118633E	02	0.121687E	02
12	0.126825E	02	0.130412E	02	0.134121E	02
13	0.138093E	02	0.142368E	02	0.146803E	02
14	0.149474E	02	0.154504E	02	0.159739E	02
15	0.160969E	02	0.166821E	02	0.172934E	02
16	0.172579E	02	0.179324E	02	0.186393E	02
17	0.184304E	02	0.192014E	02	0.200121E	02
18	0.196147E	02	0.204894E	02	0.214123E	02
19	0.208109E	02	0.217967E	02	0.228406E	02
20	0.220190E	02	0.231237E	02	0.242974E	02
21	0.232392E	02	0.244705E	02	0.257833E	02
22	0.244716E	02	0.258376E	02	0.272990E	02
23	0.257163E	02	0.272251E	02	0.288450E	02
24	0.269735E	02	0.286335E	02	0.304219E	02
25	0.282432E	02	0.300630E	02	0.320303E	02
26	0.295256E	02	0.315140E	02	0.336709E	02
27	0.308209E	02	0.329867E	02	0.353443E	02
28	0.321291E	02	0.344815E	02	0.370512E	02
29	0.334504E	02	0.359987E	02	0.387922E	02
30	0.347849E	02	0.375387E	02	0.405681E	02
31	0.361327E	02	0.391018E	02	0.423794E	02
32	0.374941E	02	0.406883E	02	0.442270E	02
33	0.388690E	02	0.422986E	02	0.461116E	02
34	0.402577E	02	0.439331E	02	0.480338E	02
35	0.416603E	02	0.455921E	02	0.499945E	02
36	0.430769E	02	0.472760E	02	0.519944E	02
37	0.445076E	02	0.489851E	02	0.540343E	02
38	0.459527E	02	0.507199E	02	0.561149E	02
39	0.474123E	02	0.524807E	02	0.582372E	02
40	0.488864E	02	0.542679E	02	0.604020E	02
41	0.503752E	02	0.560819E	02	0.626100E	02
42	0.518790E	02	0.579231E	02	0.648622E	02
43	0.533978E	02	0.597920E	02	0.671595E	02
44	0.549318E	02	0.616889E	02	0.695027E	02
45	0.564811E	02	0.636142E	02	0.718927E	02
46	0.580459E	02	0.655684E	02	0.743306E	02
47	0.596263E	02	0.675519E	02	0.768172E	02
48	0.612226E	02	0.695652E	02	0.793535E	02
49	0.628348E	02	0.716087E	02	0.819406E	02
50	0.644632E	02	0.736828E	02	0.845794E	02

Table 3 (Continued). *Value of I per Period, n Periods Hence at Interest Rate i per Period*

$$F(i, n) = \frac{(1 + i)^n - 1}{i}$$

.03	.04	.05
1.000000E 00	1.000000E 00	1.000000E 00
0.203000E 01	0.204000E 01	0.205000E 01
0.309090E 01	0.312160E 01	0.315250E 01
0.418363E 01	0.424646E 01	0.431013E 01
0.530914E 01	0.541632E 01	0.552563E 01
0.646841E 01	0.663298E 01	0.680191E 01
0.766246E 01	0.789829E 01	0.814201E 01
0.889234E 01	0.921423E 01	0.954911E 01
0.101591E 02	0.105828E 02	0.110266E 02
0.114639E 02	0.120061E 02	0.125779E 02
0.128078E 02	0.134864E 02	0.142068E 02
0.141920E 02	0.150258E 02	0.159171E 02
0.156178E 02	0.166268E 02	0.177130E 02
0.170863E 02	0.182919E 02	0.195986E 02
0.185989E 02	0.200236E 02	0.215786E 02
0.201569E 02	0.218245E 02	0.236575E 02
0.217616E 02	0.236975E 02	0.258404E 02
0.234144E 02	0.256454E 02	0.281324E 02
0.251169E 02	0.276712E 02	0.305390E 02
0.268704E 02	0.297781E 02	0.330660E 02
0.286765E 02	0.319692E 02	0.357193E 02
0.305368E 02	0.342480E 02	0.385052E 02
0.324529E 02	0.366179E 02	0.414305E 02
0.344265E 02	0.390826E 02	0.445020E 02
0.364593E 02	0.416459E 02	0.477271E 02
0.385530E 02	0.443117E 02	0.511135E 02
0.407096E 02	0.470842E 02	0.546691E 02
0.429309E 02	0.499676E 02	0.584026E 02
0.452189E 02	0.529663E 02	0.623227E 02
0.475754E 02	0.560849E 02	0.664388E 02
0.500027E 02	0.593283E 02	0.707608E 02
0.525028E 02	0.627015E 02	0.752988E 02
0.550778E 02	0.662095E 02	0.800638E 02
0.577302E 02	0.698579E 02	0.850670E 02
0.604621E 02	0.736522E 02	0.903203E 02
0.632759E 02	0.775983E 02	0.958363E 02
0.661742E 02	0.817022E 02	0.101628E 03
0.691594E 02	0.859703E 02	0.107710E 03
0.722342E 02	0.904091E 02	0.114095E 03
0.754013E 02	0.950255E 02	0.120800E 03
0.786633E 02	0.998265E 02	0.127840E 03
0.820232E 02	0.104820E 03	0.135232E 03
0.854839E 02	0.110012E 03	0.142993E 03
0.890484E 02	0.115413E 03	0.151143E 03
0.927199E 02	0.121029E 03	0.159700E 03
0.965015E 02	0.126871E 03	0.168685E 03
0.100397E 03	0.132945E 03	0.178119E 03
0.104408E 03	0.139263E 03	0.188025E 03
0.108541E 03	0.145834E 03	0.198427E 03
0.112797E 03	0.152667E 03	0.209348E 03

Table 3 (Continued).   *Value of I per Period, n Periods Hence at Interest Rate i per Period*

$$F(i, n) = \frac{(1 + i)^n - 1}{i}$$

.06	.08	.10
1.000000E 00	1.000000E 00	1.000000E 00
0.206000E 01	0.208000E 01	0.210000E 01
0.318360E 01	0.324640E 01	0.331000E 01
0.437462E 01	0.450611E 01	0.464100E 01
0.563709E 01	0.586660E 01	0.610510E 01
0.697532E 01	0.733593E 01	0.771561E 01
0.839384E 01	0.892280E 01	0.948717E 01
0.989747E 01	0.106366E 02	0.114359E 02
0.114913E 02	0.124876E 02	0.135795E 02
0.131808E 02	0.144866E 02	0.159374E 02
0.149716E 02	0.166455E 02	0.185312E 02
0.168699E 02	0.189771E 02	0.213843E 02
0.188821E 02	0.214953E 02	0.245227E 02
0.210151E 02	0.242149E 02	0.279750E 02
0.232760E 02	0.271521E 02	0.317725E 02
0.256725E 02	0.303243E 02	0.359497E 02
0.282129E 02	0.337502E 02	0.405447E 02
0.309057E 02	0.374502E 02	0.455992E 02
0.337600E 02	0.414463E 02	0.511591E 02
0.367856E 02	0.457620E 02	0.572750E 02
0.399927E 02	0.504229E 02	0.640025E 02
0.433923E 02	0.554568E 02	0.714027E 02
0.469958E 02	0.608933E 02	0.795430E 02
0.508156E 02	0.667648E 02	0.884973E 02
0.548645E 02	0.731059E 02	0.983471E 02
0.591564E 02	0.799544E 02	0.109182E 03
0.637058E 02	0.873508E 02	0.121100E 03
0.685281E 02	0.953388E 02	0.134210E 03
0.736398E 02	0.103966E 03	0.148631E 03
0.790582E 02	0.113283E 03	0.164494E 03
0.848017E 02	0.123346E 03	0.181943E 03
0.908898E 02	0.134214E 03	0.201138E 03
0.973432E 02	0.145951E 03	0.222252E 03
0.104184E 03	0.158627E 03	0.245477E 03
0.111435E 03	0.172317E 03	0.271024E 03
0.119121E 03	0.187102E 03	0.299127E 03
0.127268E 03	0.203070E 03	0.330039E 03
0.135904E 03	0.220316E 03	0.364043E 03
0.145058E 03	0.238941E 03	0.401448E 03
0.154762E 03	0.259057E 03	0.442593E 03
0.165048E 03	0.280781E 03	0.487852E 03
0.175951E 03	0.304244E 03	0.537637E 03
0.187508E 03	0.329583E 03	0.592401E 03
0.199758E 03	0.356950E 03	0.652641E 03
0.212744E 03	0.386506E 03	0.718905E 03
0.226508E 03	0.418426E 03	0.791795E 03
0.241099E 03	0.452900E 03	0.871975E 03
0.256565E 03	0.490132E 03	0.960172E 03
0.272958E 03	0.530343E 03	0.105719E 04
0.290336E 03	0.573770E 03	0.116391E 04

Table 3 (Continued). *Value of l per Period, n Periods Hence at Interest Rate i per Period*

$$F(i, n) = \frac{(1 + i)^n - 1}{i}$$

n	.12	.15	.20
1	1.000000E 00	1.000000E 00	0.100000E 01
2	0.212000E 01	0.215000E 01	0.220000E 01
3	0.337440E 01	0.347250E 01	0.364000E 01
4	0.477933E 01	0.499338E 01	0.536800E 01
5	0.635285E 01	0.674238E 01	0.744160E 01
6	0.811519E 01	0.875374E 01	0.992992E 01
7	0.100890E 02	0.110668E 02	0.129159E 02
8	0.122997E 02	0.137268E 02	0.164991E 02
9	0.147757E 02	0.167858E 02	0.207989E 02
10	0.175487E 02	0.203037E 02	0.259587E 02
11	0.206546E 02	0.243493E 02	0.321504E 02
12	0.241331E 02	0.290017E 02	0.395805E 02
13	0.280291E 02	0.343519E 02	0.484966E 02
14	0.323926E 02	0.405047E 02	0.591959E 02
15	0.372797E 02	0.475804E 02	0.720351E 02
16	0.427533E 02	0.557175E 02	0.874421E 02
17	0.488837E 02	0.650751E 02	0.105931E 03
18	0.557497E 02	0.758364E 02	0.128117E 03
19	0.634397E 02	0.882118E 02	0.154740E 03
20	0.720524E 02	0.102444E 03	0.186688E 03
21	0.816987E 02	0.118810E 03	0.225026E 03
22	0.925026E 02	0.137632E 03	0.271031E 03
23	0.104603E 03	0.159276E 03	0.326237E 03
24	0.118155E 03	0.184168E 03	0.392484E 03
25	0.133334E 03	0.212793E 03	0.471981E 03
26	0.150334E 03	0.245712E 03	0.567377E 03
27	0.169374E 03	0.283569E 03	0.681853E 03
28	0.190699E 03	0.327104E 03	0.819223E 03
29	0.214583E 03	0.377170E 03	0.984068E 03
30	0.241333E 03	0.434745E 03	0.118188E 04
31	0.271293E 03	0.500957E 03	0.141926E 04
32	0.304848E 03	0.577100E 03	0.170411E 04
33	0.342429E 03	0.664666E 03	0.204593E 04
34	0.384521E 03	0.765365E 03	0.245612E 04
35	0.431663E 03	0.881170E 03	0.294834E 04
36	0.484463E 03	0.101435E 04	0.353901E 04
37	0.543599E 03	0.116750E 04	0.424781E 04
38	0.609831E 03	0.134362E 04	0.509837E 04
39	0.684010E 03	0.154617E 04	0.611905E 04
40	0.767091E 03	0.177909E 04	0.734386E 04
41	0.860142E 03	0.204695E 04	0.881363E 04
42	0.964359E 03	0.235500E 04	0.105774E 05
43	0.108108E 04	0.270925E 04	0.126938E 05
44	0.121181E 04	0.311663E 04	0.152336E 05
45	0.135823E 04	0.358513E 04	0.182813E 05
46	0.152222E 04	0.412390E 04	0.219386E 05
47	0.170588E 04	0.474348E 04	0.263273E 05
48	0.191159E 04	0.545600E 04	0.315937E 05
49	0.214198E 04	0.627541E 04	0.379135E 05
50	0.240002E 04	0.721772E 04	0.454972E 05

Table 3 (Continued). **Value of I per Period, n Periods Hence at Interest Rate i per Period**

$$F(i, n) = \frac{(1 + i)^n - 1}{i}$$

.25	.30	.35
0.100000E 01	0.100000E 01	1.000000E 00
0.225000E 01	0.230000E 01	0.235000E 01
0.381250E 01	0.399000E 01	0.417250E 01
0.576563E 01	0.618700E 01	0.663288E 01
0.820703E 01	0.904310E 01	0.995438E 01
0.112588E 02	0.127560E 02	0.144384E 02
0.150735E 02	0.175828E 02	0.204919E 02
0.198419E 02	0.238577E 02	0.286640E 02
0.258023E 02	0.320150E 02	0.396964E 02
0.332529E 02	0.426195E 02	0.545902E 02
0.425661E 02	0.564053E 02	0.746967E 02
0.542077E 02	0.743270E 02	0.101841E 03
0.687596E 02	0.976250E 02	0.138485E 03
0.869495E 02	0.127913E 03	0.187954E 03
0.109687E 03	0.167286E 03	0.254738E 03
0.138109E 03	0.218472E 03	0.344897E 03
0.173636E 03	0.285014E 03	0.466611E 03
0.218045E 03	0.371518E 03	0.630925E 03
0.273556E 03	0.483973E 03	0.852748E 03
0.342945E 03	0.630165E 03	0.115221E 04
0.429681E 03	0.820215E 03	0.155648E 04
0.538101E 03	0.106728E 04	0.210225E 04
0.673626E 03	0.138846E 04	0.283904E 04
0.843033E 03	0.180600E 04	0.383371E 04
0.105479E 04	0.234880E 04	0.517650E 04
0.131949E 04	0.305444E 04	0.698928E 04
0.165036E 04	0.397178E 04	0.943653E 04
0.206395E 04	0.516431E 04	0.127403E 05
0.258094E 04	0.671460E 04	0.172004E 05
0.322717E 04	0.872999E 04	0.232216E 05
0.403497E 04	0.113500E 05	0.313501E 05
0.504471E 04	0.147560E 05	0.423237E 05
0.630689E 04	0.191838E 05	0.571379E 05
0.788461E 04	0.249399E 05	0.771372E 05
0.985676E 04	0.324229E 05	0.104136E 06
0.123220E 05	0.421507E 05	0.140585E 06
0.154034E 05	0.547969E 05	0.189791E 06
0.192553E 05	0.712370E 05	0.256218E 06
0.240701E 05	0.926091E 05	0.345896E 06
0.300887E 05	0.120393E 06	0.466960E 06
0.376118E 05	0.156512E 06	0.630398E 06
0.470158E 05	0.203466E 06	0.851038E 06
0.587707E 05	0.264507E 06	0.114890E 07
0.734644E 05	0.343860E 06	0.155102E 07
0.918315E 05	0.447019E 06	0.209388E 07
0.114790E 06	0.581126E 06	0.282673E 07
0.143489E 06	0.755465E 06	0.381609E 07
0.179362E 06	0.982106E 06	0.515172E 07
0.224204E 06	0.127674E 07	0.695483E 07
0.280256E 06	0.165976E 07	0.938902E 07

Table 3 (Continued). *Value of l per Period, n Periods Hence at Interest Rate i per Period*

$$F(i, n) = \frac{(1 + i)^n - 1}{i}$$

.40	.45	.50
0.100000E 01	0.100000E 01	0.100000E 01
0.240000E 01	0.245000E 01	0.250000E 01
0.436000E 01	0.455250E 01	0.475000E 01
0.710400E 01	0.760113E 01	0.812500E 01
0.109456E 02	0.120216E 02	0.131875E 02
0.163238E 02	0.184314E 02	0.207813E 02
0.238534E 02	0.277255E 02	0.321719E 02
0.343947E 02	0.412019E 02	0.492578E 02
0.491526E 02	0.607428E 02	0.748867E 02
0.698137E 02	0.890771E 02	0.113330E 03
0.987391E 02	0.130162E 03	0.170995E 03
0.139235E 03	0.189735E 03	0.257493E 03
0.195929E 03	0.276115E 03	0.387239E 03
0.275300E 03	0.401367E 03	0.581859E 03
0.386420E 03	0.582982E 03	0.873788E 03
0.541988E 03	0.846324E 03	0.131168E 04
0.759784E 03	0.122817E 04	0.196852E 04
0.106470E 04	0.178185E 04	0.295378E 04
0.149158E 04	0.258468E 04	0.443168E 04
0.208921E 04	0.374878E 04	0.664851E 04
0.292589E 04	0.543673E 04	0.997377E 04
0.409724E 04	0.788426E 04	0.149617E 05
0.573714E 04	0.114332E 05	0.224435E 05
0.803300E 04	0.165791E 05	0.336662E 05
0.112472E 05	0.240407E 05	0.505003E 05
0.157471E 05	0.348600E 05	0.757515E 05
0.220469E 05	0.505481E 05	0.113628E 06
0.308667E 05	0.732957E 05	0.170443E 06
0.432143E 05	0.106280E 06	0.255666E 06
0.605011E 05	0.154107E 06	0.383500E 06
0.847025E 05	0.223456E 06	0.575251E 06
0.118585E 06	0.324012E 06	0.862878E 06
0.166019E 06	0.469818E 06	0.129432E 07
0.232428E 06	0.681237E 06	0.194148E 07
0.325400E 06	0.987794E 06	0.291222E 07
0.455561E 06	0.143230E 07	0.436833E 07
0.637787E 06	0.207684E 07	0.655249E 07
0.892903E 06	0.301142E 07	0.982874E 07
0.125006E 07	0.436656E 07	0.147431E 08
0.175009E 07	0.633151E 07	0.221147E 08
0.245013E 07	0.918069E 07	0.331720E 08
0.343018E 07	0.133120E 08	0.497580E 08
0.480226E 07	0.193024E 08	0.746370E 08
0.672316E 07	0.279885E 08	0.111955E 09
0.941242E 07	0.405833E 08	0.167933E 09
0.131774E 08	0.588458E 08	0.251900E 09
0.184484E 08	0.853264E 08	0.377850E 09
0.258277E 08	0.123723E 09	0.566775E 09
0.361588E 08	0.179399E 09	0.850162E 09
0.506223E 08	0.260128E 09	0.127524E 10

Table 4.   Present Value of 1 per Period at Interest Rate i per Period

$$P(i, n) = \frac{1 - (1 + i)^{-n}}{i}$$

n	.01		.015		.02	
1	0.990099E	00	0.985222E	00	0.980392E	00
2	0.197040E	01	0.195588E	01	0.194156E	01
3	0.294099E	01	0.291220E	01	0.288388E	01
4	0.390197E	01	0.385438E	01	0.380773E	01
5	0.485343E	01	0.478264E	01	0.471346E	01
6	0.579548E	01	0.569719E	01	0.560143E	01
7	0.672819E	01	0.659821E	01	0.647199E	01
8	0.765168E	01	0.748593E	01	0.732548E	01
9	0.856602E	01	0.836052E	01	0.816224E	01
10	0.947130E	01	0.922218E	01	0.898259E	01
11	0.103676E	02	0.100711E	02	0.978685E	01
12	0.112551E	02	0.109075E	02	0.105753E	02
13	0.121337E	02	0.117315E	02	0.113484E	02
14	0.130037E	02	0.125434E	02	0.121062E	02
15	0.138651E	02	0.133432E	02	0.128493E	02
16	0.147179E	02	0.141313E	02	0.135777E	02
17	0.155623E	02	0.149076E	02	0.142919E	02
18	0.163983E	02	0.156726E	02	0.149920E	02
19	0.172260E	02	0.164262E	02	0.156785E	02
20	0.180456E	02	0.171686E	02	0.163514E	02
21	0.188570E	02	0.179001E	02	0.170112E	02
22	0.196604E	02	0.186208E	02	0.176580E	02
23	0.204558E	02	0.193309E	02	0.182922E	02
24	0.212434E	02	0.200304E	02	0.189139E	02
25	0.220232E	02	0.207196E	02	0.195235E	02
26	0.227952E	02	0.213986E	02	0.201210E	02
27	0.235596E	02	0.220676E	02	0.207069E	02
28	0.243164E	02	0.227267E	02	0.212813E	02
29	0.250658E	02	0.233761E	02	0.218444E	02
30	0.258077E	02	0.240158E	02	0.223965E	02
31	0.265423E	02	0.246461E	02	0.229377E	02
32	0.272696E	02	0.252671E	02	0.234683E	02
33	0.279897E	02	0.258790E	02	0.239886E	02
34	0.287027E	02	0.264817E	02	0.244986E	02
35	0.294086E	02	0.270756E	02	0.249986E	02
36	0.301075E	02	0.276607E	02	0.254888E	02
37	0.307995E	02	0.282371E	02	0.259695E	02
38	0.314847E	02	0.288051E	02	0.264406E	02
39	0.321630E	02	0.293646E	02	0.269026E	02
40	0.328347E	02	0.299158E	02	0.273555E	02
41	0.334997E	02	0.304590E	02	0.277995E	02
42	0.341581E	02	0.309941E	02	0.282348E	02
43	0.348100E	02	0.315212E	02	0.286616E	02
44	0.354555E	02	0.320406E	02	0.290800E	02
45	0.360945E	02	0.325523E	02	0.294902E	02
46	0.367272E	02	0.330565E	02	0.298923E	02
47	0.373537E	02	0.335532E	02	0.302866E	02
48	0.379740E	02	0.340426E	02	0.306731E	02
49	0.385881E	02	0.345247E	02	0.310521E	02
50	0.391961E	02	0.349997E	02	0.314236E	02

Table 4 (*Continued*). **Present Value of I per Period at Interest Rate**
i per Period

$$P(i, n) = \frac{1 - (1 + i)^{-n}}{i}$$

.03	.04	.05
0.970874E 00	0.961538E 00	0.952381E 00
0.191347E 01	0.188609E 01	0.185941E 01
0.282861E 01	0.277509E 01	0.272325E 01
0.371710E 01	0.362990E 01	0.354595E 01
0.457971E 01	0.445182E 01	0.432948E 01
0.541719E 01	0.524214E 01	0.507569E 01
0.623028E 01	0.600205E 01	0.578637E 01
0.701969E 01	0.673274E 01	0.646321E 01
0.778611E 01	0.743533E 01	0.710782E 01
0.853020E 01	0.811090E 01	0.772173E 01
0.925262E 01	0.876048E 01	0.830641E 01
0.995400E 01	0.938507E 01	0.886325E 01
0.106350E 02	0.998565E 01	0.939357E 01
0.112961E 02	0.105631E 02	0.989864E 01
0.119379E 02	0.111184E 02	0.103797E 02
0.125611E 02	0.116523E 02	0.108378E 02
0.131661E 02	0.121657E 02	0.112741E 02
0.137535E 02	0.126593E 02	0.116896E 02
0.143238E 02	0.131339E 02	0.120853E 02
0.148775E 02	0.135903E 02	0.124622E 02
0.154150E 02	0.140292E 02	0.128212E 02
0.159369E 02	0.144511E 02	0.131630E 02
0.164436E 02	0.148568E 02	0.134886E 02
0.169355E 02	0.152470E 02	0.137986E 02
0.174131E 02	0.156221E 02	0.140939E 02
0.178768E 02	0.159828E 02	0.143752E 02
0.183270E 02	0.163296E 02	0.146430E 02
0.187641E 02	0.166631E 02	0.148981E 02
0.191885E 02	0.169837E 02	0.151411E 02
0.196004E 02	0.172920E 02	0.153725E 02
0.200004E 02	0.175885E 02	0.155928E 02
0.203888E 02	0.178736E 02	0.158027E 02
0.207658E 02	0.181476E 02	0.160025E 02
0.211318E 02	0.184112E 02	0.161929E 02
0.214872E 02	0.186646E 02	0.163742E 02
0.218323E 02	0.189083E 02	0.165469E 02
0.221672E 02	0.191426E 02	0.167113E 02
0.224925E 02	0.193679E 02	0.168679E 02
0.228082E 02	0.195845E 02	0.170170E 02
0.231148E 02	0.197928E 02	0.171591E 02
0.234124E 02	0.199931E 02	0.172944E 02
0.237014E 02	0.201856E 02	0.174232E 02
0.239819E 02	0.203708E 02	0.175459E 02
0.242543E 02	0.205488E 02	0.176628E 02
0.245187E 02	0.207200E 02	0.177741E 02
0.247754E 02	0.208847E 02	0.178801E 02
0.250247E 02	0.210429E 02	0.179810E 02
0.252667E 02	0.211951E 02	0.180772E 02
0.255017E 02	0.213415E 02	0.181687E 02
0.257298E 02	0.214822E 02	0.182559E 02

Table 4 (Continued). **Present Value of 1 per Period at Interest Rate** *i per Period*

$$P(i, n) = \frac{1 - (1 + i)^{-n}}{i}$$

.06	.08	.10
0.943396E 00	0.925926E 00	0.909091E 00
0.183339E 01	0.178326E 01	0.173554E 01
0.267301E 01	0.257710E 01	0.248685E 01
0.346511E 01	0.331213E 01	0.316987E 01
0.421236E 01	0.399271E 01	0.379079E 01
0.491732E 01	0.462288E 01	0.435526E 01
0.558238E 01	0.520637E 01	0.486842E 01
0.620979E 01	0.574664E 01	0.533493E 01
0.680169E 01	0.624689E 01	0.575902E 01
0.736009E 01	0.671008E 01	0.614457E 01
0.788687E 01	0.713896E 01	0.649506E 01
0.838384E 01	0.753608E 01	0.681369E 01
0.885268E 01	0.790378E 01	0.710336E 01
0.929498E 01	0.824424E 01	0.736669E 01
0.971225E 01	0.855948E 01	0.760608E 01
0.101059E 02	0.885137E 01	0.782371E 01
0.104773E 02	0.912164E 01	0.802155E 01
0.108276E 02	0.937189E 01	0.820141E 01
0.111581E 02	0.960360E 01	0.836492E 01
0.114699E 02	0.981815E 01	0.851356E 01
0.117641E 02	0.100168E 02	0.864869E 01
0.120416E 02	0.102007E 02	0.877154E 01
0.123034E 02	0.103711E 02	0.888322E 01
0.125504E 02	0.105288E 02	0.898474E 01
0.127834E 02	0.106748E 02	0.907704E 01
0.130032E 02	0.108100E 02	0.916095E 01
0.132105E 02	0.109352E 02	0.923722E 01
0.134062E 02	0.110511E 02	0.930657E 01
0.135907E 02	0.111584E 02	0.936961E 01
0.137648E 02	0.112578E 02	0.942691E 01
0.139291E 02	0.113498E 02	0.947901E 01
0.140840E 02	0.114350E 02	0.952638E 01
0.142302E 02	0.115139E 02	0.956943E 01
0.143681E 02	0.115869E 02	0.960857E 01
0.144982E 02	0.116546E 02	0.964416E 01
0.146210E 02	0.117172E 02	0.967651E 01
0.147368E 02	0.117752E 02	0.970592E 01
0.148460E 02	0.118289E 02	0.973265E 01
0.149491E 02	0.118786E 02	0.975696E 01
0.150463E 02	0.119246E 02	0.977905E 01
0.151380E 02	0.119672E 02	0.979914E 01
0.152245E 02	0.120067E 02	0.981740E 01
0.153062E 02	0.120432E 02	0.983400E 01
0.153832E 02	0.120771E 02	0.984909E 01
0.154558E 02	0.121084E 02	0.986281E 01
0.155244E 02	0.121374E 02	0.987528E 01
0.155890E 02	0.121643E 02	0.988662E 01
0.156500E 02	0.121891E 02	0.989693E 01
0.157076E 02	0.122122E 02	0.990630E 01
0.157619E 02	0.122335E 02	0.991481E 01

Table 4 (Continued).   **Present Value of 1 per Period at Interest Rate**
i per Period

$$P(i, n) = \frac{1 - (1 + i)^{-n}}{i}$$

n	.12		.15		.20	
1	0.892857E	00	0.869565E	00	0.833333E	00
2	0.169005E	01	0.162571E	01	0.152778E	01
3	0.240183E	01	0.228323E	01	0.210648E	01
4	0.303735E	01	0.285498E	01	0.258873E	01
5	0.360478E	01	0.335216E	01	0.299061E	01
6	0.411141E	01	0.378448E	01	0.332551E	01
7	0.456376E	01	0.416042E	01	0.360459E	01
8	0.496764E	01	0.448732E	01	0.383716E	01
9	0.532825E	01	0.477158E	01	0.403097E	01
10	0.565022E	01	0.501877E	01	0.419247E	01
11	0.593770E	01	0.523371E	01	0.432706E	01
12	0.619437E	01	0.542062E	01	0.443922E	01
13	0.642355E	01	0.558315E	01	0.453268E	01
14	0.662817E	01	0.572448E	01	0.461057E	01
15	0.681086E	01	0.584737E	01	0.467547E	01
16	0.697399E	01	0.595423E	01	0.472956E	01
17	0.711963E	01	0.604716E	01	0.477463E	01
18	0.724967E	01	0.612797E	01	0.481219E	01
19	0.736578E	01	0.619828E	01	0.484350E	01
20	0.746944E	01	0.625933E	01	0.486958E	01
21	0.756200E	01	0.631246E	01	0.489132E	01
22	0.764465E	01	0.635866E	01	0.490943E	01
23	0.771843E	01	0.639884E	01	0.492453E	01
24	0.778432E	01	0.643377E	01	0.493710E	01
25	0.784314E	01	0.646415E	01	0.494759E	01
26	0.789566E	01	0.649056E	01	0.495632E	01
27	0.794255E	01	0.651353E	01	0.496360E	01
28	0.798442E	01	0.653351E	01	0.496967E	01
29	0.802181E	01	0.655088E	01	0.497472E	01
30	0.805518E	01	0.656598E	01	0.497894E	01
31	0.808499E	01	0.657911E	01	0.498245E	01
32	0.811159E	01	0.659053E	01	0.498537E	01
33	0.813535E	01	0.660046E	01	0.498781E	01
34	0.815656E	01	0.660910E	01	0.498984E	01
35	0.817550E	01	0.661661E	01	0.499154E	01
36	0.819241E	01	0.662314E	01	0.499295E	01
37	0.820751E	01	0.662881E	01	0.499412E	01
38	0.822099E	01	0.663375E	01	0.499510E	01
39	0.823303E	01	0.663805E	01	0.499592E	01
40	0.824378E	01	0.664178E	01	0.499660E	01
41	0.825337E	01	0.664502E	01	0.499717E	01
42	0.826194E	01	0.664785E	01	0.499764E	01
43	0.826959E	01	0.665030E	01	0.499803E	01
44	0.827642E	01	0.665244E	01	0.499836E	01
45	0.828252E	01	0.665429E	01	0.499863E	01
46	0.828796E	01	0.665591E	01	0.499886E	01
47	0.829282E	01	0.665731E	01	0.499905E	01
48	0.829716E	01	0.665853E	01	0.499921E	01
49	0.830104E	01	0.665959E	01	0.499934E	01
50	0.830450E	01	0.666051E	01	0.499945E	01

Table 4 (*Continued*).   *Present Value of I per Period at Interest Rate i per Period*

$$P(i, n) = \frac{1 - (1 + i)^{-n}}{i}$$

.25	.30	.35
0.800000E 00	0.769231E 00	0.740741E 00
0.144000E 01	0.136095E 01	0.128944E 01
0.195200E 01	0.181611E 01	0.169588E 01
0.236160E 01	0.216624E 01	0.199695E 01
0.268928E 01	0.243557E 01	0.221996E 01
0.295142E 01	0.264275E 01	0.238516E 01
0.316114E 01	0.280211E 01	0.250752E 01
0.332891E 01	0.292470E 01	0.259817E 01
0.346313E 01	0.301900E 01	0.266531E 01
0.357050E 01	0.309154E 01	0.271504E 01
0.365640E 01	0.314734E 01	0.275188E 01
0.372512E 01	0.319026E 01	0.277917E 01
0.378010E 01	0.322328E 01	0.279939E 01
0.382408E 01	0.324867E 01	0.281436E 01
0.385926E 01	0.326821E 01	0.282545E 01
0.388741E 01	0.328324E 01	0.283367E 01
0.390993E 01	0.329480E 01	0.283975E 01
0.392794E 01	0.330369E 01	0.284426E 01
0.394235E 01	0.331053E 01	0.284760E 01
0.395388E 01	0.331579E 01	0.285008E 01
0.396311E 01	0.331984E 01	0.285191E 01
0.397049E 01	0.332296E 01	0.285327E 01
0.397639E 01	0.332535E 01	0.285427E 01
0.398111E 01	0.332719E 01	0.285502E 01
0.398489E 01	0.332861E 01	0.285557E 01
0.398791E 01	0.332970E 01	0.285598E 01
0.399033E 01	0.333054E 01	0.285628E 01
0.399226E 01	0.333118E 01	0.285650E 01
0.399381E 01	0.333168E 01	0.285667E 01
0.399505E 01	0.333206E 01	0.285679E 01
0.399604E 01	0.333235E 01	0.285688E 01
0.399683E 01	0.333258E 01	0.285695E 01
0.399746E 01	0.333275E 01	0.285700E 01
0.399797E 01	0.333289E 01	0.285704E 01
0.399838E 01	0.333299E 01	0.285706E 01
0.399870E 01	0.333307E 01	0.285708E 01
0.399896E 01	0.333313E 01	0.285710E 01
0.399917E 01	0.333318E 01	0.285711E 01
0.399934E 01	0.333321E 01	0.285712E 01
0.399947E 01	0.333324E 01	0.285713E 01
0.399957E 01	0.333326E 01	0.285713E 01
0.399966E 01	0.333328E 01	0.285713E 01
0.399973E 01	0.333329E 01	0.285714E 01
0.399978E 01	0.333330E 01	0.285714E 01
0.399983E 01	0.333331E 01	0.285714E 01
0.399986E 01	0.333331E 01	0.285714E 01
0.399989E 01	0.333332E 01	0.285714E 01
0.399991E 01	0.333332E 01	0.285714E 01
0.399993E 01	0.333332E 01	0.285714E 01
0.399994E 01	0.333333E 01	0.285714E 01

Table 4 (Continued). **Present Value of I per Period at Interest Rate**
i per Period

$$P(i, n) = \frac{1 - (1 + i)^{-n}}{i}$$

.40	.45	.50
0.714286E 00	0.689655E 00	0.666667E 00
0.122449E 01	0.116528E 01	0.111111E 01
0.158892E 01	0.149330E 01	0.140741E 01
0.184923E 01	0.171951E 01	0.160494E 01
0.203516E 01	0.187553E 01	0.173663E 01
0.216797E 01	0.198312E 01	0.182442E 01
0.226284E 01	0.205733E 01	0.188294E 01
0.233060E 01	0.210850E 01	0.192196E 01
0.237900E 01	0.214379E 01	0.194798E 01
0.241357E 01	0.216813E 01	0.196532E 01
0.243826E 01	0.218492E 01	0.197688F 01
0.245590E 01	0.219650E 01	0.198459E 01
0.246850E 01	0.220448E 01	0.198972E 01
0.247750E 01	0.220999E 01	0.199315E 01
0.248393E 01	0.221378E 01	0.199543E 01
0.248852E 01	0.221640E 01	0.199696E 01
0.249180E 01	0.221821E 01	0.199797E 01
0.249414E 01	0.221945E 01	0.199865E 01
0.249582E 01	0.222031E 01	0.199910E 01
0.249701E 01	0.222091E 01	0.199940E 01
0.249787E 01	0.222131E 01	0.199960E 01
0.249848E 01	0.222160E 01	0.199973E 01
0.249891E 01	0.222179E 01	0.199982E 01
0.249922E 01	0.222192E 01	0.199988E 01
0.249944E 01	0.222202E 01	0.199992E 01
0.249960E 01	0.222208E 01	0.199995E 01
0.249972E 01	0.222212E 01	0.199996E 01
0.249980E 01	0.222215E 01	0.199998E 01
0.249986E 01	0.222218E 01	0.199998E 01
0.249990E 01	0.222219E 01	0.199999E 01
0.249993E 01	0.222220E 01	0.199999E 01
0.249995E 01	0.222221E 01	0.200000E 01
0.249996E 01	0.222221E 01	0.200000E 01
0.249997E 01	0.222221E 01	0.200000E 01
0.249998E 01	0.222222E 01	0.200000E 01
0.249999E 01	0.222222E 01	0.200000E 01
0.249999E 01	0.222222E 01	0.200000E 01
0.249999E 01	0.222222E 01	0.200000E 01
0.250000E 01	0.222222E 01	0.200000E 01
0.250000E 01	0.222222E 01	0.200000E 01
0.250000E 01	0.222222E 01	0.200000E 01
0.250000E 01	0.222222E 01	0.200000E 01
0.250000E 01	0.222222E 01	0.200000E 01
0.250000E 01	0.222222E 01	0.200000E 01
0.250000E 01	0.222222E 01	0.200000E 01
0.250000E 01	0.222222E 01	0.200000E 01
0.250000E 01	0.222222E 01	0.200000E 01
0.250000E 01	0.222222E 01	0.200000E 01
0.250000E 01	0.222222E 01	0.200000E 01
0.250000E 01	0.222222E 01	0.200000E 01

Table 5.   Value of 1 *n* Periods Hence with Continuous Compounding at Rate δ

$$F(\delta, n) = e^{\delta n}$$

n	.01	.015	.02
1	0.101005E 01	0.101511E 01	0.102020E 01
2	0.102020E 01	0.103045E 01	0.104081E 01
3	0.103045E 01	0.104603E 01	0.106184E 01
4	0.104081E 01	0.106184E 01	0.108329E 01
5	0.105127E 01	0.107788E 01	0.110517E 01
6	0.106184E 01	0.109417E 01	0.112750E 01
7	0.107251E 01	0.111071E 01	0.115027E 01
8	0.108329E 01	0.112750E 01	0.117351E 01
9	0.109417E 01	0.114454E 01	0.119722E 01
10	0.110517E 01	0.116183E 01	0.122140E 01
11	0.111628E 01	0.117939E 01	0.124608E 01
12	0.112750E 01	0.119722E 01	0.127125E 01
13	0.113883E 01	0.121531E 01	0.129693E 01
14	0.115027E 01	0.123368E 01	0.132313E 01
15	0.116183E 01	0.125232E 01	0.134986E 01
16	0.117351E 01	0.127125E 01	0.137713E 01
17	0.118530E 01	0.129046E 01	0.140495E 01
18	0.119722E 01	0.130996E 01	0.143333E 01
19	0.120925E 01	0.132976E 01	0.146228E 01
20	0.122140E 01	0.134986E 01	0.149182E 01
21	0.123368E 01	0.137026E 01	0.152196E 01
22	0.124608E 01	0.139097E 01	0.155271E 01
23	0.125860E 01	0.141199E 01	0.158407E 01
24	0.127125E 01	0.143333E 01	0.161607E 01
25	0.128403E 01	0.145499E 01	0.164872E 01
26	0.129693E 01	0.147698E 01	0.168203E 01
27	0.130996E 01	0.149930E 01	0.171601E 01
28	0.132313E 01	0.152196E 01	0.175067E 01
29	0.133643E 01	0.154496E 01	0.178604E 01
30	0.134986E 01	0.156831E 01	0.182212E 01
31	0.136343E 01	0.159201E 01	0.185893E 01
32	0.137713E 01	0.161607E 01	0.189648E 01
33	0.139097E 01	0.164050E 01	0.193479E 01
34	0.140495E 01	0.166529E 01	0.197388E 01
35	0.141907E 01	0.169046E 01	0.201375E 01
36	0.143333E 01	0.171601E 01	0.205443E 01
37	0.144773E 01	0.174194E 01	0.209594E 01
38	0.146228E 01	0.176827E 01	0.213828E 01
39	0.147698E 01	0.179499E 01	0.218147E 01
40	0.149182E 01	0.182212E 01	0.222554E 01
41	0.150682E 01	0.184966E 01	0.227050E 01
42	0.152196E 01	0.187761E 01	0.231637E 01
43	0.153726E 01	0.190599E 01	0.236316E 01
44	0.155271E 01	0.193479E 01	0.241090E 01
45	0.156831E 01	0.196403E 01	0.245960E 01
46	0.158407E 01	0.199372E 01	0.250929E 01
47	0.159999E 01	0.202385E 01	0.255998E 01
48	0.161607E 01	0.205443E 01	0.261170E 01
49	0.163232E 01	0.208548E 01	0.266446E 01
50	0.164872E 01	0.211700E 01	0.271828E 01

Table 5 *(Continued).* **Value of** *I n* **Periods Hence with Continuous Compounding at Rate** δ

$$F(\delta, n) = e^{\delta n}$$

.03·	.04	.05
0.103045E 01	0.104081E 01	0.105127E 01
0.106184E 01	0.108329E 01	0.110517E 01
0.109417E 01	0.112750E 01	0.116183E 01
0.112750E 01	0.117351E 01	0.122140E 01
0.116183E 01	0.122140E 01	0.128403E 01
0.119722E 01	0.127125E 01	0.134986E 01
0.123368E 01	0.132313E 01	0.141907E 01
0.127125E 01	0.137713E 01	0.149182E 01
0.130996E 01	0.143333E 01	0.156831E 01
0.134986E 01	0.149182E 01	0.164872E 01
0.139097E 01	0.155271E 01	0.173325E 01
0.143333E 01	0.161607E 01	0.182212E 01
0.147698E 01	0.168203E 01	0.191554E 01
0.152196E 01	0.175067E 01	0.201375E 01
0.156831E 01	0.182212E 01	0.211700E 01
0.161607E 01	0.189648E 01	0.222554E 01
0.166529E 01	0.197388E 01	0.233965E 01
0.171601E 01	0.205443E 01	0.245960E 01
0.176827E 01	0.213828E 01	0.258571E 01
0.182212E 01	0.222554E 01	0.271828E 01
0.187761E 01	0.231637E 01	0.285765E 01
0.193479E 01	0.241090E 01	0.300417E 01
0.199372E 01	0.250929E 01	0.315819E 01
0.205443E 01	0.261170E 01	0.332012E 01
0.211700E 01	0.271828E 01	0.349034E 01
0.218147E 01	0.282922E 01	0.366930E 01
0.224791E 01	0.294468E 01	0.385743E 01
0.231637E 01	0.306485E 01	0.405520E 01
0.238691E 01	0.318993E 01	0.426311E 01
0.245960E 01	0.332012E 01	0.448169E 01
0.253451E 01	0.345561E 01	0.471147E 01
0.261170E 01	0.359664E 01	0.495303E 01
0.269123E 01	0.374342E 01	0.520698E 01
0.277319E 01	0.389619E 01	0.547395E 01
0.285765E 01	0.405520E 01	0.575460E 01
0.294468E 01	0.422070E 01	0.604965E 01
0.303436E 01	0.439295E 01	0.635982E 01
0.312677E 01	0.457223E 01	0.668589E 01
0.322199E 01	0.475882E 01	0.702869E 01
0.332012E 01	0.495303E 01	0.738906E 01
0.342123E 01	0.515517E 01	0.776790E 01
0.352542E 01	0.536556E 01	0.816617E 01
0.363279E 01	0.558453E 01	0.858486E 01
0.374342E 01	0.581244E 01	0.902501E 01
0.385743E 01	0.604965E 01	0.948774E 01
0.397490E 01	0.629654E 01	0.997418E 01
0.409596E 01	0.655350E 01	0.104856E 02
0.422070E 01	0.682096E 01	0.110232E 02
0.434924E 01	0.709933E 01	0.115883E 02
0.448169E 01	0.738906E 01	0.121825E 02

Table 5 (*Continued*). *Value of* I *n* Periods Hence with Continuous Compounding at Rate δ

$$F(\delta, n) = e^{\delta n}$$

.06	.08	.10
0.106184E 01	0.108329E 01	0.110517E 01
0.112750E 01	0.117351E 01	0.122140E 01
0.119722E 01	0.127125E 01	0.134986E 01
0.127125E 01	0.137713E 01	0.149182E 01
0.134986E 01	0.149182E 01	0.164872E 01
0.143333E 01	0.161607E 01	0.182212E 01
0.152196E 01	0.175067E 01	0.201375E 01
0.161607E 01	0.189648E 01	0.222554E 01
0.171601E 01	0.205443E 01	0.245960E 01
0.182212E 01	0.222554E 01	0.271828E 01
0.193479E 01	0.241090E 01	0.300417E 01
0.205443E 01	0.261170E 01	0.332012E 01
0.218147E 01	0.282922E 01	0.366930E 01
0.231637E 01	0.306485E 01	0.405520E 01
0.245960E 01	0.332012E 01	0.448169E 01
0.261170E 01	0.359664E 01	0.495303E 01
0.277319E 01	0.389619E 01	0.547395E 01
0.294468E 01	0.422070E 01	0.604965E 01
0.312677E 01	0.457223E 01	0.668589E 01
0.332012E 01	0.495303E 01	0.738906E 01
0.352542E 01	0.536556E 01	0.816617E 01
0.374342E 01	0.581244E 01	0.902501E 01
0.397490E 01	0.629654E 01	0.997418E 01
0.422070E 01	0.682096E 01	0.110232E 02
0.448169E 01	0.738906E 01	0.121825E 02
0.475882E 01	0.800447E 01	0.134637E 02
0.505309E 01	0.867114E 01	0.148797E 02
0.536556E 01	0.939333E 01	0.164446E 02
0.569734E 01	0.101757E 02	0.181741E 02
0.604965E 01	0.110232E 02	0.200855E 02
0.642374E 01	0.119413E 02	0.221980E 02
0.682096E 01	0.129358E 02	0.245325E 02
0.724274E 01	0.140132E 02	0.271126E 02
0.769061E 01	0.151803E 02	0.299641E 02
0.816617E 01	0.164446E 02	0.331155E 02
0.867114E 01	0.178143E 02	0.365982E 02
0.920733E 01	0.192980E 02	0.404473E 02
0.977668E 01	0.209052E 02	0.447012E 02
0.103812E 02	0.226464E 02	0.494024E 02
0.110232E 02	0.245325E 02	0.545982E 02
0.117048E 02	0.265758E 02	0.603403E 02
0.124286E 02	0.287892E 02	0.666863E 02
0.131971E 02	0.311870E 02	0.736998E 02
0.140132E 02	0.337844E 02	0.814509E 02
0.148797E 02	0.365982E 02	0.900171E 02
0.157998E 02	0.396464E 02	0.994843E 02
0.167769E 02	0.429484E 02	0.109947E 03
0.178143E 02	0.465255E 02	0.121510E 03
0.189158E 02	0.504004E 02	0.134290E 03
0.200855E 02	0.545982E 02	0.148413E 03

Table 5 (Continued). **Value of 1 *n* Periods Hence with Continuous Compounding at Rate** δ

$$F(\delta, n) = e^{\delta n}$$

n	.12		.15		.20	
1	0.112750E	01	0.116183E	01	0.122140E	01
2	0.127125E	01	0.134986E	01	0.149182E	01
3	0.143333E	01	0.156831E	01	0.182212E	01
4	0.161607E	01	0.182212E	01	0.222554E	01
5	0.182212E	01	0.211700E	01	0.271828E	01
6	0.205443E	01	0.245960E	01	0.332012E	01
7	0.231637E	01	0.285765E	01	0.405520E	01
8	0.261170E	01	0.332012E	01	0.495303E	01
9	0.294468E	01	0.385743E	01	0.604965E	01
10	0.332012E	01	0.448169E	01	0.738906E	01
11	0.374342E	01	0.520698E	01	0.902501E	01
12	0.422070E	01	0.604965E	01	0.110232E	02
13	0.475882E	01	0.702869E	01	0.134637E	02
14	0.536556E	01	0.816617E	01	0.164446E	02
15	0.604965E	01	0.948774E	01	0.200855E	02
16	0.682096E	01	0.110232E	02	0.245325E	02
17	0.769061E	01	0.128071E	02	0.299641E	02
18	0.867114E	01	0.148797E	02	0.365982E	02
19	0.977668E	01	0.172878E	02	0.447012E	02
20	0.110232E	02	0.200855E	02	0.545982E	02
21	0.124286E	02	0.233361E	02	0.666863E	02
22	0.140132E	02	0.271126E	02	0.814509E	02
23	0.157998E	02	0.315004E	02	0.994843E	02
24	0.178143E	02	0.365982E	02	0.121510E	03
25	0.200855E	02	0.425211E	02	0.148413E	03
26	0.226464E	02	0.494024E	02	0.181272E	03
27	0.255337E	02	0.573975E	02	0.221406E	03
28	0.287892E	02	0.666863E	02	0.270426E	03
29	0.324597E	02	0.774785E	02	0.330300E	03
30	0.365982E	02	0.900171E	02	0.403429E	03
31	0.412644E	02	0.104585E	03	0.492749E	03
32	0.465255E	02	0.121510E	03	0.601845E	03
33	0.524573E	02	0.141175E	03	0.735095E	03
34	0.591455E	02	0.164022E	03	0.897847E	03
35	0.666863E	02	0.190566E	03	0.109663E	04
36	0.751886E	02	0.221406E	03	0.133943E	04
37	0.847749E	02	0.257238E	03	0.163598E	04
38	0.955835E	02	0.298867E	03	0.199820E	04
39	0.107770E	03	0.347234E	03	0.244060E	04
40	0.121510E	03	0.403429E	03	0.298096E	04
41	0.137003E	03	0.468717E	03	0.364095E	04
42	0.154470E	03	0.544572E	03	0.444707E	04
43	0.174164E	03	0.632702E	03	0.543166E	04
44	0.196370E	03	0.735095E	03	0.663424E	04
45	0.221406E	03	0.854059E	03	0.810308E	04
46	0.249635E	03	0.992275E	03	0.989713E	04
47	0.281463E	03	0.115286E	04	0.120884E	05
48	0.317348E	03	0.133943E	04	0.147648E	05
49	0.357809E	03	0.155620E	04	0.180337E	05
50	0.403429E	03	0.180804E	04	0.220265E	05

Table 5 (Continued). **Value of** I n **Periods Hence with Continuous Compounding at Rate** δ

$$F(\delta, n) = e^{\delta n}$$

.25 ·	.30	.35
0.128403E 01	0.134986E 01	0.141907E 01
0.164872E 01	0.182212E 01	0.201375E 01
0.211700E 01	0.245960E 01	0.285765E 01
0.271828E 01	0.332012E 01	0.405520E 01
0.349034E 01	0.448169E 01	0.575460E 01
0.448169E 01	0.604965E 01	0.816617E 01
0.575460E 01	0.816617E 01	0.115883E 02
0.738906E 01	0.110232E 02	0.164446E 02
0.948774E 01	0.148797E 02	0.233361E 02
0.121825E 02	0.200855E 02	0.331155E 02
0.156426E 02	0.271126E 02	0.469931E 02
0.200855E 02	0.365982E 02	0.666863E 02
0.257903E 02	0.494024E 02	0.946324E 02
0.331155E 02	0.666863E 02	0.134290E 03
0.425211E 02	0.900171E 02	0.190566E 03
0.545982E 02	0.121510E 03	0.270426E 03
0.701054E 02	0.164022E 03	0.383753E 03
0.900171E 02	0.221406E 03	0.544572E 03
0.115584E 03	0.298867E 03	0.772784E 03
0.148413E 03	0.403429E 03	0.109663E 04
0.190566E 03	0.544572E 03	0.155620E 04
0.244692E 03	0.735095E 03	0.220835E 04
0.314191E 03	0.992275E 03	0.313379E 04
0.403429E 03	0.133943E 04	0.444707E 04
0.518013E 03	0.180804E 04	0.631069E 04
0.665142E 03	0.244060E 04	0.895529E 04
0.854059E 03	0.329447E 04	0.127082E 05
0.109663E 04	0.444707E 04	0.180337E 05
0.140810E 04	0.600291E 04	0.255911E 05
0.180804E 04	0.810308E 04	0.363155E 05
0.232157E 04	0.109380E 05	0.515342E 05
0.298096E 04	0.147648E 05	0.731304E 05
0.382763E 04	0.199304E 05	0.103777E 06
0.491477E 04	0.269032E 05	0.147267E 06
0.631069E 04	0.363155E 05	0.208981E 06
0.810308E 04	0.490208E 05	0.296559E 06
0.104046E 05	0.661712E 05	0.420837E 06
0.133597E 05	0.893217E 05	0.597196E 06
0.171542E 05	0.120572E 06	0.847461E 06
0.220265E 05	0.162755E 06	0.120260E 07
0.282825E 05	0.219696E 06	0.170658E 07
0.363155E 05	0.296559E 06	0.242175E 07
0.466300E 05	0.400312E 06	0.343662E 07
0.598741E 05	0.540365E 06	0.487680E 07
0.768799E 05	0.729416E 06	0.692051E 07
0.987158E 05	0.984609E 06	0.982067E 07
0.126754E 06	0.132908E 07	0.139362E 08
0.162755E 06	0.179407E 07	0.197764E 08
0.208981E 06	0.242175E 07	0.280641E 08
0.268337E 06	0.326902E 07	0.398248E 08

Table 5 (Continued). **Value of 1** *n* **Periods Hence with Continuous Compounding at Rate** δ

$$F(\delta, n) = e^{\delta n}$$

.40		.45		.50	
0.149182E	01	0.156831E	01	0.164872E	01
0.222554E	01	0.245960E	01	0.271828E	01
0.332012E	01	0.385743E	01	0.448169E	01
0.495303E	01	0.604965E	01	0.738906E	01
0.738906E	01	0.948774E	01	0.121825E	02
0.110232E	02	0.148797E	02	0.200855E	02
0.164446E	02	0.233361E	02	0.331155E	02
0.245325E	02	0.365982E	02	0.545982E	02
0.365982E	02	0.573975E	02	0.900171E	02
0.545982E	02	0.900171E	02	0.148413E	03
0.814509E	02	0.141175E	03	0.244692E	03
0.121510E	03	0.221406E	03	0.403429E	03
0.181272E	03	0.347234E	03	0.665142E	03
0.270426E	03	0.544572E	03	0.109663E	04
0.403429E	03	0.854059E	03	0.180804E	04
0.601845E	03	0.133943E	04	0.298096E	04
0.897847E	03	0.210065E	04	0.491477E	04
0.133943E	04	0.329447E	04	0.810308E	04
0.199820E	04	0.516675E	04	0.133597E	05
0.298096E	04	0.810308E	04	0.220265E	05
0.444707E	04	0.127082E	05	0.363155E	05
0.663424E	04	0.199304E	05	0.598741E	05
0.989713E	04	0.312570E	05	0.987158E	05
0.147648E	05	0.490208E	05	0.162755E	06
0.220265E	05	0.768799E	05	0.268337E	06
0.328596E	05	0.120572E	06	0.442413E	06
0.490208E	05	0.189094E	06	0.729416E	06
0.731304E	05	0.296559E	06	0.120260E	07
0.109098E	06	0.465096E	06	0.198276E	07
0.162755E	06	0.729416E	06	0.326902E	07
0.242802E	06	0.114395E	07	0.538970E	07
0.362217E	06	0.179407E	07	0.888611E	07
0.540365E	06	0.281367E	07	0.146507E	08
0.806130E	06	0.441271E	07	0.241550E	08
0.120260E	07	0.692051E	07	0.398248E	08
0.179407E	07	0.108535E	08	0.656600E	08
0.267645E	07	0.170217E	08	0.108255E	09
0.399279E	07	0.266954E	08	0.178482E	09
0.595654E	07	0.418666E	08	0.294268E	09
0.888611E	07	0.656600E	08	0.485165E	09
0.132565E	08	0.102975E	09	0.799902E	09
0.197764E	08	0.161497E	09	0.131882E	10
0.295029E	08	0.253278E	09	0.217436E	10
0.440132E	08	0.397220E	09	0.358491E	10
0.656600E	08	0.622964E	09	0.591052E	10
0.979532E	08	0.977003E	09	0.974480E	10
0.146129E	09	0.153225E	10	0.160665E	11
0.217999E	09	0.240304E	10	0.264891E	11
0.325216E	09	0.376872E	10	0.436732E	11
0.485165E	09	0.591052E	10	0.720049E	11

Table 6. Present Value, P, of I to be Received n Periods Hence with Continuous Compounding at Rate δ

$$P(\delta, n) = e^{-\delta n}$$

n	.01		.015		.02	
1	0.990050E	00	0.985112E	00	0.980199E	00
2	0.980199E	00	0.970446E	00	0.960789E	00
3	0.970446E	00	0.955997E	00	0.941765E	00
4	0.960789E	00	0.941765E	00	0.923116E	00
5	0.951229E	00	0.927743E	00	0.904837E	00
6	0.941765E	00	0.913931E	00	0.886920E	00
7	0.932394E	00	0.900325E	00	0.869358E	00
8	0.923116E	00	0.886920E	00	0.852144E	00
9	0.913931E	00	0.873716E	00	0.835270E	00
10	0.904837E	00	0.860708E	00	0.818731E	00
11	0.895834E	00	0.847894E	00	0.802519E	00
12	0.886920E	00	0.835270E	00	0.786628E	00
13	0.878095E	00	0.822835E	00	0.771052E	00
14	0.869358E	00	0.810584E	00	0.755784E	00
15	0.860708E	00	0.798516E	00	0.740818E	00
16	0.852144E	00	0.786628E	00	0.726149E	00
17	0.843665E	00	0.774916E	00	0.711770E	00
18	0.835270E	00	0.763379E	00	0.697676E	00
19	0.826959E	00	0.752014E	00	0.683861E	00
20	0.818731E	00	0.740818E	00	0.670320E	00
21	0.810584E	00	0.729789E	00	0.657047E	00
22	0.802519E	00	0.718924E	00	0.644036E	00
23	0.794534E	00	0.708220E	00	0.631284E	00
24	0.786628E	00	0.697676E	00	0.618783E	00
25	0.778801E	00	0.687289E	00	0.606531E	00
26	0.771052E	00	0.677057E	00	0.594521E	00
27	0.763379E	00	0.666977E	00	0.582748E	00
28	0.755784E	00	0.657047E	00	0.571209E	00
29	0.748264E	00	0.647265E	00	0.559898E	00
30	0.740818E	00	0.637628E	00	0.548812E	00
31	0.733447E	00	0.628135E	00	0.537944E	00
32	0.726149E	00	0.618783E	00	0.527292E	00
33	0.718924E	00	0.609571E	00	0.516851E	00
34	0.711770E	00	0.600496E	00	0.506617E	00
35	0.704688E	00	0.591555E	00	0.496585E	00
36	0.697676E	00	0.582748E	00	0.486752E	00
37	0.690734E	00	0.574072E	00	0.477114E	00
38	0.683861E	00	0.565525E	00	0.467666E	00
39	0.677057E	00	0.557106E	00	0.458406E	00
40	0.670320E	00	0.548812E	00	0.449329E	00
41	0.663650E	00	0.540641E	00	0.440432E	00
42	0.657047E	00	0.532592E	00	0.431711E	00
43	0.650509E	00	0.524663E	00	0.423162E	00
44	0.644036E	00	0.516851E	00	0.414783E	00
45	0.637628E	00	0.509156E	00	0.406570E	00
46	0.631284E	00	0.501576E	00	0.398519E	00
47	0.625002E	00	0.494109E	00	0.390628E	00
48	0.618783E	00	0.486752E	00	0.382893E	00
49	0.612626E	00	0.479505E	00	0.375311E	00
50	0.606531E	00	0.472367E	00	0.367879E	00

Table 6 (Continued). Present Value, P, of 1 to be Received n Periods Hence with Continuous Compounding at Rate δ

$$P(\delta, n) = e^{-\delta n}$$

.03	.04	.05
0.970446E 00	0.960789E 00	0.951229E 00
0.941765E 00	0.923116E 00	0.904837E 00
0.913931E 00	0.886920E 00	0.860708E 00
0.886920E 00	0.852144E 00	0.818731E 00
0.860708E 00	0.818731E 00	0.778801E 00
0.835270E 00	0.786628E 00	0.740818E 00
0.810584E 00	0.755784E 00	0.704688E 00
0.786628E 00	0.726149E 00	0.670320E 00
0.763379E 00	0.697676E 00	0.637628E 00
0.740818E 00	0.670320E 00	0.606531E 00
0.718924E 00	0.644036E 00	0.576950E 00
0.697676E 00	0.618783E 00	0.548812E 00
0.677057E 00	0.594521E 00	0.522046E 00
0.657047E 00	0.571209E 00	0.496585E 00
0.637628E 00	0.548812E 00	0.472367E 00
0.618783E 00	0.527292E 00	0.449329E 00
0.600496E 00	0.506617E 00	0.427415E 00
0.582748E 00	0.486752E 00	0.406570E 00
0.565525E 00	0.467666E 00	0.386741E 00
0.548812E 00	0.449329E 00	0.367879E 00
0.532592E 00	0.431711E 00	0.349938E 00
0.516851E 00	0.414783E 00	0.332871E 00
0.501576E 00	0.398519E 00	0.316637E 00
0.486752E 00	0.382893E 00	0.301194E 00
0.472367E 00	0.367879E 00	0.286505E 00
0.458406E 00	0.353455E 00	0.272532E 00
0.444858E 00	0.339596E 00	0.259240E 00
0.431711E 00	0.326280E 00	0.246597E 00
0.418952E 00	0.313486E 00	0.234570E 00
0.406570E 00	0.301194E 00	0.223130E 00
0.394554E 00	0.289384E 00	0.212248E 00
0.382893E 00	0.278037E 00	0.201897E 00
0.371577E 00	0.267135E 00	0.192050E 00
0.360595E 00	0.256661E 00	0.182684E 00
0.349938E 00	0.246597E 00	0.173774E 00
0.339596E 00	0.236928E 00	0.165299E 00
0.329559E 00	0.227638E 00	0.157237E 00
0.319819E 00	0.218712E 00	0.149569E 00
0.310367E 00	0.210136E 00	0.142274E 00
0.301194E 00	0.201897E 00	0.135335E 00
0.292293E 00	0.193980E 00	0.128735E 00
0.283654E 00	0.186374E 00	0.122456E 00
0.275271E 00	0.179066E 00	0.116484E 00
0.267135E 00	0.172045E 00	0.110803E 00
0.259240E 00	0.165299E 00	0.105399E 00
0.251579E 00	0.158817E 00	0.100259E 00
0.244143E 00	0.152590E 00	0.953692E-01
0.236928E 00	0.146607E 00	0.907180E-01
0.229925E 00	0.140858E 00	0.862936E-01
0.223130E 00	0.135335E 00	0.820850E-01

Table 6 (Continued). **Present Value, P, of 1 to be Received n Periods Hence with Continuous Compounding at Rate** δ

$$P(\delta, n) = e^{-\delta n}$$

.06	.08	.10
0.941765E 00	0.923116E 00	0.904837E 00
0.886920E 00	0.852144E 00	0.818731E 00
0.835270E 00	0.786628E 00	0.740818E 00
0.786628E 00	0.726149E 00	0.670320E 00
0.740818E 00	0.670320E 00	0.606531E 00
0.697676E 00	0.618783E 00	0.548812E 00
0.657047E 00	0.571209E 00	0.496585E 00
0.618783E 00	0.527292E 00	0.449329E 00
0.582748E 00	0.486752E 00	0.406570E 00
0.548812E 00	0.449329E 00	0.367879E 00
0.516851E 00	0.414783E 00	0.332871E 00
0.486752E 00	0.382893E 00	0.301194E 00
0.458406E 00	0.353455E 00	0.272532E 00
0.431711E 00	0.326280E 00	0.246597E 00
0.406570E 00	0.301194E 00	0.223130E 00
0.382893E 00	0.278037E 00	0.201897E 00
0.360595E 00	0.256661E 00	0.182684E 00
0.339596E 00	0.236928E 00	0.165299E 00
0.319819E 00	0.218712E 00	0.149569E 00
0.301194E 00	0.201897E 00	0.135335E 00
0.283654E 00	0.186374E 00	0.122456E 00
0.267135E 00	0.172045E 00	0.110803E 00
0.251579E 00	0.158817E 00	0.100259E 00
0.236928E 00	0.146607E 00	0.907180E-01
0.223130E 00	0.135335E 00	0.820850E-01
0.210136E 00	0.124930E 00	0.742736E-01
0.197899E 00	0.115325E 00	0.672055E-01
0.186374E 00	0.106459E 00	0.608101E-01
0.175520E 00	0.982736E-01	0.550232E-01
0.165299E 00	0.907180E-01	0.497871E-01
0.155673E 00	0.837432E-01	0.450492E-01
0.146607E 00	0.773047E-01	0.407622E-01
0.138069E 00	0.713613E-01	0.368832E-01
0.130029E 00	0.658748E-01	0.333733E-01
0.122456E 00	0.608101E-01	0.301974E-01
0.115325E 00	0.561348E-01	0.273237E-01
0.108609E 00	0.518189E-01	0.247235E-01
0.102284E 00	0.478349E-01	0.223708E-01
0.963276E-01	0.441572E-01	0.202419E-01
0.907180E-01	0.407622E-01	0.183156E-01
0.854350E-01	0.376283E-01	0.165727E-01
0.804596E-01	0.347353E-01	0.149956E-01
0.757740E-01	0.320647E-01	0.135686E-01
0.713613E-01	0.295994E-01	0.122773E-01
0.672055E-01	0.273237E-01	0.111090E-01
0.632918E-01	0.252230E-01	0.100518E-01
0.596059E-01	0.232837E-01	0.909528E-02
0.561348E-01	0.214936E-01	0.822975E-02
0.528657E-01	0.198411E-01	0.744658E-02
0.497871E-01	0.183156E-01	0.673795E-02

Table 6 (Continued).   **Present Value, P, of 1 to be Received n Periods Hence with Continuous Compounding at Rate** δ

$$P(\delta, n) = e^{-\delta n}$$

n	.12	.15	.20
1	0.886920E 00	0.860708E 00	0.818731E 00
2	0.786628E 00	0.740818E 00	0.670320E 00
3	0.697676E 00	0.637628E 00	0.548812E 00
4	0.618783E 00	0.548812E 00	0.449329E 00
5	0.548812E 00	0.472367E 00	0.367879E 00
6	0.486752E 00	0.406570E 00	0.301194E 00
7	0.431711E 00	0.349938E 00	0.246597E 00
8	0.382893E 00	0.301194E 00	0.201897E 00
9	0.339596E 00	0.259240E 00	0.165299E 00
10	0.301194E 00	0.223130E 00	0.135335E 00
11	0.267135E 00	0.192050E 00	0.110803E 00
12	0.236928E 00	0.165299E 00	0.907180E-01
13	0.210136E 00	0.142274E 00	0.742736E-01
14	0.186374E 00	0.122456E 00	0.608101E-01
15	0.165299E 00	0.105399E 00	0.497871E-01
16	0.146607E 00	0.907180E-01	0.407622E-01
17	0.130029E 00	0.780817E-01	0.333733E-01
18	0.115325E 00	0.672055E-01	0.273237E-01
19	0.102284E 00	0.578443E-01	0.223708E-01
20	0.907180E-01	0.497871E-01	0.183156E-01
21	0.804596E-01	0.428521E-01	0.149956E-01
22	0.713613E-01	0.368832E-01	0.122773E-01
23	0.632918E-01	0.317456E-01	0.100518E-01
24	0.561348E-01	0.273237E-01	0.822975E-02
25	0.497871E-01	0.235177E-01	0.673795E-02
26	0.441572E-01	0.202419E-01	0.551656E-02
27	0.391639E-01	0.174224E-01	0.451658E-02
28	0.347353E-01	0.149956E-01	0.369786E-02
29	0.308074E-01	0.129068E-01	0.302755E-02
30	0.273237E-01	0.111090E-01	0.247875E-02
31	0.242340E-01	0.956160E-02	0.202943E-02
32	0.214936E-01	0.822975E-02	0.166156E-02
33	0.190631E-01	0.708341E-02	0.136037E-02
34	0.169075E-01	0.609675E-02	0.111378E-02
35	0.149956E-01	0.524752E-02	0.911882E-03
36	0.132999E-01	0.451658E-02	0.746586E-03
37	0.117959E-01	0.388746E-02	0.611253E-03
38	0.104621E-01	0.334597E-02	0.500451E-03
39	0.927901E-02	0.287990E-02	0.409735E-03
40	0.822975E-02	0.247875E-02	0.335463E-03
41	0.729913E-02	0.213348E-02	0.274654E-03
42	0.647375E-02	0.183630E-02	0.224867E-03
43	0.574170E-02	0.158052E-02	0.184106E-03
44	0.509243E-02	0.136037E-02	0.150733E-03
45	0.451658E-02	0.117088E-02	0.123410E-03
46	0.400585E-02	0.100779E-02	0.101039E-03
47	0.355287E-02	0.867409E-03	0.827241E-04
48	0.315111E-02	0.746586E-03	0.677287E-04
49	0.279479E-02	0.642592E-03	0.554516E-04
50	0.247875E-02	0.553084E-03	0.453999E-04

Table 6 (Continued).   **Present Value, P, of I to be Received n Periods Hence with Continuous Compounding at Rate** δ

$$P(\delta, n) = e^{-\delta n}$$

.25	.30	.35
0.778801E 00	0.740818E 00	0.704688E 00
0.606531E 00	0.548812E 00	0.496585E 00
0.472367E 00	0.406570E 00	0.349938E 00
0.367879E 00	0.301194E 00	0.246597E 00
0.286505E 00	0.223130E 00	0.173774E 00
0.223130E 00	0.165299E 00	0.122456E 00
0.173774E 00	0.122456E 00	0.862936E-01
0.135335E 00	0.907180E-01	0.608101E-01
0.105399E 00	0.672055E-01	0.428521E-01
0.820850E-01	0.497871E-01	0.301974E-01
0.639279E-01	0.368832E-01	0.212797E-01
0.497871E-01	0.273237E-01	0.149956E-01
0.387742E-01	0.202419E-01	0.105672E-01
0.301974E-01	0.149956E-01	0.744658E-02
0.235177E-01	0.111090E-01	0.524752E-02
0.183156E-01	0.822975E-02	0.369786E-02
0.142642E-01	0.609675E-02	0.260584E-02
0.111090E-01	0.451658E-02	0.183630E-02
0.865170E-02	0.334597E-02	0.129402E-02
0.673795E-02	0.247875E-02	0.911882E-03
0.524752E-02	0.183630E-02	0.642592E-03
0.408677E-02	0.136037E-02	0.452827E-03
0.318278E-02	0.100779E-02	0.319102E-03
0.247875E-02	0.746586E-03	0.224867E-03
0.193045E-02	0.553084E-03	0.158461E-03
0.150344E-02	0.409735E-03	0.111666E-03
0.117088E-02	0.303539E-03	0.786896E-04
0.911882E-03	0.224867E-03	0.554516E-04
0.710174E-03	0.166586E-03	0.390761E-04
0.553084E-03	0.123410E-03	0.275364E-04
0.430743E-03	0.914242E-04	0.194046E-04
0.335463E-03	0.677287E-04	0.136742E-04
0.261259E-03	0.501747E-04	0.963604E-05
0.203468E-03	0.371703E-04	0.679040E-05
0.158461E-03	0.275364E-04	0.478512E-05
0.123410E-03	0.203995E-04	0.337202E-05
0.961117E-04	0.151123E-04	0.237622E-05
0.748518E-04	0.111955E-04	0.167449E-05
0.582947E-04	0.829382E-05	0.118000E-05
0.453999E-04	0.614421E-05	0.831529E-06
0.353575E-04	0.455174E-05	0.585968E-06
0.275364E-04	0.337202E-05	0.412925E-06
0.214454E-04	0.249805E-05	0.290983E-06
0.167017E-04	0.185060E-05	0.205052E-06
0.130073E-04	0.137096E-05	0.144498E-06
0.101301E-04	0.101563E-05	0.101826E-06
0.788932E-05	0.752398E-06	0.717556E-07
0.614421E-05	0.557390E-06	0.505653E-07
0.478512E-05	0.412925E-06	0.356328E-07
0.372665E-05	0.305902E-06	0.251100E-07

Table 6 (Continued). **Present Value, P, of I to be Received n Periods Hence with Continuous Compounding at Rate** δ

$$P(\delta, n) = e^{-\delta n}$$

.40	.45	.50
0.670320E 00	0.637628E 00	0.606531E 00
0.449329E 00	0.406570E 00	0.367879E 00
0.301194E 00	0.259240E 00	0.223130E 00
0.201897E 00	0.165299E 00	0.135335E 00
0.135335E 00	0.105399E 00	0.820850E-01
0.907180E-01	0.672055E-01	0.497871E-01
0.608101E-01	0.428521E-01	0.301974E-01
0.407622E-01	0.273237E-01	0.183156E-01
0.273237E-01	0.174224E-01	0.111090E-01
0.183156E-01	0.111090E-01	0.673795E-02
0.122773E-01	0.708341E-02	0.408677E-02
0.822975E-02	0.451658E-02	0.247875E-02
0.551656E-02	0.287990E-02	0.150344E-02
0.369786E-02	0.183630E-02	0.911882E-03
0.247875E-02	0.117088E-02	0.553084E-03
0.166156E-02	0.746586E-03	0.335463E-03
0.111378E-02	0.476044E-03	0.203468E-03
0.746586E-03	0.303539E-03	0.123410E-03
0.500451E-03	0.193545E-03	0.748518E-04
0.335463E-03	0.123410E-03	0.453999E-04
0.224867E-03	0.786896E-04	0.275364E-04
0.150733E-03	0.501747E-04	0.167017E-04
0.101039E-03	0.319928E-04	0.101301E-04
0.677287E-04	0.203995E-04	0.614421E-05
0.453999E-04	0.130073E-04	0.372665E-05
0.304325E-04	0.829382E-05	0.226033E-05
0.203995E-04	0.528837E-05	0.137096E-05
0.136742E-04	0.337202E-05	0.831529E-06
0.916609E-05	0.215009E-05	0.504348E-06
0.614421E-05	0.137096E-05	0.305902E-06
0.411859E-05	0.874162E-06	0.185539E-06
0.276077E-05	0.557390E-06	0.112535E-06
0.185060E-05	0.355408E-06	0.682560E-07
0.124050E-05	0.226618E-06	0.413994E-07
0.831529E-06	0.144498E-06	0.251100E-07
0.557390E-06	0.921360E-07	0.152300E-07
0.373630E-06	0.587485E-07	0.923745E-08
0.250452E-06	0.374597E-07	0.560280E-08
0.167883E-06	0.238854E-07	0.339827E-08
0.112535E-06	0.152300E-07	0.206115E-08
0.754346E-07	0.971106E-08	0.125015E-08
0.505653E-07	0.619205E-08	0.758256E-09
0.338949E-07	0.394822E-08	0.459906E-09
0.227205E-07	0.251750E-08	0.278947E-09
0.152300E-07	0.160523E-08	0.169190E-09
0.102090E-07	0.102354E-08	0.102619E-09
0.684327E-08	0.652637E-09	0.622414E-10
0.458718E-08	0.416140E-09	0.377513E-10
0.307488E-08	0.265342E-09	0.228973E-10
0.206115E-08	0.169190E-09	0.138879E-10

Table 7. Value of I Received Uniformly per Period, n Periods Hence, with Continuous Compounding at Effective Rate i per Period

$$F(\delta, n) = \frac{e^{\delta n} - 1}{\delta} \qquad \delta = \ln(1 + i)$$

i	.01	.015	.02
δ	0.00995	0.01489	0.01980

n			
1	0.100499E 01	0.100748E 01	0.100997E 01
2	0.202003E 01	0.203007E 01	0.204013E 01
3	0.304523E 01	0.306801E 01	0.309090E 01
4	0.408067E 01	0.412151E 01	0.416269E 01
5	0.512647E 01	0.519081E 01	0.525591E 01
6	0.618272E 01	0.627616E 01	0.637099E 01
7	0.724954E 01	0.737778E 01	0.750838E 01
8	0.832703E 01	0.849593E 01	0.866852E 01
9	0.941529E 01	0.963085E 01	0.985185E 01
10	0.105144E 02	0.107828E 02	0.110589E 02
11	0.116246E 02	0.119520E 02	0.122900E 02
12	0.127458E 02	0.131388E 02	0.135458E 02
13	0.138783E 02	0.143433E 02	0.148267E 02
14	0.150220E 02	0.155660E 02	0.161332E 02
15	0.161772E 02	0.168069E 02	0.174658E 02
16	0.173440E 02	0.180665E 02	0.188251E 02
17	0.185224E 02	0.193450E 02	0.202115E 02
18	0.197127E 02	0.206427E 02	0.216257E 02
19	0.209148E 02	0.219598E 02	0.230682E 02
20	0.221289E 02	0.232967E 02	0.245395E 02
21	0.233552E 02	0.246536E 02	0.260403E 02
22	0.245937E 02	0.260309E 02	0.275711E 02
23	0.258447E 02	0.274288E 02	0.291325E 02
24	0.271081E 02	0.288477E 02	0.307251E 02
25	0.283842E 02	0.302879E 02	0.323495E 02
26	0.296730E 02	0.317497E 02	0.340065E 02
27	0.309747E 02	0.332335E 02	0.356966E 02
28	0.322895E 02	0.347394E 02	0.374205E 02
29	0.336174E 02	0.362680E 02	0.391789E 02
30	0.349585E 02	0.378195E 02	0.409724E 02
31	0.363131E 02	0.393943E 02	0.428018E 02
32	0.376812E 02	0.409927E 02	0.446678E 02
33	0.390630E 02	0.426151E 02	0.465712E 02
34	0.404587E 02	0.442618E 02	0.485126E 02
35	0.418682E 02	0.459332E 02	0.504928E 02
36	0.432919E 02	0.476297E 02	0.525126E 02
37	0.447298E 02	0.493516E 02	0.545728E 02
38	0.461821E 02	0.510993E 02	0.566742E 02
39	0.476489E 02	0.528733E 02	0.588177E 02
40	0.491304E 02	0.546739E 02	0.610040E 02
41	0.506267E 02	0.565015E 02	0.632341E 02
42	0.521380E 02	0.583565E 02	0.655087E 02
43	0.536643E 02	0.602393E 02	0.678288E 02
44	0.552060E 02	0.621504E 02	0.701954E 02
45	0.567630E 02	0.640901E 02	0.726093E 02
46	0.583356E 02	0.660590E 02	0.750714E 02
47	0.599240E 02	0.680573E 02	0.775828E 02
48	0.615282E 02	0.700857E 02	0.801444E 02
49	0.631485E 02	0.721444E 02	0.827573E 02
50	0.647850E 02	0.742341E 02	0.854224E 02

Table 7 (Continued).   *Value of I Received Uniformly per Period, n Periods Hence, with Continuous Compounding at Effective Rate i per Period*

$$F(\delta, n) = \frac{e^{\delta n} - 1}{\delta} \qquad \delta = \ln (1 + i)$$

.03	.04	.05
0.02956	0.03922	0.04879

0.101493E	01	0.101987E	01	0.102480E	01
0.206030E	01	0.208053E	01	0.210083E	01
0.313704E	01	0.318362E	01	0.323067E	01
0.424607E	01	0.433084E	01	0.441700E	01
0.538838E	01	0.552394E	01	0.566265E	01
0.656496E	01	0.676477E	01	0.697058E	01
0.777683E	01	0.805523E	01	0.834390E	01
0.902506E	01	0.939731E	01	0.978590E	01
0.103107E	02	0.107931E	02	0.113000E	02
0.116350E	02	0.122447E	02	0.128898E	02
0.129990E	02	0.137543E	02	0.145591E	02
0.144039E	02	0.153244E	02	0.163118E	02
0.158509E	02	0.169572E	02	0.181522E	02
0.173414E	02	0.186554E	02	0.200846E	02
0.188765E	02	0.204214E	02	0.221136E	02
0.204577E	02	0.222582E	02	0.242441E	02
0.220864E	02	0.241684E	02	0.264811E	02
0.237639E	02	0.261550E	02	0.288300E	02
0.254918E	02	0.282210E	02	0.312963E	02
0.272714E	02	0.303697E	02	0.338859E	02
0.291045E	02	0.326044E	02	0.366050E	02
0.309926E	02	0.349285E	02	0.394600E	02
0.329373E	02	0.373455E	02	0.424578E	02
0.349403E	02	0.398591E	02	0.456055E	02
0.370035E	02	0.424734E	02	0.489106E	02
0.391285E	02	0.451922E	02	0.523809E	02
0.413173E	02	0.480197E	02	0.560247E	02
0.435717E	02	0.509604E	02	0.598508E	02
0.458938E	02	0.540187E	02	0.638681E	02
0.482855E	02	0.571993E	02	0.680863E	02
0.507490E	02	0.605071E	02	0.725154E	02
0.532864E	02	0.639473E	02	0.771660E	02
0.558999E	02	0.675251E	02	0.820491E	02
0.585919E	02	0.712459E	02	0.871763E	02
0.613645E	02	0.751156E	02	0.925600E	02
0.642204E	02	0.791401E	02	0.982127E	02
0.671619E	02	0.833256E	02	0.104148E	03
0.701917E	02	0.876785E	02	0.110380E	03
0.733124E	02	0.922055E	02	0.116924E	03
0.765267E	02	0.969136E	02	0.123795E	03
0.798374E	02	0.101810E	03	0.131010E	03
0.832475E	02	0.106902E	03	0.138585E	03
0.867598E	02	0.112198E	03	0.146539E	03
0.903776E	02	0.117706E	03	0.154891E	03
0.941038E	02	0.123434E	03	0.163660E	03
0.979418E	02	0.129391E	03	0.172868E	03
0.101895E	03	0.135587E	03	0.182536E	03
0.105967E	03	0.142030E	03	0.192688E	03
0.110161E	03	0.148731E	03	0.203347E	03
0.114480E	03	0.155700E	03	0.214539E	03

Table 7 (Continued).   *Value of I Received Uniformly per Period, n Periods Hence, with Continuous Compounding at Effective Rate i per Period*

$$F(\delta, n) = \frac{e^{\delta n} - 1}{\delta} \qquad \delta = \ln(1 + i)$$

.06	.08	.10
0.05827	0.07696	0.09531

0.102971E 01	0.103949E 01	0.104921E 01
0.212120E 01	0.216213E 01	0.220333E 01
0.327818E 01	0.337459E 01	0.347287E 01
0.450458E 01	0.468404E 01	0.486936E 01
0.580456E 01	0.609826E 01	0.640551E 01
0.718255E 01	0.762560E 01	0.809526E 01
0.864321E 01	0.927514E 01	0.995400E 01
0.101915E 02	0.110566E 02	0.119986E 02
0.118327E 02	0.129807E 02	0.142477E 02
0.135724E 02	0.150586E 02	0.167216E 02
0.154164E 02	0.173028E 02	0.194430E 02
0.173711E 02	0.197265E 02	0.224365E 02
0.194431E 02	0.223441E 02	0.257294E 02
0.216394E 02	0.251711E 02	0.293515E 02
0.239675E 02	0.282243E 02	0.333359E 02
0.264352E 02	0.315217E 02	0.377187E 02
0.290510E 02	0.350829E 02	0.425397E 02
0.318238E 02	0.389290E 02	0.478429E 02
0.347630E 02	0.430829E 02	0.536764E 02
0.378784E 02	0.475690E 02	0.600933E 02
0.411809E 02	0.524140E 02	0.671518E 02
0.446814E 02	0.576466E 02	0.749162E 02
0.483920E 02	0.632978E 02	0.834570E 02
0.523252E 02	0.694011E 02	0.928519E 02
0.564945E 02	0.759927E 02	0.103186E 03
0.609138E 02	0.831116E 02	0.114554E 03
0.655984E 02	0.908000E 02	0.127059E 03
0.705640E 02	0.991035E 02	0.140814E 03
0.758275E 02	0.108071E 03	0.155944E 03
0.814069E 02	0.117756E 03	0.172588E 03
0.873210E 02	0.128216E 03	0.190896E 03
0.935900E 02	0.139513E 03	0.211035E 03
0.100235E 03	0.151714E 03	0.233188E 03
0.107279E 03	0.164890E 03	0.257556E 03
0.114745E 03	0.179121E 03	0.284360E 03
0.122660E 03	0.194490E 03	0.313846E 03
0.131049E 03	0.211089E 03	0.346279E 03
0.139942E 03	0.229016E 03	0.381957E 03
0.149368E 03	0.248376E 03	0.421201E 03
0.159360E 03	0.269286E 03	0.464371E 03
0.169951E 03	0.291868E 03	0.511857E 03
0.181178E 03	0.316257E 03	0.564092E 03
0.193078E 03	0.342597E 03	0.621550E 03
0.205693E 03	0.371045E 03	0.684755E 03
0.219064E 03	0.401768E 03	0.754279E 03
0.233237E 03	0.434948E 03	0.830756E 03
0.248261E 03	0.470784E 03	0.914881E 03
0.264187E 03	0.509486E 03	0.100742E 04
0.281068E 03	0.551284E 03	0.110921E 04
0.298961E 03	0.596427E 03	0.122118E 04

Table 7 (Continued).   *Value of I Received Uniformly per Period, n Periods Hence, with Continuous Compounding at Effective Rate i per Period*

$$F(\delta, n) = \frac{e^{\delta n} - 1}{\delta} \qquad \delta = \ln (1 + i)$$

i	.12	.15	.20
δ	0.11333	0.13976	0.18232

n			
1	0.105887E 01	0.107325E 01	0.109696E 01
2	0.224480E 01	0.230750E 01	0.241332E 01
3	0.357304E 01	0.372687E 01	0.399295E 01
4	0.506067E 01	0.535916E 01	0.588850E 01
5	0.672682E 01	0.723628E 01	0.816316E 01
6	0.859291E 01	0.939498E 01	0.108928E 02
7	0.106829E 02	0.118775E 02	0.141683E 02
8	0.130237E 02	0.147324E 02	0.180989E 02
9	0.156455E 02	0.180155E 02	0.228156E 02
10	0.185818E 02	0.217910E 02	0.284757E 02
11	0.218705E 02	0.261329E 02	0.352678E 02
12	0.255538E 02	0.311261E 02	0.434183E 02
13	0.296791E 02	0.368683E 02	0.531990E 02
14	0.342995E 02	0.434718E 02	0.649357E 02
15	0.394743E 02	0.510658E 02	0.790198E 02
16	0.452700E 02	0.597990E 02	0.959208E 02
17	0.517613E 02	0.698421E 02	0.116202E 03
18	0.590315E 02	0.813916E 02	0.140539E 03
19	0.671742E 02	0.946736E 02	0.169744E 03
20	0.762940E 02	0.109948E 03	0.204790E 03
21	0.865081E 02	0.127513E 03	0.246845E 03
22	0.979479E 02	0.147714E 03	0.297311E 03
23	0.110761E 03	0.170944E 03	0.357870E 03
24	0.125111E 03	0.197659E 03	0.430541E 03
25	0.141183E 03	0.228381E 03	0.517746E 03
26	0.159184E 03	0.263711E 03	0.622392E 03
27	0.179345E 03	0.304341E 03	0.747967E 03
28	0.201925E 03	0.351066E 03	0.898658E 03
29	0.227215E 03	0.404799E 03	0.107949E 04
30	0.255539E 03	0.466592E 03	0.129648E 04
31	0.287263E 03	0.537654E 03	0.155687E 04
32	0.322793E 03	0.619375E 03	0.186935E 04
33	0.362587E 03	0.713355E 03	0.224431E 04
34	0.407157E 03	0.821431E 03	0.269427E 04
35	0.457074E 03	0.945719E 03	0.323422E 04
36	0.512982E 03	0.108865E 04	0.388216E 04
37	0.575599E 03	0.125302E 04	0.465969E 04
38	0.645729E 03	0.144205E 04	0.559273E 04
39	0.724276E 03	0.165943E 04	0.671237E 04
40	0.812248E 03	0.190941E 04	0.805594E 04
41	0.910776E 03	0.219690E 04	0.966823E 04
42	0.102113E 04	0.252751E 04	0.116030E 05
43	0.114472E 04	0.290771E 04	0.139247E 05
44	0.128315E 04	0.334494E 04	0.167107E 05
45	0.143818E 04	0.384775E 04	0.200539E 05
46	0.161183E 04	0.442599E 04	0.240658E 05
47	0.180630E 04	0.509096E 04	0.288801E 05
48	0.202412E 04	0.585568E 04	0.346572E 05
49	0.226807E 04	0.673510E 04	0.415897E 05
50	0.254130E 04	0.774644E 04	0.499087E 05

Table 7 (Continued). *Value of I Received Uniformly per Period, n Periods Hence, with Continuous Compounding at Effective Rate i per Period*

$$F(\delta, n) = \frac{e^{\delta n} - 1}{\delta} \qquad \delta = \ln (1 + i)$$

.25	.30	.35
0.22314	0.26236	0.30010

0.112036E 01	0.114345E 01	0.116626E 01
0.252080E 01	0.262993E 01	0.274071E 01
0.427135E 01	0.456236E 01	0.486622E 01
0.645955E 01	0.707452E 01	0.773566E 01
0.919479E 01	0.103403E 02	0.116094E 02
0.126138E 02	0.145859E 02	0.168389E 02
0.168877E 02	0.201051E 02	0.238988E 02
0.222299E 02	0.272800E 02	0.334297E 02
0.289078E 02	0.366075E 02	0.462963E 02
0.372551E 02	0.487332E 02	0.636663E 02
0.476892E 02	0.644966E 02	0.871158E 02
0.607318E 02	0.849890E 02	0.118773E 03
0.770351E 02	0.111629E 03	0.161509E 03
0.974143E 02	0.146261E 03	0.219204E 03
0.122888E 03	0.191283E 03	0.297091E 03
0.154731E 03	0.249812E 03	0.402240E 03
0.194534E 03	0.325899E 03	0.544190E 03
0.244287E 03	0.424812E 03	0.735822E 03
0.306480E 03	0.553399E 03	0.994526E 03
0.384220E 03	0.720562E 03	0.134378E 04
0.481395E 03	0.937874E 03	0.181526E 04
0.602864E 03	0.122038E 04	0.245177E 04
0.754701E 03	0.158764E 04	0.331106E 04
0.944496E 03	0.206507E 04	0.447110E 04
0.118174E 04	0.268574E 04	0.603715E 04
0.147830E 04	0.349260E 04	0.815132E 04
0.184899E 04	0.454152E 04	0.110054E 05
0.231236E 04	0.590512E 04	0.148585E 05
0.289157E 04	0.767780E 04	0.200602E 05
0.361558E 04	0.998229E 04	0.270824E 05
0.452060E 04	0.129781E 05	0.365624E 05
0.565187E 04	0.168727E 05	0.493604E 05
0.706595E 04	0.219356E 05	0.666377E 05
0.883356E 04	0.285175E 05	0.899621E 05
0.110431E 05	0.370739E 05	0.121450E 06
0.138050E 05	0.481972E 05	0.163959E 06
0.172573E 05	0.626575E 05	0.221345E 06
0.215728E 05	0.814559E 05	0.298817E 06
0.269671E 05	0.105894E 06	0.403405E 06
0.337100E 05	0.137663E 06	0.544597E 06
0.421386E 05	0.178963E 06	0.735207E 06
0.526744E 05	0.232653E 06	0.992531E 06
0.658441E 05	0.302450E 06	0.133992E 07
0.823062E 05	0.393187E 06	0.180889E 07
0.102884E 06	0.511144E 06	0.244200E 07
0.128606E 06	0.664488E 06	0.329671E 07
0.160759E 06	0.863835E 06	0.445055E 07
0.200949E 06	0.112299E 07	0.600825E 07
0.251188E 06	0.145988E 07	0.811114E 07
0.313986E 06	0.189785E 07	0.109500E 08

Table 7 (*Continued*).   **Value of** *I* **Received Uniformly per Period,** *n*
Periods Hence, with Continuous Compounding at Effective Rate *i*
per Period

$$F(\delta, n) = \frac{e^{\delta n} - 1}{\delta} \qquad \delta = \ln (1 + i)$$

.40	.45	.50
0.33647	0.37156	0.40547

0.118881E 01	0.121110E 01	0.123315E 01
0.285313E 01	0.296719E 01	0.308288E 01
0.518319E 01	0.551353E 01	0.585747E 01
0.844527E 01	0.920571E 01	0.100194E 02
0.130122E 02	0.145594E 02	0.162622E 02
0.194059E 02	0.223222E 02	0.256264E 02
0.283570E 02	0.335783E 02	0.396728E 02
0.408886E 02	0.498996E 02	0.607424E 02
0.584329E 02	0.735655E 02	0.923467E 02
0.829949E 02	0.107881E 03	0.139753E 03
0.117382E 03	0.157639E 03	0.210863E 03
0.165523E 03	0.229787E 03	0.317528E 03
0.232921E 03	0.334403E 03	0.477524E 03
0.327278E 03	0.486095E 03	0.717520E 03
0.459378E 03	0.706049E 03	0.107751E 04
0.644319E 03	0.102498E 04	0.161750E 04
0.903235E 03	0.148743E 04	0.242749E 04
0.126572E 04	0.215799E 04	0.364246E 04
0.177319E 04	0.313030E 04	0.546493E 04
0.248366E 04	0.454014E 04	0.819863E 04
0.347831E 04	0.658442E 04	0.122992E 05
0.487083E 04	0.954862E 04	0.184500E 05
0.682035E 04	0.138467E 05	0.276762E 05
0.954967E 04	0.200789E 05	0.415156E 05
0.133707E 05	0.291157E 05	0.622746E 05
0.187202E 05	0.422189E 05	0.934131E 05
0.262095E 05	0.612187E 05	0.140121E 06
0.366945E 05	0.887683E 05	0.210183E 06
0.513734E 05	0.128715E 06	0.315275E 06
0.719240E 05	0.186638E 06	0.472914E 06
0.100695E 06	0.270627E 06	0.709372E 06
0.140974E 06	0.392410E 06	0.106406E 07
0.197365E 06	0.568996E 06	0.159609E 07
0.276312E 06	0.825045E 06	0.239414E 07
0.386838E 06	0.119632E 07	0.359121E 07
0.541574E 06	0.173466E 07	0.538681E 07
0.758205E 06	0.251526E 07	0.808022E 07
0.106149E 07	0.364713E 07	0.121203E 08
0.148608E 07	0.528833E 07	0.181805E 08
0.208052E 07	0.766808E 07	0.272707E 08
0.291273E 07	0.111187E 08	0.409061E 08
0.407782E 07	0.161221E 08	0.613592E 08
0.570895E 07	0.233771E 08	0.920387E 08
0.799253E 07	0.338968E 08	0.138058E 09
0.111895E 08	0.491504E 08	0.207087E 09
0.156654E 08	0.712681E 08	0.310631E 09
0.219315E 08	0.103339E 09	0.465946E 09
0.307041E 08	0.149841E 09	0.698919E 09
0.429857E 08	0.217270E 09	0.104838E 10
0.601800E 08	0.315041E 09	0.157257E 10

Table 8. Present Value of 1 Received Uniformly per Period
with Continuous Compounding at Effective Rate i per Period

$$P(\delta, n) = \frac{1 - e^{-\delta n}}{\delta} \qquad \delta = \ln(1 + i)$$

i	.01	.015	.02
δ	0.00995	0.01489	0.01980

n			
1	0.995041E 00	0.992593E 00	0.990164E 00
2	0.198023E 01	0.197052E 01	0.196091E 01
3	0.295567E 01	0.293399E 01	0.291263E 01
4	0.392144E 01	0.388322E 01	0.384568E 01
5	0.487766E 01	0.481843E 01	0.476044E 01
6	0.582441E 01	0.573981E 01	0.565726E 01
7	0.676178E 01	0.664758E 01	0.653650E 01
8	0.768987E 01	0.754193E 01	0.739849E 01
9	0.860878E 01	0.842307E 01	0.824359E 01
10	0.951858E 01	0.929118E 01	0.907211E 01
11	0.104194E 02	0.101465E 02	0.988439E 01
12	0.113113E 02	0.109891E 02	0.106807E 02
13	0.121943E 02	0.118193E 02	0.114615E 02
14	0.130686E 02	0.126372E 02	0.122269E 02
15	0.139343E 02	0.134431E 02	0.129773E 02
16	0.147913E 02	0.142370E 02	0.137130E 02
17	0.156399E 02	0.150192E 02	0.144343E 02
18	0.164801E 02	0.157898E 02	0.151415E 02
19	0.173120E 02	0.165491E 02	0.158347E 02
20	0.181356E 02	0.172971E 02	0.165144E 02
21	0.189511E 02	0.180341E 02	0.171808E 02
22	0.197585E 02	0.187601E 02	0.178340E 02
23	0.205579E 02	0.194755E 02	0.184745E 02
24	0.213494E 02	0.201803E 02	0.191024E 02
25	0.221331E 02	0.208746E 02	0.197180E 02
26	0.229090E 02	0.215587E 02	0.203216E 02
27	0.236772E 02	0.222327E 02	0.209133E 02
28	0.244378E 02	0.228967E 02	0.214934E 02
29	0.251909E 02	0.235510E 02	0.220621E 02
30	0.259365E 02	0.241955E 02	0.226197E 02
31	0.266748E 02	0.248305E 02	0.231663E 02
32	0.274057E 02	0.254562E 02	0.237022E 02
33	0.281294E 02	0.260726E 02	0.242277E 02
34	0.288459E 02	0.266798E 02	0.247428E 02
35	0.295554E 02	0.272782E 02	0.252478E 02
36	0.302578E 02	0.278676E 02	0.257429E 02
37	0.309533E 02	0.284484E 02	0.262283E 02
38	0.316418E 02	0.290206E 02	0.267042E 02
39	0.323236E 02	0.295843E 02	0.271707E 02
40	0.329986E 02	0.301397E 02	0.276281E 02
41	0.336669E 02	0.306868E 02	0.280766E 02
42	0.343286E 02	0.312259E 02	0.285162E 02
43	0.349838E 02	0.317571E 02	0.289472E 02
44	0.356324E 02	0.322803E 02	0.293698E 02
45	0.362747E 02	0.327959E 02	0.297841E 02
46	0.369106E 02	0.333038E 02	0.301903E 02
47	0.375402E 02	0.338042E 02	0.305884E 02
48	0.381635E 02	0.342972E 02	0.309788E 02
49	0.387807E 02	0.347830E 02	0.313616E 02
50	0.393918E 02	0.352615E 02	0.317368E 02

Table 8 (Continued).   **Present Value of I Received Uniformly per Period with Continuous Compounding at Effective Rate i per Period**

$$P(\delta, n) = \frac{1 - e^{-\delta n}}{\delta} \qquad \delta = \ln(1 + i)$$

.03	.04	.05
0.02956	0.03922	0.04879

0.985365E 00	0.980644E 00	0.975997E 00
0.194203E 01	0.192357E 01	0.190552E 01
0.287083E 01	0.283023E 01	0.279078E 01
0.377258E 01	0.370202E 01	0.363388E 01
0.464806E 01	0.454028E 01	0.443683E 01
0.549805E 01	0.534629E 01	0.520155E 01
0.632328E 01	0.612131E 01	0.592986E 01
0.712447E 01	0.686652E 01	0.662348E 01
0.790233E 01	0.758307E 01	0.728407E 01
0.865753E 01	0.827205E 01	0.791321E 01
0.939073E 01	0.893454E 01	0.851239E 01
0.101026E 02	0.957155E 01	0.908303E 01
0.107937E 02	0.101841E 02	0.962650E 01
0.114647E 02	0.107730E 02	0.101441E 02
0.121161E 02	0.113393E 02	0.106370E 02
0.127486E 02	0.118838E 02	0.111065E 02
0.133626E 02	0.124074E 02	0.115536E 02
0.139588E 02	0.129108E 02	0.119795E 02
0.145376E 02	0.133949E 02	0.123850E 02
0.150995E 02	0.138604E 02	0.127712E 02
0.156451E 02	0.143079E 02	0.131391E 02
0.161748E 02	0.147382E 02	0.134894E 02
0.166890E 02	0.151520E 02	0.138230E 02
0.171883E 02	0.155499E 02	0.141408E 02
0.176731E 02	0.159325E 02	0.144434E 02
0.181437E 02	0.163003E 02	0.147316E 02
0.186006E 02	0.166540E 02	0.150061E 02
0.190442E 02	0.169941E 02	0.152676E 02
0.194749E 02	0.173212E 02	0.155165E 02
0.198930E 02	0.176356E 02	0.157536E 02
0.202990E 02	0.179380E 02	0.159795E 02
0.206931E 02	0.182287E 02	0.161945E 02
0.210757E 02	0.185082E 02	0.163994E 02
0.214473E 02	0.187770E 02	0.165944E 02
0.218079E 02	0.190355E 02	0.167802E 02
0.221581E 02	0.192840E 02	0.169572E 02
0.224981E 02	0.195229E 02	0.171257E 02
0.228282E 02	0.197527E 02	0.172862E 02
0.231487E 02	0.199736E 02	0.174390E 02
0.234598E 02	0.201860E 02	0.175846E 02
0.237619E 02	0.203903E 02	0.177232E 02
0.240551E 02	0.205867E 02	0.178552E 02
0.243399E 02	0.207755E 02	0.179810E 02
0.246163E 02	0.209571E 02	0.181008E 02
0.248847E 02	0.211317E 02	0.182148E 02
0.251453E 02	0.212996E 02	0.183234E 02
0.253982E 02	0.214610E 02	0.184269E 02
0.256438E 02	0.216163E 02	0.185254E 02
0.258823E 02	0.217655E 02	0.186192E 02
0.261138E 02	0.219090E 02	0.187086E 02

Table 8 (Continued). *Present Value of I Received Uniformly per Period with Continuous Compounding at Effective Rate i per Period*

$$P(\delta, n) = \frac{1 - e^{-\delta n}}{\delta} \qquad \delta = \ln(1 + i)$$

.06	.08	.10
0.05827	0.07696	0.09531

0.971423E 00	0.962488E 00	0.953824E 00
0.188786E 01	0.185368E 01	0.182094E 01
0.275242E 01	0.267886E 01	0.260922E 01
0.356805E 01	0.344291E 01	0.332584E 01
0.433751E 01	0.415037E 01	0.397732E 01
0.506341E 01	0.480542E 01	0.456957E 01
0.574823E 01	0.541195E 01	0.510797E 01
0.639428E 01	0.597356E 01	0.559744E 01
0.700376E 01	0.649356E 01	0.604240E 01
0.757875E 01	0.697504E 01	0.644692E 01
0.812118E 01	0.742086E 01	0.681466E 01
0.863292E 01	0.783365E 01	0.714897E 01
0.911568E 01	0.821587E 01	0.745288E 01
0.957113E 01	0.856978E 01	0.772917E 01
0.100008E 02	0.889747E 01	0.798034E 01
0.104061E 02	0.920088E 01	0.820868E 01
0.107885E 02	0.948182E 01	0.841626E 01
0.111493E 02	0.974195E 01	0.860497E 01
0.114896E 02	0.998282E 01	0.877652E 01
0.118107E 02	0.102058E 02	0.893248E 01
0.121136E 02	0.104123E 02	0.907426E 01
0.123993E 02	0.106035E 02	0.920315E 01
0.126689E 02	0.107806E 02	0.932032E 01
0.129232E 02	0.109445E 02	0.942685E 01
0.131631E 02	0.110963E 02	0.952368E 01
0.133895E 02	0.112368E 02	0.961172E 01
0.136030E 02	0.113670E 02	0.969175E 01
0.138044E 02	0.114875E 02	0.976450E 01
0.139945E 02	0.115990E 02	0.983065E 01
0.141738E 02	0.117023E 02	0.989077E 01
0.143429E 02	0.117980E 02	0.994544E 01
0.145025E 02	0.118865E 02	0.999513E 01
0.146530E 02	0.119685E 02	0.100403E 02
0.147950E 02	0.120445E 02	0.100814E 02
0.149290E 02	0.121148E 02	0.101187E 02
0.150554E 02	0.121799E 02	0.101526E 02
0.151746E 02	0.122401E 02	0.101835E 02
0.152871E 02	0.122960E 02	0.102116E 02
0.153932E 02	0.123476E 02	0.102371E 02
0.154933E 02	0.123955E 02	0.102602E 02
0.155877E 02	0.124398E 02	0.102813E 02
0.156768E 02	0.124808E 02	0.103005E 02
0.157609E 02	0.125188E 02	0.103179E 02
0.158402E 02	0.125540E 02	0.103337E 02
0.159150E 02	0.125865E 02	0.103481E 02
0.159856E 02	0.126167E 02	0.103612E 02
0.160522E 02	0.126446E 02	0.103731E 02
0.161150E 02	0.126704E 02	0.103839E 02
0.161742E 02	0.126944E 02	0.103937E 02
0.162301E 02	0.127165E 02	0.104027E 02

Table 8 (Continued).   *Present Value of I Received Uniformly per Period with Continuous Compounding at Effective Rate i per Period*

$$P(\delta, n) = \frac{1 - e^{-\delta n}}{\delta} \qquad \delta = \ln(1 + i)$$

i	.12	.15	.20
δ	0.11333	0.13976	0.18232

n			
1	0.945417E 00	0.933264E 00	0.914136E 00
2	0.178954E 01	0.174480E 01	0.167592E 01
3	0.254322E 01	0.245048E 01	0.231073E 01
4	0.321615E 01	0.306412E 01	0.283975E 01
5	0.381698E 01	0.359771E 01	0.328059E 01
6	0.435343E 01	0.406171E 01	0.364796E 01
7	0.483241E 01	0.446519E 01	0.395410E 01
8	0.526007E 01	0.481603E 01	0.420922E 01
9	0.564191E 01	0.512112E 01	0.442182E 01
10	0.598283E 01	0.538641E 01	0.459899E 01
11	0.628723E 01	0.561710E 01	0.474662E 01
12	0.655902E 01	0.581770E 01	0.486966E 01
13	0.680168E 01	0.599213E 01	0.497218E 01
14	0.701835E 01	0.614381E 01	0.505762E 01
15	0.721180E 01	0.627571E 01	0.512882E 01
16	0.738452E 01	0.639040E 01	0.518815E 01
17	0.753874E 01	0.649014E 01	0.523760E 01
18	0.767644E 01	0.657686E 01	0.527880E 01
19	0.779938E 01	0.665227E 01	0.531314E 01
20	0.790915E 01	0.671785E 01	0.534175E 01
21	0.800716E 01	0.677487E 01	0.536559E 01
22	0.809466E 01	0.682446E 01	0.538546E 01
23	0.817279E 01	0.686757E 01	0.540202E 01
24	0.824255E 01	0.690507E 01	0.541582E 01
25	0.830484E 01	0.693767E 01	0.542732E 01
26	0.836045E 01	0.696602E 01	0.543690E 01
27	0.841011E 01	0.699067E 01	0.544489E 01
28	0.845444E 01	0.701211E 01	0.545154E 01
29	0.849403E 01	0.703075E 01	0.545709E 01
30	0.852937E 01	0.704696E 01	0.546171E 01
31	0.856092E 01	0.706106E 01	0.546556E 01
32	0.858910E 01	0.707331E 01	0.546877E 01
33	0.861426E 01	0.708397E 01	0.547144E 01
34	0.863672E 01	0.709324E 01	0.547367E 01
35	0.865677E 01	0.710130E 01	0.547553E 01
36	0.867468E 01	0.710831E 01	0.547708E 01
37	0.869066E 01	0.711440E 01	0.547837E 01
38	0.870494E 01	0.711970E 01	0.547944E 01
39	0.871768E 01	0.712431E 01	0.548034E 01
40	0.872906E 01	0.712831E 01	0.548108E 01
41	0.873922E 01	0.713180E 01	0.548171E 01
42	0.874829E 01	0.713483E 01	0.548222E 01
43	0.875639E 01	0.713746E 01	0.548266E 01
44	0.876363E 01	0.713975E 01	0.548302E 01
45	0.877008E 01	0.714174E 01	0.548332E 01
46	0.877585E 01	0.714348E 01	0.548357E 01
47	0.878100E 01	0.714498E 01	0.548377E 01
48	0.878559E 01	0.714629E 01	0.548395E 01
49	0.878970E 01	0.714743E 01	0.548409E 01
50	0.879336E 01	0.714842E 01	0.548421E 01

Table 8 (Continued).   **Present Value of 1 Received Uniformly per Period with Continuous Compounding at Effective Rate** *i* **per Period**

$$P(\delta, n) = \frac{1 - e^{-\delta n}}{\delta} \qquad \delta = \ln(1 + i)$$

.25	.30	.35
0.22314	0.26236	0.30010

0.896284E 00	0.879576E 00	0.863896E 00
0.161331E 01	0.155617E 01	0.150382E 01
0.218693E 01	0.207663E 01	0.197784E 01
0.264583E 01	0.247698E 01	0.232896E 01
0.301295E 01	0.278495E 01	0.258905E 01
0.330664E 01	0.302184E 01	0.278171E 01
0.354160E 01	0.320407E 01	0.292442E 01
0.372956E 01	0.334425E 01	0.303014E 01
0.387993E 01	0.345207E 01	0.310844E 01
0.400023E 01	0.353502E 01	0.316645E 01
0.409647E 01	0.359882E 01	0.320941E 01
0.417346E 01	0.364790E 01	0.324124E 01
0.423505E 01	0.368565E 01	0.326481E 01
0.428433E 01	0.371469E 01	0.328228E 01
0.432374E 01	0.373703E 01	0.329521E 01
0.435528E 01	0.375421E 01	0.330479E 01
0.438051E 01	0.376743E 01	0.331189E 01
0.440069E 01	0.377760E 01	0.331715E 01
0.441684E 01	0.378542E 01	0.332104E 01
0.442975E 01	0.379144E 01	0.332393E 01
0.444009E 01	0.379607E 01	0.332607E 01
0.444835E 01	0.379963E 01	0.332765E 01
0.445497E 01	0.380237E 01	0.332882E 01
0.446026E 01	0.380447E 01	0.332969E 01
0.446449E 01	0.380609E 01	0.333033E 01
0.446788E 01	0.380734E 01	0.333081E 01
0.447058E 01	0.380830E 01	0.333116E 01
0.447275E 01	0.380904E 01	0.333142E 01
0.447449E 01	0.380960E 01	0.333162E 01
0.447587E 01	0.381004E 01	0.333176E 01
0.447698E 01	0.381038E 01	0.333187E 01
0.447787E 01	0.381063E 01	0.333195E 01
0.447858E 01	0.381083E 01	0.333200E 01
0.447915E 01	0.381099E 01	0.333205E 01
0.447960E 01	0.381110E 01	0.333208E 01
0.447997E 01	0.381119E 01	0.333210E 01
0.448026E 01	0.381126E 01	0.333212E 01
0.448049E 01	0.381132E 01	0.333213E 01
0.448068E 01	0.381136E 01	0.333214E 01
0.448082E 01	0.381139E 01	0.333215E 01
0.448094E 01	0.381141E 01	0.333216E 01
0.448104E 01	0.381143E 01	0.333216E 01
0.448112E 01	0.381145E 01	0.333216E 01
0.448118E 01	0.381146E 01	0.333217E 01
0.448122E 01	0.381147E 01	0.333217E 01
0.448126E 01	0.381147E 01	0.333217E 01
0.448130E 01	0.381148E 01	0.333217E 01
0.448132E 01	0.381148E 01	0.333217E 01
0.448134E 01	0.381148E 01	0.333217E 01
0.448136E 01	0.381149E 01	0.333217E 01

Table 8 (Continued). **Present Value of I Received Uniformly per Period with Continuous Compounding at Effective Rate** *i* **per Period**

$$P(\delta, n) = \frac{1 - e^{-\delta n}}{\delta} \qquad \delta = \ln (1 + i)$$

.40	.45	.50
0.33647	0.37156	0.40547

0.849147E 00	0.835240E 00	0.822101E 00
0.145568E 01	0.141127E 01	0.137017E 01
0.188892E 01	0.180853E 01	0.173555E 01
0.219837E 01	0.208250E 01	0.197913E 01
0.241941E 01	0.227145E 01	0.214152E 01
0.257730E 01	0.240176E 01	0.224978E 01
0.269007E 01	0.249162E 01	0.232196E 01
0.277063E 01	0.255360E 01	0.237007E 01
0.282817E 01	0.259634E 01	0.240215E 01
0.286927E 01	0.262582E 01	0.242353E 01
0.289862E 01	0.264615E 01	0.243779E 01
0.291959E 01	0.266017E 01	0.244729E 01
0.293457E 01	0.266984E 01	0.245363E 01
0.294527E 01	0.267651E 01	0.245786E 01
0.295291E 01	0.268111E 01	0.246067E 01
0.295837E 01	0.268428E 01	0.246255E 01
0.296227E 01	0.268647E 01	0.246380E 01
0.296505E 01	0.268798E 01	0.246463E 01
0.296704E 01	0.268902E 01	0.246519E 01
0.296846E 01	0.268974E 01	0.246556E 01
0.296948E 01	0.269023E 01	0.246581E 01
0.297020E 01	0.269057E 01	0.246597E 01
0.297072E 01	0.269081E 01	0.246608E 01
0.297109E 01	0.269097E 01	0.246616E 01
0.297135E 01	0.269108E 01	0.246621E 01
0.297154E 01	0.269116E 01	0.246624E 01
0.297168E 01	0.269121E 01	0.246626E 01
0.297177E 01	0.269125E 01	0.246627E 01
0.297184E 01	0.269127E 01	0.246628E 01
0.297189E 01	0.269129E 01	0.246629E 01
0.297193E 01	0.269130E 01	0.246629E 01
0.297195E 01	0.269131E 01	0.246630E 01
0.297197E 01	0.269132E 01	0.246630E 01
0.297198E 01	0.269132E 01	0.246630E 01
0.297199E 01	0.269132E 01	0.246630E 01
0.297200E 01	0.269133E 01	0.246630E 01
0.297200E 01	0.269133E 01	0.246630E 01
0.297201E 01	0.269133E 01	0.246630E 01
0.297201E 01	0.269133E 01	0.246630E 01
0.297201E 01	0.269133E 01	0.246630E 01
0.297201E 01	0.269133E 01	0.246630E 01
0.297201E 01	0.269133E 01	0.246630E 01
0.297201E 01	0.269133E 01	0.246630E 01
0.297201E 01	0.269133E 01	0.246630E 01
0.297201E 01	0.269133E 01	0.246630E 01
0.297201E 01	0.269133E 01	0.246630E 01
0.297201E 01	0.269133E 01	0.246630E 01
0.297201E 01	0.269133E 01	0.246630E 01

APPENDIX C

Summary of Procedure for Reducing Polynomial Functions of Second Degree in Two Independent Variables to Standard Form[1]

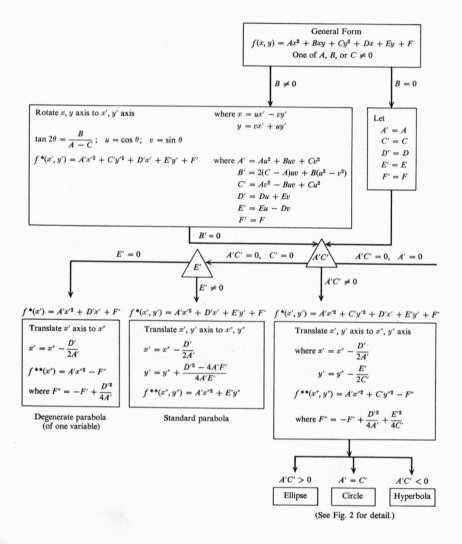

General Form

$$f(x, y) = Ax^2 + Bxy + Cy^2 + Dx + Ey + F$$

One of A, B, or $C \neq 0$

$B \neq 0$ $B = 0$

Rotate x, y axis to x', y' axis   where $x = ux' - vy'$

$y = vx' + uy'$

$\tan 2\theta = \dfrac{B}{A - C}$; $\quad u = \cos\theta; \quad v = \sin\theta$

$f^*(x', y') = A'x'^2 + C'y'^2 + D'x' + E'y' + F'$ where $A' = Au^2 + Buv + Cv^2$

$B' = 2(C - A)uv + B(u^2 - v^2)$

$C' = Av^2 - Buv + Cu^2$

$D' = Du + Ev$

$E' = Eu - Dv$

$F' = F$

Let

$A' = A$
$C' = C$
$D' = D$
$E' = E$
$F' = F$

$B' = 0$

$E' = 0$ E' $A'C' = 0, \ C' = 0$ $A'C'$ $A'C' = 0, \ A' = 0$

$E' \neq 0$ $A'C' \neq 0$

$f^*(x') = A'x'^2 + D'x' + F'$

Translate x' axis to x''

$x' = x'' - \dfrac{D'}{2A'}$

$f^{**}(x'') = A'x''^2 - F''$

where $F'' = -F' + \dfrac{D'^2}{4A'}$

Degenerate parabola
(of one variable)

$f^*(x', y') = A'x'^2 + D'x' + E'y' + F'$

Translate x', y' axis to x'', y''

$x' = x'' - \dfrac{D'}{2A'}$

$y' = y'' + \dfrac{D'^2 - 4A'F'}{4A'E'}$

$f^{**}(x'', y'') = A'x''^2 + E'y''$

Standard parabola

$f^*(x', y') = A'x'^2 + C'y'^2 + D'x' + E'y' + F'$

Translate x', y' axis to x'', y'' axis

where $x' = x'' - \dfrac{D'}{2A'}$

$y' = y'' - \dfrac{E'}{2C'}$

$f^{**}(x'', y'') = A'x''^2 + C'y''^2 - F''$

where $F'' = -F' + \dfrac{D'^2}{4A'} + \dfrac{E'^2}{4C'}$

$A'C' > 0$ $A' = C'$ $A'C' < 0$

Ellipse   Circle   Hyperbola

(See Fig. 2 for detail.)

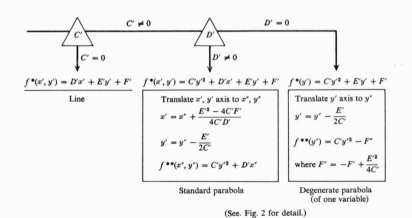

$C' \neq 0$ $D' = 0$

C'

$C' = 0$

D'

$D' \neq 0$

$f*(x', y') = D'x' + E'y' + F'$ $f*(x', y') = C'y'^2 + D'x' + E'y' + F'$ $f*(y') = C'y'^2 + E'y' + F'$

Line	Translate x', y' axis to x'', y''	Translate y' axis to y''
	$x' = x'' + \dfrac{E'^2 - 4C'F'}{4C'D'}$	$y' = y'' - \dfrac{E'}{2C'}$
	$y' = y'' - \dfrac{E'}{2C'}$	$f**(y'') = C'y''^2 - F''$
	$f**(x'', y'') = C'y''^2 + D'x''$	where $F'' = -F' + \dfrac{E'^2}{4C'}$
	Standard parabola	Degenerate parabola (of one variable)

(See. Fig. 2 for detail.)

---

[1] In using this figure to graph the equation $f(x, y) = K$, where $K \neq 0$, the two transformations must be performed on the function $f(x, y) - K$. This is equivalent to letting $F' = F - K$.

Figure 2

Name	Equation		Diagram
Ellipse	$\dfrac{x''^2}{a^2} + \dfrac{y''^2}{b^2} = 1$ $a^2 = \dfrac{F'}{A'}$ $b^2 = \dfrac{F''}{C}$ a^2 and b^2 same signs	The locus of a point P such that the sum of its distances from two fixed points Q' and Q is constant $= 2a$ $Q'P + PQ = 2a$ from the equation $A'x''^2 + C'y''^2 = F''$ if $a^2 > 0$, ellipse is real if $a^2 < 0$, ellipse is imaginary if $F'' = 0$, ellipse degenerates to a point	
Circle	$x''^2 + y''^2 = a^2$ $a^2 = \dfrac{F''}{A'} = \dfrac{F''}{C}$	The locus of a point P such that its distance from a fixed point $(0, 0)$ is constant $= a$ from the equation $A'x''^2 + C'y''^2 = F''$ if $a^2 > 0$, circle is real if $a^2 < 0$, circle is imaginary if $F'' = 0$, circle degenerates to a point	
Hyperbola	$\dfrac{x''^2}{a^2} + \dfrac{y''^2}{b^2} = 1$ $a^2 = \dfrac{F'}{A'}$ $b^2 = \dfrac{F''}{C}$ a^2 and b^2 opposite signs	The locus of a point P such that the difference of its distances from two fixed points Q' and Q is a constant $= 2a$ $PQ' - PQ = 2a$ from the equation $A'x''^2 + C'y''^2 = F''$ F'' can be > 0 or < 0 and the hyperbola is real. If $F'' = 0$, then hyperbola degenerates to a pair of straight lines intersecting at the origin.	

Parabola (x independent, y dependent)	$x''^2 = 2ay''$ $2a = -\dfrac{E'}{A'}$	The locus of a point P such that its distance from a fixed point Q is equal to its distance from a fixed line $y'' = -a/2$ $PQ = PN$	from the equation $A'x''^2 = -E'y''$ if $E' \neq 0$, then a parabola exists if $E' = 0$, the parabola is imaginary, or degenerates into two lines parallel to the y'' axis or to the y'' axis itself.	
Parabola (y independent, x dependent)	$y''^2 = 2bx''$ $2b = -\dfrac{D'}{C'}$	The locus of a point P such that its distance from a fixed point Q is equal to its distance from a fixed line $x'' = -b/2$ $PQ = PN$	from the equation $C'y''^2 = -D'x''$ if $D' \neq 0$, then a parabola exists if $D' = 0$, the parabola is imaginary, or degenerates into two lines parallel to the x'' axis or to the x'' axis itself.	

Answers to Selected Exercises

Chapter 1

Section A

1. (*b*) Sales could decrease by approximately 25%. (*d*) Sales must increase by approximately 25%.

Section B
1. 5500 units
2. (*a*) $300, $90

Chapter 2

Section B
1. (*b*) 87.79; $\lim_{N \to \infty} 1000(1 - 2/N)^N = 1000e^{-2} = 135.34$
3. They cross for $2 < t < 3$.
5. *Hint:* see answer to 1b

Chapter 3

Section A

5. $P = \left[x + \dfrac{y}{i} \right] \left[\dfrac{1 - v^n}{i} \right] - \dfrac{nyv^n}{i}$

7. 31.82

Section B
5. $156.25, yes.

Section D
1. Unique IRR $= 50\%$
3. IRR $= 0$ and 100%; $r = 2 - [2/(1 + k)]$

Chapter 4

Section B
1. $C(y) = (c_o r/y) + (c_c y/2)$ where $y =$ number of units per order, $y^* = \sqrt{2c_o r/c_c}$

2. Approximately 10 cents

5. $E(x) = pr - c_o x - (rc_c/2x) - ur$; $x^* = \sqrt{rc_c/2c_o}$; Solution is the same.

Section D

2. Vibration, Distortion, Electrical, Shock, Visual

Chapter Exercises

1. Assign D to intersection of 102 and 2 and E to intersection of 104 and 3. (Assume distance between aisles in both directions is equal.)

Chapter 5

Section A

1. $g' = a_1 + 2a_2 x + 3a_3 x^2 + 4a_4 x^3$; $g'' = 2a_2 + 6a_3 x + 12a_4 x^2$

2. $g' = a/x$; $g'' = -ax^{-2}$

3. $g' = dhe^{-hx-m}$; $g'' = -dh^2 e^{-hx-m}$

7. $g' = kn^v v^n[\ln v + vn^{-1}]$; $g'' = kn^v v^n[(\ln v + vn^{-1})^2 - vn^{-2}]$

8. $g' = \ln c + cx^{-2}(1 - \ln x) - 1 - \ln x$; $g'' = -cx^{-3}(3 - 2\ln x) - x^{-1}$

Section B

1. 33.994

Section C

1. Critical points are $(-\infty; 1, \infty)$. Global minimum: $x = 1$; global maximum: $x = \pm\infty$. Increasing for $x > 1$; decreasing for $x < 1$.

2. Critical points $(0, \infty)$. Global minimum: $x = 0$; global maximum: $x = \infty$. Increasing for $x > 0$.

3. Critical points $(0, \infty)$. Global minimum: $x = 0$; global maximum: $x = \infty$. Increasing for $x \geq 0$.

7. Critical points $(-\infty, -2/\ln 2, 0, \infty)$. Global minimum: $n = -\infty$; $n = 0$; global maximum: $n = +\infty$. Increasing for $-\infty < n < -2/\ln 2$ and for $n > 0$. Decreasing for $-2/\ln 2 < n < 0$.

8. Critical points $(-\infty, -1, \frac{1}{2}, 2, \infty)$. Global minima: $x = -1$, $x = 2$; global maxima: $x = -\infty$; $x = +\infty$. Increasing for $-1 < x < \frac{1}{2}$ and $2 < x < \infty$. Decreasing for $-\infty < x < -1$; $\frac{1}{2} < n < 2$.

11. 5

13. $4 - \sqrt{5}$

Section D

1. (a) Concave for $0.036 < x < 0.52$; convex for $-\infty < x < 0.036$ and $0.52 < x < +\infty$. (b) None. (c) None. (d) One unique inverse for $x \leq 1$ and another for $x \geq 1$.

2. (a) Concave for $x > 0$; (b) $x = 0$ as $x \to -\infty$; (c) none; (d) $x > 0$.

3. (a) Concave for $x \geq 0$; (b) $g = 2$ as $x \to \infty$; (c) none; (d) $x \geq 0$.

7. (a) Concave for $-4.93 < n < -0.85$; convex for $-\infty < n < -4.93$ and $-0.85 < n < \infty$. (b) $g = 0$ as $n \to -\infty$. (c) none. (d) $-\infty < n \leq -2.89$; $-2.89 \leq n \leq 0$; $0 \leq n < \infty$.

8. (a) Concave for $-0.365 < x < 1.365$; convex for $-\infty < x < -0.365$ and $1.365 < x < \infty$. (b) none. (c) Symmetrical about its local maximum. (d) $-\infty < x \leq -1$; $-1 \leq x \leq \frac{1}{2}$; $\frac{1}{2} \leq x \leq 2$; $2 \leq x < \infty$.

Section E
1. $\alpha > b$

Chapter Exercises
2. (a) $60,000 to A; $20,000 to B; $30,000 to C; $40,000 to D; and $50,000 to E.
(b) Another increment of sales support is added to region x if the increment of return is greater than the increment of return from any other region. This procedure is continued until all funds are allocated.

Chapter 6

Section A

1. $P(i) = -C + \sum_{j=1}^{n} a_j(1 + i)^{-j}$; $\quad P'(i) = - \sum_{j=1}^{n} ja_j(1 + i)^{-j-1} < 0$

$P(0) = -C + \sum_{j=1}^{n} a_j > 0$ by assumption; $\quad P(\infty) = -C$

Under the given conditions, $P(0) > 0$; $P(i)$ is monotonically decreasing; $P(\infty) < 0$; $P(i)$ is continuous; therefore, there is a single value of i for which $P(i) = 0$.

Section B
1. When $y = 30$, x should also be 30. This imposes one constraint on the parameters:

$$30 = \left[\frac{a + b}{2(a + c)}\right]30 + \frac{20(a + c) + 30(c - 2000) + 2000}{2(a + c)}$$

Chapter 7

Section A
4. (b) If each component has the same initial cost and the same value of the parameter b. (c) $U(i) = U(1)[i^{-b+1} - (i - 1)^{-b+1}] \simeq U(1)(1 - b)i^{-b}$ when i is large.

Section B
1. 122.14
3. 383.71
6. 1117.67
8. (a) 8514.19; (b) 8660.58

Section C
2. Same as if the objective is to maximize $P(k, t)$.
3. (a) 16,332

Chapter Exercises
1. (c) $x \simeq 3$ years and 9 months

Chapter 8

Section A

7. $2^x \left[\dfrac{x}{\ln 2} - \dfrac{1}{(\ln 2)^2}\right] + C$

8. $\dfrac{x^2}{2} + 2x + \frac{27}{4} \ln (x - 3) + \frac{1}{4} \ln (x + 1) + C$

11. 1

Section B

7. $\dfrac{x^2}{2} + \dfrac{1}{y} = C$

12. $2x^2 + 2xy + 3y^2 = C$

14. $y = \frac{1}{8}e^{2x} + Ce^{-3x}$

19. $S(t) = e^{\delta t} - 1 \left[\dfrac{\alpha}{\delta} + \dfrac{\beta}{\delta^2} + \dfrac{2\gamma}{\delta^3} \right] - \dfrac{\gamma t^2}{\delta} - \dfrac{2\gamma t}{\delta^2} - \dfrac{\beta t}{\delta}$

Chapter 9

Section B

2. $f_x = -6x + 60 - y$; $f_y = -x - 5y + 53.5$; $f_{xx} = -6$; $f_{yy} = -5$; $f_{xy} = -1$

5. $f_x = (x + \sqrt{y})^{-1}$; $f_y = (\frac{1}{2})(x + \sqrt{y})^{-1}y^{-\frac{1}{2}}$
    $f_{xx} = -(x + \sqrt{y})^{-2}$; $f_{xy} = -(x + \sqrt{y})^{-2}(\frac{1}{2})y^{-\frac{1}{2}}$
    $f_{yy} = (-\frac{1}{4})(x + \sqrt{y})^{-1}y^{-3/2} - (\frac{1}{4})y^{-1}(x + \sqrt{y})^{-2}$

10. $\dfrac{dy}{dx} = -\dfrac{f_x}{f_y} = -\dfrac{(4 + y - 2x)}{(5 + x - 2y)}$;   at $x = 6, y = 0.75$; $dy/dx = 0.762$; at $x = 2$, $y = 8$; $dy/dx = 0.89$

12. $E(y, q) = yf(y, q) - f(y, q)A(x, q)$

$$\dfrac{\partial E}{\partial y} = f(y, q) + y\dfrac{\partial f}{\partial y} - A(x, q)\dfrac{\partial f}{\partial y} - f(y, q)\dfrac{\partial A}{\partial x}\dfrac{\partial x}{\partial y}$$

$$\dfrac{\partial E}{\partial q} = y\dfrac{\partial f}{\partial q} - A(x, q)\dfrac{\partial f}{\partial q} - f(y, q)\left(\dfrac{\partial A}{\partial q} + \dfrac{\partial A}{\partial x}\dfrac{\partial x}{\partial q}\right)$$

Section C

1. $f_x = 0 = f_y$ gives $x^* = \frac{13}{3}$, $y^* = \frac{14}{3}$ as the single stationary point.
   $\Delta_1 = 2A = -2 < 0$ and $\Delta_2 = 4AC - B^2 = 4(-1)(-1) - 1 = 3 > 0$
The stationary point is a global maximum and the function is concave throughout.
   2. $x^* = 8.5$, $y^* = 9$, $\Delta_1 < 0$, $\Delta_2 > 0$. The function has a global maximum at x^*, y^* and is concave throughout.

Section D

2. From Example 10,

$$\dfrac{\partial E}{\partial y} = x - \eta x + \eta\dfrac{x}{y}\dfrac{\partial C}{\partial x} = 0 \quad \text{or} \quad \eta = \dfrac{1}{1 - (1/y)(\partial C/\partial x)}$$

$$\dfrac{\partial E}{\partial z} = \mu - \dfrac{\mu}{y}\dfrac{\partial C}{\partial x} - 1 = 0 \quad \text{or} \quad \mu = \dfrac{1}{1 - (1/y)(\partial C/\partial x)}$$

Therefore $\eta = \mu$ at a stationary point.

Chapter 10

Section B

2. $\Delta_2 = 4[n\Sigma x_i^2 - (\Sigma x_i)^2]$; let $\bar{x} = \dfrac{1}{n} \Sigma x_i$; then $\Sigma(x_i - \bar{x})^2 > 0$.

But $n\Sigma(x_i - \bar{x})^2 = n[\Sigma x_i^2 - 2\bar{x}\Sigma x_i + n\bar{x}^2]$

$$= n\Sigma x_i^2 - (\Sigma x_i)^2$$

Therefore $\Delta_2 > 0$ unless $x_i = \bar{x}$ for all i.

Chapter 11

Section A

1. $x^* = \dfrac{2acC + abE - bcB - Db^2}{2AB^2 - 2Bab + 2Ca^2}$; $y^* = \dfrac{c}{b} - \dfrac{a}{b}x^*$

7. Let x_i = number of units per order

Total cost = ordering cost + holding cost

$$h = C_o\left[\frac{R_1}{x_1} + \frac{R_2}{x_2}\right] + \frac{I}{2}[U_1 x_1 + U_2 x_2] - \lambda\left[\frac{U_1 x_1 + U_2 x_2}{2} - K\right]$$

$$x_i^* = \frac{K\sqrt{2C_o R_i / U_i}}{\sqrt{U_1 C_o R_1 / 2} + \sqrt{U_2 C_o R_2 / 2}}$$

$$\Delta_3 = -\frac{U_1^2 C_o R_2}{2x_2^3} - \frac{U_2^2 C_o R_1}{2x_1^3} < 0; \quad \text{solution is a minimum.}$$

Section B

1. (a) $x^* = \dfrac{2acC + abE - bcB - Db^2}{2Ab^2 - 2Bba + 2Ca^2}$; $y^* = \dfrac{c}{b} - \dfrac{a}{b}x^*$

$$\lambda = \frac{1}{b^2}[(Bb - 2aC)x^* + 2cC + Eb]$$

If $\lambda \geq 0$, x^*, y^* is an extreme point.

If $\lambda < 0$, $x^* = \dfrac{2CD - BE}{B^2 - 4AC}$; $y^* = \dfrac{2AE - DB}{B^2 - 4AC}$

Section C

1. Let $g_1(x, y) = ax + by - c$; $g_2(x, y) = -x$; $g_3(x, y) = -y$

Form the Lagrangian function:

$$h(x, y, \lambda_1, \lambda_2, \lambda_3) = f(x, y) - \lambda_1 g_1 - \lambda_2 g_2 - \lambda_3 g_3$$

The necessary conditions are:

$$2Ax + By + D - \lambda_1 a + \lambda_2 = 0$$
$$2Cy + Bx + E - \lambda_1 b + \lambda_3 = 0 \qquad \text{and}$$
$$\lambda_i g_i = 0; \quad g_i \leq 0 \quad \text{for } i = 1, 2, 3$$

There are 8 possible solutions satisfying the necessary conditions:

Case	λ_1	g_1	λ_2	g_2	λ_3	g_3	λ_1 or g_1	λ_2 or x	λ_3 or y
1	0	$\neq 0$	0	$\neq 0$	0	$\neq 0$	$g_1 = ax + by - c$	$x = \dfrac{2CD - BE}{B^2 - 4AC}$	$y = \dfrac{2AE - BD}{B^2 - 4AC}$
2	0	$\neq 0$	$\neq 0$	$\neq 0$	$\neq 0$	0	$g_1 = ax - c$	$x = -\dfrac{D}{2A}$	$\lambda_3 = \dfrac{BD}{2A} - E$
3	0	$\neq 0$	$\neq 0$	0	0	$\neq 0$	$g_1 = by - c$	$\lambda_2 = -D + \dfrac{BE}{2C}$	$y = -\dfrac{E}{2C}$
4	0	$\neq 0$	$\neq 0$	0	$\neq 0$	0	$g_1 = -c$	$\lambda_2 = -D$	$\lambda_3 = -E$
5	$\neq 0$	0	$\neq 0$	0	0	$\neq 0$	$\lambda_1 = \dfrac{1}{b^2}[(Bb - 2aC)x^* + 2cC + Eb]$	x^*	y^*
6	$\neq 0$	0	$\neq 0$	0	$\neq 0$	0	$\lambda_1 = \dfrac{b(2Ax + D)}{a}$	$x = \dfrac{c}{a}$	$\lambda_3 = -\dfrac{b(2Ax + D) - a(Bx + E)}{a}$
7	$\neq 0$	0	0	$\neq 0$	0	$\neq 0$	$\lambda_1 = \dfrac{(2Cy + E)}{b}$	$\lambda_2 = \dfrac{a(2Cy + E) - b(By + D)}{b}$	$y = \dfrac{c}{b}$
8	$\neq 0$	0	0	$\neq 0$	0	0		Not possible if $c \neq 0$	

$$x^* = \frac{2acC + abE - bcB - b^2 D}{2Ab^2 - 2abB + 2Ca^2}$$

$$y^* = \frac{2bcA + abD - acB - a^2 E}{2Ab^2 - 2abB + 2Ca^2}$$

The optimum solution is the case for which $\lambda_i \geq 0$ and $g_i \leq 0$ for $i = 1, 2, 3$. The conditions are sufficient if $f(x, y)$ is concave; i.e., if $A < 0$ and $4AC - B^2 > 0$.

Chapter 12

Section A

4. Let $U^* = [3 \quad 4 \quad 6 \quad 3]$ denote sales to consumers (rows) by product (columns) for area U and $V^* = [4 \quad 5 \quad 3 \quad 6]$ be the same matrix for area V. Then the total sales to consumers by products =

$$U^* + V^* = [3 + 4 \quad 4 + 5 \quad 6 + 3 \quad 3 + 6] = [7 \quad 9 \quad 9 \quad 9]$$

9. Let $A = \begin{bmatrix} 6 & 2 & 5 & 3 \\ 7 & 1 & 4 & 1 \end{bmatrix}$ denote sales to retailers and wholesalers (rows 1 and 2, respectively) by product (columns) for the area U and $B = \begin{bmatrix} 7 & 2 & 8 & 0 \\ 7 & 2 & 4 & 1 \end{bmatrix}$ be the same matrix for the area V. Then the difference in sales to retailers and wholesalers by product between the two areas =

$$A - B = \begin{bmatrix} 6-7 & 2-2 & 5-8 & 3-0 \\ 7-7 & 1-2 & 4-4 & 1-1 \end{bmatrix} = \begin{bmatrix} -1 & 0 & -3 & 3 \\ 0 & -1 & 0 & 0 \end{bmatrix}$$

13. $AX = a_1x_1 + a_2x_2$
19. $[15 \quad 56 \quad 17]'$
25. Let S be a 1×4 row vector which gives unit sales (rows) by products (columns); then $S = KU = [16 \quad 7 \quad 15 \quad 7]$.

Chapter 13

Section E

2.

x_1	x_2	x_3	z (\$)
0	0	0	0
1,200	0	0	60.00
0	370	0	14.80
0	0	2,400	48.00
1,100	200	0	63.00
800	0	1,600	72.00
0	-533	5,867	not feasible

The optimum product mix is $x_1 = 800$; $x_2 = 0$; $x_3 = 1,600$; and $z = 72.00$.

Chapter 14

Section B

2. (a) \$1.6875 per pound of *YIP* and \$2.25 per pound of *ZIP*.

Section C

1. $\begin{bmatrix} 854.7 \\ 827.4 \end{bmatrix}$

Chapter 15

Section B

1. $x_1 = 0$; $x_2 = 0$; $x_3 = 2,400$; $z = 9,600$

3. If $x_2 = 300$, then from $L_4, x_3 = 1,600 - 8(300) = -800$. Thus L_3 and L_4 give an infeasible solution and (16) cannot apply. The optimum feasible solution is $x_1 = 450$, $x_2 = 300$, $x_3 = 0$; then $z = 3,450$.

5. $x_1 = 25,000$; $x_2 = 300,000$; and maximum profit = \$725,000

Section C

1. (a) Max $z = 3x_1 + 5x_2 + 4x_3 + 0x_4 + 0x_5$

subject to $4x_1 + 2x_2 + x_3 + x_4 \qquad = 4,800$

$2x_1 + 13x_2 + 2x_3 + \qquad x_5 = 4,800$

$x_i \geq 0; \qquad i = 1, 2, \ldots, 5$

(b) x_4 is the number of minutes of idle time on the slotting machine; x_5 is the number of minutes of idle time on the threading machine.

(c) $x_1 = 0$; $x_2 = 0$; $x_3 = 2,400$; $x_4 = 2,400$; $x_5 = 0$

$x_3 + 0x_4 = 2,400 - x_1 - 6.5x_2 - 0.5x_5$

$0x_3 + x_4 = 2,400 - 3x_1 + 4.5x_2 + 0.5x_5$

$z = 3x_1 + 5x_2 + 4[2,400 - x_1 - 6.5x_2 - 0.5x_5] = 9,600 - x_1 - 21x_2 - 2x_5$

(d) Basic variables:

$x_3 = 2,400$: produce 2,400 units of aluminum screws
$x_4 = 2,400$: slotting machine is idle 2,400 minutes

Non-basic variables:

$x_1 = 0$; $c_1' = 1$: to produce one unit of x_1 reduces profit by 1
$x_2 = 0$; $c_2' = 21$: to produce one unit of x_2 reduces profit by 21
$x_5 = 0$; $c_3' = 2$: each additional minute of threading machine time increases profit by 2 cents

(e) Set of basic variables remains unchanged if threading machine time is changed by $\pm 4,800$.

Section D

1.

		1	8	0	0	$-z$		
BV	UP	x_1	x_2	x_3	x_4	b	Check	Ratio
x_3	0	4	2	1	0	4,800	4,807	2,400
x_4	0	2	13	0	1	4,800	4,816	4,800/13 →
ΔP		1	8	0	0	0	9	
			*					
x_3	0	48/13	0	1	−2/13	11(4,800)/13	52,859/13	
x_2	8	2/13	1	0	1/13	4,800/13	4,816/13	
ΔP		−3/13	0	0	−8/13	−8(4,800)/13	−38,411/13	

Chapter 16

Section A

3.

BV	UP	x_1 (A₁) 3.0	x_2 (A₂) 2.5	x_3 (B₁) 3.5	x_4 (B₂) 4.0	x_5 (C₁) 5.0	x_6 (C₂) 4.5	x_7 0	x_8 0	x_9 0	x_{10} 0	x_{11} −6	x_{12} 0	Amt 0	
x_{11}	−6	1	1					−1				1		40	40→
x_8	0			1	1				1					35	
x_9	0					1	1			1				35	
x_{10}	0	1	1	1	1	1	1				1			100	100
x_{12}	0	1		1		1							1	50	50
ΔP		9.0*	8.5	3.5	4.0	5.0	4.5	−6				0	0	240	
x_1	3.0	1	1					−1				1		40	
x_8	0			1	1				1					35	
x_9	0					1	1			1				35	
x_{10}	0	0	0	1	1	1	1	1			1	−1		60	60
x_{12}	0	0	−1	1		1		1				−1	1	10	10→
ΔP		0	−0.5	3.5	4.0	5.0*	4.5	3				−9.0		−120	
x_1	3.0	1	1					−1				1		40	
x_8	0			1	1				1					35	
x_9	0	0	1	−1		0	1	−1		1		1	−1	25	25→
x_{10}	0	0	1	0	1	0	1	0			1	0	−1	50	50
x_5	5.0	0	−1	1		1		1				−1	1	10	
ΔP		0	4.5	−1.5	4.0	0	4.5*	−2				−4.0	−5	−170	
x_1	3.0	1	1					−1				1		40	
x_8	0			1	1				1					35	35
x_6	4.5	0	1	−1		0	1	−1		1		1	−1	25	
x_{10}	0	0	0	1	1	0	0	1		−1	1	−1		25	25→
x_5	5.0	0	−1	1		1		1				−1	1	10	
ΔP		0	0	3.0	4.0*	0	0	2.5		−4.5		−8.5	−0.5	−282.5	
x_1	3.0	1	1					−1				1		40	
x_8	0			0	0			−1	1	1	−1	1		10	
x_6	4.5		1	−1		1		−1		1		1	−1	25	
x_4	4.0			1	1			1		−1	1	−1		25	
x_5	5.0		−1	1		1		1				−1	1	10	
ΔP		0	0	−1	0	0	0	−1.5		−0.5	−4.0	−4.5	−0.5	−382.5	

The optimum solution is to invest 40% in A_1, 25% in B_2, 10% in C_1, and 25% in C_2. This satisfies all the constraints and yields a return of 3.825%.

Section B

2. The slack variable x_{41} is basic; therefore additional machine capacity on machine I would not change the solution. Additional time, 5 hours, on machine II would change the solution as follows:

$$x_{11} = 90; \quad x_{22} = 80; \quad x_{31} = 40 - 5(0.95) = 35.25; \quad x_{32} = 20 + 5(0.95) = 24.75.$$

Total cost is reduced by $5(0.286) = 1.43$.

Section C

4. The solution is unique if no non-basic variable has a zero change in profit coefficient. In this case, z_{12} is a non-basic variable which has a zero change in profit coefficient. This means that, if additional cash were available in period 2, no profit would be lost by not using this cash to buy until the next period because the purchase price does not change.

Section D

1. Let X, Y, S, T, U, V, R, Z_1, and Z_2 be $n \times 1$ column vectors and let **A** and **B** be two $n \times n$ matrices:

$$\mathbf{A} = \begin{bmatrix} 1 & & & & & \\ -1 & 1 & & & & \\ & -1 & 1 & & 0 & \\ & & 0 & \cdot & & \\ & & & & \cdot & \\ & & & & & \cdot \\ & & & & -1 & 1 \end{bmatrix} ;$$

$$\mathbf{B} = \begin{bmatrix} 1 & & & & & \\ -2 & 1 & & & & \\ 1 & -2 & 1 & & 0 & \\ & 1 & -2 & 1 & & \\ & & & \cdot & & \\ 0 & & & & \cdot & \\ & & & & 1 & -2 & 1 \end{bmatrix}$$

A has 1's down the main diagonal and -1's to the left of each 1. **B** has 1's down the main diagonal and the numbers [1 -2] to the left of each 1. The linear programming tableau becomes:

U	V	X	Y	S	T	Z_1	Z_2	=	rhs	
A	$-$A					$-$I		=	$-$R	non-negative production
A	$-$A		$-\frac{1}{k}$I	$\frac{1}{k}$I			$-$I	=	$-$R	non-negative work force
B	$-$B	$-\frac{1}{k}$I	$\frac{1}{k}$I	$-\frac{1}{k}$A	$\frac{1}{k}$A			=	$-$AR	

The initial work force and $1/k$ times the initial inventory is subtracted from the right hand side (rhs) of the first set of equations in the third set. The initial inventory is added to the first equation in the first and second set.

Let $\vec{x} = \begin{bmatrix} U \\ V \\ X \\ Y \\ S \\ T \end{bmatrix}$; $\vec{a}$ the matrix of the LP tableau for $\vec{x}$; $\vec{z} = \begin{bmatrix} Z_1 \\ Z_2 \end{bmatrix}$;

$\vec{I} = \begin{bmatrix} -I & 0 \\ 0 & -I \\ 0 & 0 \end{bmatrix}$; and $\vec{c}$ the cost vector associated with $\vec{x}$; $\vec{d} = \begin{bmatrix} -R \\ -R \\ -AR \end{bmatrix}$

Then the model is minimize $\vec{c}\vec{x}$ subject to $\vec{a}\vec{x} \geq \vec{d}$; $\vec{x} \geq 0$ or

$$\vec{a}\vec{x} + \vec{I}\vec{z} = \vec{d}; \quad \vec{z} \geq 0; \quad \vec{x} \geq 0$$

Chapter 17

Section A

1. $X = \begin{bmatrix} 1 & 4 & 0 \\ 1 & 0 & 2 \end{bmatrix}$ or $\begin{bmatrix} 2 & 3 & 0 \\ 0 & 1 & 2 \end{bmatrix}$

Section B

2. A to 4; B to 2; C to 5; D to 3; E to 1.

Section C

1. Primal problem:

$\max z = 5x_1 + 4x_2 + kx_3 + 0x_4 + 0x_5$

subject to
$$x_1 + x_2 + x_3 = 1{,}200$$
$$4x_1 + 2x_2 + x_4 = 4{,}800$$
$$2x_1 + 13x_2 - x_5 = 4{,}800$$
$$x_1 \geq 0; \quad x_2 \geq 0; \quad x_3 \geq 0; \quad x_4 \geq 0; \quad x_5 \geq 0; \quad k < 0$$

The basic variables are x_1, x_2, x_4 and
$$x_1 = (1/11)[10{,}800 - 13x_3 - x_5]$$
$$x_2 = (1/11)[2{,}400 + 2x_3 + x_5]$$
$$x_4 = (1/11)[4{,}800 + 48x_3 + 2x_5]$$
$$\text{and } z = (1/11)[53(1{,}200) - (57 - 11k)x_3 - x_5]$$

The dual problem is minimize $y = 1{,}200u_1 + 4{,}800u_2 - 4{,}800u_3$ subject to
$$u_1 + 4u_2 - 2u_3 - u_4 = 5$$
$$u_1 + 2u_2 - 13u_3 - u_5 = 4$$
$$u_i \geq 0; \quad i = 1, 2, \ldots, 5$$

The basic variables are u_1 and u_3 and
$$u_1 = (1/11)[57 - 48u_2 + 13u_4 - 2u_5]$$
$$u_3 = (1/11)[1 - 2u_2 + u_4 - u_5]$$
$$\text{and } y = (1/11)[53(1{,}200) + 4{,}800u_2 + 9(1{,}200)u_4 + 2{,}400u_5]$$

Chapter 18

Section A

1. (a) $f_{x_1} = 2x_1 + 4$; $f_{x_2} = 2x_2 + 2$; $f_{x_3} = 2x_3$

$f_{x_1 x_1} = 2$; $f_{x_1 x_2} = f_{x_1 x_3} = 0$; $f_{x_2 x_2} = 2$; $f_{x_2 x_3} = 0$; $f_{x_3 x_3} = 2$

(b) Stationary point $x_1 = -2$; $x_2 = -1$; $x_3 = 0$

(c) $\Delta_1 > 0$; $\Delta_2 = \begin{vmatrix} 2 & 0 \\ 0 & 2 \end{vmatrix} = 4$;

$\Delta_3 = \begin{vmatrix} 2 & 0 & 0 \\ 0 & 2 & 0 \\ 0 & 0 & 2 \end{vmatrix} = 8$

(d) Convex everywhere

8. (a) $E_i(y_i, z_i) = (y_i - c)s_i(y, z) - z_i$

Total earnings are:

$$E = \Sigma E_i = \sum_{i=1}^{n} \left(\frac{y_i - c}{n}\right)(\alpha - \beta y_i)(1 + \gamma\sqrt{n\bar{z}})\left[(1 - \delta)\frac{z_i}{n\bar{z}} + \delta\right] - n\bar{z}$$

$$\frac{\partial E}{\partial y_i} = \left(\frac{y_i - c}{n}\right)(-\beta) + (\alpha - \beta y_i)\frac{1}{n} = 0$$

$$y_i{}^* = \frac{c\beta + \alpha}{2\beta}$$

Since $y_i{}^*$ is the same for all i, let $A = \left(\frac{y - c}{n}\right)(\alpha - \beta y)$

$$E = A(1 + \gamma\sqrt{n\bar{z}})\left(\frac{(1 - \delta)}{n\bar{z}}\Sigma z_i + n\delta\right) - n\bar{z}; \quad n\bar{z} = (z_1 + z_2 + \cdots + z_n)$$

$$= A(1 + \gamma\sqrt{n\bar{z}})(1 + \delta(n - 1)) - n\bar{z}$$

$$\frac{\partial E}{\partial z_i} = A(1 + \delta(n - 1))\left[\frac{\gamma}{2\sqrt{n\bar{z}}}\right] - 1 \quad \text{or} \quad A(1 + \delta(n - 1))\frac{\gamma}{2} = \sqrt{n\bar{z}}$$

$$n\bar{z}^* = \frac{A^2\gamma^2}{4}(1 + \delta(n - 1))^2 = \frac{[1 + \delta(n - 1)]^2\gamma^2(\alpha - c\beta)^2}{16\beta n^2} = \sum_{i=1}^{n} z_i{}^*$$

Section B

1. Objective $E(x_i) = y(\Sigma x_i) - \Sigma x_i{}^2 - \lambda(\Sigma a_i x_i - K)$

$$\frac{\partial E(x_i)}{\partial x_i} = 0; \quad y - 2x_i - \lambda a_i = 0; \quad \Sigma a_i x_i = K; \quad x_i{}^* = \frac{y - \lambda a_i}{2}$$

$$a_i y - 2x_i a_i - \lambda a_i{}^2 = 0$$

$$y\Sigma a_i - 2\Sigma x_i a_i - \lambda\Sigma a_i{}^2 = 0$$

$$y\Sigma a_i - \lambda\Sigma a_i{}^2 - 2K = 0$$

$$\frac{y\Sigma a_i - 2K}{\Sigma a_i{}^2} = \lambda$$

To verify the necessary conditions, compute the principal minors of

$$\Delta_{n+1} = \begin{vmatrix} 0 & a_1 & a_2 & \cdots & a_n \\ a_1 & -2 & 0 & \cdots & 0 \\ a_2 & 0 & -2 & \cdots & 0 \\ \cdot & \cdot & \cdot & & \cdot \\ \cdot & \cdot & \cdot & & \cdot \\ \cdot & \cdot & \cdot & & \cdot \\ a_n & 0 & 0 & \cdots & -2 \end{vmatrix}$$

$$\Delta_3 = 2(a_1{}^2 + a_2{}^2) > 0; \quad \Delta_4 = -4(a_1{}^2 + a_2{}^2 + a_3{}^2) < 0;$$
$$\Delta_5 = 8(a_1{}^2 a_2{}^2 + a_3{}^2 + a_4{}^2) > 0$$

$$\Delta_{n+1} = (-)^{n+1} 2^{n-1} \sum_{i=1}^{n} a_i{}^2$$

Therefore the solution is a maximum.

6. Maximize $E_1 + E_2$ subject to $x_1 + x_2 = 8$ and $y_1 + y_2 = 7$.

$$h(x_1, x_2, y_1, y_2, \lambda_1, \lambda_2) = 4x_1 + 5y_1 + x_1y_1 - x_1{}^2 - y_1{}^2 + 5 + 4x_2 + 2y_2 + 2x_2y_2$$
$$- 2x_2{}^2 - y_2{}^2 - 5 - \lambda_1[x_1 + x_2 - 8] - \lambda_2[y_1 + y_2 - 7]$$

$$\frac{\partial h}{\partial x_1} = 4 + y_1 - 2x_1 - \lambda_1 = 0$$

$$\frac{\partial h}{\partial x_2} = 4 + 2y_2 - 4x_2 - \lambda_1 = 0$$

$$\frac{\partial h}{\partial y_1} = 5 + x_1 - 2y_1 - \lambda_2 = 0$$

$$\frac{\partial h}{\partial y_2} = 2 + 2x_2 - 2y_2 - \lambda_2 = 0$$

$$\frac{\partial h}{\partial \lambda_1} = -[x_1 + x_2 - 8] = 0; \quad \frac{\partial h}{\partial \lambda_2} = -[y_1 + y_2 - 7] = 0$$

The solution to this set of equations is:

$$x_1{}^* = 5, x_2{}^* = 3, y_1{}^* = 4, y_2{}^* = 3, \lambda_1 = -2, \lambda_2 = 2$$

$$\Delta_6 = \begin{vmatrix} 0 & 0 & 1 & 1 & 0 & 0 \\ 0 & 0 & 0 & 0 & 1 & 1 \\ 1 & 0 & -2 & 0 & 1 & 0 \\ 1 & 0 & 0 & -4 & 0 & 2 \\ 0 & 1 & 1 & 0 & -2 & 0 \\ 0 & 1 & 0 & 2 & 0 & -2 \end{vmatrix}$$

$\Delta_5 = -6, \Delta_6 = 9$ The solution is a local maximum.

Section C

1. Since λ_1 is negative, the constraint $g_1(x_1, x_2) = x_1 + x_2 - 8$ will be satisfied as an inequality, i.e., $\lambda_1 = 0$. The optimum solution is

$$x_1{}^* = 4; \quad x_2{}^* = 2.5; \quad y_1{}^* = 4; \quad y_2{}^* = 3; \quad \lambda_1 = 0; \quad \lambda_2 = 1$$

Chapter 19

Section A

1. Let $\mathbf{X}' = [x_1 \quad x_2 \quad x_3]$. Then $g(\mathbf{X}) = \mathbf{X}'\mathbf{AX} + \mathbf{B}'\mathbf{X} + c$ where

$$\mathbf{A} = \begin{bmatrix} 1 & 0 & 0 \\ 0 & 1 & 0 \\ 0 & 0 & 1 \end{bmatrix}; \quad \mathbf{B} = \begin{bmatrix} 4 \\ 2 \\ 0 \end{bmatrix}; \quad c = -40$$

$$\mathbf{X}^* = -\frac{1}{2}\begin{bmatrix} 1 & 0 & 0 \\ 0 & 1 & 0 \\ 0 & 0 & 1 \end{bmatrix}\begin{bmatrix} 4 \\ 2 \\ 0 \end{bmatrix} = \begin{bmatrix} -2 \\ -1 \\ 0 \end{bmatrix}; \quad 2\mathbf{A} = \begin{bmatrix} 2 & 0 & 0 \\ 0 & 2 & 0 \\ 0 & 0 & 2 \end{bmatrix} = \Delta; \quad \begin{matrix} \Delta_1 = 2; \\ \Delta_2 = 4; \quad \Delta_3 = 8 \end{matrix}$$

Therefore $\mathbf{X}^*$ is a minimum

Section D

2. $z_1 = 0.312$; $z_2 = 0.688$; $z_3 = 0$; $v = 35.90$

Chapter 20

Section A

1. $A = \begin{bmatrix} -60 & 50 \\ 50 & -60 \end{bmatrix}$; $B = \begin{bmatrix} 1{,}760 \\ 1{,}320 \end{bmatrix}$; $P^{-1} = \begin{bmatrix} 1 & -\frac{5}{6} \\ 0 & 1 \end{bmatrix}$; $P = \begin{bmatrix} 1 & \frac{5}{6} \\ 0 & 1 \end{bmatrix}$

$$K = -\tfrac{1}{2}A^{-1}B = -\frac{1}{2200}\begin{bmatrix} -60 & -50 \\ -50 & -60 \end{bmatrix}\begin{bmatrix} 1{,}760 \\ 1{,}320 \end{bmatrix} = \begin{bmatrix} 78 \\ 76 \end{bmatrix}$$

$$Q = P'AP = \begin{bmatrix} 1 & 0 \\ \frac{5}{6} & 1 \end{bmatrix}\begin{bmatrix} -60 & 50 \\ 50 & -60 \end{bmatrix}\begin{bmatrix} 1 & \frac{5}{6} \\ 0 & 1 \end{bmatrix} = \begin{bmatrix} -60 & 0 \\ 0 & -110/6 \end{bmatrix}$$

$$P(z_1, z_2) = -60z_1{}^2 - \tfrac{110}{6}z_2{}^2 + k$$

where $k = K'AK + B'K - 5{,}000 = 113{,}800$

Chapter 21

Section A

3. $x_3{}^* = 15 - z_3$; $x_2{}^* = 12.5 - \dfrac{c}{4b} - \dfrac{z_2}{2}$; $x_1{}^* = 10 - \dfrac{c}{2b} - \dfrac{z_1}{3}$

Section B

2. $x_1{}^* = y_1 + z_1 - z_0$; $x_2{}^* = \dfrac{1}{2}\left[y_1 + y_2 + \dfrac{c}{2b} + z_2 - z_0 \right]$;

$$x_3{}^* = \frac{1}{3}\left[y_1 + y_2 + y_3 + z_3 + \frac{3c}{2b} - z_0 \right]$$

Author Index

Ackoff, R. L., 539
Albers, H. H., 109
Allen, R. G. D., 152
Allen, R. L., 414
Arnoff, E. L., 539
Averink, G. J. A., 590

Bass, F. M., *et al.*, 241, 278
Baumol, W. J., 152
Beckmann, M. J., 52
Bellman, R., 636
Bernhard, R., 84
Bhavnani, K. H., 636
Bierman, H., 84
Birkoff, G., 356
Blattner, W. O., 500
Brachen, J., 84
Buffa, E. S., 109

Cahn, A. S., 502
Charnes, A., 468, 502, 539, 568
Chen, K., 636
Christenson, C., 84
Churchman, C. W., 84
Churchman, C. W., *et al.*, 109, 539
Conway, R. W., 52
Cooper, W. W., 468, 502, 539, 568
Courant, R., 52, 152

Dantzig, G. B., 468
Data Processing Digest, 67

Debreu, G., 568
Dorfman, R., 240, 241, 278, 294, 564, 568
Dorn, W. S., 540, 564, 568
Dougall, H. E., 84
Dwight, H. B., 240

Eilon, S., 153
Erdei, M. J., 414
Everett III, H., 321

Farrar, D. E., 591
Ford, L. R., 240
Ford, L. R., Jr., 540
Fordham, S., 48
Friedman, L., 540
Frommer, A. M., 21
Fulkerson, D. R., 540

Gass, S. I., 468
Gee, R., 502
Glicksman, A. M., 468
Gomory, R. E., 540
Grant, E. L., 20, 84
Grobner, W., 240

Hadley, G. F., 153
Hamming, R. W., 279, 562
Hancock, H., 278, 568
Hanssmann, F., 485, 502
Henderson, J. M., 153

Hess, S. W., 485
Hicks, J. R., 568
Hildreth, C., 204
Hitchcock, F. L., 540
Hohn, F. E., 356
Holt, C. C., 294
Holton, R. H., 4
Householder, A. S., 279, 562
Houthakker, H. S., 540
Hunt, P., 227, 241

IBM Corporation, 414
Ireson, W. G., 20, 84

Johnson, R. E., 152
Jolley, L. B. W., 52
Jones, M. H., 109

Karlin, S., 468
Kibby, D. E., 240
Kiokemeister, F. E., 152
Koopmans, T. C., 540
Kuhn, H. W., 564, 568

Leontief, W. W., 414
Levary, G., 84
Lutz, F., 204
Lutz, V. L., 204

Manne, A., 540
Markowitz, H., 590, 591
McConnell, C. R., 43
McGee, C. G., 21
McKean, R. N., 84
McLane, S., 356
Milne, W. E., 279
Mitten, L. G., 109
Modigliani, F., 294
Murdoch, D. C., 356
Muth, J. F., 294
Myers, J. H., 52

National Association of Accountants, 84
Nering, E. D., 356
Newman, J. R., 21

Orden, A., 540
Ozya, S. A., 241

Patrick, A. W., 21
Pinger, R. W., 84
Polya, G., 21
Price, H. W., 110

Quandt, R. E., 153

Reddich, H. W., 240
Reisman, A., 109
Riley, V., 414, 468
Robichek, A. A., 165

Samuelson, P. A., 564, 568, 604
Sasieni, M., 540
Schultz, A., 52
Shubik, M., 568
Silander, F. S., 109
Simon, H. A., 294
Smidt, S., 84
Smith, L. W., Jr., 414
Solomon, E., 84
Solow, R. M., 568
Steinberg, A. W., 414
Steiner, P., 240, 241, 278, 294
Swalm, R. O., 84

Taylor, H. E., 152
Teichroew, D., 165
Tse, J. W. D., 21
Tucker, A. W., 564

U.S. Treasury Department, 84

Vajda, S., 468, 500, 564, 568
van de Panne, C., 590
Van Ness, P. H., 52
Vazsonyi, A., 21, 278, 414
Vidale, M. L., 241, 540

Wade, T. L., 152
Wasserman, P., 109
Waterman, R., 502
Wilde, D. J., 564, 568
Willson, J. D., 21
Wolfe, H. B., 241

Yaspan, A., 540
Young, B., 84

Subject Index

Administrative costs, 42
Advertising model, 205, 228, 302, 557
Alcatraz National Bank model, 492
Algebraic functions, 180
Assignment problem, 520
Asymptotes, 142
Average function, 150

Break-even analysis, 14, 21
Burden, 18

Chain rule, 261, 545
Combinations, 638
Compounding, 53, 185
Concavity and convexity, 139, 273, 548
Constraints, equality, 295, 551
    inequality, 302, 561
Continuity, 225, 544
Continuous compounding, 185, 225, 227
Contour lines, 252, 690
Cost allocation, 18, 21
    in joint production, 398
Costs, fixed and variable, 14, 20, 99
Cost-volume-profit relationship, 13, 21; see also Earnings function
Cramer's rule, 347, 368
Critical point, 134
Curve fitting by least squares, 284, 580

Decision rule, 97
Decision variables, 90
Definite integral, 213
Degeneracy, 425, 515
Depreciation, 32, 52, 84
Determinant, 346, 363, 369
Differential equations, 220
Differentiation, 116, 255, 544
    implicit function, 118
    inverse function, 118
Diffusion models, 232
Dimensional analysis, 11, 171, 419
Dual problem, 527
Dynamic programming, 610

Earnings function, 14, 146, 216, 237, 262, 266, 275, 287, 463, 465, 546, 549
    consulting firm, 246
Economic order quantity, 96, 99, 259, 554
Elasticity, 151, 184, 278
Enumeration of alternatives, 94, 110, 415, 422
Equation, 8
    linear, 343, 362, 368, 378
    non-linear, 123, 562
Expansion by minors, 369
Exponential function, 181
Extreme values, 129, 134, 266, 295, 420, 547

Functions, 9, 116, 245, 544
Future value, 54, 185

Global extrema, 134
Graphical solution, 95, 252, 289, 420
Greek alphabet, 638
Grocery store sales model, 199, 302

Holt, Modigliani, Muth model, 280,
    485, 569, 574

Implicit functions, 118, 262
Inequalities, 9, 302, 417, 561
Infinite series, 28, 52, 121, 264, 605
Input-output model, 411
Integer programming, 503
Integer solutions, 108, 419
Integration, 208
Interest, 53, 185, 227
    tables, 84, 185, 637
Internal rate of return, 75, 159, 161,
    190, 254, 266
Internal Revenue Code, 1954, 32
Interpolation method, 123
Inventory model, 302, 563, 610
Inverse functions, 143
Investment model, 165, 470, 500
Investment rule, 62, 64, 190

Kuhn-Tucker conditions, 306, 309,
    415, 447, 539, 562, 563

Lagrange multipliers, 296, 320, 552,
    579
Learning curves, 29, 52, 184, 219
Least-cost testing sequence, 104
Least squares, 284, 580
Life insurance investment decision,
    165, 319
Linear combination, 348
Linear equations, 343, 378
Linear independence, 348
Linear programming, 415
    dual and primal, 527
    enumeration, 422
    graphical solution, 420
    Kuhn-Tucker conditions, 313, 447
    slack variables, 434
    verification of optimal solutions, 442

Local extrema, 129, 269, 547, 562
Logarithmic function, 181, 195

Machine loading, 475, 500
Management science models, 89, 107
Marginal analysis, 148, 153, 179
Marketing model, 205, 228, 302, 557
Matrices, 325, 569
    definiteness, 601
    operations, 331
    partitioning, 373
Matrix inversion, 357, 386, 395
    determinants, 360, 364
    partitioning, 375
Minor of a determinant, 369, 547
Mixed partial derivatives, 257, 544
Models, 3, 92
Monotonic function, 128

Newton's method, 124
Non-negativity constraints, 315
Numerical analysis, 279, 562

Objective, 91
Optimization, 108, 128, 266, 547, 561
    equality constraints, 295, 551, 579
    inequality constraints, 302, 320, 415,
        468
Organizational efficiency, 48

Parallelepiped, 551, 560, 620
Parameters, 7
Partial derivative, 256, 545
Parts explosion, 387
Payback period, 83, 184
Periodic functions, 142
Permissible range, 154
Permutation, 369, 637
Personal Toiletries Company model,
    498
Piecewise linear function, 156
Polynomials, 157, 250, 265, 272, 569
Portfolio selection, 584
Positive definite, 601
Present value, 55, 185, 190
Price war model, 161
Production and employment schedul-
    ing, 280, 485, 502, 569, 574
Production scheduling, 22

Progression, arithmetic, 24
  geometric, 26
  harmonic, 32

Quadratic form, 598

Rational functions, 160, 171
  integration, 211
Rent or buy decision, 67
Replacement problem, 100

Sensitivity analysis, 259
Simplex method, 449, 517, 519, 525, 536
Sinking fund, 60
Solution, 94; *see also* Optimization
  analytic, 96
  enumeration of alternatives, 94, 110, 415, 422
  graphic, 95, 252, 289, 420
Stationary point, 129
Sum of squares, 598
Symbols, 5

Symmetrical functions, 143
Systematic elimination, 350, 366

Taylor expansion, 121, 154, 264, 605
Theory of the firm, 43
Total differential, 258
  constrained variables, 299
Trading on the equity, 227
Transformations, 195, 592
Translation, 594
Transportation model, 504

Uncontrollable variables, 90

Variable project life models, 190
Variables, 7
  decision, 90
  discrete, 9
  independent, 8
  uncontrollable, 90
Variance, volume, 18

Warehousing model, 477, 502